Solutions manual to accompany

# Elements of Physical Chemistry

Sixth Edition

David Smith
*University of Bristol*

OXFORD
UNIVERSITY PRESS

W. H. FREEMAN AND COMPANY

OXFORD
UNIVERSITY PRESS

Great Clarendon Street, Oxford, OX2 6DP,
United Kingdom

Oxford University Press is a department of the University of Oxford.
It furthers the University's objective of excellence in research, scholarship,
and education by publishing worldwide. Oxford is a registered trade mark of
Oxford University Press in the UK and in certain other countries



Fifth Edition published 2010
Fourth Edition published 2006
Third Edition published 2000



Published in the United States of America by Oxford University Press
198 Madison Avenue, New York, NY 10016, United States of America

British Library Cataloguing in Publication Data
Data available

ISBN 978–0–19–967449–7

# Contents

# Chapter 0

# Foundations

## Answers to discussion questions

**D0.1** A gas is a form of matter that fills the container it occupies and is compressible under ordinary atmospheric conditions. It is composed of separated particles in continuous rapid, disordered motion during which particles often travel several diameters before colliding. Consequently, the particles are separated by considerable empty space, a condition that results in compressibility. The interactions between particles are negligibly weak except when they are colliding.

The particles of liquids and solids are in continuous contact with their neighbours, a condition that causes liquids and solids to be incompressible. All particles are in constant motion but they travel only a fraction of a diameter before colliding with a neighbour. The microscopic particles of the liquid phase can slip past each other, a condition that results in a non-rigid fluidity of the macroscopic phase. Microscopic particles of a solid cannot slip past each other. They can only oscillate about an average position within the solid, a condition that results in macroscopic rigidity of the solid. The interactions between particles within the liquid or solid phases are relatively strong.

**D0.2** The force $F$ acting on any object of mass $m$ equals the mass multiplied by the acceleration $a$ of the object. This is Newton's second law of motion: $F = ma$.

The work done on an object when moving the object against an opposing force equals the opposing force multiplied by the distance over which the object is moved:

$$\text{Work done on an object} = \text{opposing force} \times \text{distance}\,.$$

Energy is the capacity to do work. Kinetic energy is the energy that a mass $m$ has because of its speed $v$

$$E_{\mathrm{k}} = \tfrac{1}{2}mv^2$$

The potential energy, $E_{\mathrm{p}}$, of an object is the energy it possesses due to its position. The potential energy of an object may be due to gravitational, electrical, or magnetic forces. In particular, the Coulombic potential resulting from the presence of electrical charges is especially important in chemistry.

**D0.3** When there are equal gas pressures on both sides of a macroscopic object such as a movable, stationary, frictionless piston confined in a cylinder, there is no net force acting upon the object. Such an object will not accelerate in either direction and is said to be in **mechanical equilibrium**. Two objects that exhibit no net flow of energy between them upon contact are in **thermal equilibrium**. These objects have the same temperature. Mechanical equilibrium is a dynamic process because the rates of molecule–wall collisions are extremely large on each side of the movable object and it is the opposing, but equal, collision rates that produce the equilibrium. Similarly, molecular, atomic, or ionic collisions at the contact surface between two macroscopic objects produce a continuous, dynamic transfer of energy between the two objects even though the objects may be at thermal equilibrium. Equal and directionally opposing rates of energy transfer balance to produce equilibrium. When objects are not at thermal equilibrium, atomic scale collisions always cause the transfer of energy from high temperature to low temperature.

**D0.4** By specifying the **state of matter** we identify whether matter is gaseous(g), liquid(l), or solid(s). The **state symbol** within a chemical reaction equation may indicate that water, for example, is a gas, a liquid, or a solid by writing $H_2O(g)$, $H_2O(l)$, or $H_2O(s)$, respectively.

The description of the **physical state** of bulk matter includes the state of the matter along with information about physical properties such as volume, pressure, temperature, amount of substance present, and density. Two samples of a substance that have the same physical properties are in the same **state**.

**D0.5** The relative population of any pair of quantum states is given by the Boltzmann equation, eqn 0.18,

$$\frac{N_2}{N_1} = \mathrm{e}^{-(\epsilon_2-\epsilon_1)/kT} = \mathrm{e}^{-(E_2-E_1)/RT}$$

where $E_1 = N_A\epsilon_1$ and $E_2 = N_A\epsilon_2$ are the energies of the two states. Thus, for a fixed difference in energy, the relative population depends only upon the temperature, $T$. The form of the function means that the population of the state with the lower energy is greater than that of the upper state. The relative population of the upper state does, however, increase with temperature. Only at a theoretical infinite temperature do the populations of the two states become equal.

If, instead, we consider a system with more than two quantum states, we can see that at low temperatures, only the lowest states will be populated. However, as temperature increases, higher energy states become populated.

## Solutions to exercises

**E0.1** The molar mass of glucose is

$$M = \{(6 \times 12.01) + (12 \times 1.01) + (6 \times 16.00)\}\,\mathrm{g\,mol^{-1}} = 180.18\,\mathrm{g\,mol^{-1}}$$

Thus, the amount of glucose molecules is, from eqn 0.2,

$$n = m/M = (10.0\ \text{g})\,/(180.18\ \text{g mol}^{-1}) = 55.6 \times 10^{-3}\text{mol} = \mathbf{55.6\ mmol}$$

**E0.2** The molar mass of the fullerene is

$$M = 60\ \times\ (12.01\ \text{g mol}^{-1}) = 720.6\ \text{g mol}^{-1}$$

The molecular mass is thus

$$m = \frac{M}{N_A} = \frac{720.6\ \text{g mol}^{-1}}{6.022\ \times\ 10^{23}\ \text{mol}^{-1}} = 1.197 \times 10^{-21}\text{g} = \mathbf{1.197 \times 10^{-24}kg}$$

**E0.3** Combining eqns 0.1 and 0.2, the number of myoglobin molecules is

$$\begin{aligned} N &= n \times N_A = (m/M) \times N_A \\ &= \{(1.0 \times 10^{-3}\text{kg})/(16.1\ \text{kg mol}^{-1})\} \times 6.022 \times 10^{23}\text{mol}^{-1} = \mathbf{3.7 \times 10^{19}} \end{aligned}$$

**E0.4** We may express the mass of a haemoglobin molecule in terms of the molar mass of myoglobin. Thus, denoting haemoglobin as Hb and myoglobin as Mb, then the fraction of the mass of the cell that is haemoglobin is

$$\begin{aligned} \frac{m_{\text{Hb}}}{m_{\text{cell}}} &= \frac{\overbrace{N_{\text{Hb}}}^{\text{number of Hb molecules}} \times \overbrace{m_{\text{Hb}}}^{\text{mass of one Hb molecule}}}{\underbrace{m_{\text{cell}}}_{\text{total mass of cell}}} = \frac{N_{\text{Hb}} \times \overbrace{(4 \times m_{\text{Mb}})}^{m_{\text{Hb}}}}{m_{\text{cell}}} = \frac{N_{\text{Hb}} \times 4 \times \overbrace{(M_{\text{Mb}}/N_A)}^{m_{\text{Mb}}}}{m_{\text{cell}}} \\ &= \frac{(3 \times 10^{8}) \times 4 \times \{(16.1 \times 10^{3}\text{g})/(6.022 \times 10^{23}\text{mol}^{-1})\}}{3.33 \times 10^{-11} g} \\ &= \mathbf{0.97}\ \text{or}\ \mathbf{97\ per\ cent} \end{aligned}$$

**E0.5** The balanced equation for the reduction is

$$Fe_2O_3(s) + 3\ CO(g) \rightarrow 2\ Fe(s) + 3\ CO_2(g).$$

The stoichiometry of the reactions such that the amount of carbon monoxide molecules required, $n_{CO}$, is three times the amount of iron(III)oxide, $n_{Fe_2CO_3}$. Thus,

$$\begin{aligned} m_{\text{CO}} &= n_{\text{CO}} \times \overbrace{M_{\text{CO}}}^{\text{molar mass of CO}} = (3n_{\text{Fe}_2\text{CO}_3})M_{\text{CO}} = 3\left(\overbrace{m_{\text{Fe}_2\text{CO}_3}}^{\text{mass of Fe}_2\text{CO}_3} / \overbrace{M_{\text{Fe}_2\text{CO}_3}}^{\text{molar mass of Fe}_2\text{CO}_3}\right) M_{\text{CO}} \\ &= 3 \times \left\{\overbrace{(1 \times 10^{6}\text{g})}^{m_{\text{Fe}_2\text{CO}_3}} / \overbrace{(159.69\ \text{g mol}^{-1})}^{M_{\text{Fe}_2\text{CO}_3}}\right\} \times \overbrace{(28.01\ \text{g mol}^{-1})}^{M_{\text{CO}}} \\ &= 5.3 \times 10^{5}\text{g} = \mathbf{0.53\ t} \end{aligned}$$

Note that its is good practice to perform the calculation as a single step in order to avoid the magnification of successive rounding errors. This approach also allows for an easy visual check that the units cancel to yield a quantity with the correct dimensions.

**E0.6** Noting that 1 $dm^3 = 10^{-3}$ $m^3 = 10^3$ $cm^3$,

$$V = 50\ \mathrm{dm^3} = 50\ \mathrm{dm^3} \times (10^{-3}\mathrm{m^3/dm^3}) = \mathbf{0.050\ m^3}$$
$$= 50\ \mathrm{dm^3} \times (10^3\ \mathrm{cm^3/dm^3}) = \mathbf{5.0 \times 10^4\ cm^3}$$

**E0.7** The volume of the spherical drop is $V = (4/3)\pi r^3$ where $r$ is the radius. Substituting into eqn 0.3 gives a mass density of

$$\rho = \frac{m}{V} = \frac{3m}{4\pi r^3} = \frac{3 \times (20.4 \times 10^{-6}\ \mathrm{kg})}{4\pi \times (1.74 \times 10^{-3}\ \mathrm{m})^3} = 926\ \mathrm{kg\ m^{-3}} = \mathbf{0.926\ g\ cm^{-3}}$$

**E0.8** We may derive an expression for the amount of octane molecules by combining eqns 0.2 and 0.3. Thus, noting that a volume of 1 $dm^3$ is equivalent to $10^3$ $cm^3$,

$$n_{\mathrm{C_3H_{18}}} \overset{\text{eqn 0.2}}{=} m_{\mathrm{C_3H_{18}}}/M_{\mathrm{C_3H_{18}}} \overset{\text{eqn 0.3}}{=} \left(\overbrace{\rho_{\mathrm{C_3H_{18}}}}^{\text{mass density}}\overbrace{V_{\mathrm{C_3H_{18}}}}^{\text{volume}}\right)/\overbrace{M_{\mathrm{C_3H_{18}}}}^{\text{molar mass}}$$
$$= \{(0.703\ \mathrm{g\ cm^{-3}}) \times \overbrace{(1.00 \times 10^3\ \mathrm{cm^3})}^{1\ \mathrm{dm^3} = 10^3\ \mathrm{cm^3}}\}/(114.23\ \mathrm{g\ mol^{-1}})$$
$$= \mathbf{6.15\ mol}$$

Writing the solution in this way, as a single step, allows us to minimise the propogation of errors due to rounding and to check that the units cancel properly.

**E0.9** The chemical equation for the complete combustion of octane is

$$C_8H_{18}(g) + 12\tfrac{1}{2}\ O_2(g) \rightarrow 8\ CO_2(g) + 9\ H_2O(l)$$

so that each molecule of octane produces eight molecules of carbon dioxide. We may calculate the amount of octane molecules from the density and molar mass using eqns 0.2 and 0.3. Thus,

$$m_{\mathrm{CO_2}} = n_{\mathrm{CO_2}}M_{\mathrm{CO_2}} = (8 \times n_{\mathrm{C_3H_{18}}})M_{\mathrm{CO_2}} = 8 \times \overbrace{(m_{\mathrm{C_3H_{18}}}/M_{\mathrm{C_3H_{18}}})}^{n_{\mathrm{C_3H_{18}}}}M_{\mathrm{CO_2}}$$
$$= 8 \times (\overbrace{\rho_{\mathrm{C_3H_{18}}}V_{\mathrm{C_3H_{18}}}}^{m_{\mathrm{C_3H_{18}}}}/M_{\mathrm{C_3H_{18}}})M_{\mathrm{CO_2}}$$
$$= 8 \times \{(0.703\ \mathrm{g\ cm^{-3}}) \times (1.00 \times 10^3\mathrm{cm^3})/(114.23\ \mathrm{g\ mol^{-1}})\} \times (44.01\ \mathrm{g\ mol^{-1}})$$
$$= 2.17 \times 10^3\mathrm{g} = \mathbf{2.17\ kg}$$

**E0.10** Extensive properties are those that depend upon the amount of substance; intensive properties are those that do not depend upon the amount of substance. Thus, only volume and amount of substance are extenive properties. Molar volume, however, is the volume per mole of substance, and is therefore an intesive property. Mass density is, from eqn 0.3, the ratio of mass to volume. Although both mass and volume are extensive properties, their ratio is not.

$$\rho = m/V = \overbrace{\underbrace{(nM)}_{\text{extensive}}}^{m} \;/\; \overbrace{\underbrace{(nV_\mathrm{m})}_{\text{extensive}}}^{V} = \overbrace{\underbrace{M}_{\text{intensive}}}^{\text{molar mass}} \;/\; \overbrace{\underbrace{V_\mathrm{m}}_{\text{intensive}}}^{\text{molar volume}}$$

Thus, mass density is an intensive property. Finally, temperature is an intesive property; its value does not depend upon the amount of subtance.

**E0.11** Molar volume, $V_\mathrm{m}$, is, from eqn 0.4, the ratio of the total volume to the amount of substance. We may, however, use eqn 0.2 to express the amount of substance as the ratio of the mass to the molar mass. Thus, substituting,

$$V_\mathrm{m} = \frac{V}{n} = \frac{V}{m/M} = \frac{MV}{m}$$

$$= \frac{\overbrace{(26.05\ \mathrm{g\ mol^{-1}})}^{\text{molar mass},M} \times \overbrace{(2.19 \times 10^{-3}\ \mathrm{dm^3})}^{\text{volume},V}}{\underbrace{45.2\ \mathrm{g}}_{\text{mass},m}} = \mathbf{1.26 \times 10^{-3}\ dm^3\ mol^{-1}}$$

**E0.12** The energy required to ionize a single sodium atom is given by the molar ionization energy divided by Avogadro's number, which is the number of molecules per mole

$$E = I/N_\mathrm{A} = (495.8 \times 10^3\ \mathrm{J\ mol^{-1}})/(6.022 \times 10^{23}\ \mathrm{mol^{-1}}) = \mathbf{8.23 \times 10^{-19} J}$$

**E0.13** The linear momentum of a molecule is, from eqn 0.5, $p = mv$, where $m$ is the molecular mass and $v$ the speed of the molecule. Thus, using eqn 0.2 to express the molecular mass in terms of the molar mass, $M$, and Avogadro's number, $N_\mathrm{A}$

$$\begin{aligned} p &= mv = (M/N_A)v \\ &= \{(32.00 \times 10^{-3}\ \mathrm{kg\ mol^{-1}})/(6.022 \times 10^{23}\ \mathrm{J\ mol^{-1}})\} \times 482\ \mathrm{m\ s^{-1}} \\ &= \mathbf{2.56 \times 10^{-23}\ kg\ m\ s^{-1}} \end{aligned}$$

**E0.14** Following *Brief Illustration 0.5*, the moment of inertia of the $H_2$ molecule is given by the sum of the product of each mass multiplied by the square of the perpendicular distance from the axis of rotation. For $H_2$, the axis of rotation runs through the centre of the molecule, so if the bond length is $R$, then the distance of each atom from the axis of rotation is $R/2$. Hence,

$$I = \sum_i m_i r_i^2 = 2m_\mathrm{H} \overbrace{r_\mathrm{H}^2}^{(R/2)^2} = ½ m_\mathrm{H} R_\mathrm{H}^2$$

Rearranging, and noting that the mass of an individual hydrogen atom is $m_\mathrm{H} = M_\mathrm{H} / N_\mathrm{A} = 1.01 m_\mathrm{u}$

$$\begin{aligned} R_\mathrm{H} &= (2I/m_\mathrm{H})^{1/2} \\ &= \{2 \times (4.61 \times 10^{-48} \mathrm{kg\ m^2})/(1.01\ m_\mathrm{u})\}^{1/2} \\ &= [\{2 \times (4.61 \times 10^{-48} \mathrm{kg\ m^2})\}/\{1.01 \times (1.661 \times 10^{-27} \mathrm{kg})\}]^{1/2} \end{aligned}$$

$$= 74.1 \times 10^{-12}\text{m} = \mathbf{74.1\ pm}$$

**E0.15** (a) Acceleration is the rate of change of velocity. If the acceleration is constant, such as when a charged particle is accelerated by a uniform electric field, then the magnitude of the acceleration is given by $a = \Delta v / \Delta t$. The electron is accelerated from rest, so that the change in speed $\Delta v$ is $42.0 \times 10^6$ m s$^{-1}$. Thus,

$$a = (42 \times 10^4 \text{ m s}^{-1})/(10 \times 10^{-6}\text{s}) = \mathbf{4.2 \times 10^{10} m\ s^{-2}}$$

(b) The force acting is given by Newton's second law of motion, eqn 0.7

$$F = m_e a = (9.109 \times 10^{-31}\text{kg}) \times (4.2 \times 10^{10}\text{m s}^{-2}) = \mathbf{3.8 \times 10^{-20}\ N}$$

(c) The kinetic energy acquired is, from eqn 0.11a,

$$E_k = \tfrac{1}{2}m_e v^2 = \tfrac{1}{2} \times (9.109 \times 10^{-31}\text{ kg}) \times (42 \times 10^4 \text{ m s}^{-1})^2 = \mathbf{8.0 \times 10^{-20}\ J}$$

(d) The work done is equivalent to the kinetic energy acquired.

**E0.16** Assuming that an average human has a mass of 70 kg, then, following the method used in *Brief Illustration 0.6*

$$F_{\text{gravitational}} = mg = (70\text{ kg}) \times \overbrace{(9.81 \text{ m s}^{-2})}^{\substack{\text{acceleration}\\ \text{of free fall}}} = 700 \text{ kg m s}^{-2} = \mathbf{700\ N}$$

**E0.17** Weight is simply the gravitational force. Thus, the percentage difference in the weight of a body between the Equator and the North Pole is

$$\frac{W_{\text{North Pole}} - W_{\text{Equator}}}{W_{\text{North Pole}}} = 1 - \frac{W_{\text{Equator}}}{W_{\text{North Pole}}} = 1 - \frac{mg_{\text{Equator}}}{mg_{\text{North Pole}}} = 1 - \frac{g_{\text{Equator}}}{g_{\text{North Pole}}}$$

$$= 1 - \frac{9.832 \text{ ms}^{-2}}{9.789 \text{ ms}^{-2}} = \mathbf{-0.004393} \text{ or } \mathbf{-0.4393\ per\ cent}$$

**E0.18** Conversion factors are given in Table 0.1.

(a) If 1 Torr is equivalent to 133.32 Pa, then 1 Pa is equivalent to (1 / 133.32) Torr. Thus, 108 kPa is equal to

$$(108 \times 10^3 \text{ Pa}) \times (1/133.32)\text{Torr Pa}^{-1} = \mathbf{810\ Torr}$$

(b) 1 atm is equivalent to 1.01325 bar, so that 1 bar is equivalent to (1 / 1.01325) atm. Thus, 0.975 bar is equal to

$$(0.975 \text{ bar}) \times (1/1.01325)\text{bar atm}^{-1} = \mathbf{0.962\ atm}$$

(c) In the same way, 1 atm is equivalent to 101.325 kPa, so that 1 kPa is equivalent to (1 / 101.325) atm. Thus, 22.5 kPa is equal to

$$(22.5 \text{ kPa}) \times (1/101.325) \text{ kPa atm}^{-1} = \mathbf{0.222\ atm}$$

(d) 1 Torr is equal to 133.32 Pa, so that 770 Torr is equivalent to

$$770\ \text{Torr} \times 133.32\ \text{Pa Torr}^{-1} = \mathbf{103 \times 10^3\ Pa}$$

**E0.19** The kinetic energy of a rotating body is given by eqn 0.12,

$$E_\text{k} = \tfrac{1}{2}I\omega^2$$

where $\omega$ is the angular speed and the moment of inertia is given by $I = mr^2$. Substituting the values for the effective mass and radius of the rotor arm

$$\begin{aligned} E_\text{k} &= \tfrac{1}{2}I\omega^2 = \tfrac{1}{2}m \times r^2 \times \omega^2 \\ &= \tfrac{1}{2} \times (2.0\ \text{kg}) \times (20 \times 10^{-2}\text{m})^2 \times (400\ \text{rad s}^{-1})^2 \\ &= 6.4 \times 10^3\ \text{J} = \mathbf{6.4\ kJ} \end{aligned}$$

**E0.20** The mechanical work done in moving a mass $m$ through a distance $h$ against the gravitational force of the Earth is, from eqn 0.11, $w = mgh$, where $g$ is the acceleration of free fall. Thus,

$$\begin{aligned} w &= mgh \\ &= (65\ \text{kg}) \times (9.81\ \text{ms}^{-2}) \times (4.0\ \text{m}) \\ &= 2.6 \times 10^3\ \text{kg m s}^{-2} = 2.6 \times 10^3\text{J} = \mathbf{2.6\ kJ} \end{aligned}$$

**E0.21** Applying eqn 0.12a,

$$E_\text{k} = \tfrac{1}{2}mv^2 = \tfrac{1}{2} \times (58 \times 10^{-3}\text{kg}) \times (35\ \text{m s}^{-1})^2 = 36\ \text{kg m s}^{-2} = \mathbf{36\ J}$$

**E0.22** The kinetic energy of the car is, from eqn 0.12a,

$$\begin{aligned} E_\text{k} &= \tfrac{1}{2}mv^2 \\ &= \tfrac{1}{2} \times (1.5 \times 10^3\ \text{kg}) \times \overbrace{\{(50 \times 10^3/3600\ )\text{m s}^{-1}\}^2}^{1\ \text{km h}^{-1} = (10^3\text{m})/(3600\ \text{s})} \\ &= 140 \times 10^3\ \text{kg m s}^{-2} = \mathbf{140\ kJ} \end{aligned}$$

**E0.23** The total translational kinetic energy is, from eqn 0.12a,

$$\begin{aligned} E_\text{k} &= \overbrace{N}^{\text{number of molecules}} \times \overbrace{(\tfrac{1}{2}mv^2)}^{\text{kinetic energy of one molecule}} = \overbrace{(nN_\text{A})}^{n} \times (\tfrac{1}{2}mv^2) = \tfrac{1}{2}n\,\overbrace{N_\text{A}m}^{\text{molar mass}}\,v^2 = \tfrac{1}{2}nMv^2 \\ &= \tfrac{1}{2} \times (1\ \text{mol}\ ) \times (26 \times 10^{-3}\text{kg mol}^{-1}) \times (400\ \text{m s}^{-1})^2 \\ &= 2.1 \times 10^3\ \text{kg m s}^{-2} = \mathbf{2.1\ kJ} \end{aligned}$$

**E0.24** The minimum energy that the bird must expend is equivalent to the mechanical work done in raising its mass against the gravitational force. Thus, from eqn 0.11,

$$E = mgh = (25 \times 10^{-3}\text{kg}) \times (9.81\ \text{m s}^{-2}) \times (50\ \text{m}) = 12\ \text{kg m s}^{-2} = \mathbf{12\ J}$$

**E0.25** The electrostatic potential energy of interaction between two charges $Q_1$ and $Q_2$ in vacuum is, from eqn 0.15

$$E_p = \frac{Q_1 Q_2}{4\pi\epsilon_0 r}$$

where $\epsilon_0 = 8.854 \times 10^{-12}\,\mathrm{J^{-1}C^2m^{-1}}$ is the vacuum permittivity. For a proton and electron, the charges are $+e$ and $-e$ where $e = 1.602 \times 10^{-19}$ C is the elementary charge. Thus, substituting,

$$E_p = -\frac{(1.602 \times 10^{-19}\ \mathrm{C})^2}{4\pi \times 8.854 \times 10^{-12}\mathrm{J^{-1}C^2m^{-1}} \times 52.9 \times 10^{-12}\mathrm{m}}$$
$$= -4.36 \times 10^{-18}\ \mathrm{J} = \mathbf{-4.36\ aJ}$$

The energy is negative, indicating that the force between the proton and electron is attractive.

**E0.26** To determine the equivalent molar energy, we must first convert the work function from units of electronvolts to joules and then multiply by Avogadro's constant

$$(2.30\ \mathrm{eV}) \times (1.602 \times 10^{-19}\ \mathrm{J\ eV^{-1}}) \times (6.022 \times 10^{23}\ \mathrm{mol^{-1}})$$
$$= 222 \times 10^3\ \mathrm{J\ mol^{-1}} = \mathbf{222\ kJ\ mol^{-1}}$$

**E0.27** At $T = 0$, $\theta_{\mathrm{Celsius}}/°\mathrm{C} = -273.15$. Rearranging,

$$(\theta_{\mathrm{Fahrenheit}}/°\mathrm{F}) = \{9/5(\theta_{\mathrm{Celsius}}/°\mathrm{C})\} + 32 = \{(9/5) \times -273.15\} + 32$$
$$= -459.67$$

Hence, absolute zero is equivalent to **–459.67 °F**.

**E0.28** At the freezing point of water $\theta/°\mathrm{C} = 0$ and $\theta'/°\mathrm{C}' = 100$ and at the boiling point of water $\theta/°\mathrm{C} = 100$ and $\theta'/°\mathrm{C}' = 0$. The reverse symmetry of the values suggest that the simple relation is

$$\boldsymbol{\theta'}/°\mathrm{C}' = -(\boldsymbol{\theta}/°\mathrm{C}) + \mathbf{100} \text{ or } \boldsymbol{\theta}/°\mathrm{C} = \mathbf{100} - (\boldsymbol{\theta'}/°\mathrm{C}')$$

**E0.29** We may write the relationship between the Plutonium and Celsius scales as

$$\theta_{\mathrm{Plutonium}}/°\mathrm{P} = a(\theta_{\mathrm{Celsius}}/°\mathrm{C}) + b$$

so that

$$0 = a \times (-209.9) + b$$
$$100 = a \times (-195.8) + b$$

Solving these two equations simultaneously gives $a = 7.092$ and $b = 1488.6$, so that

$$\theta_{\mathrm{Plutonium}}/°\mathrm{P} = 7.092(\theta_{\mathrm{Celsius}}/°\mathrm{C}) + 1488.6$$

(a) Substituting the relationship between temperatures on the Celsius and Kelvin scales, gives

$$\theta_{\text{Plutonium}}/°\text{P} = 7.092\overbrace{\{(T/K) - 273.15\}}^{\theta_{\text{Celsius}}/°\text{C}} + 1488.6 = \mathbf{7.092(T/K) - 448.6}$$

(b) and in the same way for the Fahrenheit scale,

$$\begin{aligned}\theta_{\text{Plutonium}}/°\text{P} &= 7.092\{(5/9)(\theta_{\text{Fahrenheit}}/°\text{F}) - 32\} + 1488.6 \\ &= \mathbf{3.940(\theta_{Fahrenheit}/°F) + 1261.7}\end{aligned}$$

**E0.30** On the Rankine scale, 0 °F = 459.67 °R and the degree size is identical to that of the Fahrenheit scale. Hence, the relationship between the Rankine scale and the Fahrenheit scale is

$$\theta_{\text{Rankine}}/°\text{R} = \theta_{\text{Fahrenheit}}/°\text{F} + 459.67$$

so that, at the boiling temperature of water, 212 °F,

$$\theta_{\text{Rankine}}/°\text{R} = 212 + 459.67 = 672$$

**E0.31** The relative population of two states is given by eqn 0.17,

$$\frac{N_2}{N_1} = \mathrm{e}^{-(\epsilon_2-\epsilon_1)/kT}$$

At a temperature of $T = \epsilon/k$ the denominator in the exponent becomes

$$kT = k \times \frac{\epsilon}{k} = \epsilon$$

Thus, the population of the first five excited states relative to the lowest state, which has an energy of 0, are

$$\begin{aligned}N_1/N_0 &= \mathrm{e}^{-(\epsilon-0)/\epsilon} = \mathrm{e}^{-1} = \mathbf{0.37} \\ N_2/N_0 &= \mathrm{e}^{-(2\epsilon-0)/\epsilon} = \mathrm{e}^{-2} = \mathbf{0.14} \\ N_3/N_0 &= \mathrm{e}^{-(3\epsilon-0)/\epsilon} = \mathrm{e}^{-3} = \mathbf{0.05} \\ N_4/N_0 &= \mathrm{e}^{-(4\epsilon-0)/\epsilon} = \mathrm{e}^{-4} = \mathbf{0.01} \\ N_5/N_0 &= \mathrm{e}^{-(5\epsilon-0)/\epsilon} = \mathrm{e}^{-4} = \mathbf{0.00}\end{aligned}$$

**E0.32** The total number of molecules is

$$\begin{aligned}N_{\text{tot}} = \sum_{i=1}^{\infty} N_i &= N_0 + N_1 + N_2 + N_3 + N_4 \\ &= N_0 + 0.37N_0 + 0.14N_0 + 0.05N_0 + 0.01N_0 \\ &= 1.57N_0\end{aligned}$$

where we have truncated the series after the fourth excited state because higher states are not populated at this temperature. Thus, for a system with 100 molecules

$$N_0 = N_{\text{tot}}/1.57 = 100/1.57$$

The total energy of the system is given by

$$E = \sum_{i=0}^{\infty} N_i E_i$$

where $N_i$ is the population of the state with energy $E_i$. Evaluating this sum directly gives

$$\begin{aligned} E &= (0.37N_0 \times \epsilon) + (0.14N_0 \times 2\epsilon) + (0.05N_0 \times 3\epsilon) + (0.01N_0 \times 4\epsilon) \\ &= 0.79N_0 \\ &= 0.79 \times (100/1.57) \\ &= \mathbf{50\epsilon} \end{aligned}$$

**E0.33** According to *Brief Illustration 0.12*, the average translational kinetic energy of a molecule is

$$E_{\text{trans}} = \frac{3}{2}kT = \frac{3}{2} \times 1.381 \times 10^{-23}\,\text{J K}^{-1} \times 298\,\text{K} = 6.17 \times 10^{-21}\,\text{J}$$

The translational kinetic energy is, from eqn 0.11a

$$E_{\text{trans}} = \frac{1}{2}mv^2$$

so that, rearranging

$$v = (2E_{\text{trans}}/m)^{1/2}$$

where $m = M / N_A$ is the molecular mass. Thus,

$$\begin{aligned} v &= (2N_A E_{\text{trans}}/M)^{1/2} \\ &= \left(\frac{2 \times 6.022 \times 10^{23}\,\text{mol}^{-1} \times 6.17 \times 10^{-21}\,\text{J}}{28.02 \times 10^{-3}\,\text{kg mol}^{-1}}\right)^{1/2} \\ &= \mathbf{515\ ms^{-1}} \end{aligned}$$

**E0.34** Using the arguments given in *Brief Illustration 0.12*,

$$E_{\text{rot}} = 3 \times \tfrac{1}{2}RT = \frac{3}{2} \times (8.3145\,\text{J K}^{-1}\text{mol}^{-1}) \times (298\,\text{K}) = \mathbf{3.72\ J\ mol^{-1}}$$

**E0.35** From eqn 0.20, the wavenumber of the emitted radiation is

$$\tilde{\nu} = 1/\lambda = 1/(632.8 \times 10^{-9}\text{m}) = 1.580 \times 10^{6}\,\text{m}^{-1} = \mathbf{1.580 \times 10^{4}\ cm^{-1}}$$

and, from eqn 0.19, the frequency is

$$\begin{aligned} \nu &= c/\nu \\ &= (2.998 \times 10^{8}\text{m s}^{-1})/(632.8 \times 10^{-9}\,\text{m}) = 4.738 \times 10^{14}\,\text{s}^{-1} = \mathbf{473.8\ THz} \end{aligned}$$

Using eqn 0.21b, the energy of each photon is

$$E = hc/\lambda = (6.626 \times 10^{-34}\,\text{J s}) \times (2.998 \times 10^{8}\text{m s}^{-1})/(632.8 \times 10^{-9}\,\text{m})$$

$= \mathbf{3.139 \times 10^{-19} J}$

**E0.36** The energy per photon is from eqn 0.21b, $E = hc / \lambda$, with the energy per mole of photons given by $N_A E$, where $N_A$ is Avogadro's constant.

(a) Thus, for red light with a wavelength of exactly 600 nm, the energy of an individual photon is

$$E = hc/\lambda = (6.626 \times 10^{-34}\ \text{J s}) \times (2.998 \times 10^{8}\ \text{m s}^{-1})/(600 \times 10^{-9}\ \text{m})$$
$$= \mathbf{3.31 \times 10^{-19}\ J}$$

with a molar energy

$$N_A E = (6.022 \times 10^{23}\ \text{mol}^{-1}) \times (3.31 \times 10^{-19}\ \text{J}) = 199 \times 10^{3}\ \text{J mol}^{-1}$$
$$= \mathbf{199\ kJ\ mol^{-1}}$$

(b) In the same way for yellow light of wavelength exactly 550 nm,

$$E = hc/\lambda = (6.626 \times 10^{-34}\ \text{J s}) \times (2.998 \times 10^{8}\ \text{m s}^{-1})/(550 \times 10^{-9}\ \text{m})$$
$$= \mathbf{3.61 \times 10^{-19}\ J}$$

with a molar energy

$$N_A E = (6.022 \times 10^{23}\ \text{mol}^{-1}) \times (3.61 \times 10^{-19}\ \text{J}) = 218 \times 10^{3}\ \text{J mol}^{-1}$$
$$= \mathbf{218\ kJ\ mol^{-1}}$$

(c) For violet light of wavelength exactly 400 nm,

$$E = hc/\lambda = (6.626 \times 10^{-34}\ \text{J s}) \times (2.998 \times 10^{8}\ \text{m s}^{-1})/(400 \times 10^{-9}\ \text{m})$$
$$= \mathbf{4.97 \times 10^{-19}\ J}$$

with a molar energy

$$N_A E = (6.022 \times 10^{23}\ \text{mol}^{-1}) \times (4.97 \times 10^{-19}\ \text{J}) = 218 \times 10^{3}\ \text{J mol}^{-1}$$
$$= \mathbf{299\ kJ\ mol^{-1}}$$

(d) For ultraviolet radiation of wavelength exactly 200 nm,

$$E = hc/\lambda = (6.626 \times 10^{-34}\ \text{J s}) \times (2.998 \times 10^{8}\ \text{m s}^{-1})/(200 \times 10^{-9}\ \text{m})$$
$$= \mathbf{9.93 \times 10^{-19}\ J}$$

with a molar energy

$$N_A E = (6.022 \times 10^{23}\ \text{mol}^{-1}) \times (9.93 \times 10^{-19}\ \text{J}) = 218 \times 10^{3}\ \text{J mol}^{-1}$$
$$= \mathbf{598\ kJ\ mol^{-1}}$$

(e) For X-rays of wavelength exactly 150 pm,

$$E = hc/\lambda = (6.626 \times 10^{-34}\ \text{J s}) \times (2.998 \times 10^{8}\ \text{m s}^{-1})/(150 \times 10^{-9}\ \text{m})$$
$$= \mathbf{1.32 \times 10^{-18}\ J}$$

with a molar energy

$$N_AE = (6.022\times10^{23}\ \text{mol}^{-1})\times(1.32\times10^{-19}\ \text{J}) = 798\times10^{3}\ \text{J mol}^{-1}$$
$$= \mathbf{798\ kJ\ mol^{-1}}$$

(f) For microwave radiation of wavelength 1.0 cm,

$$E = hc/\lambda = (6.626\times10^{-34}\ \text{J s})\times(2.998\times10^{8}\ \text{m s}^{-1})/(1.0\times10^{-2}\ \text{m})$$
$$= \mathbf{1.99\times10^{-23}\ J}$$

with a molar energy

$$N_AE = (6.022\times10^{23}\ \text{mol}^{-1})\times(1.99\times10^{-23}\ \text{J}) = \mathbf{12\ J\ mol^{-1}}$$

**E0.37** The energy of each photon is given by eqn 0.21b,

$$E = \frac{hc}{\lambda}$$

Denoting the rate at which energy is produced quantity as $P$, and assuming that the photodetector is 100% efficient, the number of photons detected per second is thus

$$n = \frac{P}{E} = \frac{P\lambda}{hc} = \frac{(0.68\times10^{-3}\ \text{J s}^{-1})\times(245\times10^{-9}\text{m})}{(6.626\times10^{-34}\ \text{J s})\times(2.998\times10^{8}\ \text{m s}^{-1})} = \mathbf{8.39\times10^{11}\ s^{-1}}$$

**E0.38** The energy of each photon is given by eqn 0.21b,

$$E = \frac{hc}{\lambda}$$

Denoting the rate at which the lamp emits energy as $P$, the number of photons emitted per second is thus, for a power of 1.00 W,

$$n = \frac{P}{E} = \frac{P\lambda}{hc} = \frac{\overbrace{(1.00\ \text{J s}^{-1})}^{1.00\ \text{W}}\times(380\times10^{-9}\text{m})}{(6.626\times10^{-34}\ \text{J s})\times(2.998\times10^{8}\ \text{m s}^{-1})} = \mathbf{1.91\times10^{11}\ s^{-1}}$$

and for 100 W,

$$n = \frac{P}{E} = \frac{P\lambda}{hc} = \frac{\overbrace{(100\ \text{J s}^{-1})}^{100\ \text{W}}\times(380\times10^{-9}\text{m})}{(6.626\times10^{-34}\ \text{J s})\times(2.998\times10^{8}\ \text{m s}^{-1})} = \mathbf{1.91\times10^{13}\ s^{-1}}$$

**E0.39** The energy of 1.00 mol of photons is given by the product of the number of photons, $N$, and the energy of an individual photon $E$,

$$E_{\text{total}} = NE = \overbrace{(nN_A)}^{\text{eqn 0.1}}\times\overbrace{(hc/\lambda)}^{\text{eqn 0.21b}}$$

However, the time required for the generation of these photons, $\delta t$, depends upon the rate at which energy is emitted, $P$,

$$\delta t = E_{\text{total}}/P = \frac{nN_A hc}{\lambda P}$$

$$= \frac{(1.00\ \text{mol}) \times (6.022 \times 10^{23}\ \text{mol}^{-1}) \times (6.626 \times 10^{-34}\ \text{J s}) \times (2.998 \times 10^{8}\ \text{m s}^{-1})}{(590 \times 10^{-9}\ \text{m}) \times \underbrace{(100\ \text{J s}^{-1})}_{1\ \text{W}=1\ \text{J s}^{-1}}}$$

$$= \mathbf{2030\ s}$$

Once again, by including the units for each quantity in the calculation, we can ensure that the result has the correct units of, in this case, seconds.

**E0.40** The energy of each photon is given by eqn 0.21b,

$$E = \frac{hc}{\lambda}$$

The rate at which energy is emitted is the power of the laser. Denoting this quantity as $P$, the number of photons emitted per second is then

$$n = \frac{P}{E} = \frac{P\lambda}{hc} = \frac{(1.05 \times 10^{-3}\ \text{J s}^{-1}) \times (1.13 \times 10^{-6}\text{m})}{(6.626 \times 10^{-34}\ \text{J s}) \times (2.998 \times 10^{8}\ \text{m s}^{-1})} = \mathbf{5.97 \times 10^{15}\ s^{-1}}$$

# Chapter 1

# The properties of gases

## Answers to discussion questions

**D1.1** An equation of state is an equation that relates the variables that define the state of a system to each other. In principle, we could choose many variables to define the state of the system, but for a gas, we usually use the amount of gas, $n$, pressure, $p$, volume, $V$, and temperature, $T$. Boyle, Charles, and Avogadro established relations between these variables for gases at low pressures by appropriate experiments. Boyle determined how volume varies with pressure $V \propto 1/p$, Charles how volume varies with temperature $V \propto T$, and Avogadro how volume varies with amount of gas $V \propto n$. Combining all of these proportionalities into one, we find

$$V \propto nT/p$$

Inserting a constant of proportionality, $R$, yields the equation

$$V = R(nT/p)$$

The constant $R$ is called the gas constant and has the value 8.3145 J K$^{-1}$ mol$^{-1}$. The expression may thus be rearranged into the familiar form of the perfect gas equation

$$pV = nRT$$

The experiments of Boyle, Charles and Avogadro were all performed at relatively low pressures, where the deviations in the behaviour of real gases from the perfect gas model are not significant.

**D1.2** The partial pressure of a gas in a mixture of gases is the pressure the gas would exert if it alone occupied the same container as the mixture at the same temperature. It is a limiting law because it holds exactly only under conditions where the gases have no effect upon each other. This can only be true in the limit of zero pressure where molecules of the gas are separated by many molecular diameters on the average. Hence, Dalton's law holds exactly only for a mixture of perfect gases; for real gases, the law is only an approximation.

**D1.3** We may conclude by combining eqns 1.15 and 1.17, that basic kinetic theory predicts that the average speed of molecules, $\bar{v}$, decreases by a factor of $M^{-1/2}$ as the molar mass increases

$$\bar{v} = \left(\frac{8}{3\pi}\right)^{1/2} v_{\mathrm{rms}} = \left(\frac{8}{3\pi}\right)^{1/2} \overbrace{\left(\frac{3RT}{M}\right)^{1/2}}^{v_{\mathrm{rms}}} = \left(\frac{8RT}{\pi M}\right)^{1/2}$$

On average, light molecules therefore move more quickly than heavy ones. The very light molecules of hydrogen, $H_2$, and helium, He, with molar masses of 2.02 g mol$^{-1}$ and 4.00 g mol$^{-1}$ respectively, are rare in the Earth's atmosphere because at atmospheric temperatures, a significant fraction of these molecules travel at sufficiently high speeds to escape from the planet's gravitational attraction. Only a very small fraction of the heavier molecules oxygen, $O_2$, carbon dioxide, $CO_2$ and nitrogen, $N_2$, with molar masses of 32.00 g mol$^{-1}$, 44.01 g mol$^{-1}$, and 28.02 g mol$^{-1}$ respectively, have a speed sufficiently large to escape from the Earth's gravitational pull.

**D1.4** Simple molecular kinetic theory proposes that the rate of gaseous diffusion and effusion is proportional to the average speed of the molecules. We may see from eqn 1.17, that the average speed is proportional to $T^{1/2}$, but inversely proportional to $M^{1/2}$

$$v_{\mathrm{rms}} = \left(\frac{3RT}{M}\right)^{1/2}$$

which is consistent with Graham's law, eqn 1.19.

**D1.5** For a perfect gas, the compression factor $Z = 1$. However, for a real gas, at low pressure the attractive force between molecules dominates and causes the compression factor to be less than 1, while at high pressure the repulsive force of molecules in close contact dominates and causes the compression factor to be greater than 1. An increase in temperature at a given pressure causes an increase in the mean kinetic energy relative to attractive and repulsive potential energies, which do not depend upon temperature. Thus, an increase in temperature diminishes the deviation of a real gas from perfect gas behaviour and the compression factor approaches the value of a perfect gas at both low and high pressure. These qualitative characteristics are quantified in Figure 1.1, which shows how the compression factor for gaseous ethene varies with pressure plots at 300 K, 400 K, and 500 K. The lines on the plot are called isotherms, because they show how the characteristics of the gas change at constant temperature. The critical temperature of ethene is 283.1 K so ethene is properly called a gas at the temperatures of these isotherms.

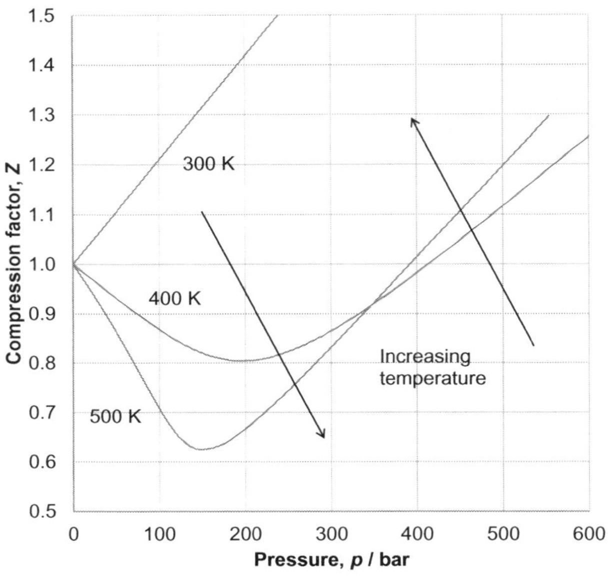


**Figure 1.1**

**D1.6** The critical point of a substance is a single ($p$, $T$, $V_m$) point that is characterized by the critical constants ($p_c$, $T_c$, $V_c$). Consider a liquid in equilibrium with its vapour. As the substance is heated, the density of the liquid phase decreases but the density of the vapour phase increases. The densities of the two phases converge, so that at the critical point, the liquid and vapour phases become indistinguishable. At temperatures above the critical temperature a gaseous substance cannot be liquefied by the application of pressure alone while at temperatures below the critical temperature the vapour can be condensed by the application of pressure.

**D1.7** The van der Waals equation of state, eqn 1.26a,

$$p = \frac{nRT}{V - nb} - a\left(\frac{n}{V}\right)^2$$

accounts for both the attractive and repulsive interactions between molecules.

Use of the equation supposes that the repulsive interactions cause the molecules to behave as small but impenetrable spheres. The nonzero volume of the molecules implies that instead of moving in a volume $V$ they are restricted to a smaller volume ($V - nb$), where $b$ is approximately four times the molar volume of the molecules ($b = 4V_{\text{molecule}}N_A$). This argument suggests that the perfect gas law, $p = nRT/V$, should be replaced by $p = nRT/(V - nb)$ when repulsions are significant.

The pressure depends on both the frequency of collisions with the walls and the force of each collision. Both the frequency of the collisions and their force are reduced by the attractive forces, which act with a strength proportional to the molar concentration, $n/V$, of molecules in the sample. Therefore, because the attractive forces reduce both the frequency and the force of the collisions, the pressure is reduced in proportion to the square of this concentration. If the reduction of pressure is written as $-a(n/V)^2$, where $a$ is a positive constant characteristic of each gas, the combined effect of the repulsive and attractive forces is the van der Waals equation of state.

## Solutions to exercises

**E1.1** Applying the perfect gas equation of state, eqn 1.2a, and paying particular attention to the units,

$$\begin{aligned} p &= \frac{nRT}{V} = \frac{\overbrace{(m/M)}^{\text{eqn 0.2}}RT}{V} \\ &= \frac{\{(3.055\ \text{g})/(28.02\ \text{g mol}^{-1})\}\times(8.3145\ \text{J K}^{-1}\text{mol}^{-1})\times(273.15+32)\ \text{K}}{\underbrace{(3.00\times10^{-3}\ \text{m}^3)}_{1\ \text{dm}^3=10^{-3}\ \text{m}^3}} \\ &= \underbrace{92.1\times10^3\ \text{J m}^{-3}}_{1\ \text{J m}^{-3}=1\ \text{Pa}} = 92.1\times10^3\ \text{Pa} = \mathbf{92.1\ kPa} \end{aligned}$$

**E1.2** Applying the perfect gas equation of state, eqn 1.2a, and using eqn 0.2 to express the amount of neon in terms of the mass and molar mass,

$$\begin{aligned} p &= \frac{nRT}{V} = \frac{\overbrace{(m/M)}^{\text{eqn 0.2}}RT}{V} \\ &= \frac{\{(425\times10^{-3}\ \text{g})/(20.18\ \text{g mol}^{-1})\}\times(8.3145\ \text{J K}^{-1}\text{mol}^{-1})\times(77\ \text{K})}{\underbrace{(6.00\times10^{-3}\ \text{m}^3)}_{1\ \text{dm}^3=10^{-3}\ \text{m}^3}} \\ &= \underbrace{2.25\times10^3\text{J m}^{-3}}_{1\ \text{J m}^{-3}=1\ \text{Pa}} = 2.25\times10^3\ \text{Pa} = \mathbf{2.25\ kPa} \end{aligned}$$

**E1.3** Rearranging the perfect gas equation, eqn 1.2a,

$$\begin{aligned} n &= \frac{pV}{RT} = \frac{(34.5\times10^3\ \text{Pa})\times\overbrace{(300.0\times10^{-6}\ \text{m}^3)}^{1\ \text{cm}^3=10^{-6}\text{m}^3}}{(8.3145\ \text{J K}^{-1}\text{mol}^{-1})\times(273.15+14.5)\ \text{K}} \\ &= 4.33\times10^{-3}\ \text{mol} = \mathbf{4.33\ mmol} \end{aligned}$$

**E1.4** We may use the difference in mass between the full and empty cylinder, along with eqn 0.2 to derive an expression for the amount of carbon dioxide molecules present

$$n = m/M = (m_{\text{full}} - m_{\text{empty}})/M$$

Substituting into the perfect gas equation, eqn 1.2a,

$$p = \frac{nRT}{V} = \frac{(m_{\text{full}} - m_{\text{empty}})RT}{MV}$$

$$= \frac{\{(1.04 - 0.74)\text{ kg}\} \times (8.3145\text{ J K}^{-1}\text{mol}^{-1}) \times \{(273.15 + 20)\text{K}\}}{(44.01 \times 10^{-3}\text{ kg mol}^{-1}) \times \underbrace{(250 \times 10^{-6}\text{ m}^3)}_{1\text{ cm}^3 = 10^{-6}\text{m}^3}}$$

$$= 6.64 \times 10^7\text{ Pa} = \mathbf{665\ bar}$$

**E1.5** Boyle's law, eqn 1.3, states that $p$ is inversely proportional to $V$ at constant temperature, $p \propto 1 / V$. It follows from eqn 1.7, that if temperature is constant,

$$p_1V_1 = p_2V_2 = \cdots$$

Thus, denoting the original conditions as $p_1$ and $V_1$ and the final conditions as $p_2$ and $V_2$,

$$p_2 = \frac{p_1V_1}{V_2} = \frac{(1.00\text{ atm}) \times (1.00\text{ dm}^3)}{\underbrace{(100 \times 10^{-3}\text{ dm}^3)}_{1\text{ cm}^3 = 10^{-3}\text{dm}^3}} = \mathbf{10.0\ atm}$$

**E1.6** For a perfect gas, pressure is proportional to temperature. We may see from eqn 1.7, that for a fixed volume and amount of gas, the ratio of pressure and temperature remains constant

$$\frac{p_1}{T_1} = \frac{p_2}{T_2}$$

Thus, denoting the original conditions as $p_1$ and $T_1$ and the final conditions as $p_2$ and $T_2$,

$$p_2 = \frac{p_1T_2}{T_1} = \frac{125\text{ kPa} \times (273.15 + 700)\text{K}}{(273.15 + 18)\text{K}} = \mathbf{418\ kPa}$$

**E1.7** Following the method used in Exercise 1.5,

$$p_2 = \frac{p_1V_1}{V_2} = \frac{(101\text{ kPa}) \times (7.20\text{ dm}^3)}{(4.21\text{ dm}^3)} = \mathbf{173\ kPa}$$

**E1.8** Charles's law, eqn 1.4b, states that volume is proportional to temperature at constant pressure. It follows from eqn 1.7, that if pressure is constant,

$$\frac{V_1}{T_1} = \frac{V_2}{T_2} = \cdots$$

Thus, denoting the original conditions as $V_1$ and $T_1$ and the final conditions as $V_2$ and $T_2$,

$$T_2 = \frac{V_2T_1}{V_1} = \frac{(0.100\text{ dm}^3) \times (273.15 + 22.2)\text{K}}{(1.00\text{ dm}^3)} = 29.5\text{ K}$$

which is equivalent to

$$\theta = (29.5 - 273.15)\ ^\circ\text{C} = \mathbf{-243.6\ ^\circ C}$$

**E1.9** We may follow the same method as in the previous exercise. If the volume of the sample increases by 25 per cent, then $V_2 / V_1 = 1.25$, so that the temperature of the air must be heated to

$$T_2 = \frac{V_2}{V_1} T_1 = 1.25 \times (315\ \text{K}) = \mathbf{394\ K}$$

**E1.10** Rearranging eqn 1.7, which expresses the relationship between the pressure, volume and temperature for a fixed amount of gas

$$V_2 = \frac{p_1 V_1}{T_1} \times \frac{T_2}{p_2}$$

(a) Thus, for a pressure of 52 kPa,

$$V_2 = \frac{(104\ \text{kPa}) \times (2.0\ \text{m}^3)}{(273.15 - 21.1)\ \text{K}} \times \frac{(273.15 - 5.0)\ \text{K}}{(52\ \text{kPa})} = \mathbf{3.6\ m^3}$$

(b) and 0.880 kPa,

$$V_2 = \frac{(104\ \text{kPa}) \times (2.0\ \text{m}^3)}{(273.15 - 21.1)\ \text{K}} \times \frac{(273.15 - 52.0)\ \text{K}}{(0.880\ \text{kPa})} = \mathbf{178\ m^3}$$

**E1.11** Boyle's law states that pressure is inversely proportional to volume at constant temperature. Thus, applying eqn 1.17 for a constant temperature,

$$V_2 = \frac{p_1 V_1}{p_2}$$

where $p_1$ and $V_1$ are the presure and volume at the surface, and $p_2$ and $V_2$ are the pressure and volume when submerged. The pressure is greater than that at the surface because of the hydrostatic pressure of the sea water. This hydrostatic pressure depends upon the depth, $h$, the density of the fluid, $\rho$, and the acceleration due to free fall, $g$, so that

$$p_2 = \overbrace{p_1}^{\text{surface pressure}} + \overbrace{h\rho g}^{\text{hydrostatic pressure}}$$

Hence, assuming that the pressure at the surface is 1 atm = $1.01 \times 10^5$ Pa, and noting that a density of 1.025 g cm$^{-3}$ is equivalent to $1.025 \times 10^3$ kg m$^{-3}$,

$$\begin{aligned} V_2 &= \frac{p_1 V_1}{p_1 + h\rho g} \\ &= \frac{(1.01 \times 10^5\ \text{Pa}) \times (3.0\ \text{m}^3)}{(1.01 \times 10^5\ \text{Pa}) + \{(50\ \text{m}) \times (1.025 \times 10^3\ \text{kg m}^{-3}) \times (9.81\ \text{m s}^{-2})\}} \\ &= \mathbf{0.50\ m^3} \end{aligned}$$

**E1.12** Air is roughly 80 per cent $N_2(g)$ and 20 per cent $O_2(g)$. We may therefore take the molar mass of air as

$$M_{\text{air}} = 0.80\, M_{N_2} + 0.20\, M_{O_2}$$

$$= \{(0.80 \times 28.02) + (0.20 \times 32.00)\}\ \text{g mol}^{-1} = \mathbf{28.82\ g\ mol^{-1}}$$

so that the ratio of the mass densities is

$$M_{H_2}/M_{\text{air}} = (2.01\ \text{g mol}^{-1})/(28.82\ \text{g mol}^{-1}) = 0.069$$

The volume of air displaced by the balloon is equal to the volume occupied by 10 kg of hydrogen. The perfect gas equation of state indicates that this volume will contain the same amount, $n$, of air and hydrogen. Thus the balloon will displace air of mass

$$m_{\text{air}} = \overbrace{n_{\text{air}}M_{\text{air}}}^{\text{eqn 0.2}} = \overbrace{(m_{H_2}/M_{H_2})}^{n_{\text{air}}=n_{H_2}} M_{\text{air}} = m_{H_2}(M_{\text{air}}/M_{H_2})$$

The payload is the difference between the mass of displaced air and the mass of the hydrogen,

$$\begin{aligned} m_{\text{air}} - m_{H_2} &= \{m_{H_2}(M_{\text{air}}/M_{H_2}) - m_{H_2}\} = m_{H_2}\{(M_{\text{air}}/M_{H_2}) - 1\} \\ &= 10\ \text{kg} \times \{(28.82\ \text{g mol}^{-1})/(2.01\ \text{g mol}^{-1}) - 1\} \\ &= \mathbf{130\ kg} \end{aligned}$$

**E1.13** Applying the perfect gas equation of state, eqn 1.17, and using eqn 0.2 to express the amount of gas in terms of the mass, $m$, and molar mass, $M$,

$$\begin{aligned} V &= \frac{\overbrace{n}^{m/M} RT}{p} = \frac{mRT}{Mp} \\ &= \frac{\overbrace{(250 \times 10^3\ \text{kg})}^{\text{mass of } SO_2} \times (8.3145\ \text{J K}^{-1}\text{mol}^{-1}) \times (273.15 + 800)\text{K}}{(64.06 \times 10^{-3}\text{kg mol}^{-1}) \times \underbrace{(1.01325 \times 10^5\ \text{Pa})}_{1\ \text{atm}=\ 1.01325\times10^5\ \text{Pa}}} \\ &= \mathbf{3.4 \times 10^5\ m^3} \end{aligned}$$

**E1.14** Applying eqn 1.17, and assuming that the balloon is spoherical, so that its volume may be expressed as $V = 4/3\pi r^3$

$$\begin{aligned} p_2 &= \frac{p_1V_1}{T_1} \times \frac{T_2}{V_2} = p_1 \times \frac{T_2}{T_1} \times \frac{V_1}{V_2} = p_1 \times \frac{T_2}{T_1} \times \frac{(4/3)\pi r_1^3}{(4/3)\pi r_2^3} = p_1 \times \frac{T_2}{T_1} \times \left(\frac{r_1}{r_2}\right)^3 \\ &= \overbrace{(1.01325 \times 10^5\ \text{Pa})}^{\text{atmospheric pressure at sea level}} \times \frac{(273.15 - 25.0)\ \text{K}}{(273.15 + 20.0)\ \text{K}} \times \left(\frac{1.5\ \text{m}}{3.5\ \text{m}}\right)^3 \\ &= 6.8 \times 10^3\ \text{Pa} = \mathbf{6.8\ kPa} \end{aligned}$$

**E1.15** (a) We may consider partial pressure as the pressure that a component of a gaseous mixture would exert if it alone occupied the container. Thus, considering the partial presure of nitrogen, and using the perfect gas equation of state to express the total volume in terms of the pressure, temperature and amount of nitrogen gas,

$$V = \frac{n_{N_2}RT}{p_{N2}} = \frac{(m_{N_2}/M_{N_2})RT}{p_{N2}}$$

$$= \frac{\{(225 \times 10^{-3}\,\mathrm{g})/(28.02\,\mathrm{g\,mol^{-1}})\} \times (8.3145\,\mathrm{J\,K^{-1}mol^{-1}}) \times (300\,\mathrm{K})}{(15.2 \times 10^{3}\,\mathrm{Pa})}$$
$$= \mathbf{1.32 \times 10^{-3}\,m^{3}}$$

(b) The partial pressure of nitrogen is, however, defined in terms of the mole fraction and total pressure, through eqn 1.9. Thus, rearranging and expressing the amount of the each component in terms of the mass and molar mass

$$p = \frac{p_{\mathrm{N_2}}}{x_{\mathrm{N_2}}} = \frac{p_{\mathrm{N_2}}}{(n_{\mathrm{N_2}}/n)} = \frac{\overbrace{\left(n_{\mathrm{CH_4}} + n_{\mathrm{Ar}} + n_{\mathrm{N_2}}\right)}^{\text{total amount of gas},n} p_{\mathrm{N_2}}}{n_{\mathrm{N_2}}}$$
$$= \frac{\left\{\overbrace{\left(m_{\mathrm{CH_4}}/M_{\mathrm{CH_4}}\right)}^{n_{\mathrm{CH_4}}} + \overbrace{\left(m_{\mathrm{Ar}}/M_{\mathrm{Ar}}\right)}^{n_{\mathrm{Ar}}} + \overbrace{\left(m_{\mathrm{N_2}}/M_{\mathrm{N_2}}\right)}^{n_{\mathrm{N_2}}}\right\} p_{\mathrm{N_2}}}{n_{\mathrm{N_2}}}$$
$$= \frac{\left\{\left(\frac{320 \times 10^{-3}\,\mathrm{g}}{16.05\,\mathrm{g\,mol^{-1}}}\right) + \left(\frac{175 \times 10^{-3}\,\mathrm{g}}{39.95\,\mathrm{g\,mol^{-1}}}\right) + \left(\frac{225 \times 10^{-3}\,\mathrm{g}}{28.02\,\mathrm{g\,mol^{-1}}}\right)\right\} \times 15.2 \times 10^{3}\,\mathrm{Pa}}{\left(\frac{225 \times 10^{-3}\,\mathrm{g}}{28.02\,\mathrm{g\,mol^{-1}}}\right)}$$
$$= \mathbf{61.2 \times 10^{3}\,Pa}$$

**E1.16** Applying Dalton's law, eqn 1.8, the total pressure is equal to the sum of the partial pressure of the dry air and the vapour pressure of the water

$$p = p_{\text{dry air}} + p_{\text{water vapour}}$$

so that

$$p_{\text{dry air}} = p - p_{\text{water vapour}} = (760\,\mathrm{Torr}) - (47\,\mathrm{Torr}) = \mathbf{713\,Torr}$$

**E1.17** From the definition of mass density, eqn 0.3, and applying the perfect gas equation of state, eqn 1.2,

$$\rho = \frac{m}{V} = \frac{nM}{V} = \frac{(pV/RT)M}{V} = \frac{pM}{RT}$$

Thus, rearranging,

$$M = \frac{RT\rho}{p} = \frac{(8.3145\,\mathrm{J\,K^{-1}mol^{-1}}) \times (330\,\mathrm{K}) \times \overbrace{(1.23\,\mathrm{kg\,m^{-3}})}^{1\,\mathrm{g\,dm^{-3}}=1\,\mathrm{kg\,m^{-3}}}}{25.5 \times 10^{3}\,\mathrm{Pa}}$$
$$= 132 \times 10^{-3}\,\mathrm{kg\,mol^{-1}} = \mathbf{132\,g\,mol^{-1}}$$

**E1.18** Rearranging the perfect gas equation of state, eqn 1.2, and expressing the amount of gas in terms of the mass and molar mass,

$$p = \frac{nRT}{V} = \frac{(m/M)RT}{V}$$

so that

$$M=\frac{mRT}{pV}=\frac{(33.5\times10^{-6}\text{ kg})\times(8.3145\text{ J K}^{-1}\text{mol}^{-1})\times(298\text{ K})}{\{(152\text{ Torr})\times(133.32\text{ Pa Torr}^{-1})\}\times(250\times10^{-6}\text{ m}^3)}$$
$$=16.4\times10^{-3}\text{ kg mol}^{-1}=\mathbf{16.4\ g\ mol^{-1}}$$

**E1.19** (a) The partial pressure of a component is defined in terms of the mole fraction and total pressure through eqn 1.9,

$$p_{H_2}=x_{H_2}p=\overbrace{(n_{H_2}/n)}^{x_{H_2}}\overbrace{(nRT/V)}^{p}=\frac{n_{H_2}RT}{V}$$
$$=\frac{(2.0\text{ mol})\times(8.3145\text{ J K}^{-1}\text{mol}^{-1})\times(273.15\text{ K})}{(22.4\times10^{-3}\text{ m}^3)}$$
$$=2.0\times10^5\text{ Pa}=\mathbf{200\ kPa}$$

In the same way,

$$p_{N_2}=\frac{(1.0\text{ mol})\times(8.3145\text{ J K}^{-1}\text{mol}^{-1})\times(273.15\text{ K})}{(22.4\times10^{-3}\text{ m}^3)}$$
$$=2.0\times10^5\text{ Pa}=\mathbf{100\ kPa}$$

(b) The total pressure is, from Dalton's law, eqn 1.8, therefore

$$p=p_{H_2}+p_{N_2}=200\text{ kPa}+100\text{ kPa}=\mathbf{300\ kPa}$$

**E1.20** The root-mean-square speed of molecules is given by eqn 1.17.

$$v_{rms}=\left(\frac{3RT}{M}\right)^{1/2}$$

(a) Thus, for $N_2$

$$v_{rms}=\left\{\frac{3\times(8.3145\text{ J K}^{-1}\text{mol}^{-1})\times(273\text{ K})}{(28.02\times10^{-3}\text{ kg mol}^{-1})}\right\}^{1/2}=\mathbf{492\ m\ s^{-1}}$$

(b) and for $H_2O$,

$$v_{rms}=\left\{\frac{3\times(8.3145\text{ J K}^{-1}\text{mol}^{-1})\times(273\text{ K})}{(18.02\times10^{-3}\text{ kg mol}^{-1})}\right\}^{1/2}=\mathbf{614\ m\ s^{-1}}$$

**E1.21** The translational kinetic energy of an atom or molecule depends upon the square of its speed, through eqn 0.12a. The average kinetic energy of an atom or molecule in a gas is therefore

$$\langle E_k\rangle=\tfrac{1}{2}m\langle v^2\rangle$$

However, the equipartition theorem states that quadratic terms such as this contribute, on average, $\tfrac{1}{2}kT$ to the total energy. Thus, because the atoms or molecules in a gas move in three dimensions, the total average translational kinetic energy according to the equipartition theorem is

$$\langle E_{\text{trans}} \rangle = 3 \times \tfrac{1}{2}kT$$

Equating these two expressions,

$$\tfrac{1}{2}m\langle v^2 \rangle = 3 \times \tfrac{1}{2}kT$$

so that

$$\langle v^2 \rangle = \frac{3kT}{m} = \frac{3\overbrace{N_A k}^{R} T}{\underbrace{N_A m}_{M}} = \frac{3RT}{M}$$

and therefore

$$v_{\text{rms}} = \langle v^2 \rangle^{1/2} = \left(\frac{3RT}{M}\right)^{1/2}$$

**E1.22** Combining eqns 1.13 and 1,17, the mean speed is

$$\bar{v} = \left(\frac{8}{3\pi}\right)^{1/2} v_{\text{rms}} = \left(\frac{8}{3\pi}\right)^{1/2} \left(\frac{3RT}{M}\right)^{1/2} = \left(\frac{8RT}{\pi M}\right)^{1/2}$$

Hence, for He atoms, with a molar mass of $M = 4.00 \text{ g mol}^{-1}$,

$$\bar{v}_{\text{He}}(79 \text{ K}) = \left\{\frac{8 \times (8.3145 \text{ J K}^{-1}\text{mol}^{-1}) \times (79 \text{ K})}{\pi \times (4.00 \times 10^{-3} \text{ kg mol}^{-1})}\right\}^{1/2}$$
$$= \mathbf{647 \text{ m s}^{-1}}$$

$$\bar{v}_{\text{He}}(315 \text{ K}) = \left\{\frac{8 \times (8.3145 \text{ J K}^{-1}\text{mol}^{-1}) \times (315 \text{ K})}{\pi \times (4.00 \times 10^{-3} \text{ kg mol}^{-1})}\right\}^{1/2}$$
$$= 1.29 \times 10^3 \text{ m s}^{-1} = \mathbf{1.29 \text{ km s}^{-1}}$$

$$\bar{v}_{\text{He}}(1500 \text{ K}) = \left\{\frac{8 \times (8.3145 \text{ J K}^{-1}\text{mol}^{-1}) \times (1500 \text{ K})}{\pi \times (4.00 \times 10^{-3} \text{ kg mol}^{-1})}\right\}^{1/2}$$
$$= 2.82 \times 10^3 \text{ m s}^{-1} = \mathbf{2.82 \text{ km s}^{-1}}$$

and for methane molecules, with a molar mass of $M = 16.04 \text{ g mol}^{-1}$

$$\bar{v}_{CH_4}(79 \text{ K}) = \left\{\frac{8 \times (8.3145 \text{ J K}^{-1}\text{mol}^{-1}) \times (79 \text{ K})}{\pi \times (4.00 \times 10^{-3} \text{ kg mol}^{-1})}\right\}^{1/2}$$
$$= \mathbf{323 \text{ m s}^{-1}}$$

$$\bar{v}_{CH_4}(315 \text{ K}) = \left\{\frac{8 \times (8.3145 \text{ J K}^{-1}\text{mol}^{-1}) \times (315 \text{ K})}{\pi \times (4.00 \times 10^{-3} \text{ kg mol}^{-1})}\right\}^{1/2}$$
$$= \mathbf{645 \text{ m s}^{-1}}$$

$$\bar{v}_{CH_4}(1500 \text{ K}) = \left\{\frac{8 \times (8.3145 \text{ J K}^{-1}\text{mol}^{-1}) \times (1500 \text{ K})}{\pi \times (4.00 \times 10^{-3} \text{ kg mol}^{-1})}\right\}^{1/2}$$
$$= 1.41 \times 10^3 \text{ m s}^{-1} = \mathbf{1.41 \text{ km s}^{-1}}$$

**E1.23** (a) From the perfect gas equation of state, eqn 1.2, the temperature is

$$T=\frac{pV}{nR}=\frac{pV}{(N/N_A)R}=\frac{N_ApV}{NR}$$

$$=\frac{(6.022\times10^{23}\,\text{mol}^{-1})\times\overbrace{(100\times10^{3}\,\text{Pa})}^{1\,\text{Pa}=1\,\text{J m}^{-3}}\times\overbrace{(1.0\times10^{-3}\,\text{m}^3)}^{1\,\text{dm}^3=10^{-3}\text{m}^3}}{(1.0\times10^{23})\times(8.3145\,\text{J K}^{-1}\text{mol}^{-1})}=\mathbf{72\,K}$$

(b) The root-mean-square speed follows from eqn 1.15

$$v_{\text{rms}}=\left(\frac{3RT}{M}\right)^{1/2}=\left\{\frac{3\times(8.3145\,\text{J K}^{-1}\text{mol}^{-1})\times(72\,\text{K})}{(2.02\times10^{-3}\,\text{kg mol}^{-1})}\right\}^{1/2}=\mathbf{944\,m\,s^{-1}}$$

(c) The temperature would not be different if the molecules were oxygen, $O_2$, rather than hydrogen, $H_2$, providing given the same pressure in the same volume, but the root mean square speed would be different.

**E1.24** According to Graham's law, eqn 1.19, the rate of effusion is inversely proportional to the square root of the molar mass. Thus, the relative rate at which the hydrogen and carbon monoxide leak from the cylinder is

$$\frac{v_{H_2}}{v_{CO}}=\left(\frac{M_{CO}}{M_{H_2}}\right)^{1/2}=\left(\frac{28.01\,\text{g mol}^{-1}}{2.02\,\text{g mol}^{-1}}\right)^{1/2}=\mathbf{3.72}$$

**E1.25** The number of molecules escaping per second depends, according to Graham's law of effusion, on the molar mass through eqn 1.19

$$v\propto\frac{1}{M^{1/2}}$$

Thus, the relative number of molecules escaping in a given time period is

$$\frac{n_{N_2}}{n_{CO_2}}=\left(\frac{M_{CO_2}}{M_{N_2}}\right)^{1/2}$$

The amount of molecules is related to the mass and molar mass through eqn 0.2, $n=m/M$, so that

$$n_{N_2}=\left(\frac{M_{CO_2}}{M_{N_2}}\right)^{1/2}\left(\frac{m_{CO_2}}{M_{CO_2}}\right)$$

and therefore

$$m_{N_2}=n_{N_2}M_{N_2}=\left(\frac{M_{N_2}}{M_{CO_2}}\right)^{1/2}m_{CO_2}=\left(\frac{28.01\,\text{g mol}^{-1}}{44.01\,\text{g mol}^{-1}}\right)^{1/2}\times1.0\,\text{g}=\mathbf{0.80\,g}$$

In the same way,

$$m_{He}=\left(\frac{4.00\,\text{g mol}^{-1}}{44.01\,\text{g mol}^{-1}}\right)^{1/2}\times1.0\,\text{g}=\mathbf{0.30\,g}$$

**E1.26** The volume of a spherical vessel of diameter $d$ is

$$V = (4/3)\pi(d/2)^3 = \pi d^3/6$$

so that, rearranging,

$$d = (6V/\pi)^{1/3}$$

The mean free path of a molecule is given by eqn 1.21

$$\lambda = kT/\sigma p$$

Equating these two quantities and rearranging for pressure,

$$\begin{aligned} p &= \frac{kT}{\sigma(6V/\pi)^{1/3}} \\ &= \frac{(1.381\times10^{-23}\,\mathrm{J\,K^{-1}})\times(273.15+25)\mathrm{K}}{\underbrace{(0.36\times10^{-18}\mathrm{m^2})}_{1\,\mathrm{nm^2}=10^{-18}\mathrm{m^2}}\times\{6\times\underbrace{(1.0\times10^{-3}\mathrm{m^3})}_{1\,\mathrm{dm^3}=10^{-3}\mathrm{m^3}}/\pi\}^{1/3}} \\ &= \underbrace{0.092\,\mathrm{J\,m^{-3}}}_{1\,\mathrm{J\,m^{-3}}=1\,\mathrm{Pa}} = \mathbf{92\ mPa} \end{aligned}$$

A more sophisticated treatment of kinetic theory that takes into account the relative speed of the molecules rather than the absolute speed suggest that a more accurate expression for the mean free path is $\lambda = kT/\sqrt{2}\sigma p$. The resulting pressure is then 65 mPa.

**E1.27** The cross-sectional area of an atom is, from Figure 1.12, $\sigma = \pi d^2$, so that, rearranging, we may express the diameter as

$$d = (\sigma/\pi)^{1/2}$$

The mean free path of a molecule is, however, given by eqn 1.21

$$\lambda = kT/\sigma p$$

Equating these two quantities and rearranging for pressure,

$$\begin{aligned} p &= \frac{kT}{\sigma(\sigma/\pi)^{1/2}} = \frac{\pi^{1/2}kT}{\sigma^{3/2}} \\ &= \frac{\pi^{1/2}\times(1.381\times10^{-23}\,\mathrm{J\,K^{-1}})\times(273.15+25)\mathrm{K}}{\underbrace{(0.36\times10^{-18}\mathrm{m^2})^{3/2}}_{1\,\mathrm{nm^2}=10^{-18}\mathrm{m^2}}} \\ &= \overbrace{33\times10^{6}\,\mathrm{J\,m^{-3}}}^{1\,\mathrm{J\,m^{-3}}=1\,\mathrm{Pa}} = \mathbf{33\ MPa} \end{aligned}$$

Once again, a more accurate treatment of kinetic theory suggests that the mean free path is shorter by a factor of $2^{1/2}$ than predicted here. The pressure calculated using this more advanced theory, will also therefore be lower by an equivalent factor.

**E1.28** The mean free path of a molecule is given by eqn 1.21

$$\lambda = \frac{kT}{\sigma p} = \frac{(1.381\times10^{-23}\ \mathrm{J\,K^{-1}})\times(217\ \mathrm{K})}{\underbrace{(0.43\times10^{-18}\mathrm{m^2})}_{1\ \mathrm{nm^2}=10^{-18}\ \mathrm{m^2}}\times\underbrace{(0.050\ \mathrm{atm}\times1.01325\times10^5\ \mathrm{Pa\,atm^{-1}})}_{1\ \mathrm{atm}=1.01325\times10^5\ \mathrm{Pa}}}$$
$$= 1.37\times10^{-6}\ \mathrm{m} = \mathbf{1.37\ \mu m}$$

**E1.29** The number of collisions made by an atom or molecule is given by the product of the collision frequency $z$ and the time interval $\delta t$. We may, however, express the collision frequency in terms of the temperature and pressure using eqns 1.17 and 1.21

$$Z = \frac{\sigma v_{\mathrm{rms}} p}{kT} = \frac{\sigma(3RT/M)^{1/2}p}{kT} = \frac{\sigma(3kT/m)^{1/2}p}{kT} = \frac{\sqrt{3}\sigma p}{(mkT)^{1/2}}$$

Thus, taking the collision cross-section to be 0.36 nm$^2$ from Table 1.4, the number of collisions in 1 s at a presure of 10 bar is

$$N = Z\delta t = \frac{\sqrt{3}\sigma p\delta t}{(mkT)^{1/2}}$$
$$= \frac{\sqrt{3}\times\overbrace{(0.36\times10^{-18}\ \mathrm{m^2})}^{1\ \mathrm{nm^2}=10^{-18}\mathrm{m^2}}\times(10\ \mathrm{bar}\times\ 10^5\ \mathrm{Pa\,bar^{-1}})\times(1\ \mathrm{s})}{\{39.95m_u\times(1.38\times10^{-23}\ \mathrm{J\,K^{-1}})\times(273.15+25)\ \mathrm{K}\}^{1/2}}$$
$$= \frac{\sqrt{3}\times\overbrace{(0.36\times10^{-18}\ \mathrm{m^2})}^{1\ \mathrm{nm^2}=10^{-18}\mathrm{m^2}}\times(10\ \mathrm{bar}\times\ 10^5\ \mathrm{Pa\,bar^{-1}})\times(1\ \mathrm{s})}{\{39.95\times(1.602\times10^{-27}\ \mathrm{kg})\times(1.38\times10^{-23}\ \mathrm{J\,K^{-1}})\times(273.15+25)\ \mathrm{K}\}^{1/2}}$$
$$= \mathbf{4.0\times10^{10}}$$

The number of collisions is directly proportional to the pressure, so that, for a pressure of 100 kPa, which is one hundreth of that used above,

$$N = 4.0\times10^8$$

and for a pressure of 1 Pa, which is a factor of $10^{-6}$ of the original pressure,

$$N = 4.0\times10^4$$

**E1.30** The total number of collisions per second is proportional to the collision frequency, which is the number of collisions per second for an individual atom, and the number of atoms. We must also be careful not to double count every collision. Hence, for a pressure of 10 bar = $10^6$ Pa, temperature of 25 °C = 298 K and volume of 1 dm$^3$ = $10^{-3}$ m$^3$,

$$N_{\mathrm{total}} = \tfrac{1}{2}(N_{\mathrm{A}}n)\times z$$
$$= \tfrac{1}{2}N_{\mathrm{A}}\left(\frac{pV}{RT}\right)\times\frac{\sigma v_{\mathrm{rms}}p}{kT} = N_{\mathrm{A}}\left(\frac{pV}{RT}\right)\frac{\sigma(3RT/M)^{1/2}p}{(R/N_{\mathrm{A}})T} = \frac{\sqrt{3}N_{\mathrm{A}}^2p^2V}{M^{1/2}(RT)^{3/2}}$$
$$= \frac{\sqrt{3}\times(0.36\times10^{-18}\ \mathrm{m^2})\times(6.022\times10^{23}\ \mathrm{mol^{-1}})^2\times(10^6\ \mathrm{Pa})^2\times(10^{-3}\ \mathrm{m^3})}{2\times(39.95\times10^{-3}\ \mathrm{kg\,mol^{-1}})^{1/2}\times\{(8.3145\ \mathrm{J\,K^{-1}mol^{-1}})\times(298\ \mathrm{K})\}^{3/2}}$$
$$= \mathbf{4.6\times10^{33}\ s^{-1}}$$

The number of collisions depends upon the square of the pressure. Thus, for a pressure of 100 kPa = $10^5$ Pa, which is a factor of $10^{-1}$ times smaller than above, the number of collisions will be smaller by a factor of $10^{-2}$, and so

$$N_{\text{total}} = \mathbf{4.6 \times 10^{31}\ s^{-1}}$$

In the same way, a pressure of 1.0 Pa is a factor of $10^{-6}$ times smaller than the original conditions, so that the number of collisions will be smaller by a factor of $10^{-12}$, so that

$$N_{\text{total}} = \mathbf{4.6 \times 10^{21}\ s^{-1}}$$

**E1.31** The collision frequency of a molecule is given by eqn 1.22, with the root-mean-square speed given by eqn 1.17. Thus, using the value for the collision cross section from Table 1.4,

$$\begin{aligned} z &= \frac{\sigma v_{\text{rms}} p}{kT} = \frac{\sigma(3RT/M)^{1/2} p}{(R/N_{\text{A}})T} = \frac{\sqrt{3}\sigma N_{\text{A}} p}{(RTM)^{1/2}} \\ &= \frac{\sqrt{3} \times (0.43 \times 10^{-18}\ \text{m}^2) \times (6.022 \times 10^{23} \text{mol}^{-1}) \times (0.050\ \text{atm} \times 1.01325 \times 10^5\ \text{Pa atm}^{-1})}{\{(8.3145\ \text{J K}^{-1}\text{mol}^{-1}) \times (217\ \text{K}) \times (28.02 \times 10^{-3} \text{kg mol}^{-1})\}^{1/2}} \\ &= \mathbf{3.2 \times 10^8\ s^{-1}} \end{aligned}$$

**E1.32** The mean free path of an atom or molecule is given by eqn 1.21. Thus, manipulating the equation and recognising that we may use the perfect gas law, eqn 1.2, to replace some terms

$$\lambda = \frac{kT}{\sigma p} = \frac{(R/N_{\text{A}})T}{\sigma p} = \frac{RT}{p} \times \frac{1}{N_{\text{A}}\sigma} = \frac{V}{n} \times \frac{1}{N_{\text{A}}\sigma} = \frac{V}{nN_{\text{A}}\sigma}$$

Thus, the mean free path is directly proportional to the volume of the container for a fixed amount of gas and is not dependent upon temperature.

**E1.33** The mean free path of an atom or molecule is given by eqn 1.21. Thus, assuming that air may be represented by nitrogen molecules, $N_2$, and using the value for the collision cross section from Table 1.4, at 10 bar,

$$\begin{aligned} \lambda &= \frac{kT}{\sigma p} \\ &= \frac{(1.38 \times 10^{-23}\ \text{J K}^{-1}) \times (298\ \text{K})}{(0.43 \times 10^{-18}\ \text{m}^2) \times (10\ \text{bar} \times 10^5\ \text{Pa bar}^{-1})} = 9.6 \times 10^{-9}\ \text{m} = \mathbf{9.6\ nm} \end{aligned}$$

The mean free path is inversely proportional to pressure. Thus, for a pressure of 103 kPa, which is approximately one tenth of the pressure above, the mean free path will be ten times the original result

$$\lambda = \mathbf{96\ nm}$$

In the same way, at a pressure of 1.0 Pa, which is $10^{-6}$ times lower than in the original calculation, the mean free path will be $10^{6}$ times greater

$$\lambda = 9.6 \times 10^{-3}\ \text{m} = \mathbf{9.6\ mm}$$

**E1.34** From the definition of the compression factor, eqn 1.23b, and being careful to convert the quantities to SI base units

$$\begin{aligned} Z_c &= \frac{p_c V_{m,c}}{RT_c} \\ &= \frac{111.3\ \text{atm} \times (1.013 \times 10^5\ \text{atm Pa}^{-1}) \times (7.25 \times 10^{-5}\ \text{m}^3\ \text{mol}^{-1})}{(8.3145\ \text{J K}^{-1}\text{mol}^{-1}) \times (405.5\ \text{K})} \\ &= \mathbf{0.242} \end{aligned}$$

The compression factor $Z_c < 1$, indicating that attractive interactions must be dominant at the critical point.

**E1.35** Rearranging the truncated form of the virial equation of state, and substituting the definition of the compression factor, eqn 1.23b

$$\begin{aligned} B' &= \frac{Z-1}{p} = \frac{pV_m/RT - 1}{p} = \frac{V_m}{RT} - \frac{1}{p} \\ &= \left\{\frac{(5.53 \times 10^{-5}\ \text{m}^3\ \text{mol}^{-1})}{(8.3145\ \text{J K}^{-1}\text{mol}^{-1}) \times (647.4\ \text{K})}\right\} \\ &\qquad - \left\{\frac{1}{(218.3\ \text{atm}) \times (1.01325 \times 10^5\ \text{Pa atm}^{-1})}\right\} \\ &= \mathbf{-3.49 \times 10^{-8}\ Pa^{-1}} \end{aligned}$$

The value of the second virial coefficient is negative, indicating that for water at the critical point, attractive interactions dominate.

**E1.36** (a) Applying the perfect gas equation of state, eqn 1.2, the pressure exerted at 273.15 K and 22.414 $\text{dm}^3$ is

$$\begin{aligned} p &= \frac{nRT}{V} \\ &= \frac{(1.0\ \text{mol}) \times (8.3145\ \text{J K}^{-1}\text{mol}^{-1}) \times (273.15\ \text{K})}{\underbrace{(22.414 \times 10^{-3}\ \text{m}^3)}_{1\ \text{dm}^3 = 10^{-3}\ \text{m}^3}} = 101 \times 10^3\ \text{Pa} = \mathbf{101\ kPa} \end{aligned}$$

and at 1000 K and 100 $\text{cm}^3$,

$$\begin{aligned} p &= \frac{nRT}{V} \\ &= \frac{(1.0\ \text{mol}) \times (8.3145\ \text{J K}^{-1}\text{mol}^{-1}) \times (1000\ \text{K})}{\underbrace{(100 \times 10^{-6}\ \text{m}^3)}_{1\ \text{cm}^3 = 10^{-6}\text{m}^3}} = 8.31 \times 10^7\ \text{Pa} = \mathbf{83.1\ MPa} \end{aligned}$$

(b) Applying eqn 1.26a,

$$a = \overbrace{(5.507 \times 10^{-6})}^{1\,\text{dm}^3=10^{-1}\text{m}^3} \times \overbrace{(1.01325 \times 10^5)}^{1\,\text{atm}=1.01325\times10^5\,\text{Pa}}\ \text{m}^3\ \text{Pa}^{-1}\ \text{mol}^{-2}$$
$$= 0.5580\ \text{m}^3\text{Pa}^{-1}\text{mol}^{-2}$$

$$b = 0.0651 \times \overbrace{10^{-3}}^{1\,\text{dm}^3=10^{-1}\text{m}^3}\ \text{m}^3\text{mol}^{-1} = 6.51 \times 10^{-5}\ \text{m}^3\text{mol}^{-1}$$

at 273.15 K and 22.414 $\text{dm}^3$ the pressure is

$$p = \frac{nRT}{V - nb} - a\left(\frac{n}{V}\right)^2$$
$$= \left[\frac{(1.0\ \text{mol}) \times (8.3145\ \text{J K}^{-1}\text{mol}^{-1}) \times (273.15\ \text{K})}{(22.414 \times 10^{-3}\ \text{m}^3) - \{(1.0\ \text{mol}) \times (6.51 \times 10^{-5}\text{m}^3\ \text{mol}^{-1})\}}\right] - \left(\frac{(0.5436\ \text{m}^3\text{Pa}^{-1}\text{mol}^{-2}) \times (1.0\ \text{mol})}{(22.414 \times 10^{-3}\ \text{m}^3)}\right)^2$$
$$= 1.01 \times 10^5\ \text{Pa} = \mathbf{101\ kPa}$$

and at 1000 K and 100 $\text{cm}^3$,

$$p = \frac{nRT}{V - nb} - a\left(\frac{n}{V}\right)^2$$
$$= \left[\frac{(1.0\ \text{mol}) \times (8.3145\ \text{J K}^{-1}\text{mol}^{-1}) \times (1000\ \text{K})}{(100 \times 10^{-6}\ \text{m}^3) - \{(1.0\ \text{mol}) \times (6.51 \times 10^{-5}\text{m}^3\ \text{mol}^{-1})\}}\right] - \left(\frac{(0.5436\ \text{m}^3\text{Pa}^{-1}\text{mol}^{-2}) \times (1.0\ \text{mol})}{(100 \times 10^{-6}\ \text{m}^3)}\right)^2$$
$$= 8.37 \times 10^6\ \text{Pa} = \mathbf{83.7\ MPa}$$

Thus, at 273.15 K and 22.414 $\text{dm}^3$, the pressure is the same for both the perfect and van der Waals gases. However, at 1000 K and 100 $\text{cm}^3$, the interactions between the molecules become significant; the pressure of the van der Waals gas is greater than that of the perfect gas under these conditions, indicating that repulsive interactions dominate.

**E1.37** Using the perfect gas and van der Waals equations of state, eqns 1.2 and 1.26 respectively, and, taking the values of the van der Waals parameters for carbon dioxide from Table 1.6,

$$p_{\text{perfect}} = \left(\frac{nRT}{V}\right) = \left(\frac{m}{M}\right)\left(\frac{RT}{V}\right) = \frac{mRT}{MV}$$
$$= \frac{(10.00\ \text{g}) \times (8.3145\ \text{J K}^{-1}\text{mol}^{-1}) \times (298.15\ \text{K})}{(44.01\ \text{g mol}^{-1}) \times (100 \times 10^{-6}\text{m}^3)}$$
$$= 5.633 \times 10^6\ \text{Pa} = 5.633\ \text{MPa}$$

$$p_{\text{vdW}} = \left(\frac{nRT}{V - nb}\right) - a\left(\frac{n}{V}\right)^2 = \left\{\frac{(m/M)RT}{V - (m/M)b}\right\} - a\left\{\frac{(m/M)}{V}\right\}^2$$
$$= \frac{\{(10.00\ \text{g})/(44.01\ \text{g mol}^{-1})\} \times (8.3145\ \text{J K}^{-1}\text{mol}^{-1}) \times (298.15\ \text{K})}{(100 \times 10^{-6}\text{m}^3) - \{(10.00\ \text{g}) \times (4.29 \times 10^{-5}\text{m}^3\ \text{mol}^{-1})/(44.01\ \text{g mol}^{-1})\}}$$
$$- (0.3119\ \text{m}^3\text{Pa}^{-1}\text{mol}^{-2})\left(\frac{(10.00\ \text{g})/(44.01\ \text{g mol}^{-1})}{100 \times 10^{-6}\ \text{m}^3}\right)^2$$

$$= 4.631 \text{ MPa}$$

The difference is therefore

$$\Delta p = p_{\text{perfect}} - p_{\text{vdW}} = 5.633 \text{ MPa} - 4.631 \text{ MPa} = \mathbf{1.002\ MPa}$$

which is equivalent to 17 per cent of the perfect-gas pressure.

**E1.38** Rearranging the van der Waals equation of state, eqn 1.21b,

$$\begin{aligned} b &= \frac{V}{n} - \frac{RT}{\{p + a(n/V)^2\}} = V_{\text{m}} - \frac{RT}{\{p + a/V_{\text{m}}^2\}} \\ &= (5.00 \times 10^{-4} \text{ m}^3 \text{ mol}^{-1}) \\ &\quad - \left[\frac{(8.3145 \text{ J K}^{-1}\text{mol}^{-1}) \times (273 \text{ K})}{(3.0 \times 10^6 \text{ Pa}) + \{(0.50 \text{ m}^6 \text{ Pa mol}^{-2})/(5.00 \times 10^{-4} \text{ m}^3 \text{ mol}^{-1})^2\}}\right] \\ &= \mathbf{4.6 \times 10^{-5}\ m^3\ mol^{-1}} \end{aligned}$$

The compression factor is therefore, from eqn 1.23b,

$$Z = \frac{pV_{\text{m}}}{RT} = \frac{(3.0 \times 10^6 \text{ Pa}) \times (5.00 \times 10^{-4} \text{ m}^3 \text{ mol}^{-1})}{(8.3145 \text{ J K}^{-1}\text{mol}^{-1}) \times (273 \text{ K})} = \mathbf{0.66}$$

**E1.39** We may express the van der Waals equation of state, eqn 1.26a, as

$$p = \frac{RT}{(V_{\text{m}} - b)} - \frac{a}{V_{\text{m}}^2} = \left\{\frac{RT}{V_{\text{m}}} \times \frac{1}{(1 - b/V_{\text{m}})}\right\} - \frac{a}{V_{\text{m}}^2}$$

Because $b/V_{\text{m}} \ll 1$, it is possible to expand the factor $(1 - b / V_{\text{m}})^{-1}$ as a Taylor series for which higher order terms become negligibly small:

$$\begin{aligned} (1 - x)^{-1} &= 1 + x + x^2 + \cdots \\ (1 - b/V_{\text{m}})^{-1} &= 1 + (b/V_{\text{m}}) + (b/V_{\text{m}})^2 + \cdots \end{aligned}$$

Thus,

$$\begin{aligned} p &= \left[\frac{RT}{V_{\text{m}}} \times \{1 + (b/V_{\text{m}}) + (b/V_{\text{m}})^2 + \cdots\}\right] - \frac{a}{V_{\text{m}}^2} \\ &= (RT/V_{\text{m}})[1 + \{b - (a/RT)\}/V_{\text{m}} + b^2/V_{\text{m}}^2 + \cdots] \end{aligned}$$

Comparsion with the virial equation of state, eqn 1.25,

$$p = (RT/V_{\text{m}})\{1 + B/V_{\text{m}} + C/V_{\text{m}}^2 + \cdots\}$$

shows that

$$B = \{b - (a/RT)\}$$

and

$$C = b^2$$

**E1.40** Combining the relationships between the virial coefficients $B$ and $C$ and the van der Waals parameters $a$ and $b$ derived in the previous exercise, $B = \{b - (a / RT)\}$ and $C = b^2$,

$$b = C^{1/2} = \underbrace{(1200 \times 10^{-12}\text{m}^6\text{mol}^{-2})}_{1\text{ cm}^3=10^{-2}\text{ m}^3}{}^{1/2} = \mathbf{3.5 \times 10^{-5}m^3\ mol^{-1}}$$

and

$$\begin{aligned} a &= RT(b - B) \\ &= (8.3145\text{ J K}^{-1}\text{mol}^{-1}) \times (273\text{ K}) \\ &\qquad \times \{(1200 \times 10^{-12}\text{m}^6\text{mol}^{-2})^{1/2} - (-21.7 \times 10^{-6}\text{m}^3\text{mol}^{-1})\} \\ &= \underbrace{0.128\text{ J m}^3\text{mol}^{-1}}_{1\text{ J}=1\text{ Pa m}^3} = \mathbf{0.128\ Pa\ m^6\ mol^{-1}} \end{aligned}$$

**E1.41** Using the expression for the second virial coefficient $B$ in terms of the van der Waals parameters $a$ and $b$ derived in Exercise 1.39, if $B = \{b - (a / RT)\} = 0$, then

$$b = \frac{a}{RT}$$

and so, using the values for the van der Waals parameters for carbon dioxide from Table 1.6, $a = 3.119 \times 10^2$ kPa dm$^6$ mol$^{-2}$ and $b = 4.29 \times 10^{-2}$ dm$^3$ mol$^{-1}$,

$$T_{B=0} = \frac{a}{Rb} = \frac{\overbrace{(0.3119 \times \text{Pa m}^6\text{mol}^{-2})}^{1\text{ dm}^6=10^{-6}\text{ m}^6}}{(8.3145\text{ J K}^{-1}\text{mol}^{-1}) \times \underbrace{(4.29 \times 10^{-5}\text{m}^3\text{ mol}^{-1})}_{1\text{ dm}^3=10^{-3}\text{ m}^3}} = \mathbf{874\ K}$$

At this temperature, known as the Boyle temperature, carbon dioxide behaves as if a perfect gas, with the compression factor, $Z = 1$.

**E1.42** From the relationships in eqns 1.27,

$$V_c = 3b, T_c = \frac{8a}{27Rb} \text{ and } p_c = \frac{a}{27b^2}$$

so that

$$b = V_c/3 = 148\text{ cm}^3\text{mol}^{-1}/3 = 49.3\text{ cm}^3\text{ mol}^{-1} = \mathbf{4.93 \times 10^{-5}\ m^3\ mol^{-1}}$$

The parameter $b$ may be considered to be the molar volume occupied by the molecules themselves, so that

$$b = (4/3)\pi r^3 N_A$$

Rearranging,

$$r = \left(\frac{3b}{4\pi N_A}\right)^{1/3} = \left\{\frac{3 \times 148 \times 10^{-6}\text{ m}^3\text{mol}^{-1}}{4\pi \times (6.022 \times 10^{23}\text{mol}^{-1})}\right\}^{1/3} = 3.9 \times 10^{-10}\text{ m} = \mathbf{0.39\ nm}$$

We may calculate the value of $a$ in different ways, because we have three crictical parameters, $p_{c}$, $V_c$ and $T_c$, but only two unknowns, $a$ and $b$. Using the expression for $T_c$,

$$\begin{aligned} a &= (27/8)RbT_c = (27/8)R(V_c/3)T_c = (9/8)RV_cT_c \\ &= (9/8) \times (8.3145\ \mathrm{J\ K^{-1}mol^{-1}}) \times (148 \times 10^{-6}\mathrm{m^3mol^{-1}}) \times (305.4\ \mathrm{K}) \\ &= 0.423\ \mathrm{J\ m^3\ mol^{-1}} = \mathbf{0.423\ Pa\ m^6\ mol^{-1}} \end{aligned}$$

or the expression for $p_c$

$$\begin{aligned} a &= 27b^2p_c = 27(V_c/3)^2p_c = 3V_c/p_c \\ &= 3 \times (148 \times 10^{-6}\mathrm{m^3mol^{-1}})^2 \times \{(48.20\ \mathrm{atm}) \times (1.01325 \times 10^5\ \mathrm{Pa\ atm^{-1}})\} \\ &= \mathbf{0.321\ Pa\ m^6\ mol^{-1}} \end{aligned}$$

## Answers to projects

**P1.43** (a) For continuous variables, such as speed, we may calculate an average by calculating the integral of the variable multiplied by the probability distribution function. For a Maxwellian distribution of speeds, the probability distribution is given by eqn 1.18. Thus, the average speed is given by the integral

$$\begin{aligned} \langle v\rangle &= \int_0^\infty v\,P(v)\,\mathrm{d}v \\ &= \int_0^\infty v\left\{4\pi\left(\frac{M}{2\pi RT}\right)^{3/2} v^2\mathrm{e}^{-Mv^2/2RT}\right\}\mathrm{d}v \\ &= 4\pi\left(\frac{M}{2\pi RT}\right)^{3/2}\int_0^\infty v^3\mathrm{e}^{-Mv^2/2RT}\,\mathrm{d}v \end{aligned}$$

This integral is of the standard form

$$\int_0^\infty x^{2n+1}\mathrm{e}^{-ax^2}\,\mathrm{d}x = \frac{n!}{2a^2} \text{ with } n = 1 \text{ and } a = \frac{M}{2RT}$$

Thus,

$$\langle v\rangle = 4\pi\left(\frac{M}{2\pi RT}\right)^{3/2} \times \left\{\frac{1!}{2(M/2RT)^2}\right\} = \left(\frac{8RT}{\pi M}\right)^{1/2}$$

(b) In the same way, the average squared speed is

$$\begin{aligned} \langle v^2\rangle &= \int_0^\infty v\,P(v)\,\mathrm{d}v \\ &= \int_0^\infty v^2\left\{4\pi\left(\frac{M}{2\pi RT}\right)^{3/2} v^2\mathrm{e}^{-Mv^2/2RT}\right\}\mathrm{d}v \\ &= 4\pi\left(\frac{M}{2\pi RT}\right)^{3/2}\int_0^\infty v^4\mathrm{e}^{-Mv^2/2RT}\,\mathrm{d}v \end{aligned}$$

This integral is of the standard form

$$\int_0^{\infty} x^4 e^{-ax^2}\,dx = \frac{3}{8a^2}\left(\frac{\pi}{a}\right)^{1/2} \quad \text{with } a = \frac{M}{2RT}$$

so that

$$\langle v^2\rangle = 4\pi\left(\frac{M}{2\pi RT}\right)^{3/2} \times \frac{3}{8(M/2RT)^2}\left\{\frac{\pi}{(M/2RT)}\right\}^{1/2} = \frac{3RT}{M}$$

Thus, the root-mean-square speed is

$$v_{\text{rms}} = \langle v^2\rangle^{1/2} = \left(\frac{3RT}{M}\right)^{1/2}$$

(c) The most probable speed corresponds to the maximum in the probability distribution function $P(v)$. The most probable speed may therefore be found by differentiating, and solving

$$\frac{dP(v)}{dv} = 0$$

Hence,

$$\frac{dP(v)}{dv} = \frac{d}{dv}\left\{4\pi\left(\frac{M}{2\pi RT}\right)^{3/2} v^2 e^{-Mv^2/2RT}\right\} = 4\pi\left(\frac{M}{2\pi RT}\right)^{3/2}\frac{d}{dv}\left(v^2 e^{-Mv^2/2RT}\right)$$

This differential is of the form

$$\frac{d}{dx}(fg) = f\frac{dg}{dx} + g\frac{df}{dx}$$

so that

$$\begin{aligned}\frac{dP(v)}{dv} &= 4\pi\left(\frac{M}{2\pi RT}\right)^{3/2} \times \left[v^2\frac{d}{dv}\left(e^{-Mv^2/2RT}\right) + e^{-Mv^2/2RT}\frac{d}{dv}(v^2)\right] \\ &= 4\pi\left(\frac{M}{2\pi RT}\right)^{3/2}\left[\left\{v^2 \times \overbrace{\left(-\frac{Mv}{RT}\right) \times e^{-Mv^2/2RT}}^{\frac{d}{dx}e^{f(x)} = \left(\frac{d}{dx}f(x)\right)e^{f(x)}}\right\} + \left\{e^{-Mv^2/2RT} \times (2v)\right\}\right] \\ &= 0\end{aligned}$$

Thus,

$$-\frac{Mv^3}{RT} \times e^{-Mv^2/2RT} + 2v\,e^{-Mv^2/2RT} = 0$$

Dividing through by the common factor $\left(v\,e^{-Mv^2/2RT}\right)$ and rearranging,

$$v^2 = 2RT/M$$

so that the most probable speed is

$$v^* = (2RT/M)^{1/2}$$

(e) The fraction of molecules with speeds in a small range $\delta v$ is given by the product

$$f(v, v+\delta v) = P(v)\delta v = \left\{4\pi\left(\frac{M}{2\pi RT}\right)^{3/2} v^2 e^{-Mv^2/2RT}\right\}\delta v$$

This expression is valid only if the range is sufficiently small that the probability may be assumed to be constant. For the interval $290\ \text{m s}^{-1} \le v \le 300\ \text{m s}^{-1}$, we may use the value for the probability at $295\ \text{m s}^{-1}$ as an average across the entire range. Thus,

$$\begin{aligned}
f &= P(295\ \text{m s}^{-1}) \times \overbrace{(300\ \text{ms}^{-1} - 290\ \text{ms}^{-1})}^{\delta v} \\
&= 4\pi\left\{\frac{(28.02\times10^{-3}\ \text{kg mol}^{-1})}{2\pi(8.3145\ \text{J K}^{-1}\text{mol}^{-1})\times(500\ \text{K})}\right\}^{3/2} \times (295\ \text{m s}^{-1})^2 \\
&\qquad \times e^{-\frac{(28.02\times10^{-3}\ \text{kg mol}^{-1})\times(295\ \text{m s}^{-1})^2}{\{2\times(8.3145\ \text{J K}^{-1}\text{mol}^{-1})\times(500\ \text{K})\}}} \times (10\ \text{m s}^{-1})
\end{aligned}$$

$$= 9.06\times10^{-3} \approx \mathbf{10^{-2}}$$

The fraction of $N_2$ molecules with speeds in the range 290 to 300 m $s^{-1}$ is thus about 1 per cent of the total number.

We cannot use this expression to calculate the fraction with speeds over a wider range because the probability may change significantly over the interval. Instead, we must integrate

$$f(v_1, v_2) = \int_{v_1}^{v_2} P(v)\,dv = \int_{v_1}^{v_2} \left\{4\pi\left(\frac{M}{2\pi RT}\right)^{3/2} v^2 e^{-Mv^2/2RT}\right\} dv$$

**P1.44** (a) If

$$p = \frac{nRT}{V-nb} - a\left(\frac{n}{V}\right)^2 = \frac{RT}{V_m - b} - \frac{a}{V_m^2}$$

then

$$\begin{aligned}
\left(\frac{\partial p}{\partial V_m}\right)_T &= \frac{\partial}{\partial V_m}\left(\frac{RT}{V_m - b} - \frac{a}{V_m^2}\right) \\
&= -RT(V_m - b)^{-2} + 2aV_m^{-3} = 0
\end{aligned}$$

Rearranging, and adding a subscript to indicate that the expressions are valid only at the critical point,

$$V_c^3 = \frac{2a(V_c - b)^2}{RT_c}$$

In the same way,

$$\left(\frac{\partial^2 p}{\partial V_m^2}\right)_T = \frac{\partial}{\partial V_m}\left(\frac{\partial p}{\partial V_m}\right)_T = \frac{\partial}{\partial V_m}\{-RT(V_m - b)^{-2} + 2aV_m^{-3}\}$$
$$= 2RT(V_m - b)^{-3} - 6aV_m^{-4} = 0$$

so that

$$V_c^4 = \frac{3a(V_c - b)^4}{RT_c}$$

Dividing these expressions for $V_c^{\,3}$ and $V_c^{\,4}$ leads to

$$V_c = (3/2)(V_c - 3b)$$

Solving for $V_c$,

$$\boldsymbol{V_c = 3b}$$

Substituting this result leads to an expression for the critical temperature

$$V_c^3 = \frac{2a(V_c - b)^2}{RT_c}$$
$$(3b)^3 = \frac{2a(3b - b)^2}{RT_c}$$
$$27b^3 = \frac{8a}{RT_c}$$
$$\boldsymbol{T_c = \frac{8a}{27bR}}$$

and for the critical pressure

$$p_c = \frac{RT_c}{V_c - b} - \frac{a}{V_c^2}$$
$$= \frac{R\{8a/(27bR)\}}{3b - b} - \frac{a}{(3b)^2} = \frac{4a}{27b^2} - \frac{a}{9b^2}$$
$$= \boldsymbol{\frac{a}{27b^2}}$$

(c) Hence, at the critical point, the compression factor is

$$z = \frac{p_c V_c}{RT_c} = \frac{\overbrace{\{a/(27b^2)\}}^{p_c} \times \overbrace{3b}^{V_c}}{R\underbrace{\{8a/(27bR)\}}_{T_c}} = \frac{3}{8}$$

This result is valid for all gases that obey the van der Waals equation.

**P1.45** (a) As for any perfect gas, the pressure in the interior of the Sun is related to the mass density, $\rho = m/V$, by

$$p = \frac{nRT}{V} = \frac{mRT}{MV} = \frac{\rho RT}{M}$$

Atoms are stripped of their electrons in the interior of stars, so if we suppose that the interior consists of a gas of ionized hydrogen atoms and free electrons, the mean molar mass is half the molar mass of hydrogen, or 0.5 g mol$^{-1}$, being the mean of the molar mass of $H^+$ and $e^-$, the latter being almost 0. Halfway to the centre of the Sun, the pressure is thus

$$p = \frac{(1.20 \times 10^3 \text{ kg m}^{-3}) \times (8.3145 \text{ J K}^{-1}\text{mol}^{-1}) \times (3.6 \times 10^6 \text{ K})}{(0.50 \times 10^{-3} \text{ kg mol}^{-1})}$$
$$= 7.2 \times 10^{13} \text{ Pa} = \mathbf{720\ Mbar}$$

(b) The total kinetic energy of $N$ atoms or molecules is $N$ times the average kinetic energy of one atom or molecule, so that the energy density is

$$\rho_k = \frac{E_{k,\text{total}}}{V} = \frac{N \times \tfrac{1}{2} m v_{\text{rms}}^2}{V} = \frac{N m v_{\text{rms}}^2}{2V}$$

But, from the kinetic model, eqn 1.11,

$$p = \frac{nMv_{\text{rms}}^2}{3V} = \frac{n \times (N_A m) \times v_{\text{rms}}^2}{3V} = \frac{nN_A \times m v_{\text{rms}}^2}{3V} = \frac{N m v_{\text{rms}}^2}{3V}$$

Comparison of the two expressions shows that

$$p = (2/3)\rho_k$$

(c) Thus, using the results derived in parts (a) and (b),

$$\rho_k = (3/2)p = (3/2) \times (7.2 \times 10^{13}\ Pa) = \overbrace{1.1 \times 10^{14} \text{ J m}^{-3}}^{1\ \text{Pa}=1\ \text{J m}^{-3}}$$

The ratio of the kinetic energy density halfway to the centre of the Sun to the kinetic energy density of our atmosphere is therefore

$$(1.1 \times 10^{14} \text{ J m}^{-3})/(1.5 \times 10^5 \text{ J m}^{-3}) = 7.3 \times 10^8$$

(d) The complete ionization of carbon atoms results in a $C^{6+}$ ion and six electrons. Thus, we may take the average molar mass of the particles in the gas to be

$$M = \frac{m_{C^+} + 6m_e}{7} = \frac{\{12 + (6 \times 0)\} \text{ g mol}^{-1}}{7} = 1.7 \text{ g mol}^{-1}$$

Following the same method as in part (a),

$$p = \frac{(1.20 \times 10^3 \text{ kg m}^{-3}) \times (8.3145 \text{ J K}^{-1}\text{mol}^{-1}) \times (3.5 \times 10^3 \text{ K})}{(1.7 \times 10^{-3} \text{ kg mol}^{-1})}$$
$$= 2.1 \times 10^{10} \text{ Pa} = \mathbf{0.21\ Mbar}$$

(e) If the atoms are not ionized, then the average mass is just that of a neutral carbon atom. Thus,

$$p = \frac{(1.20 \times 10^3 \text{ kg m}^{-3}) \times (8.3145 \text{ J K}^{-1}\text{mol}^{-1}) \times (3.5 \times 10^3 \text{ K})}{(12 \times 10^{-3} \text{ kg mol}^{-1})}$$
$$= 2.9 \times 10^7 \text{ Pa} = \mathbf{0.029\ Mbar}$$

# Chapter 2

# Thermodynamics: the First Law

## Answers to discussion questions

**D2.1** The **system** is the part of the world in which we have a special interest. It may be a reaction vessel, an engine, an electrochemical cell, a biological cell, and so on. The **surroundings** comprise the region outside the system and are where we make our measurements. The system is **open** if matter can be transferred between the system and surroundings. Otherwise, it is **closed**. If no heat can be transferred between the system and surroundings, the boundary is **adiabatic**; otherwise, it is **diathermic**. An **isolated system** can exchange neither matter nor energy with its surroundings.

The choice between what is the system of interest and what is the surroundings depends upon the phenomena and substance of interest but the division is often dictated by physical boundaries. The container wall at which a confined gas has contact logically provides the boundary between the system (the gas) and the surroundings (the contact surface and everything beyond it). Yet, if liquid properties alone are the focus of interest, the vapour of the liquid may be considered part of the surroundings and the liquid-gas interface separates the system of interest from the surroundings. In the case for which liquid-gas equilibrium is the centre of focus, both liquid and vapour become part of the system of interest and surroundings begin with the container walls. It is not always necessary to have a boundary that separates the system from surroundings. When discussing stratospheric ozone, it may be convenient to consider the nitrogen and oxygen of the stratosphere to be the surrounding environment of the ozone; energy and mass transfers between the system and surroundings may then be the focus of analysis. Always attempt to clearly define the system and its surroundings so that work, heat, energy, and mass transfers can be correctly accounted for.

**D2.2** (a) **Open** systems are those in which both energy and matter may be exchanged with the surroundings. Examples include a reaction mixture in a non-insulated, unstoppered flask; reactants may be added, gas may be produced, or solvent may evaporate and be lost from the system to the surroundings. Energy may also be exchanged as either heat or work.

(b) **Closed** systems allow the exchange of energy, but not matter and examples include: a reaction mixture in a non-insulated, stoppered flask; although the reactants and products remain within the container, heat may still be exchanged with the surroundings.

(c) **Isolated** systems do not allow any exchange of either energy or matter, and examples include a reaction mixture in an insulated, stoppered flask, such as an adiabatic calorimeter.

**D2.3** (a) **Temperature**, $T$, is an intensive property of a system. It is often said to measure the hotness or coldness of a system in the sense that heat always flows from high temperature to lower temperature. If two objects are at the same temperature, they are in **thermal equilibrium** and there is no net flow of heat between them when they are in contact. Temperature is the single parameter that tells us the relative molecular (and/or atomic) populations over the available energy levels of a system.

(b) **Heat**, $q$, is energy in transit as a result of a temperature difference. It is characterized by energy transfer that the causes or utilizes chaotic, disorderly motion in the surroundings and it depends upon molecular collisions.

(c) **Work**, $w$, is done when a body is moved against an opposing force. If the opposing force is constant, then the work done is given by the product of the magnitude of the opposing force, $F$, and the distance, $d$, through which the body is moved. The magnitude of the work done is thus given by eqn 0.10

$$w = Fd$$

By considering examples of work, such as the raising of a weight against the force of gravity, we may infer that work is the mode of transfer of energy that achieves or utilizes uniform motion in the surroundings.

(d) **Energy** is the capacity to do work. **Internal energy**, $U$, is the sum of all the kinetic and potential contributions to the energy of all the atoms, ions, and molecules in the system. It is the total energy of the system. According to the First Law of Thermodynamics, internal energy is a state property and a change in internal energy, $\Delta U$, occurs because of the surroundings doing work on the system and transferring heat to the system, may be expressed as eqn 2.7:

$$\Delta U = w + q$$

The internal energy of an isolated system is a constant; it is conserved.

**D2.4** At the molecular level, work is a transfer of energy that results in orderly motion of the atoms and molecules in a system; heat is a transfer of energy that results in disorderly motion.

**D2.5** The **law of conservation of energy** states that energy can be neither created nor destroyed but merely converted from one form into another or moved from place to place. The law of conservation of energy, belonging to the field of classical mechanics, considers energy to be the sum of kinetic and potential energies and either one of these can convert to the other. Work is the transfer mode for energy and mechanics does not deal with the concept of heat. The **first law of thermodynamics** adds the transfer of energy via heat to that of work and the sum relates to the internal energy $U$, which becomes the conserved state property. Furthermore, with the recognition that transfers of internal energy occur between the system and surroundings, the first law emphasizes that the transfers change the system's internal energy according to the relation $\Delta U = q + w$, which is eqn 2.7. The heat and work transfers may be very complex but $\Delta U = 0$ for an isolated system; $U$ is conserved.

**D2.6** The most general expression for **expansion work** is

$$dw = -p_{ex}dV$$

The relationship is expressed in terms of differentials, which are neither numbers nor functions, and the expression must be integrated using the concepts and rules of the integral calculus for the particulars of an application. When the expansion work is against a constant external pressure, the integration gives a relation between functions that is computationally practical:

$$w = -p_{ex}\Delta V = -p_{ex} \times (V_f - V_i)$$

which is eqn 2.1 that is valid for expansion work against constant pressure.

We need only specify the values of $p_{ex}$, $V_i$, and $V_f$ before calculating the value of $w$ in this specific process. For example, suppose that $p_{ex} = 1.00$ bar, $V_i = 5.20$ dm$^3$, and $V_f = 6.30$ dm$^3$, we then find that

$$w = -(1.00\text{ bar}) \times (6.30 - 5.20)\text{dm}^3 = -1.10\text{ bar dm}^3 = -110\text{ J}$$

Remarkably, the computation does not depend upon whether the system is gaseous, liquid, or solid; it does not even depend upon the composition of the system. Independence of composition and phase is a powerful generality of thermodynamics. This particular example has only the single restriction that the expansion be against a constant external pressure. Other computations have further, or different, restrictions.

When the expansion work is reversible, the external pressure is balanced at all times by the pressure of the system, $p = p_{ex}$. The external pressure is therefore not constant, but varies as the system expands. Thus, substituting

$$dw = -p\, dV$$

so that

$$w = -\int_{V_i}^{V_f} p\, dV$$

and further information is needed before the general expression can be integrated further. If the behavior of $p$ with changing $V$ is known, the expression may be integrated and the work calculated.

If we consider the example of the reversible, isothermal expansion work of a perfect gas, which is analyzed in *Derivation 2.2*, then we find that,

$$w = -nRT\ln(V_f/V_i)$$

Alternatively, suppose that during a particular reversible expansion the pressure and volume are maintained in the linear correspondence: $p = a + bV$ between $V_i = 5.20\ \text{dm}^3$ and $V_f = 6.30\ \text{dm}^3$ where $a$ and $b$ are the constants $a = 1.00$ bar and $b = -0.30\ \text{bar dm}^{-3}$. The value of the expansion work is now restricted by the reversible condition and the particulars of the $p(V)$ relation during the expansion.

$$\begin{aligned} w &= -\int_{V_i}^{V_f} p\,dV \\ &= -\int_{V_i}^{V_f} (a + bV)\,dV = -\int_{V_i}^{V_f} a\,dV - \int_{V_i}^{V_f} bV\,dV \\ &= [-aV - ½bV^2]_{V_i}^{V_f} \\ &= -a(V_f - V_i) - ½b(V_f^2 - V_i^2) \end{aligned}$$

Now we may substitute values and perform the calculation:

$$\begin{aligned} w &= -\{(1.00\ \text{bar}) \times (6.30\ \text{dm}^3 - 5.20\ \text{dm}^3)\} \\ &\qquad - ½[(-0.30\ \text{bar dm}^{-3}) \times \{(6.30\ \text{dm}^3)^2 - (5.20\ \text{dm}^3)^2\}] \\ &= -1.10\ \text{bar dm}^3 + 1.90\ \text{bar dm}^3 \\ &= \underbrace{+0.80\ \text{bar dm}^3}_{1\ \text{bar dm}^3 = 10^2\ \text{J}} = +80\ \text{J} \end{aligned}$$

These examples demonstrate that work depends upon the particulars, or so-called path, of the process. Work, like heat, is not a state function and thus not a property of the system. Consequently, great care must always be taken to select, or derive, the work relation that is applicable to a particular process.

**D2.7** A **reversible** expansion is one that may be reversed by an *infinitesimal* change in a variable—in this case, the pressure. This condition implies that for a reversible expansion, the external pressure and internal pressure are equal

$$p = p_{ex}$$

For a reversible expansion, the system and surroundings are therefore in mechanical equilibrium because the forces acting are balanced. The work done during an isothermal reversible expansion is thus

$$w_{rev} = -nRT\ln(V_f/V_i)$$

For an **irreversible** expansion, however, the system and surroundings are not necessarily I mechanical equilibirum and the internal and external pressure are not, therefore, equal. The system does work against the force exterted as a result of the external pressure. If the external pressure is contant, then the work done is

$$w_{\text{irrev}} = -p_{\text{ex}}(V_f - V_i)$$

The magnitude of the work done in expansion therefore depends upon whether it occurs reversibly, or irreversibly.

**D2.8** Enthalpy is defined, through eqn 2.11 as

$$H = U + pV$$

so that

$$\Delta H = \Delta U + \Delta(pV)$$

As $\Delta(pV)$ is not usually zero, except for isothermal processes in a perfect gas, the difference between $\Delta H$ and $\Delta U$ is therefore normally a non-zero quantity. The First Law of Thermodynamics, shows us that if the change occurs at constant volume, so that no expansion work is done, and if no other form of work is done, then the change in internal energy is the heat, eqn 2.9b

$$\Delta U = q_V$$

If, however, the change under consideration occurs at constant pressure, with only expansion work done, then

$$\Delta H = \Delta U + p\Delta V$$

and we can show, as in *Derivation 2.3* that the enthalpy change is equivalent to the heat

$$\Delta H = q_p$$

**D2.9** $q = nRT \ln(V_f/V_i)$ limitations: reversible, isothermal expansion of a perfect gas

$\Delta H = \Delta U + p\Delta V$ limitation: constant pressure process

$C_{p,m} - C_{V,m} = R$ limitation: perfect gas

## Solutions to exercises

**E2.1** Expansion against atmospheric pressure is an irreversible process. Thus, the work done is given by

$$w = -p_{\text{ex}}\Delta V$$

so that

(a)

$$w_{\text{expansion}} = -(1.00 \times 10^5\ \text{Pa}) \times \overbrace{(1.0 \times 10^{-6}\ \text{m}^3)}^{1\ \text{cm}^3 = 10^{-6}\text{m}^3} = \underbrace{-0.10\ \text{Pa m}^3}_{1\ \text{Pa m}^3 = 1\ \text{J}} = \mathbf{-0.10\ J}$$

(b)

$$w_{\text{expansion}} = -(1.00\times10^{5}\ \text{Pa})\times\overbrace{(1.0\times10^{-3}\ \text{m}^3)}^{1\ \text{dm}^3=10^{-3}\text{m}^3} = -100\ \text{Pa m}^3 = \mathbf{-100\ J}$$

The work done in a process depends upon the path taken. If we assume that the compression also occurs irreversibly at constant external pressure, then

(a) $w_{\text{compression}} = -(1.00\times10^{5}\ \text{Pa})\times-(1.0\times10^{-6}\ \text{m}^3) = \mathbf{+0.10\ J}$

(b) $w_{\text{compression}} = -(1.00\times10^{5}\ \text{Pa})\times(1.0\times10^{-3}\ \text{m}^3) = \mathbf{+100\ J}$

**E2.2** The work done when a gas expands reversibly and isothermally is, from eqn 2.2,

$$\begin{aligned} w &= -nRT\ln(V_f/V_i) \\ &= -(2.0\ \text{mol})\times(8.3145\ \text{J K}^{-1}\text{mol}^{-1})\times(300\ \text{K})\times\ln(3.0\ \text{dm}^3/1.0\ \text{dm}^3) \\ &= -5.5\times10^{3}\text{J} = \mathbf{-5.5\ kJ} \end{aligned}$$

**E2.3** (a) For an irreversible, isothermal expansion, with a change in volume of $\Delta V = 3.3\ \text{dm}^3$

$$\begin{aligned} w &= -p_{\text{ex}}\Delta V \\ &= -(30.0\times10^{3}\ \text{Pa})\times\overbrace{(3.3\times10^{-3}\text{m}^3)}^{1\ \text{dm}^3=10^{-3}\text{m}^3} = \overbrace{-99\ \text{Pa m}^3}^{1\ \text{Pa m}^3=1\ \text{J}} = \mathbf{-99\ J} \end{aligned}$$

(b) For a reversible, isothermal expansion

$$w = -nRT\ln(V_f/V_i)$$

The amount of methane molecules is the ratio of the mass to the molar mass, $n = m/M$, so that

$$\begin{aligned} w &= -\frac{\overbrace{(4.50\ \text{g})}^{\text{mass, } m}}{\underbrace{(16.04\ \text{g mol}^{-1})}_{\text{molar mass, } M}}\times(8.3145\ \text{J K}^{-1}\text{mol}^{-1})\times(310\ \text{K})\times\ln\frac{\overbrace{(12.7+3.3)\ \text{dm}^3}^{V_f}}{\underbrace{(12.7\ \text{dm}^3)}_{V_i}} \\ &= \mathbf{-167\ J} \end{aligned}$$

**E2.4** For an isothermal, irreversible process,

$$\begin{aligned} w &= -nRT\ln(V_f/V_i) \\ &= -(52.0\times10^{-3}\ \text{mol})\times(8.3145\ \text{J K}^{-1}\text{mol}^{-1})\times(260\ \text{K}) \\ &\qquad \times\ln\{(100\ \text{cm}^3/300\ \text{cm}^3)\} \\ &= \mathbf{+123\ J} \end{aligned}$$

Note that there is no need to convert the volumes from units $\text{cm}^3$, because the units cancel. The work done in compressing the gas is positive, as we should expect. It is good practice to include the sign of the work done, even if it is positive.

**E2.5** The compression is irreversible because it occurs at a constant external pressure. Thus, the work done is

$$w = -p_{ex}\Delta V$$

The change in volume is

$$\Delta V = V_f - V_i = 0.57 \times V_i$$

so that

$$w = -\overbrace{\underbrace{(95.2 \times 10^5\ \text{Pa})}_{1\ \text{bar}=10^5\text{Pa}}}^{\text{external pressure},\ p_{ex}} \times \overbrace{\{0.57 \times \underbrace{(0.550 \times 10^{-3}\ \text{m}^3)}_{1\ \text{dm}^3=10^{-3}\ \text{m}^3}\}}^{\text{change in volume},\ \Delta V}$$

$$= +\overbrace{2.99 \times 10^3 \text{Pa m}^3}^{10\text{^}3\ \text{Pa m}^3=1\ \text{kJ}} = \mathbf{+2.99\ kJ}$$

Note that, once again, we explicitly include the positive sign when quoting the work done.

**E2.6** The reaction between magnesium and dilute hydrocholoric acid generates hydrogen gas

$$Mg(s) + 2\ HCl(aq) \rightarrow H_2(g) + MgCl_2(aq)$$

The system will expand as a result of the production of the gas. If we assume that the expansion occurs irreversibly against the constant external pressure exerted by the atmosphere, then

$$w = -p_{ex}\Delta V$$

The volume of gases is very much greater than the volume of solids and liquids. It is reasonable to assume, therefore, that the change in the volume of the liquids and solids is negligible in comparison with the the change in the volume caused by the production of the gas. If we assume that the hydrogen behaves as a perfect gas, then

$$\Delta V = V_{H_2} = n_{H_2}RT/p_{ex}$$

The stoichiometry of the reaction is such that the amount of hydrogen molecules is equivalent to the amount of magnesium atoms consumed

$$n_{H_2} = n_{Mg}$$

The amount of magnesium is given by the ratio of the mass of magneisum consumed, $m$, to the molar mass, $M$,

$$n_{Mg} = m_{Mg}/M_{Mg}$$

Thus, substituting,

$$w = -p_{ex}\Delta V = -p_{ex} \times (n_{H_2}RT/p_{ex}) = -n_{Mg}RT = -(m_{Mg}/M_{Mg})RT$$
$$= -\{(12.5\ \text{g})/(24.31\ \text{g mol}^{-1})\} \times (8.3145\ \text{J K}^{-1}\text{mol}^{-1}) \times \{(273.15 + 20.2)\ \text{K}\}$$
$$= -1.25 \times 10^3\ \text{J} = \mathbf{-1.25\ kJ}$$

**E2.7** Assuming that the reaction is accompanied by an irreversible expansion, in which the system does work by expanding against a constant external pressure, then

$$w = -p_{\text{ex}}\Delta V$$

The balanced reaction equation for the complete combustion of sucrose is

$$C_{12}H_{22}O_{11}(s) + 12\ O_2(g) \rightarrow 12\ CO_2(g) + 11\ H_2O$$

In part (a), we are required to calculate the net expansion work done on the chemical system, $w$, for the case in which water is produced as a liquid. In part (b), water is considered to form as a gas. The difference is important because gases have a large molar volume compared to the negligibly small molar volumes of solids and liquids. In considering the change in volume on reaction, we may therefore assume that the change is the result only of either the consumption or production of gas

$$\Delta V = \Delta V_{\text{gas}}$$

If we define the change in the number of moles of gas

$$\Delta n_{\text{gas}} = n_{\text{gas,products}} - n_{\text{gas,reactants}}$$

and assume that the gases are perfect, then

$$\Delta V = \Delta n_{\text{gas}} RT/p_{\text{ex}}$$

so that

$$w = -p_{\text{ex}} \times (\Delta n_{\text{gas}} RT/p_{\text{ex}}) = -\Delta n_{\text{gas}} RT$$

For part (a), when the reaction is considered to produce liquid water, gaseous carbon dioxide is produced and gaseous oxygen is consumed. The combustion does not result in an overall change in the amount of gas molecules, so that

$$\Delta n_{\text{gas}} = 0$$

and therefore

$$w = \mathbf{0}$$

In part (b), the production of water vapour, causes an increase in the amount of gas. The combustion of $n_{\text{sucrose}}$ mol sucrose causes the consumption of $12n_{\text{sucrose}}$ mol of oxygen gas, but the production of $12n_{\text{sucrose}}$ mol of carbon dioxide gas and $11n_{\text{sucrose}}$ mol of water vapour. Thus,

$$\Delta n_{\text{gas}} = (12n_{\text{sucrose}} + 11n_{\text{sucrose}}) - 12n_{\text{sucrose}} = +11n_{\text{sucrose}}$$

The expansion work is therefore significant. The amount of sucrose consumed is given by the ratio of the mass of sucrose to the molar mass of sucrose

$$n_{\text{sucrose}} = m_{\text{sucrose}}/M_{\text{sucrose}}$$

Thus,

$$w = -\overbrace{11n_{\text{sucrose}}}^{\Delta n_{\text{gas}}}RT = -11(m_{\text{sucrose}}/M_{\text{sucrose}})RT$$

$$= -11 \times \frac{\overbrace{(10.0\text{ g})}^{m_{\text{sucrose}}}}{\underbrace{(342.30\text{ g mol}^{-1})}_{M_{\text{sucrose}}}} \times (8.3145\text{ J K}^{-1}\text{mol}^{-1}) \times \{(273.15+20)\text{ K}\}$$

$$= \mathbf{-782\ J}$$

The reaction therefore does 782 J of expansion work as the production of gas pushes on the surrounding atmospheric gases.

**E2.8** Assuming that the expansion caused by the chemical reaction occurs irreversibly, so that the system does work against a constant external pressure, then the work done is given by

$$w = -p_{\text{ex}}\Delta V$$

The change in volume is given by the product of the area of the piston, $A$, and the distance through which it is pushed out, $\Delta h$

$$\Delta V = A\Delta h$$

so that

$$w = -(100 \times 10^3\text{ Pa}) \times \{\overbrace{(100 \times 10^{-4}\text{ m}^2)}^{1\text{ cm}^2=10^{-4}\text{ m}^2} \times \overbrace{(10 \times 10^{-2}\text{m})}^{1\text{ cm}=10^{-2}\text{m}}\}$$
$$= -1.0 \times 10^2 \underbrace{\text{Pa m}^3}_{1\text{ Pa m}^3=1\text{ J}} = \mathbf{-100\ J}$$

The expanding gas does 100 J of work while moving the piston.

**E2.9** From eqn 2.3a

$$C = q/\Delta T = (124\text{ J})/(5.23\text{ K}) = \mathbf{23.7\ J\ K^{-1}}$$

**E2.10** We may consider the system to be isolated, so that

$$\Delta U = 0$$

If we assume that no work is done, which is not unreasonable given that the volumes of solids and liquids change very little with temperature, then

$$\Delta U = q_{\text{Fe}} + q_{\text{H}_2\text{O}} = 0$$

so that

$$q_{\text{Fe}} = -q_{\text{H}_2\text{O}}$$

and we may determine the heat supplied by the iron from the rise in the temperature of the water and the known specific heat capacity of water

$$q_{\text{Fe}} = -q_{\text{H}_2\text{O}} = -m_{\text{H}_2\text{O}}C_{\text{s,H}_2\text{O}}\Delta T_{\text{H}_2\text{O}}$$

But,

$$q_{\text{Fe}} = C_{\text{Fe}}\Delta T_{\text{Fe}}$$

Combining these expressions and rearranging allows us to calculate the heat capacity of the iron block

$$\begin{aligned} C_{\text{Fe}} &= -m_{\text{H}_2\text{O}}C_{\text{s,H}_2\text{O}}\Delta T_{\text{H}_2\text{O}}/\Delta T_{\text{Fe}} \\ &= -(100\text{ g}) \times (4.184\text{ J K}^{-1}\text{g}^{-1}) \times \{(23-20)\text{K}\}/\{(23-70)\text{ K}\} \\ &= \mathbf{27\ J\ K^{-1}} \end{aligned}$$

In the same way, the specific heat capacity is

$$C_{\text{s,Fe}} = C_{\text{Fe}}/m_{\text{Fe}} = (27\text{ J K}^{-1})/(59\text{ g}) = \mathbf{0.45\ J\ K^{-1}g^{-1}}$$

The molar heat capacity is

$$C_{\text{m,Fe}} = C_{\text{Fe}}/n_{\text{Fe}}$$

and because the amount of iron is given by the ratio of the mass of iron to the molar mass of iron

$$n_{\text{Fe}} = m_{\text{Fe}}/M_{\text{Fe}}$$

then

$$C_{\text{m,Fe}} = (27\text{ J K}^{-1})/\{(59\text{ g})/\overbrace{(55.85\text{ g mol}^{-1})}^{\text{molar mass, }M_{\text{Fe}}}\} = \mathbf{25\ J\ K^{-1}mol^{-1}}$$

Note that it is not good practice to perform the calculation of the specific and molar heat capacity in this way, using the result from the first calculation, because it may lead to the propogation of rounding errors. Much better would be to perform the calculation in a single step.

**E2.11** The heat required depends upon the molar heat capacity as

$$q = nC_{p,\text{m}}\Delta T$$

The amount of water is given by the ratio of the mass of water to the molar mass of water

$$n = m/M$$

so that, if we recognise that an increase of 40 °C is equivalent to a temperature rise of 40 K,

$$\begin{aligned} q &= (m/M) \times C_{p,\text{m}}\Delta T \\ &= \{(250\text{ g})\ /\ \underbrace{(18.02\text{ g mol}^{-1})}_{\text{molar mass, }M_{\text{H}_2\text{O}}}\} \times (75.3\text{ J K}^{-1}\text{ mol}^{-1}) \times 40\text{ K} = \mathbf{42\ kJ} \end{aligned}$$

**E2.12** The heat supplied by the source is, from eqn 2.4

$$q = I\mathcal{V}t$$
$$= (1.55\ \text{A}) \times (110\ \text{V}) \times \{(8.5 \times 60)\ \text{s}\} = \overbrace{8.7 \times 10^4\ \text{A V s}}^{1\ \text{A V s} = 1\ \text{J}} = \mathbf{87\ kJ}$$

**E2.13** The molar heat capacity at constant volume is defined, through eqn 2.3a as

$$C_V = q_V/\Delta T$$

so that the molar heat heat capacity at constant volume is

$$C_{V,\text{m}} = q_V/n\Delta T$$
$$= (229\ \text{J})/(3.00\ \text{mol}) \times (2.55\ \text{K}) = 29.9\ \text{J K}^{-1}\text{mol}^{-1}$$

For a perfect gas, from eqn 2.17,

$$C_{p,\text{m}} = C_{V,\text{m}} + R$$
$$= 29.9\ \text{J K}^{-1}\text{mol}^{-1} + (8.3145\ \text{J K}^{-1}\text{mol}^{-1}) = \mathbf{38.2\ J\ K^{-1}mol^{-1}}$$

**E2.14** The heat required is, from the definition of the molar heat capacity,

$$q = nC_\text{m}\Delta T$$

If we assume that the air in the room behaves as a perfect gas, then we may write

$$q = \overbrace{\left(\frac{pV}{RT}\right)}^{n} C_\text{m}\Delta T$$

If we take the initial room temperature and pressure to be $T = 298$ K and $p = 1.00$ atm, then

$$q = \frac{\overbrace{(1.0325 \times 10^5\ \text{Pa})}^{1\ \text{atm}=1.0325\times10^5\ \text{Pa}} \times (5.5\ \text{m} \times 6.5\ \text{m} \times 3.0\ \text{m})}{(8.3145\ \text{J K}^{-1}\text{mol}^{-1}) \times (298\ \text{K})} \times (21\ \text{J K}^{-1}\text{mol}^{-1}) \times (10\ \text{K})$$
$$= +920 \times 10^3\ \text{J} = \mathbf{+920\ kJ}$$

The power, $P$, of the heater is the rate at which it can supply energy, so that the heat supplied in a time interval $t$ is

$$q = Pt$$

Thus

$$t = q/P = (920\ \text{kJ})/(1.5\ \text{kW}) = \mathbf{610\ s}$$

In practice, the walls and furniture of a room are also heated, so this time interval will be an underestimate.

**E2.15** If the temperature of the parcel of air remains constant, then

$$\Delta U = 0$$

and from the First Law of Thermodynamics,

$$q = -w$$

For a reversible isothermal expansion, however,

$$w = -nRT\ln(V_f/V_i)$$

so that

$$q = +\overbrace{(1.00\text{ mol})}^{n} \times (8.3145\text{ J K}^{-1}\text{mol}^{-1}) \times (300\text{ K}) \times \ln\frac{\overbrace{(30.0\text{ dm}^3)}^{V_f}}{\underbrace{(22.0\text{ dm}^3)}_{V_i}}$$

$$= \mathbf{+773\ J}$$

Note that in this case there is no need to convert the initial and final volumes from units of $dm^3$ to $m^3$ because the units cancel.

**E2.16** The cooling of the block of iron is a constant-pressure process. However, the volume of solids varies very little with temperature so that

$$q_p \approx q_V$$

and we can therefore consider the process as if it were occuring at constant volume. Thus, because

$$\Delta U = q_V$$

and the heat is

$$q_V = nC_{V,m}\Delta T$$

then, because the amount of iron is given by the ratio of the mass of iron to the molar mass of iron,

$$\Delta U = \{(1.4\text{ kg})/\overbrace{(55.84 \times 10^{-3}\text{kg mol}^{-1})}^{\text{molar mass},M_{\text{Fe}}}\} \times (25.1\text{ J K}^{-1}\text{mol}^{-1}) \times (-65\text{ K})$$
$$= -41 \times 10^3\text{ J} = \mathbf{-41\ kJ}$$

**E2.17** In order to calculate the heat released by the combustion of the food, we must first derive an expression for the heat capacity, $C$, of the calorimeter. The heat provided by the electric heater, $q_e$, depends upon the current, $I$, potential difference of the source, $\mathcal{V}$, and the time for which the current flows, $t$, according to eqn 2.4

$$q_e = I\mathcal{V}t$$

We may also express the heat in terms of the heat capacity of the calorimeter, $C$, and the temperature rise, $\Delta T$,

$$q_e = C\Delta_e T$$

By equating these two expressions and rearranging, we may obtain an expression for the heat capacity

$$C = \frac{I\mathcal{V}t}{(\Delta_e T)}$$

The energy released as heat by the combustion is

$$\begin{aligned} q_c &= C(\Delta_c T) = \frac{I\mathcal{V}t}{(\Delta_e T)}(\Delta_c T) \\ &= \frac{(1.27\text{ A}) \times (12.5\text{ V}) \times (157\text{ s})}{(3.88\text{ K})} \times (2.89\text{ K}) = +1.86 \times 10^3\text{ V A s} = \mathbf{+1.86\ kJ} \end{aligned}$$

**E2.18** Assuming that the volume of the calorimeter remains constant, so that no expansion work is done, then the change in the internal energy is equal to the heat,

$$\Delta U = \overbrace{w}^{w=0} + q = q$$

The magnitude of the heat depends upon the current, $I$, potential difference of the source, $\mathcal{V}$, and the time for which the current flows, $t$. Thus, using eqn 2.4,

$$\begin{aligned} \Delta U &= q = I\mathcal{V}t \\ &= (22.22 \times 10^{-3}\text{ A}) \times (11.8\text{ V}) \times (162\text{ s}) = +42.5\text{ V A s} = \mathbf{+42.5\ J} \end{aligned}$$

**E2.19** We may assume that the pressure of the parcel of air remains constant as it is heated, and that no non-expansion work occurs. For such a process, the enthalpy change is equal to the heat, eqn 2.14b

$$\Delta H = q_p = \mathbf{+20\ kJ}$$

**E2.20** Enthalpy is defined through eqn 2.11 as

$$H = U + pV$$

so that, for a perfect gas,

$$H = U + nRT$$

Thus, the change in enthalpy is

$$\Delta H = \Delta U + \Delta(nRT)$$

and for a non reactive sample, such that the amount $n$ is constant, $\Delta n = 0$, at constant temperature, so that $\Delta T = 0$, then

$$\Delta H = \Delta U = 0$$

**E2.21** The molar enthalpy of a gas is related to the molar internal energy through eqn 2.12a

$$H_m = U_m + pV_m$$

so that the differerence

$$H_m - U_m = pV_m$$

For a perfect gas, we may simplify this expression using the relationship

$$pV_m = RT$$

The equation of state for a van der Waals gas is more complicated

$$(p + a/V_m^2)(V_m - b) = RT$$

For carbon dioxide, where $a = 3.610$ atm dm$^6$ mol$^{-2}$, $b = 0.0429$ dm$^3$ mol$^{-1}$, and, choosing units to be compatible with those of $a$ and $b$, $RT = 24.4654$ atm dm$^3$ mol$^{-1}$. This is a cubic expression in the molar volume $V_m$ so we cannot conveniently use algebra to solve for $V_m$. Rather, we need to resort to an iterative numerical procedure. We first rearrange the equation into the form

$$V_m = \frac{RT}{(p + a/V_m^2)} + b$$

Substitution of the values for the van der Waals parameters, along with $p = 1.00$ atm, gives

$$V_m = \frac{(24.4654 \text{ atm dm}^3\text{mol}^{-1})}{[1 \text{ atm} + \{(3.610 \text{ atm dm}^6\text{mol}^{-2})/V_m^2\}]} + (0.0429 \text{ dm}^3\text{mol}^{-1})$$

To derive an initial estimate of the value of $V_m$ we may substitute the value expected for a perfect gas under these conditions,

$$V_m^{\text{perfect}} = RT/p = (24.4654 \text{ atm dm}^3\text{mol}^{-1})/(1.00 \text{ atm}) = 24.4654 \text{ dm}^3\text{mol}^{-1}$$

into the denominator of the first term. This allows us to calculate an improved, more realistic, value for the molar volume of the van der Waals gas

$$V_m = 24.3616 \text{ dm}^3\text{mol}^{-1}$$

We may repeat this process, substituting this revised value into the denominator of our expression for the molar volume. We can continue to do this until the value does not change, and find that

$$V_m = 24.3604 \text{ dm}^3\text{mol}^{-1}$$

This value is self consistent, in that subsitution of this value into the right-hand side of the expression yields the same value. This procedure for finding the solution is a numerical iteration and in this example the successive iterations quickly converge to the answer.

The difference between molar enthalpy and molar energy is therefore

$$\begin{aligned} H_m - U_m &= pV_m \\ &= (1.01325 \times 10^5 \text{ Pa}) \times (24.3604 \times 10^{-3} \text{m}^3\text{mol}^{-1}) \end{aligned}$$

$$= +2.468 \times 10^3 \underbrace{\text{Pa m}^3}_{1\,\text{Pa m}^3=1\,\text{J}} \text{mol}^{-1} = +\mathbf{2.468\ kJ\ mol^{-1}}$$

**E2.22** For a change occurring at constant pressure, with no non-expansion work,

$$\Delta H = q_p$$

The serum cools, so we know that the heat leaves the sample, and hence

$$\Delta H = q_p = -\mathbf{1.2\ kJ}$$

The heat capacity is then, from eqn 2.3

$$C_p = q_p/\Delta T = (-1.2 \times 10^3\ \text{J})/\{(275\ \text{K}) - (290\ \text{K})\} = \mathbf{80\ J\ K^{-1}}$$

**E2.23** For a process occurring at constant pressure and with no non-expansion work, the heat and enthalpy change are equivalent. The heat and enthalpy change therefore both follow from the definition of the heat capacity,

$$\begin{aligned}\Delta H = q_p &= nC_{p,\text{m}}\Delta T \\ &= (3.00\ \text{mol}) \times (29.4\ \text{J K}^{-1}\text{mol}^{-1}) \times \{(285\ \text{K}) - (260\ \text{K})\} \\ &= +2.2 \times 10^3\ \text{J} = +\mathbf{2.2\ kJ}\end{aligned}$$

From the definition of enthalpy,

$$H = U + pV$$

it follows that for a perfect gas,

$$\Delta H = \Delta U + \Delta(pV) = \Delta U + \Delta(nRT)$$

Thus, rearranging

$$\begin{aligned}\Delta U &= \Delta H - nR\Delta T = nC_{p,\text{m}}\Delta T - nR\Delta T = \left(C_{p,\text{m}} - R\right)n\Delta T \\ &= \{(29.4\ \text{J K}^{-1}\text{mol}^{-1}) - (8.3145\ \text{J K}^{-1}\text{mol}^{-1})\} \times (3.00\ \text{mol}) \\ &\qquad \times \{(285\ \text{K}) - (260\ \text{K})\} \\ &= +1.6 \times 10^3\ \text{J} = +\mathbf{1.6\ kJ}\end{aligned}$$

**E2.24** The molar heat capacity at constant pressure and constant volume for a perfect gas are related through eqn 2.17

$$\begin{aligned}C_{V,\text{m}} &= C_{p,\text{m}} - R \\ &= (29.14\ \text{J K}^{-1}\text{mol}^{-1}) - (8.3145\ \text{J K}^{-1}\text{mol}^{-1}) = \mathbf{20.83\ J\ K^{-1}mol^{-1}}\end{aligned}$$

**E2.25** The change in molar enthalpy is, from eqn 2.15

$$\Delta H_\text{m} = C_{p,\text{m}}\Delta T = (29.14\ \text{J K}^{-1}\text{mol}^{-1}) \times \{(37\ \text{K}) - (15\ \text{K})\} = +\mathbf{641\ J\ mol^{-1}}$$

In the same way,

$$\Delta U_\text{m} = C_{V,\text{m}}\Delta T = (20.83\ \text{J K}^{-1}\text{mol}^{-1}) \times \{(37\ \text{K}) - (15\ \text{K})\} = +\mathbf{458\ J\ mol^{-1}}$$

## Answers to projects

**P2.26** For a reversible expansion

$$dw = -pdV$$

and because the pressure is a function of volume, we must integrate to derive an expression for the work done

$$w = -\int_{V_i}^{V_f} p\,dV$$

In order to find the work done for each of the two different equations of state, we must express the pressure explicitly as a function of temperature and volume.

(a) If

$$p = \frac{nRT}{V-b}$$

then, substituting,

$$w = -\int_{V_i}^{V_f} \frac{nRT}{(V-b)}dV = -nRT\int_{V_i}^{V_f} \frac{dV}{(V-b)}$$

where we have removed the term involving the temperature from the integrand because it is a constant for an isothermal expansion. This is a standard integral of the form

$$\int \frac{dx}{Ax+B} = \frac{1}{A}\ln(Ax+B) + c$$

with $x = V$, $A = 1$ and $B = -nb$, so that

$$\begin{aligned} w &= -nRT[\ln(V-nb)]_{V_i}^{V_f} \\ &= -nRT[\{\ln(V_f - nb)\} - \{\ln(V_i - nb)\}] \\ &= \boldsymbol{-nRT\ln\frac{(V_f - nb)}{(V_i - nb)}} \end{aligned}$$

For a perfect gas,

$$w_{\text{perfect}} = -nRT\ln(V_f/V_i)$$

and so, for the case of an expansion for which $V_f > V_i$, the value of $w$ is more negative than the value for a perfect gas.

(b) If, however,

$$p = nRT/V - n^2a/V^2$$

then, substituting,

$$w = -\int_{V_i}^{V_f}\left(\frac{nRT}{V} - \frac{n^2a}{V^2}\right)dV$$

$$= -\int_{V_i}^{V_f} \frac{nRT}{V} \mathrm{d}V + \int_{V_i}^{V_f} \frac{n^2 a}{V^2} \mathrm{d}V$$
$$= -nRT[\ln V]_{V_i}^{V_f} - \left[\frac{n^2 a}{V}\right]_{V_i}^{V_f}$$
$$= \boldsymbol{-nRT \ln(V_f/V_i) - n^2 a \left(\frac{1}{V_f} - \frac{1}{V_i}\right)}$$

which may be written as

$$w = w_{\text{perfect}} - n^2 a \left(\frac{1}{V_f} - \frac{1}{V_i}\right)$$

For an expansion, $V_f > V_i$ and the second term is positive. Thus, the work done for a gas that obeys this equation of state is more positive than for a perfect gas.

**P2.27** (a) For a reversible expansion

$$\mathrm{d}w = -p\mathrm{d}V$$

and because the pressure is a function of volume, we must integrate to derive an expression for the work done

$$w = -\int_{V_i}^{V_f} p \, \mathrm{d}V$$

For a perfect gas, $p = nRT / V$, so that

$$w = -\int_{V_i}^{V_f} \frac{nRT}{V} \mathrm{d}V$$

For this example, we must treat both volume and temperature as variables because the expansion is not isothermal. Thus, if

$$T = T_i - c(V - V_i)$$

we may write

$$w = -nR \int_{V_i}^{V_f} \frac{T}{V} \mathrm{d}V$$
$$= -nR \int_{V_i}^{V_f} \frac{T_i - c(V - V_i)}{V} \mathrm{d}V$$
$$= -nR \int_{V_i}^{V_f} \left(\frac{T_i}{V} - \mathrm{c} + \frac{cV_i}{V}\right) \mathrm{d}V$$
$$= -nRT_i[\ln V]_{V_i}^{V_f} + nRc[V]_{V_i}^{V_f} - nRcV_i[\ln V]_{V_i}^{V_f}$$
$$= -nR(T_i + cV_i)\ln(V_f/V_i) + nRc(V_f - V_i)$$

(b) In the case for which $V_f > V_i$ and $c$ is positive, the value of $w$ is made more negative than the isothermal expansion at $T_i$ by the first term while the last term makes it more positive than the value for the isothermal expansion. The balance between these two factors depends upon the values of $c$ and $V_i$.

**P2.28** The heat capacity is defined fully in terms of derivatives as

$$C_{V,m} = \left(\frac{\partial U_m}{\partial T}\right)_{V_m}$$

where the curly $\partial$ and $V_m$ subscript indicate that this is a partial derivative with respect to temperature with the molar volume held constant. For simplicity, we may write

$$C_{V,m} = \frac{dU_m}{dT}$$

as long as we remember that the molar volume is constant. We may rearrange this expression to give

$$dU = C_{V,m}dT$$

and integrate so that

$$\Delta U_m = \int_{T_i}^{T_f} C_{V,m}dT$$

(a) If the heat capacity is of the form $C_{V,m} = aT^3$, then substituting gives

$$\Delta U_m = \int_{T_i}^{T_f} aT^3 dT = [{}^1\!/_4\, aT^4]_{T_i}^{T_f} = {}^1\!/_4\, a(T_f^4 - T_i^4)$$

Let us choose $T_i$ to be the absolute zero of temperature (0 K) and let us write the $T_f$ simply as $T$, the temperature of interest ($\Delta U_m$ becomes the internal energy change that occurs as $T$ is raised above absolute zero). Then,

$$\Delta U_m = \tfrac{1}{4}\boldsymbol{aT^4}$$

and the internal energy varies as the fourth power of temperature.

(b) In the same way, if

$$U_{V,m} = a + bT + cT^2$$

then

$$C_{V,m} = \frac{dU_m}{dT} = \frac{d}{dT}(a + bT + cT^2) = \boldsymbol{b + 2cT}$$

**P2.29** Writing the molar heat capacity at constant pressure fully as

$$C_{p,m} = \left(\frac{\partial H_m}{\partial T}\right)_p$$

or, for convenience as

$$C_{p,\mathrm{m}} = \frac{\mathrm{d}H_\mathrm{m}}{\mathrm{d}T}$$

and remembering that the pressure remains constant, then, if we rearrange and integrate

$$\Delta H_\mathrm{m} = \int_{T_i}^{T_\mathrm{f}} C_{p,\mathrm{m}}\,\mathrm{d}T$$

We may now substitute the expression for the heat capacity,

$$\begin{aligned}\Delta H_\mathrm{m} &= \int_{T_i}^{T_\mathrm{f}} (a + bT + cT^{-2})\,\mathrm{d}T \\ &= [aT + ½bT^2 - cT^{-1}]_{T_\mathrm{i}}^{T_\mathrm{f}} \\ &= a(T_f - T_i) + ½b(T_f^2 - T_i^2) - c(T_f^{-1} - T_i^{-1})\end{aligned}$$

(a) At 15 °C,

$$T_\mathrm{i} = (273.15 + 15)\mathrm{K} = 288.15\ \mathrm{K}$$

and at 37 °C,

$$T_\mathrm{f} = (273.15 + 37)\mathrm{K} = 310.15\ \mathrm{K}$$

so that

$$\begin{aligned}\Delta H_\mathrm{m} &= (44.22\ \mathrm{J\ K^{-1}mol^{-1}}) \times \{(310.15\ \mathrm{K}) - (288.15\ \mathrm{K})\} \\ &\quad +½ \times (8.79 \times 10^{-3}\mathrm{J\ K^{-2}mol^{-1}})\{(310.15\ \mathrm{K})^2 - (288.15\ \mathrm{K})^2\} \\ &\quad -(-8.62 \times 10^3\mathrm{J\ K\ mol^{-1}})\{(310.15\ \mathrm{K})^{-1} - (288.15\ \mathrm{K})^{-1}\} \\ &= \mathbf{+818\ J\ mol^{-1}}\end{aligned}$$

(b) We may derive an expression for the change in molar enthalpy of carbon dioxide as it is heated from 15 °C at constant pressure by setting $T_\mathrm{i} = 288.15$ K and letting $T = T_\mathrm{f}$ be any temperature in the range $288.15\ \mathrm{K} < T < 310.15\ \mathrm{K}$. The equation of part (a) then becomes

$$\Delta H_\mathrm{m} = (aT + ½bT^2 - c/T) - 16.10\ \mathrm{kJ\ mol^{-1}}$$

Figure 2.1 shows a plot of $\Delta H_\mathrm{m}$ against $T$. Inspection of the figure shows it to be almost linear so we conclude that the last two non-linear terms of the expression do not contribute significantly over this small temperature range. This is often the case; we may usually consider $C_{p,\mathrm{m}}$ to be a constant over a small temperature range and, consequently, $\Delta H_\mathrm{m}$ is linear in temperature.

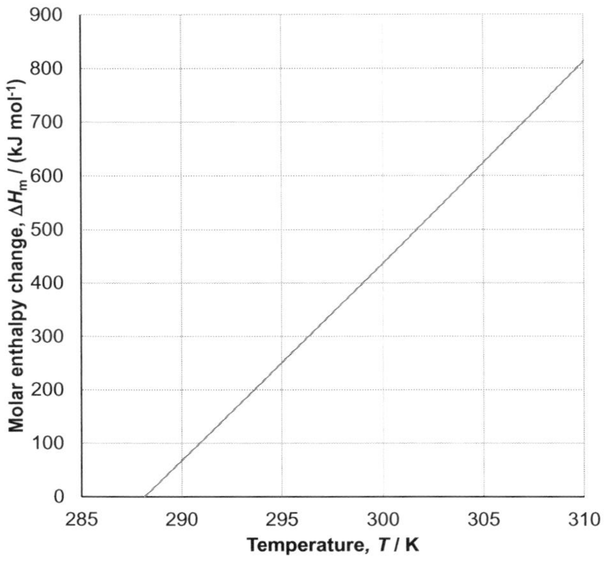


**Figure 2.1**

Figure 2.2 shows a plot of $\Delta H_m$ against $T$ over the larger temperature range 275 K $< T <$ 525 K. Inspection of the plot shows that the non-linear terms now provide a more significant contribution.

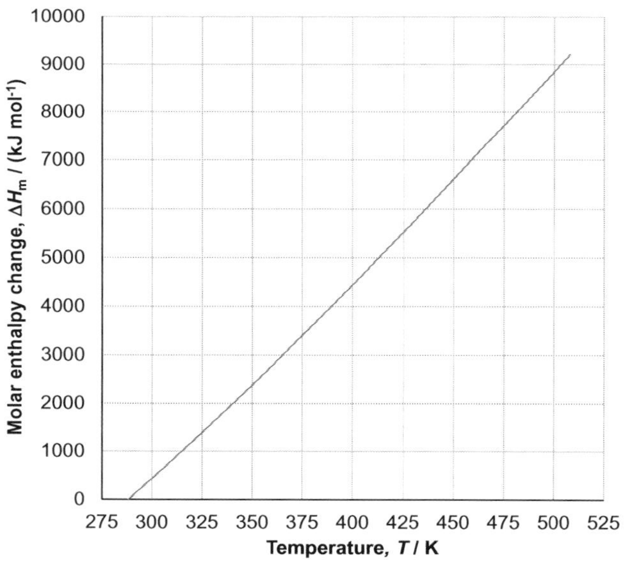


**Figure 2.2**

**P2.30** We may simplify the expressions for $\alpha$ and $\kappa$ in the case of a perfect gas by writing the differentials explicitly. Thus,

$$\alpha = \frac{1}{V}\left(\frac{\mathrm{d}V}{\mathrm{d}T}\right) = \frac{1}{V}\frac{\mathrm{d}}{\mathrm{d}T}\overbrace{\left(\frac{nRT}{p}\right)}^{V=(nRT/p)} = \frac{1}{V}\times\frac{nR}{p} = \frac{nR}{pV} = \frac{1}{T}$$

and

$$\kappa = -\frac{1}{V}\left(\frac{\mathrm{d}V}{\mathrm{d}p}\right) = -\frac{1}{V}\frac{\mathrm{d}}{\mathrm{d}p}\overbrace{\left(\frac{nRT}{p}\right)}^{V=(nRT/p)} = -\frac{1}{V}\times-\frac{nRT}{p^2} = \frac{nRT}{p^2V} = \frac{1}{p}\times\overbrace{\left(\frac{nRT}{pV}\right)}^{=1\text{ for a perfect gas}} = \frac{1}{p}$$

Thus, substituting,

$$C_p - C_V = \frac{\alpha^2 TV}{\kappa} = \frac{TVp}{T^2} = \frac{pV}{T} = nR$$

or

$$C_{p,\mathrm{m}} - C_{V,\mathrm{m}} = R$$

which is the result expected for a perfect gas, eqn 2.17.

# Chapter 3

# Thermodynamics: applications of the First Law

## Answers to discussion questions

**D3.1** The enthalpies listed are all special types of standard reaction enthalpy. The standard state of a substance is the pure substance at exactly 1 bar and so the values refer to transformations with each reactant and product at 1 bar. The standard state is denoted with the superscript $\ominus$ on the symbol. We take the temperature to be the conventional temperature 298.15 K (25 °C) unless otherwise specified. All are molar quantities, referring to the entahlpy change per mole of reaction, so have units of kJ $mol^{-1}$.

The **standard enthalpy of vaporization** is the enthalpy change per mole for a change of state from liquid to gas for a pure substance at exactly 1 bar. The value is usually quoted at the normal boiling temperature, $T_b$, but may be quoted at any temperature. It is now conventional to indicate the quantity as $\Delta_{vap}H^{\ominus}$, with the subscript vap attached to the capital delta in order to indicate that the quantity refers to vaporization. The standard enthalpy of vaporization is always positive, and it is therefore not necessary to write the sign of the quantity explicitly. For example, for the vaporization of methane:

$$CH_4(l) \rightarrow CH_4(g) \qquad \Delta_{vap}H_m^{\ominus}(T_b = 111.7\ K) = 8.18\ kJ\ mol^{-1}$$

The **standard enthalpy of fusion** is the enthalpy change per mole for a change of state from solid to liquid for a pure substance at exactly 1 bar. The value is usually quoted at the normal melting temperature, $T_f$, but may be quoted at any temperature. Just as for vaporization, there is no need to state the sign of the standard enthalpy of fusion because it is always positive. For example, for the melting of methane:

$$CH_4(s) \rightarrow CH_4(l) \qquad \Delta_{fus}H_m^{\ominus}(T_f = 90.68\ K) = 0.941\ kJ\ mol^{-1}$$

The **standard enthalpy of sublimation** is the enthalpy change per mole for a change of state from liquid to gas for a pure substance at exactly 1 bar. We usually quite the value at the conventional temperature 298.15 K (25 °C) unless otherwise specified. Thus, for the transformation of solid iodine to iodine vapour:

$$I_2\ (s) \rightarrow I_2\ (g) \qquad \Delta_{sub}H^{\ominus}(298\ K) = 62.44\ kJ\ mol^{-1}$$

The **standard enthalpy of ionization** is the standard molar enthalpy accompanying the removal of an electron from a gas-phase atom (or ion). The standard enthalpy of ionization is always positive, and there is therefore no need to include the sign explicitly. Thus, for the ionization of a hydrogen atom,

$$H(g) \rightarrow H^+(g) + e^-(g) \qquad \Delta_{ion}H^\ominus(298\text{ K}) = +1318\text{ kJ}$$

The **standard electron-gain enthalpy** is the standard molar enthalpy accompanying the capture of an electron by a gas-phase atom (or ion). The enthalpy change may be either positive or negative and it is therefore good practice always to include the sign explicitly when quoting the value. Thus, for a chlorine atom,

$$Cl(g) + e^-(g) \rightarrow Cl^-(g) \qquad \Delta_{eg}H^\ominus = -354.81\text{ kJ mol}^{-1}$$

The enthalpy of a bond is the molar enthalpy change in the dissociation, or breaking, of a chemical bond. Bond enthalpies vary from compound to compound, so we define the **mean bond enthalpy** as the average bond enthalpy over a related series of compounds. Thus, given the enthalpy of reaction for the complete dissociation of methane,

$$CH_4(g) \rightarrow C(g) + 4\,H(g) \qquad \Delta_rH^\ominus = 1648\text{ kJ mol}^{-1}$$

the bond enthalpy of the C–H bond is

$$\Delta H^\ominus_m(C-H) = (1648\text{ kJ mol}^{-1})/4 = 412\text{ kJ mol}^{-1}$$

**D3.2** (a) A **standard reaction enthalpy** is the enthalpy change with each reactant and product at 1 bar and temperature $T$. We take $T$ to be the conventional temperature 298.15 K (25 °C) unless otherwise specified. The standard state is denoted with the superscript $^\ominus$ on the symbol for the property and the general symbol for a reaction enthalpy is.$\Delta_rH^\ominus$. For example, for the reduction of iron (III) oxide using carbon monoxide,

$$Fe_2O_3(s) + 3\,CO(g) \rightarrow 2\,Fe(s) + 3\,CO_2(g) \qquad \Delta_rH^\ominus = -24.74\text{ kJ mol}^{-1}$$

(b) The **standard enthalpy of combustion** is the change in standard enthalpy per mole of combustible substance upon reaction with oxygen to produce $CO_2(g)$, $H_2O(l)$, and $N_2(g)$ from its carbon, hydrogen, and nitrogen component in addition to oxides of the remaining elements. The symbol for standard enthalpy of combustion is $\Delta_cH^\ominus$. Thus, for the combustion of propane,

$$C_3H_8(g) + 5\,O_2(g) \rightarrow 3\,CO_2(g) + 4\,H_2O(l) \qquad \Delta_cH^\ominus = -2220\text{ kJ mol}^{-1}$$

(c) The **standard enthalpy of formation** is the change in standard enthalpy per mole of substance formed from its elements in their standard reference state. The **reference state** of an element is its most stable form under the prevailing conditions. Standard entahlpies of formation are represented by the symbol $\Delta_fH^\ominus$. For example, for propane

$$3\,C(s,\text{graphite}) + 4\,H_2(g) \rightarrow C_3H_8(g) \qquad \Delta_fH^\ominus = -103.85\text{ kJ}$$

**D3.3** The vaporization of water is an endothermic transformation that cools the linen and its immediate environment:

$$H_2O(l) \rightarrow H_2O(g) \qquad \Delta_{vap}H^{\ominus} = +44.01\ \text{kJ mol}^{-1}.$$

**D3.4** The **standard state** of a substance at a specified temperature is its pure form at 1 bar. The standard state does not refer to a particular temperature, although when quoting values for standard thermodynamic quantities, it is common to do so at a temperature of 298.15 K. The **reference state** of a substance is its most stable state at 1 bar and the specified temperature. The distinction is important because formation enthalpies are for formation of a substance from the elements in their reference states under prevailing conditions but other types of reactions may list a substance in a non-reference state.

**D3.5** (a) Molar enthalpy is defined through eqn 2.11 as

$$H = U + pV$$

Thus, expressing an enthalpy of formation as the difference between the molar enthalpies of the products and reactants,

$$\Delta_f H = \Delta_f \mathrm{U} + \Delta_f(pV)$$

The volume of solids and liquids, however, is small and varies little with pressure and temperature. Thus, for condensed phases, the final term in this expression may be considered to be negligible. We may further simplify the expression if we assume that the gases are perfect. In that case,

$$pV = nRT$$

so that, substituting,

$$\Delta_f H = \Delta_f U + \Delta \nu_{gas} RT$$

where $\Delta \nu_{gas}$ is the change in the amount of gas on reaction. The relationship therefore applies to reactions for which it may assumed that the volume of the condensed, solid and liquid, phases is negligible and for which all gases may be considered to be perfect gases.

(b) The heat capacity at constant pressure is defined in full differential form as

$$C_p = \frac{\mathrm{d}H}{\mathrm{d}T}$$

If we consider the heat capacities for each reactant and product, we may write

$$\Delta_r C_p^{\ominus} = \frac{\mathrm{d}(\Delta_r H^{\ominus})}{\mathrm{d}T}$$

To obtain an expression for the enthalpy of reaction at a particular temperature, we integrate

$$\int d(\Delta_r H^\ominus) = \int \Delta_r C_p^\ominus \, dT$$

If, and only if, the heat capacities do not vary with temperature, then we may treat the quantity $\Delta_r C_p^\ominus$ as a constant and write

$$\int d(\Delta_r H^\ominus) = \Delta_r C_p^\ominus \int dT$$

Integrating between limits of $T'$ and $T$ then gives

$$\Delta_r H^\ominus(T') = \Delta_r H^\ominus(T) + \Delta_r C_p \times (T' - T)$$

This expression is therefore valid only in the limit that there is a negligible dependence of the heat capacities of the reactants and products upon temperature.

**D3.6** The heat of a reaction depends upon whether it occurs at constant pressure or temperature. However, expressions such as *heat of combustion* and *latent heat of vaporization* do not make it not clear whether the value quoted for the reaction heat is for a constant pressure process or a constant volume process. The distinction is important because generally $q_p$ does not equal $q_V$; for a reaction at constant pressure, the heat of reaction is equivalent to the enthalpy change, $\Delta H = q_p$, whereas at constant volume, the heat of reaction is equivalent to the internal energy change, $\Delta U = q_V$.

## Solutions to exercises

**E3.1** For the formation reaction:

$$C(s, graphite) + O_2(g) \rightarrow CO_2(g)$$

we may express the enthalpy of formation as

$$\Delta_f H(CO_2(g), p, T) = H_m(CO_2(g), p, T) - \overbrace{\{H_m(O_2(g), p, T) + H_m(\text{graphite}, p, T)\}}^{\text{reactants}}$$

The difference in the enthalpy of formation at two pressures is thus

$$\begin{aligned}\Delta_f H(CO_2(g), p, T) - \Delta_f H(CO_2(g), p', T) \\ = \{H_m(CO_2(g), p, T) - H_m(O_2(g), p, T) - H_m(\text{graphite}, p, T)\} \\ -\{H_m(CO_2(g), p', T) - H_m(O_2(g), p', T) - H_m(\text{graphite}, p', T)\}\end{aligned}$$

The internal energy and enthalpy of a perfect gas depend upon $T$ alone; they have no pressure dependence. To understand this, we may recall that perfect gases exhibit neither attractive nor repulsive forces between molecules and, consequently, $\Delta U_m = 0$ (eqn 2.8) for the isothermal expansion of a perfect gas. Additionally, equation 2.12b indicates that $\Delta H_m = \Delta U_m + R\Delta T$ for a perfect gas; there is no pressure dependence on the right side of this equation so $\Delta H_m$ is independent of pressure. Thus, an isothermal change in the pressure of an ideal gas leaves both the internal energy and enthalpy unchanged. Hence, because

$$H_m(CO_2,g,p,T) - H_m(CO_2,g,p',T) = 0$$
$$H_m(O_2,g,p,T) - H_m(O_2,g,p',T) = 0$$

then

$$\Delta_f H(CO_2,g,p,T) - \Delta_f H(CO_2,g,p',T) = \{H_m(\text{graphite},p,T) - H_m(\text{graphite},p',T)\}$$

Because

$$H_m = U_m + pV_m$$

$$\Delta_f H(CO_2,g,p,T) - \Delta_f H(CO_2,g,p',T) = \{U_m(\text{graphite},p,T) + pV_m(\text{graphite},p,T)\} - \{U_m(\text{graphite},p',T) + p'V_m(\text{graphite},p',T)\}$$

Then, because graphite is an incompressible solid, for pressures $p = 1\text{ atm} = 1.01325p^{\ominus}$ and $p' = p^{\ominus}$ we may assume that

$$U_m(\text{graphite},p,T) - U_m(\text{graphite},p',T) = 0$$
$$V_m(\text{graphite},p,T) - V_m(\text{graphite},p',T) = 0$$

so that

$$\Delta_f H(CO_2,g,p,T) - \Delta_f H(CO_2,g,p',T) = (p - p')V_m(\text{graphite},p',T)$$

The molar volume may be expressed in terms of the mass density, $\rho$, and molar mass, $M$,

$$V_m = M/\rho$$

The mass density of graphite is 2.260 g dm$^{-3}$ so that

$$V_m = (12.01\text{ g mol}^{-1})/(2.260\text{ g dm}^{-3})$$
$$= 5.314 \times 10^{-3}\text{ dm}^3 = 5.314 \times 10^{-6}\text{ m}^3$$

and therefore

$$\Delta_f H(CO_2,g,p,T) - \Delta_f H(CO_2,g,p',T)$$
$$= \{(1.01325 - 1) \times 10^5\text{ Pa}\} \times (5.314 \times 10^{-6}\text{ m}^3)$$
$$= +6.91 \times 10^{-3}\text{ J mol}^{-1} = \mathbf{+6.91\text{ mJ mol}^{-1}}$$

This is a negligibly small difference for all practical purposes.

**E3.2** At constant pressure, the heat, $q_p$, required to melt the sodium is equivalent to the enthalpy change. References such as the *CRC Handbook of Chemistry and Physics* give the standard enthalpy of fusion of sodium as $\Delta_{fus}H^{\ominus}(Na) = +2.60\text{ kJ mol}^{-1}$ at the normal melting temperature of 371 K. The standard enthalpy of fusion is a molar quantity, so assuming a presure of 1 bar, then

$$q_p = \Delta H = n\Delta_{fus}H^{\ominus}$$

The amount of sodium is given by the ratio of the mass of sodium, $m$, to the molar mass of sodium, $M$,

$$n = m/M$$

so that

$$\begin{aligned} q_p &= (m/M)\Delta_{\text{fus}}H^{\ominus} \\ &= \{(250\ \text{kg})/(22.99 \times 10^{-3}\text{kg mol}^{-1})\} \times (2.60\ \text{kJ mol}^{-1}) \\ &= \mathbf{+2.83 \times 10^4\ kJ} \end{aligned}$$

**E3.3** Assuming that the transformation occurs at a pressure of 1 bar, the energy that must be transferred as heat is related to the standard enthalpy of vaporization at the appropriate temperature

$$q_p = n\Delta_{\text{vap}}H^{\ominus}(T)$$

The amount of water molecules is given by the ratio of the mass of water to the molar mass of water

$$n = m/M = (1.00\ \text{kg})/(18.02 \times 10^{-3}\ \text{kg mol}^{-1})$$

(a) Values for standard enthalpies of vaporization are usually quoted at the normal boiling temperature. It is therefore necessary to adopt a slightly different approach to calculate the enthalpy change for vaporization at 25 °C. Writing the process as

$$H_2O(\text{l}, 298.15\ \text{K}) \rightarrow H_2O(\text{g}, 298.15\ \text{K})$$

it can be seen that the standard enthalpy of vaporization of water at 298.15 K is simply the difference between the standard enthalpies of formation of water vapour and liquid water at this temperature.

$$\begin{aligned} \Delta_{\text{vap}}H^{\ominus}(\text{H}_2\text{O}, 298.15\ \text{K}) &= \Delta_{\text{f}}H^{\ominus}(\text{H}_2\text{O}, \text{g}, 298.15\ \text{K}) - \Delta_{\text{f}}H^{\ominus}(\text{H}_2\text{O}, \text{l}, 298.15\ \text{K}) \\ &= (-241.82\ \text{kJ mol}^{-1}) - (-285.83\ \text{kJ mol}^{-1}) \end{aligned}$$

Thus,

$$\begin{aligned} q_p &= \frac{(1.00\ \text{kg})}{(18.02 \times 10^{-3}\ \text{kg mol}^{-1})} \times \{(-241.82\ \text{kJ mol}^{-1}) - (-285.83\ \text{kJ mol}^{-1})\} \\ &= \mathbf{+2.44\ kJ\ mol^{-1}} \end{aligned}$$

(b) The standard enthalpy of vaporization of water at 100 °C is quoted directly in many sets of data tables as 40.7 kJ mol$^{-1}$. Thus, at this temperature,

$$\begin{aligned} q_p &= \frac{(1.00\ \text{kg})}{(18.02 \times 10^{-3}\ \text{kg mol}^{-1})} \times (40.7\ \text{kJ mol}^{-1}) \\ &= \mathbf{+2.26\ kJ\ mol^{-1}} \end{aligned}$$

**E3.4** The enthalpy change on vaporization, $\Delta H$, is equal to the heat supplied at constant pressure, $q_p$, which depends upon the current, $I$, potential difference of the source, $\mathcal{V}$, and the time for which the current flows, $t$, according to eqn 2.4

$$\Delta H = q_p = I\mathcal{V}t$$

We may then calculate the molar enthalpy of vaporization of propanol at its boiling point from the enthalpy change and the amount of propanol, $n$, which in turn depends upon the mass of propanol ,$m$, and molar mass of propanol, $M$

$$\Delta_{\text{vap}}H^{\ominus} = \frac{\Delta H}{n} = \frac{I\mathcal{V}t}{m/M} = \frac{(0.812\ \text{A}) \times (11.5\ \text{V}) \times (303\ \text{s})}{\{(4.27\ \text{g})/(60.04\ \text{g mol}^{-1})\}} = \mathbf{+39.8\ kJ\ mol^{-1}}$$

**E3.5** At constant pressure, the heat, $q$, is equal to the enthalpy change

$$q = \Delta H = n\Delta_{\text{vap}}H^{\ominus} = (2.50\ \text{mol}) \times (+32.0\ \text{kJ mol}^{-1}) = \mathbf{+80.0\ kJ\ mol^{-1}}$$

Work is done when the liquid vaporizes because the volume increases. We may assume that the expansion occurs irreversibly against constant atmospheric pressure. From eqn 2.1,

$$w = -p_{\text{ex}}\Delta V$$

The change in volume is equal to the difference between the volume of the vapour and the liquid. We may, however, assume that the volume of the liquid is negligible in comparison with the volume of the vapour. If we also assume that the vapour behaves as a perfect gas, we may write

$$\Delta V = V_{\text{vap}} - V_{\text{liq}} \approx V_{\text{vap}} = nRT/p_{\text{ex}}$$

so that

$$\begin{aligned} w = -p_{\text{ex}} \times (nRT/p_{\text{ex}}) &= -nRT \\ &= (2.50\ \text{mol}) \times (8.3145\ \text{J K}^{-1}\text{mol}^{-1}) \times (250\ \text{K}) \\ &= -5.20 \times 10^{3}\ \text{J} = \mathbf{-5.20\ kJ} \end{aligned}$$

From the First Law of thermodynamics,

$$\Delta U = q + w = +80.0\ \text{kJ} - 5.20\ \text{kJ} = \mathbf{+74.8\ kJ}$$

**E3.6** At constant pressure, the energy transferred as heat is equal to the enthalpy change

$$q = \Delta H = n\Delta H_{\text{m}} = (m/M)\Delta H_{\text{m}}$$

The enthalpy change for the phase transitions are given by the enthalpies of fusion and vaporization. We may use the known heat capacity at constant pressure to calculate the enthalpy change on heating. If we assume that the heat capacity does not vary with temperature, then, from eqn 2.15,

$$\Delta H = C_p\Delta T$$

Thus, assuming that the processes occur at standard pressure,

$$q = (m/M) \times (\overbrace{\Delta_{fus}H^{\ominus}}^{\text{melting}} + \overbrace{C_p^{\ominus}\Delta T}^{\text{heating}} + \overbrace{\Delta_{vap}H^{\ominus}}^{\text{vaporization}})$$
$$= \left\{\frac{(100\text{ g})}{(18.0\text{ g mol}^{-1})}\right\}$$
$$\times [\overbrace{(6.01\text{ kJ mol}^{-1})}^{\Delta_{fus}H^{\ominus}}$$
$$+ \overbrace{\{(4.18\text{ J K}^{-1}\text{mol}^{-1}) \times (373\text{ K} - 273\text{ K})\}}^{C_p^{\ominus}\Delta T} + \overbrace{(40.7\text{ kJ mol}^{-1})}^{\Delta_{vap}H^{\ominus}}]$$
$$= \mathbf{+301\ kJ}$$

The graph of temperature against time is sketched in Figure 3.1. Note that the length of the liquid + gas, two-phase fusion line is longer than the solid + liquid vaporization line in proportion to their $\Delta_{trs}H$ values.

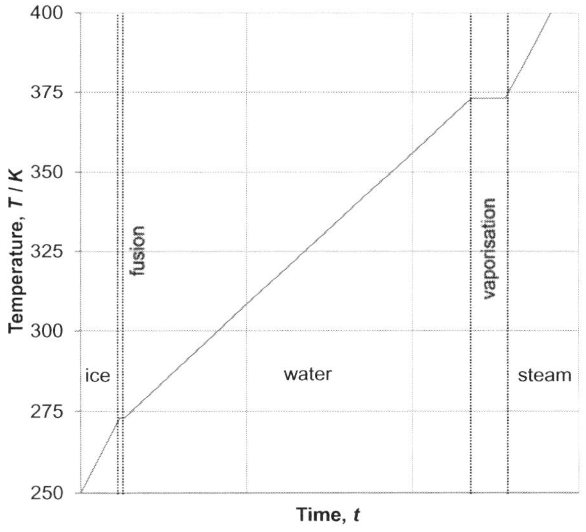


**Figure 3.1**

**E3.7** We may calculate the enthalpy change for overall process

$$Ca(s) \rightarrow Ca^{2+}(g) + 2\ e^{-}(g)$$

by separating in to three steps: sublimation, first ionization and then second ionization. The heat required at constant pressure is equal to the enthalpy change,

$$q = \Delta H = n\Delta H^{\ominus}{}_m = (m/M)\Delta H^{\ominus}{}_m = (m/M)\{\Delta_{sub}H^{\ominus} + \Delta_{ion,1}H^{\ominus} + \Delta_{ion,2}H^{\ominus}\}$$
$$= \frac{(5.0\text{ g})}{(40.08\text{ g mol}^{-1})} \times \left\{\overbrace{(178.2\text{ kJ mol}^{-1})}^{\Delta_{sub}H^{\ominus}} + \overbrace{(590\text{ kJ mol}^{-1})}^{\Delta_{ion,1}H^{\ominus}} + \overbrace{(1150\text{ kJ mol}^{-1})}^{\Delta_{ion,2}H^{\ominus}}\right\}$$

$$= \mathbf{+239\ kJ\ mol^{-1}}$$

where we have used the data from Table 3.2, and from the *Data Section*.

**E3.8** We may assume that the volume of condensed phases are neglible compared to the volume of any gas. If all gases are assumed to be perfect then we may express the relationship between the enthalpy change and internal energy change on ionization as

$$\Delta_{\text{ion}}H^{\ominus} = \Delta_{\text{ion}}U^{\ominus} + \Delta\nu_{\text{gas}}RT$$

where $\Delta\nu_{\text{gas}}$ is the difference between the sum of the stoichiometric numbers of the products and reactants. By writing out a balanced equation for the ionization,

$$Ca(g) \rightarrow Ca^{2+}(g) + 2\ e^{-}(g)$$

we can see that it results in an increase in the amount of gas so that

$$\Delta\nu_{\text{gas}} = +2$$

so that

$$\Delta_{\text{ion}}H^{\ominus} - \Delta_{\text{ion}}U^{\ominus} = \Delta\nu_{\text{gas}}RT = 2 \times (8.3145\ \text{J K}^{-1}\text{mol}^{-1}) \times (298.15\ \text{K})$$
$$= +4.96 \times 10^{3}\ \text{kJ mol}^{-1} = \mathbf{+4.96\ kJ\ mol^{-1}}$$

In practice, it is unreasonable to assume that the electrons behave as a perfect gas because of the repulsive electrostatic interactions.

**E3.9** We may follow the same approach as in the previous exercise. The process of electron gain may be written as

$$Br(g) + e^{-}(g) \rightarrow Br^{-}(g)$$

and so can be seen to correspond to a decrease in the amount of gas

$$\Delta\nu_{\text{gas}} = -1$$

Thus,

$$\Delta_{\text{ion}}H^{\ominus} - \Delta_{\text{ion}}U^{\ominus} = \Delta\nu_{\text{gas}}RT = -1 \times (8.3145\ \text{J K}^{-1}\text{mol}^{-1}) \times (298.15\ \text{K})$$
$$= -2.48 \times 10^{3}\ \text{kJ mol}^{-1} = \mathbf{-2.48\ kJ\ mol^{-1}}$$

**E3.10** We may write the overall process

$$Cl_2(g) \rightarrow Cl^{+}(g) + Cl^{-}(g)$$

as three separate steps: dissociation,

$$Cl_2(g) \rightarrow 2\ Cl\ (g)$$

for which the molar enthalpy change is twice the enthalpy of formation of a gaseous Cl atom, $2\Delta_f H(\text{Cl})$, followed by ionization

$$Cl(g) \rightarrow Cl^+(g) + e^-$$

with a molar enthalpy change $\Delta_{ion}H(Cl)$, and electron gain

$$Cl(g) + e^- \rightarrow Cl^-(g)$$

with a molar enthalpy change $\Delta_{eg}H(Cl)$. Thus,

$$\Delta_m H = 2\Delta_f H(Cl) + \Delta_{ion}H(Cl) + \Delta_{eg}H(Cl)$$

However, a mass of chlorine molecules $m$ corresponds to an amount $n = m / M$, where $M$ is the molar mass of $Cl_2$. The change occurs at standard pressure, and 298.15 K, so that, using the values from standard tables,

$$\begin{aligned}\Delta H = n\Delta_m H &= n\{2\Delta_f H^\ominus(Cl) + \Delta_{ion}H^\ominus(Cl) + \Delta_{eg}H^\ominus(Cl)\} \\ &= \frac{(10.0\ \text{g})}{(70.90\ \text{g mol}^{-1})} \times \\ &\quad \{2 \times (121.68\ \text{kJ mol}^{-1})\} + (1260\ \text{kJ mol}^{-1}) - (349\ \text{kJ mol}^{-1}) \\ &= \mathbf{+163\ kJ}\end{aligned}$$

**E3.11** (a) The ionization process

$$Cl^-(g) \rightarrow Cl(g) + e^-(g)$$

is just the reverse of electron gain, so that the standard enthalpy of ionization of $Cl^-(g)$ is

$$\Delta_{ion}H(Cl^-) = -\Delta_{eg}H(Cl) = \mathbf{+354.8\ kJ\ mol^{-1}}$$

(b) Following the same process as in the preceding exercises,

$$\Delta_{ion}U^\ominus = \Delta_{ion}H^\ominus - \Delta\nu_{gas}RT$$

There is a net increase in the amount of gas produced, so that $\Delta\nu_{gas} = +1$, and therefore

$$\begin{aligned}\Delta_{ion}U^\ominus &= (354.8 \times 10^3\ \text{J mol}^{-1}) - \{(-1) \times (8.3145\ \text{J K}^{-1}\text{mol}^{-1}) \times (298.15\ \text{K})\} \\ &= +352.3 \times 10^3\ \text{J mol}^{-1} = \mathbf{+352.3\ kJ\ mol^{-1}}\end{aligned}$$

**E3.12** (a) The mean bond enthalpy is the average of the three enthalpy changes given

$$\Delta H_B(\text{N} - \text{H}) = \left(\frac{460 + 390 + 314}{3}\right)\ \text{kJ mol}^{-1} = \mathbf{388\ kJ\ mol^{-1}}$$

(b) The bond dissociation energies and enthalpies refer to gas-phase dissociation to atoms. Because of the dissociation, the number of moles of gas-phase particles increases ($\Delta\nu_{gas} > 0$). Therefore, since

$$\Delta_{ion}U^\ominus = \Delta_{ion}H^\ominus - \Delta\nu_{gas}RT$$

the mean bond internal energy is expected to be smaller than the mean bond enthalpy.

**E3.13** (a) The enthalpy of reaction is the difference between the energy required to break the bonds in the reactant and the energy released by the formation of the bonds in the product.

The enthalpy of reaction is thus the difference between the sum of the mean bond enthalpies of the bonds in the reactant and in the product

$$\Delta_r H^\ominus = \sum \Delta H_B(\text{reactants}) - \sum \Delta H_B(\text{products})$$
$$= \sum \Delta H_B(\text{glucose}) - 2 \times \sum \Delta H_B(\text{lactic acid})$$

Consider the structures of the reactant and product

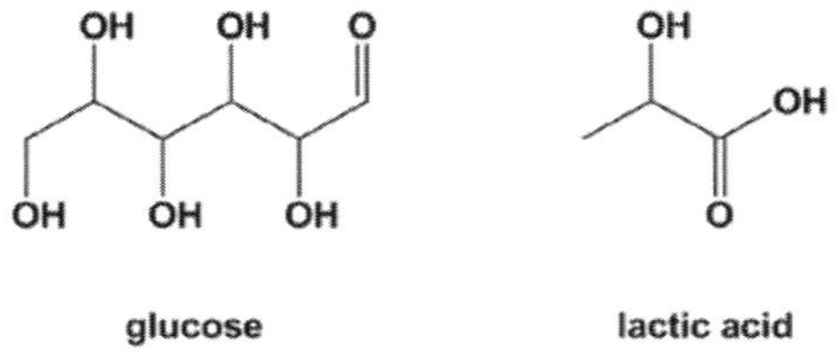


Glucose, $C_6H_{12}O_6$, contains seven C–H bonds, five O–H bonds, five C–O bonds, one C=O bond and five C=C bonds. Thus,

$$\sum \Delta H_B(\text{glucose}) = (7 \times \Delta H_B(\text{C}-\text{H})) + (5 \times \Delta H_B(\text{O}-\text{H}))$$
$$+(5 \times \Delta H_B(\text{C}-\text{O})) + \Delta H_B(\text{C}=\text{O}) + (5 \times \Delta H_B(\text{C}=\text{C}))$$
$$= \{(7 \times 412) + (5 \times 463) + (5 \times 360) + 743$$
$$+(5 \times 348)\}\ \text{kJ mol}^{-1}$$
$$= 9482\ \text{kJ mol}^{-1}$$

Similarly, lactic acid, $CH_3CH(OH)COOH$, contains four C–H bonds, two O–H bonds, two C–O bonds, one C=O bond and two C=C bonds. Thus,

$$\sum \Delta H_B(\text{lactic acid}) = (4 \times \Delta H_B(\text{C}-\text{H})) + (2 \times \Delta H_B(\text{O}-\text{H}))$$
$$+(2 \times \Delta H_B(\text{C}-\text{O})) + \Delta H_B(\text{C}=\text{O}) + (2 \times \Delta H_B(\text{C}=\text{C}))$$
$$= \{(4 \times 412) + (2 \times 463) + (2 \times 360)$$
$$+743 + (2 \times 348)\}\ \text{kJ mol}^{-1}$$
$$= 4733\ \text{kJ mol}^{-1}$$

Thus,

$$\Delta_r H^\ominus = \overbrace{(9482\ \text{kJ mol}^{-1})}^{\text{glucose}} - \overbrace{(2 \times 4733\ \text{kJ mol}^{-1})}^{\text{lactic acid}}$$
$$= \mathbf{16\ kJ\ mol^{-1}}$$

The approximate nature of this kind of calculation can be seen by comparing this value of $\Delta_r H$ to the value of $\Delta_r H^\ominus$ calculated from standard enthalpies of formation, which is

$$\Delta_r H^\ominus = -114\ \text{kJ mol}^{-1}$$

Strictly speaking, bond enthalpies apply only to gas-phase processes.

(b) In the same way for the reaction

$$C_6H_{12}O_6(aq) + 6\ O_2(g) \rightarrow 6\ CO_2(g) + 6\ H_2O(l)$$

then

$$\Delta_r H^\ominus = \overbrace{\left\{6 \times \sum \Delta H_B(CO_2) + 6 \times \sum \Delta H_B(H_2O)\right\}}^{\text{products}} - \underbrace{\left\{6 \times \Delta H_B(O_2) + \sum \Delta H_B(C_6H_{12}O_6)\right\}}_{\text{reactants}}$$

But

$$\sum \Delta H_B(CO_2) = \{2 \times \Delta H_B(C = O)\} = 2 \times (799\ \text{kJ mol}^{-1}) = 1598\ \text{kJ mol}^{-1}$$
$$\sum \Delta H_B(H_2O) = \{2 \times \Delta H_B(O - H)\} = 2 \times (492\ \text{kJ mol}^{-1}) = 984\ \text{kJ mol}^{-1}$$
$$\Delta H_B(O_2) = 497\ \text{kJ mol}^{-1}$$

so that

$$\Delta_r H^\ominus = \{\overbrace{(6 \times 497\ \text{kJ mol}^{-1})}^{O_2} + \overbrace{(9482\ \text{kJ mol}^{-1})}^{\text{glucose}}\} - \{\underbrace{(6 \times 1598\ \text{kJ mol}^{-1})}_{CO_2} + \underbrace{(6 \times 984\ \text{kJ mol}^{-1})}_{H_2O}\}$$
$$= \mathbf{-3028\ kJ\ mol^{-1}}$$

**E3.14** (a) The standard enthalpy of combustion applies to the combustion of one mole ethane. As written, however, the standard enthalpy of reaction refers to two moles of ethane, for each mole of reaction, so that

$$\Delta_c H^\ominus = (\Delta_r H^\ominus)/n = (-3120\ \text{kJ mol}^{-1})/\overbrace{\{(2\ \text{mol})/(1\ \text{mol})\}}^{\substack{\text{amount of ethane}\\ \text{per mole of reaction}}} = \mathbf{-1560\ kJ\ mol^{-1}}$$

(b) The specific enthalpy of combustion of ethane is the enthalpy change per unit mass, and thus may be calculated from the standard molar enthalpy of combustion and the molar mass

$$\Delta_c H_s^\ominus = \Delta_c H^\ominus/M = (-1560\ \text{kJ mol}^{-1})/(30.07\ \text{g mol}^{-1}) = \mathbf{+51.88\ kJ\ g^{-1}}$$

(c) In the same way, using data of Table 3.6, we find that the specific enthalpy of combustion of methane is

$$\Delta_c H_s^\ominus = \Delta_c H^\ominus/M = (-890\ \text{kJ mol}^{-1})/(16.04\ \text{g mol}^{-1}) = \mathbf{+55.5\ kJ\ g^{-1}}$$

Because the specific enthalpy of ethane is less exothermic than that of methane, ethane is a less efficient fuel.

**E3.15** The standard enthalpy of combustion of ethylbenzene may be calculated, according to Hess's law, from the standard enthalpies of formation of the products and reactants using eqn 3.5. Thus,

$$\Delta_c H^\ominus = \sum \nu\Delta_f H^\ominus(\text{products}) - \sum \nu\Delta_f H^\ominus(\text{reactants})$$

The balanced equation for the combustion of ethylbenzene is

$$C_6H_5C_2H_5(l) + 21/2\ O_2(g) \rightarrow 8\ CO_2(g) + 5\ H_2O(l)$$

Hence,

$$\Delta_c H^\ominus = \overbrace{\{8\Delta_f H^\ominus(CO_2, g) + 8\Delta_f H^\ominus(CO_2, g)\}}^{\text{products}} - \underbrace{\{\Delta_f H^\ominus(C_6H_5C_2H_5, l) + (21/2)\Delta_f H^\ominus(O_2, g)\}}_{\text{reactants}}$$

Thus,

$$\Delta_c H^\ominus = \{8 \times (-393.51\ \text{kJ mol}^{-1})\} + \{5 \times (-285.83\ \text{kJ mol}^{-1})\}$$
$$-(-12.5\ \text{kJ mol}^{-1}) - 0 = \mathbf{-4564.7\ kJ\ mol^{-1}}$$

**E3.16** We may express the reaction

$$C_6H_{10}(l) + H_2(g) \rightarrow C_6H_{12}(l)$$

as a combination of the reactions

$$C_6H_{10}(l) + 17/2\ O_2 \rightarrow 6\ CO_2\ (g) + 5\ H_2O(l) \qquad \Delta_c H^\ominus = -3752\ \text{kJ mol}^{-1} \quad (1)$$
$$C_6H_{12}(l) + 9\ O_2 \rightarrow 6\ CO_2(g) + 6\ H_2O(l) \qquad \Delta_c H^\ominus = -3953\ \text{kJ mol}^{-1} \quad (2)$$
$$H_2(g) + 1/2O_2(g) \rightarrow H_2O(l) \qquad \Delta_f H^\ominus = -286\ \text{kJ mol}^{-1} \quad (3)$$

If we sum eqn (1) and eqn (3), and the reverse of eqn (2), we get the desired reaction, so that

$$\Delta_r H^\ominus = \overbrace{-3752\ \text{kJ mol}^{-1}}^{\text{eqn (1)}} - \overbrace{-3953\ \text{kJ mol}^{-1}}^{\text{eqn (2)}} + \overbrace{-286\ \text{kJ mol}^{-1}}^{\text{eqn (3)}}$$
$$= \mathbf{-85\ kJ\ mol^{-1}}$$

**E3.17** (a) The enthalpy change for the consumption of 1.00 t of nitrogen molecules follows from the standard molar enthalpy of reaction, together with the mass, $m$, and molar mass, $M$, of nitrogen

$$\Delta H = n\Delta_r H^\ominus = (m/M)\Delta_r H^\ominus$$
$$= \{1.00 \times 10^3\ \text{kg})/(28.04 \times 10^{-3}\text{kg mol}^{-1}\} \times (-92.22\ \text{kJ mol}^{-1})$$
$$= \mathbf{-3290\ kJ}$$

(b) As written, two moles of ammonia are produced for every mole of nitrogen consumed. Thus, the enthalpy change for the production of 1.00 t of ammonia molecules is

$$\Delta H = (n/2)\Delta_r H^{\ominus} = ½(m/M)\Delta_r H^{\ominus}$$
$$= ½\{(1.00 \times 10^3 \text{ kg})/(17.05 \times 10^{-3} \text{kg mol}^{-1}\} \times (-92.22 \text{ kJ mol}^{-1})$$
$$= \mathbf{-2700 \text{ kJ}}$$

**E3.18** If we assume that the volume of condensed phases is negligibly small in compairson to the volume of gases, and that all gases behave perfectly, then we may write

$$\Delta_f U^{\ominus} = \Delta_f H^{\ominus} - \Delta\nu_{gas} RT$$

where $\Delta\nu_{gas}$ is the change in the amount of gas per mole of reaction. The formation of methyl acetate may be written as

$$3 \text{ C(s)} + 3 \text{ H}_2\text{(g)} + \text{O}_2\text{(g)} \rightarrow \text{CH}_3\text{COOCH}_3\text{(l)}$$

so that $\Delta\nu_{gas} = -4$. Thus,

$$\Delta_f U^{\ominus} = (-442 \times 10^3 \text{ J mol}^{-1}) - 4 \times (8.3145 \text{ J K}^{-1}\text{mol}^{-1}) \times (298 \text{ K})$$
$$= \mathbf{-432 \text{ kJ mol}^{-1}}$$

**E3.19** We may exploit Hess's Law by expressing the chemical equation for the formation of anthracene in terms of the combustion of anthracene and other reactions for which the enthalpy changes are known. Thus, we may write

$$14 \text{ C(s)} + 5 \text{ H}_2\text{(g)} \rightarrow \text{C}_{14}\text{H}_{10}\text{(s)}$$

as the sum of the formation reactions

$$14 \text{ C(s)} + 14 \text{ O}_2\text{(g)} \rightarrow 14 \text{ CO}_2\text{(g)} \qquad \Delta_f H^{\ominus}(\text{C(s)}) = -393.5 \text{ kJ mol}^{-1}$$
$$5 \text{ H}_2\text{(g)} + 5/2 \text{ O}_2\text{(g)} \rightarrow 5 \text{ H}_2\text{O (l)} \qquad \Delta_f H^{\ominus}(\text{H}_2\text{(g)}) = -285.8 \text{ kJ mol}^{-1}$$

minus the combustion reaction

$$\text{C}_{14}\text{H}_{10}\text{(s)} + 33/2 \text{ O}_2\text{(g)} \rightarrow 14 \text{ CO}_2\text{(g)} + 5 \text{ H}_2\text{O (l)}$$
$$\Delta_c H^{\ominus}(\text{C}_{14}\text{H}_{10}\text{(s)}) = -7163 \text{ kJ mol}^{-1}$$

Thus, taking into account the stoichiometric coefficients,

$$\Delta_f H^{\ominus}(\text{C}_{14}\text{H}_{10}, \text{s}) = \{14\Delta_f H^{\ominus}(\text{C, s}) + 5\Delta_f H^{\ominus}(\text{H}_2, \text{g})\} - \Delta_c H^{\ominus}(\text{C}_{14}\text{H}_{10}, \text{s})$$
$$= \{14 \times (-393.5 \text{ kJ mol}^{-1})\} + \{5 \times (-285.8 \text{ kJ mol}^{-1})\} - (-7163 \text{ kJ mol}^{-1})$$
$$= \mathbf{+225 \text{ kJ mol}^{-1}}$$

**E3.20** The enthalpy of combustion of naphthalene is, from the *Data Section*, $\Delta_c H^{\circ} = -5157 \text{ kJ mol}^{-1}$. Combustion in a bomb calorimeter occurs at constant volume. The heat of reaction is thus equal to the change in internal energy, rather than enthalpy

$$q_V = \Delta U^{\ominus} = n\Delta_r U^{\ominus}$$

The heat transferred to the calorimeter is thus $-q_V$ so that

$$C_V = -q_V = -n\Delta_r U^{\ominus}/\Delta T = -(m/M) \times \Delta_r U^{\ominus}/\Delta T$$

But, if we assume that only the gases make a significant contribution to the volume, and that all gases behave perfectly, then

$$\Delta_r U^{\ominus} = \Delta_r H^{\ominus} - \Delta\nu_{gas} RT$$

with, for the combustion of naphthalene,

$$C_{10}H_8(s) + 7\,O_2(g) \rightarrow 5\,CO_2(g) + 4\,H_2O(l)$$

so that $\Delta\nu_{gas} = -2$. Thus,

$$\begin{aligned} C_V &= -(m/M) \times \frac{(\Delta_r H^{\ominus} - \Delta\nu_{gas} RT)}{\Delta T} \\ &= -\frac{(320 \times 10^{-3}\ \mathrm{g})}{(128.18\ \mathrm{g\ mol^{-1}})} \\ &\quad \times \frac{(-5157 \times 10^{3}\ \mathrm{J\ mol^{-1}}) - \{-2 \times (8.3145\ \mathrm{J\ K^{-1} mol^{-1}}) \times (298\ \mathrm{K})\}}{3.05\ \mathrm{K}} \\ &= 4.22 \times 10^{3}\ \mathrm{J\ K^{-1}} = \mathbf{4.22\ kJ\ K^{-1}} \end{aligned}$$

where we have assumed an average temperature of 298 K. We may rearrange the expression for the heat capacity to allow us to calculate the rise in temperature for the combustion of the sample of phenol.

$$\Delta T = -(m/M) \times \frac{(\Delta_r H^{\ominus} - \Delta\nu_{gas} RT)}{C_V}$$

For phenol, $\Delta_c H^{\circ} = -3054\ \mathrm{kJ\ mol^{-1}}$ and complete combustion

$$C_6H_5OH(s) + 7\,O_2(g) \rightarrow 6\,CO_2(g) + 3\,H_2O(l)$$

results in a change in the amount of gas $\Delta\nu_{gas} = -1$. Thus

$$\begin{aligned} \Delta T &= -\left(\frac{100 \times 10^{-3}\ \mathrm{g}}{94.12\ \mathrm{g\ mol^{-1}}}\right) \\ &\quad \times \frac{(-3054 \times 10^{3}\mathrm{J\ mol^{-1}}) - \{-1 \times (8.3145\ \mathrm{J\ K^{-1} mol^{-1}}) \times (298\ \mathrm{K})\}}{4.22 \times 10^{3}\ \mathrm{J\ K^{-1}}} \\ &= \mathbf{+0.768\ K} \end{aligned}$$

In practice, the difference between the change in internal energy and enthalpy is negligible for both naphthalene and phenol and we would have obtained similar results had we assumed initially that

$$q = \Delta U^{\ominus} \approx \Delta H^{\ominus}$$

**E3.21** The heat released in a bomb calorimeter is equivalent to the change in internal energy because the combustion occurs at constant volume.

$$\Delta U = q_V$$

(a) If we assume that the volume of condensed phases is negligible in comparison to that of gases, and that all gases behave perfectly, then

$$\Delta_c U^\ominus = \Delta_c H^\ominus - \Delta\nu_{gas} RT$$

where $\Delta\nu_{gas}$ is the change in the amount of gas. For the combustion of glucose,

$$C_6H_{12}O_6(s) + 6\,O_2(g) \rightarrow 6\,CO_2(g) + 6\,H_2O(l)$$

then $\Delta\nu_{gas} = 0$, so that

$$\begin{aligned}\Delta_c H^\ominus = \Delta_c U^\ominus = \frac{\Delta U}{n} = \frac{q_V}{(m/M)} &= \frac{-C_V\Delta T}{(m/M)}\\ &= \frac{(641\ \mathrm{J\,K^{-1}}) \times (7.793\ \mathrm{K})}{(0.3212\ \mathrm{g})/(180.16\ \mathrm{g\,mol^{-1}})}\\ &= -2802 \times 10^3\ \mathrm{J\,mol^{-1}} = \mathbf{-2802\ kJ\,mol^{-1}}\end{aligned}$$

(b) $\Delta_c U^\ominus = \Delta_c H^\ominus = \mathbf{-2802\ kJ\,mol^{-1}}$

(c) We may express the chemical equation for the formation of glucose

$$6\,C(s) + 6\,H_2(g) + 3\,O_2(g) \rightarrow C_6H_{12}O_6(s)$$

as the sum of the formation reactions for $CO_2(g)$ and $H_2O(l)$

$$6\,C(s) + 6\,O_2\,(g) \rightarrow 6\,CO_2\,(g) \qquad \Delta H = 6 \times \Delta_f H^\ominus(CO_2, g) \quad (1)$$
$$6\,H_2(g) + 3\,O_2\,(g) \rightarrow 6\,H_2O\,(g) \qquad \Delta H = 6 \times \Delta_f H^\ominus((H_2O, l) \quad (2)$$

for which the enthalpy changes are known, minus the combustion reaction

$$C_6H_{12}O_6(s) + 6\,O_2(g) \rightarrow 6\,CO_2(g) + 6\,H_2O(l) \qquad \Delta H = \Delta_c H^\ominus(C_6H_{12}O_6\,, s) \quad (3)$$

Thus

$$\begin{aligned}&\Delta_f H^\ominus(C_6H_{12}O_6\,(s))\\ &= \{6 \times \Delta_f H^\ominus(CO_2(g)) + 6 \times \Delta_f H^\ominus(H_2O(l))\} - \Delta_c H^\ominus(C_6H_{12}O_6\,(s))\\ &= 6 \times (-393\ \mathrm{kJ\,mol^{-1}}) + 6 \times (-285\ \mathrm{kJ\,mol^{-1}}) + (2802\ \mathrm{kJ\,mol^{-1}})\\ &= \mathbf{-1.27 \times 10^3 kJ\,mol^{-1}}\end{aligned}$$

**E3.22** (a) On the assumption that the calorimeter is a constant volume bomb calorimeter, the heat released directly equals the internal energy of combustion. Therefore,

$$\Delta_c U^\ominus = q_V = \mathbf{-1333\ kJ\,mol^{-1}}$$

It is important to remember that because the combustion is exothermic, the heat released is negative.

(b) If we assume that the volumes of solids and liquids are negligible in comparison to the volume of gases, and that all gases obey the pefect gas law, then

$$\Delta_c H^\ominus = \Delta_c U^\ominus + \Delta\nu_{gas} RT$$

where $\Delta\nu_{gas}$ is the change in the amount of gas. For the combustion of fumaric acid,

$$\text{HOOCCH=CHCOOH(s)} + 6\ \text{O}_2\text{(g)} \rightarrow 4\ \text{CO}_2\text{(g)} + 2\ \text{H}_2\text{O(l)}$$

then $\Delta \nu_{\text{gas}} = +1$, so that

$$\begin{aligned}\Delta_c H^{\ominus}(\text{fumaric acid}) &= -1333 \times 10^3\ \text{J mol}^{-1} \\ &\quad +\{1 \times (8.3145\ \text{J K}^{-1}\text{mol}^{-1}) \times (298\ \text{K})\} \\ &= -1331 \times 10^3\ \text{J mol}^{-1} = \mathbf{-1331\ kJ\ mol^{-1}}\end{aligned}$$

(c) We may express the formation reaction for fumaric acid

$$4\ \text{C(s)} + 2\ \text{H}_2\text{(g)} \rightarrow \text{HOOCCH=CHCOOH(s)}$$

as the sum of the formation reactions of $CO_2(g)$ and $H_2O(l)$

$$4\ \text{C(s)} + \text{O}_2 = 4\ \text{CO}_2\text{(g)} \qquad \Delta H = 4 \times \Delta_f H^{\ominus}(\text{CO}_2, \text{g}) \quad (1)$$
$$2\ \text{H}_2\text{(g)} + \text{O}_2\ \text{(g)} \rightarrow 2\ \text{H}_2\text{O (g)} \qquad \Delta H = 2 \times \Delta_f H^{\ominus}(\text{H}_2\text{O}, \text{l}) \quad (2)$$

for which the enthalpy changes are known, minus the combustion reaction

$$\text{HOOCCH=CHCOOH(s)} + 6\ \text{O}_2\text{(g)} \rightarrow 4\ \text{CO}_2\text{(g)} + 2\ \text{H}_2\text{O(l)}$$
$$\Delta H = \Delta_c H^{\ominus}(\text{fumaric acid}) \ (3)$$

Thus,

$$\begin{aligned}\Delta_c H^{\ominus}(\text{fumaric acid}) &= \{4 \times \Delta_f H^{\ominus}(\text{CO}_2, \text{g})\} + \{2 \times \Delta_f H^{\ominus}(\text{H}_2\text{O}, \text{l})\} \\ &\qquad -\Delta_c H^{\ominus}(\text{fumaric acid, s}) \\ &= \{4 \times (-393\ \text{kJ mol}^{-1})\} + \{2 \times (-285\ \text{kJ mol}^{-1})\} \\ &\qquad -(2802\ \text{kJ mol}^{-1}) \\ &= \mathbf{-815\ kJ\ mol^{-1}}\end{aligned}$$

**E3.23** The specific enthalpy of combustion is related to the standard enthalpy of combustion through

$$\Delta_c H_s^{\ominus} = \Delta_c H^{\ominus}/M$$

where $M$ is the molar mass. The specific enthalpy of combustion therefore gives an indication of the strength of the bonds that must be broken rather than the number and type of atoms in the molecule. Combustion involves breaking the weak bonds in the fuel and oxygen molecules and the formation of the bonds in the product carbon dioxide and water molecules. By considering the balanced equations for the combustion of glucose and decanoic acid

$$\text{C}_6\text{H}_{12}\text{O}_6\text{(s)} + 6\ \text{O}_2\text{(g)} \rightarrow 6\ \text{CO}_2\ \text{(g)} + 6\ \text{H}_2\text{O (l)}$$
$$\text{C}_{10}\text{H}_{20}\text{O}_2\text{(s)} + 13\ \text{O}_2\text{(g)} \rightarrow 9\ \text{CO}_2\ \text{(g)} + 10\ \text{H}_2\text{O (l)}$$

we can see that the combustion of decanoic acid involves the formation of more strong carbon–oxygen and oxygen–hydrogen bonds than does the combustion of glucose. This more than balances the energy required in breaking the strong bonds in the reactant oxygen molecules. Thus, more energy is released in the combustion of decanoic acid than glucose. Indeed, in general, when comparing a carbon-based series of compounds, all having similar molar masses, those that are least oxidized will have the most exothermic enthalpy of combustion and thus have higher specific enthalpies.

**E3.24** The standard enthalpy of reaction may be expressed in terms of the standard enthalpies of formation of the products and reactants through eqn 3.5

$$\Delta_r H^\ominus = \sum \nu\Delta_f H^\ominus(\text{products}) - \sum \nu\Delta_f H^\ominus(\text{reactants})$$

Thus, for the dissolution of solid silver iodide, AgI(s),

$$\text{AgI(s)} \rightarrow \text{Ag}^+\text{(aq)} + \text{I}^-\text{(aq)}$$

the enthalpy of reaction is

$$\begin{aligned}\Delta_r H^\ominus &= \overbrace{\{\Delta_f H^\ominus(\text{Ag}^+,\text{aq}) + \Delta_f H^\ominus(\text{I}^-,\text{aq})\}}^{\text{product}} - \overbrace{\Delta_f H^\ominus(\text{AgI, s})}^{\text{reactant}} \\ &= (105.58\ \text{kJ mol}^{-1}) + (-55.19\ \text{kJ mol}^{-1}) - (-61.88\ \text{kJ mol}^{-1}) \\ &= \mathbf{+112.27\ kJ\ mol^{-1}}\end{aligned}$$

**E3.25** The standard enthalpy of reaction for the decomposition

$$\text{NH}_3\text{SO}_2\text{(s)} \rightarrow \text{NH}_3\text{(g)} + \text{SO}_2\text{(g)}$$

may be written in terms of the standard enthalpies of formation using eqn 3.5 as

$$\begin{aligned}\Delta_r H^\ominus &= \sum \nu\Delta_f H^\ominus(\text{products}) - \sum \nu\Delta_f H^\ominus(\text{reactants}) \\ &= \overbrace{\{\Delta_f H^\ominus(\text{NH}_3,\text{g}) + \Delta_f H^\ominus(\text{SO}_2,\text{g})\}}^{\text{products}} - \overbrace{\Delta_f H^\ominus(\text{NH}_3\text{SO}_2,\text{g})}^{\text{reactants}}\end{aligned}$$

Thus, rearranging,

$$\begin{aligned}\Delta_f H^\ominus(\text{NH}_3\text{SO}_2,\text{g}) &= \Delta_f H^\ominus(\text{NH}_3,\text{g}) + \Delta_f H^\ominus(\text{SO}_2,\text{g}) - \Delta_r H^\ominus \\ &= (-46.11\ \text{kJ mol}^{-1}) + (-296.83\ \text{kJ mol}^{-1}) - (40\ \text{kJ mol}^{-1}) \\ &= \mathbf{-383\ kJ\ mol^{-1}}\end{aligned}$$

**E3.26** The standard enthalpy of reaction for the transition

$$\text{C(graphite)} \rightarrow \text{C(diamond)}$$

may be written, by analogy with eqn 3.5, in terms of the standard enthalpies of combustion as

$$\Delta_{trs} H^\ominus = \sum \nu\Delta_c H^\ominus(\text{products}) - \sum \nu\Delta_c H^\ominus(\text{reactants})$$

because the reaction may be expressed as the combination of the combustion of graphite

$$\text{C(graphite)} + \text{O}_2\text{(g)} \rightarrow \text{CO}_2\text{(g)}$$

$$\Delta H = \Delta_c H^\ominus(\text{C, graphite}) = -393.5\ \text{kJ mol}^{-1}$$

and the reverse of the combustion of diamond

$$CO_2(g) \rightarrow C(\text{diamond}) + O_2(g)$$

$$\Delta H = -\Delta_c H^\ominus(\text{C, diamond}) = -395.4\ \text{kJ mol}^{-1}$$

Thus,

$$\begin{aligned}\Delta_{\text{trs}}H^\ominus &= \Delta_c H^\ominus(\text{C, diamond}) - \Delta_c H^\ominus(\text{C, graphite})\\ &= -(395.4\ \text{kJ mol}^{-1}) - (-393.5\ \text{kJ mol}^{-1})\\ &= \mathbf{+1.9\ kJ\ mol^{-1}}\end{aligned}$$

**E3.27** From the First Law of thermodynamics, the change in the molar internal energy is

$$\Delta_{\text{trs}}U = q + w$$

The heat transferred at constant pressure is given by the molar enthalpy change,

$$q = \Delta_{\text{trs}}H$$

and the work done by

$$w = -p_{\text{ex}}\Delta V_{\text{m}}$$

We may calculate the volume change from the mass density, because

$$\rho = m/V = M/V_{\text{m}}$$

where $M$ is the molar mass and $V_{\text{m}}$ the molar volume, so that

$$\Delta V_{\text{m}} = V_{\text{diamond}} - V_{\text{graphite}} = M(1/\rho_{\text{diamond}} - 1/\rho_{\text{graphite}})$$

Hence, if we assume that the enthalpy of transition does not vary with pressure,

$$\Delta_{\text{trs}}U = \Delta_{\text{trs}}H - p_{\text{ex}}M(1/\rho_{\text{diamond}} - 1/\rho_{\text{graphite}})$$

A pressure of 150 kbar is equivalent to $150 \times 10^8$ Pa, because 1 bar = $10^5$ Pa and a mass density of 1 g cm$^{-3}$ is equivalent to $1 \times 10^6$ g m$^{-3}$. Thus,

$$\begin{aligned}\Delta_{\text{trs}}U &= (1.9 \times 10^3\ \text{J mol}^{-1})\\ &\quad -(150 \times 10^5\ \text{Pa}) \times (12.01\ \text{g mol}^{-1})\\ &\qquad \times \left\{\left(\frac{1}{3.510 \times 10^6\ \text{g m}^{-3}}\right) - \left(\frac{1}{2.250 \times 10^6\ \text{g m}^{-3}}\right)\right\}\\ &= +30.6 \times 10^3\ \text{J mol}^{-1} = \mathbf{+30.6\ kJ\ mol^{-1}}\end{aligned}$$

**E3.28** (a) The specific heat capacity of liquid water is, from Table 2.1, 4.18 kJ kg$^{-1}$ K$^{-1}$. Thus, from the definition of specific heat capacity given in section 2.5 of the text, $q = mC_s\Delta T$, so that

$$\Delta T = q/mC_s = (10 \times 10^6\ \text{J})/\{(65\ \text{kg}) \times (4.18 \times 10^3\ \text{J kg}^{-1}\text{K}^{-1})\} = \mathbf{37\ K}$$

(b) The heat transferred through the vaporization of water at constant pressure is

$$q = n\Delta_{\text{vap}}H^\ominus = (m/M)\Delta_{\text{vap}}H^\ominus$$

Rearranging, the mass of water that must be vaporized to maintain constant temperature is

$$\begin{aligned} m &= qM/\Delta_{\text{vap}}H^{\ominus} \\ &= (10 \times 10^{6}\ \text{J}) \times (18.02 \times 10^{-3}\ \text{kg mol}^{-1})/(44 \times 10^{3}\text{J mol}^{-1}) \\ &= \mathbf{4.1\ kg} \end{aligned}$$

This estimate ignores both the conduction of heat that occurs from high temperature to low temperature without evaporation and the small amount of heat used to bring ingested water to body temperature.

**E3.29** (a) We may write the chemical equation for the combustion of liquid propane as a two-step process that involves first the vaporization of liquid propane, and second the combustion of gaseous propane

$$C_3H_8(l) + 5\ O_2(g) \rightarrow C_3H_8(g) + 5\ O_2(g) \rightarrow 3\ CO_2(g) + 4\ H_2O(l)$$

The standard enthalpy change for the combustion of liquid propane is thus the sum

$$\begin{aligned} \Delta_c H^{\ominus}(C_3H_8, l) &= \Delta_{\text{vap}}H^{\ominus}(C_3H_8) + \Delta_c H^{\ominus}(C_3H_8, g) \\ &= +15\ \text{kJ mol}^{-1} + (-2220\ \text{kJ mol}^{-1}) = \mathbf{-2205\ kJ\ mol^{-1}} \end{aligned}$$

(b) If we assume that the volume of the liquid propane and water is negligible in comparsion with the volume of the different gases, and that the gases behave perfectly, then we may express the relationship between the standard enthalpy and standard internal energy change in terms of the change in the amount of gas, $\Delta\nu_{\text{gas}}$

$$\Delta_c U^{\ominus} = \Delta_c H^{\ominus} - \Delta\nu_{\text{gas}}RT$$

For the combustion of liquid propane,

$$\Delta\nu_{\text{gas}} = 3 - 5 = -2$$

so that

$$\begin{aligned} \Delta_c U^{\ominus}(C_3H_8, l) &= (-2205 \times 10^{3}\ \text{J mol}^{-1}) \\ &\quad -\{-2 \times (8.3145\ \text{J K}^{-1}\text{mol}^{-1}) \times (298\ \text{K})\} \\ &= -2200 \times 10^{3}\text{J mol}^{-1} = \mathbf{-2205\ kJ\ mol^{-1}} \end{aligned}$$

**E3.30** (a) exothermic, because $\Delta_r H^{\ominus} < 0$.

(b) endothermic, because $\Delta H^{\ominus} > 0$.

(c) endothermic, because vaporization requires heat to be transferred, so that $\Delta_{\text{vap}}H^{\ominus} > 0$.

(d) endothermic, because fusion, which is the transition from solid to liquid, requires heat to be transferred, so that $\Delta_{\text{fus}}H^{\ominus} > 0$.

(e) endothermic, because sublimation, which is the transition from solid to vapour, requires heat to be transferred, so that $\Delta_{\text{sub}}H^{\ominus} > 0$.

**E3.31** Standard enthalpies of reaction may be written in terms of the standard enthalpies of formation using eqn 3.5 as

$$\Delta_r H^{\ominus} = \sum \nu \Delta_f H^{\ominus}(\text{products}) - \sum \nu \Delta_f H^{\ominus}(\text{reactants})$$

(a) Thus, for the reaction

$2\,NO_2(g) \rightarrow N_2O_4(g)$

$$\begin{aligned}\Delta_r H^{\ominus} &= \Delta_f H^{\ominus}(N_2O_4, g) - \{2 \times \Delta_f H^{\ominus}(NO_2, g)\}\\ &= (9.16\ \text{kJ mol}^{-1}) - 2 \times (33.18\ \text{kJ mol}^{-1}) = \mathbf{-57.20\ kJ\ mol^{-1}}\end{aligned}$$

(b) For the reaction

$NO_2(g) \rightarrow \tfrac{1}{2}N_2O_4(g)$

$$\begin{aligned}\Delta_r H^{\ominus} &= \{\tfrac{1}{2} \times \Delta_f H^{\ominus}(N_2O_4, g)\} - \Delta_f H^{\ominus}(NO_2, g)\\ &= \tfrac{1}{2} \times (9.16\ \text{kJ mol}^{-1}) - (33.18\ \text{kJ mol}^{-1}) = \mathbf{-28.6\ kJ\ mol^{-1}}\end{aligned}$$

The standard reaction enthalpy is a molar quantity and refers to the enthalpy change per mole of reaction as written. Thus, the standard enthalpy change for part (b) is half that for part (a).

(c) For the reaction

$3\,NO_2(g) + H_2O(l) \rightarrow 2HNO_3(aq) + NO(g)$

$$\begin{aligned}\Delta_r H^{\ominus} &= \{(2 \times \Delta_f H^{\ominus}(HNO_3, aq)) + \Delta_f H^{\ominus}(NO, g)\}\\ &\qquad -\{(3 \times \Delta_f H^{\ominus}(NO_2, g)) + \Delta_f H^{\ominus}(H_2O(l))\}\\ &= \{2 \times (-207.36\ \text{kJ mol}^{-1}) + (90.5\ \text{kJ mol}^{-1})\}\\ &\qquad - \{3 \times (33.18\ \text{kJ mol}^{-1}) + (-285.83\ \text{kJ mol}^{-1})\}\\ &= \mathbf{-138.2\ kJ\ mol^{-1}}\end{aligned}$$

(d) For the iosmerisation reaction,

cyclopropane(g) $\rightarrow$ propene(g)

$$\begin{aligned}\Delta_r H^{\ominus} &= \Delta_f H^{\ominus}(\text{propene}, g) - \Delta_f H^{\ominus}(\text{cyclopropane}, g)\\ &= (+20.42\ \text{kJ mol}^{-1}) - (53.30\ \text{kJ mol}^{-1})\\ &= \mathbf{-32.88\ kJ\ mol^{-1}}\end{aligned}$$

(e) In order to calculate the standard reaction enthalpy, we must first write the net ionic equation

$H^+(aq) + Cl^-(aq) + Na^+(aq) + OH^-(aq) \rightarrow Na^+(aq) + Cl^-(aq) + H_2O(l)$

Simplifying we obtain

$H^+(aq) + OH^-(aq) \rightarrow H_2O(l)$

so that

$$\begin{aligned}\Delta_r H^\ominus &= \Delta_f H^\ominus(H_2O,l) - \{\Delta_f H^\ominus(H^+,aq) + \Delta_f H^\ominus(OH^-,aq)\}\\ &= (-285.83\ \text{kJ mol}^{-1}) - \{(0\ \text{kJ mol}^{-1}) + (-229.99\ \text{kJ mol}^{-1})\}\\ &= \mathbf{-55.84\ kJ\ mol^{-1}}\end{aligned}$$

**E3.32** We may express the formation of $N_2O_5$ is the sum of the following four reactions for which the standard enthalpy of reaction is known:

| | | |
|---|---|---|
| $2\,NO(g) + O_2(g) \rightarrow 2\,NO_2(g)$ | $\Delta_r H^\ominus = -114.1\ \text{kJ mol}^{-1}$ | (1) |
| $1/2O_2(g) + 2\,NO_2(g) \rightarrow N_2O_5(g)$ | $\Delta_r H^\ominus = ½ \times (-110.2\ \text{kJ mol}^{-1})$ | (2) |
| $N_2(g) + O_2(g) \rightarrow 2\,NO(g)$ | $\Delta_r H^\ominus = +180.5\ \text{kJ mol}^{-1}$ | (3) |
| $N_2(g) + 5/2O_2(g) \rightarrow N_2O_5(g)$ | $\Delta_r H^\ominus = +11.3\ \text{kJ mol}^{-1}$ | (4) |

Therefore,

$$\begin{aligned}\Delta_f H^\ominus(N_2O_5,g) &= \overbrace{(-114.1\ \text{kJ mol}^{-1})}^{\text{reaction (1)}} + \overbrace{½(-110.2\ \text{kJ mol}^{-1})}^{\text{reaction (2)}}\\ &\quad + \underbrace{(180.51\ \text{kJ mol}^{-1})}_{\text{reaction (3)}} + \underbrace{(11.3\ \text{kJ mol}^{-1})}_{\text{reaction (4)}}\\ &= \mathbf{+11.3\ kJ\ mol^{-1}}\end{aligned}$$

**E3.33** Using Kirchoff's law, eqn 3.6,

$$\Delta_r H^\ominus(T') = \Delta_r H^\ominus(T) + \Delta_r C_p^\ominus \times (T' - T)$$

with, from eqn 3.7,

$$\begin{aligned}\Delta_r C_p^\ominus &= \sum \nu\Delta_r C_{p,m}^\ominus(\text{products}) - \sum \nu\Delta_r C_{p,m}^\ominus(\text{reactants})\\ &= C_{p,m}^\ominus(N_2O_4,g) - \{2 \times C_{p,m}^\ominus(NO_2,g)\}\\ &= (77.28\ \text{J K}^{-1}\text{mol}^{-1}) - (2 \times 37.20\ \text{J K}^{-1}\text{mol}^{-1})\\ &= +2.88\ \text{J K}^{-1}\text{mol}^{-1}\end{aligned}$$

where, once again, we have explicitly given the sign of the change. Thus,

$$\begin{aligned}\Delta_r H^\ominus(373\ \text{K}) &= \Delta_r H^\ominus(298\ \text{K}) + \Delta_r C_p^\ominus \times \{(373\ \text{K}) - (298\ \text{K})\}\\ &= (-57.20 \times 10^3\text{J mol}^{-1}) + \{(2.88\ \text{J K}^{-1}) \times (75\ \text{K})\}\\ &= \mathbf{-56.98\ kJ\ mol^{-1}}\end{aligned}$$

**E3.34** Using Kirchoff's law, eqn 3.6,

$$\Delta_{vap} H^\ominus(T') = \Delta_{vap} H^\ominus(T) + \Delta_r C_p^\ominus \times (T' - T)$$

with, from eqn 3.7,

$$\begin{aligned}\Delta_{vap} C_p^\ominus &= \sum \nu\Delta_{vap} C_{p,m}^\ominus(\text{products}) - \sum \nu\Delta_{vap} C_{p,m}^\ominus(\text{reactants})\\ &= C_{p,m}^\ominus(H_2O,g) - C_{p,m}^\ominus(H_2O,l)\\ &= (33.58\ \text{J K}^{-1}\text{mol}^{-1}) - (75.29\ \text{J K}^{-1}\text{mol}^{-1})\\ &= -41.71\ \text{J K}^{-1}\text{mol}^{-1}\end{aligned}$$

Thus,

$$\begin{aligned}\Delta_r H^{\ominus}(373\text{ K}) &= \Delta_r H^{\ominus}(298\text{ K}) + \Delta_r C_p^{\ominus} \times \{(373\text{ K}) - (298\text{ K})\}\\ &= (44.01\times 10^3\text{J mol}^{-1}) + \{(-41.71\text{ J K}^{-1})\times(75\text{ K})\}\\ &= \mathbf{+40.88\ kJ\ mol^{-1}}\end{aligned}$$

**E3.35** We may rearrange Kirchoff's law, eqn 3.6, to express the change in reaction enthalpy with an increase in temperature

$$\Delta_r H^{\ominus}(T') - \Delta_r H^{\ominus}(T) = \Delta_r C_p^{\ominus} \times (T' - T)$$

The sign of the change thus depends upon the sign of the difference in the constant pressure molar heat capacities of the products and reactants, $\Delta_r C_p^{\ominus}$. A negative value of $\Delta_r C_p^{\ominus}$ implies a decrease, a positive value an increase, with increasing $T$.

(a) For the reaction

$$2\ H_2(g) + O_2(g) \rightarrow 2H_2O(g)$$

then, if we approximate the constant pressure molar heat capacities of water as $4R$ and of hydrogen and oxygen as $3/2R$, then

$$\begin{aligned}\Delta_r C_p^{\ominus} &= \sum \nu\Delta_r C_{p,m}^{\ominus}(\text{products}) - \sum \nu\Delta_r C_{p,m}^{\ominus}(\text{reactants})\\ &= C_{p,m}^{\ominus}(H_2O,g) - \left(C_{p,m}^{\ominus}(H_2,g) + C_{p,m}^{\ominus}(O_2,g)\right)\\ &= 4R - \{(7/2)R + (7/2)R\}\\ &= -3R\end{aligned}$$

The difference is negative, $-3R < 0$, so that the standard enthalpy of reaction must **decrease** with temperature.

(b) In the same way for the reaction

$$N_2(g) + 3\ H_2(g) \rightarrow 2\ NH_3(g)$$

$$\begin{aligned}\Delta_r C_p^{\ominus} &= \sum \nu\Delta_r C_{p,m}^{\ominus}(\text{products}) - \sum \nu\Delta_r C_{p,m}^{\ominus}(\text{reactants})\\ &= 2\times C_{p,m}^{\ominus}(NH_3,g) - \left(3\times C_{p,m}^{\ominus}(H_2,g) + C_{p,m}^{\ominus}(N_2,g)\right)\\ &= (2\times 4)R - (3\times 7/2)R + (7/2)R\\ &= -6R\end{aligned}$$

and once again, the standard enthalpy of reaction must **decrease** with temperature.

(c) For the reaction

$$CH_4(g) + 2\ O_2(g) \rightarrow CO_2(g) + 2\ H_2O(g)$$

$$\begin{aligned}\Delta_r C_p^{\ominus} &= \sum \nu\Delta_r C_{p,m}^{\ominus}(\text{products}) - \sum \nu\Delta_r C_{p,m}^{\ominus}(\text{reactants})\\ &= \left(2\times C_{p,m}^{\ominus}(H_2O,g) + C_{p,m}^{\ominus}(CO_2,g)\right) - \left(C_{p,m}^{\ominus}(CH_4,g) + 2\times C_{p,m}^{\ominus}(O_2,g)\right)\\ &= \{(2\times 4)R + (7/2)R\} - \{4R + 2\times(7/2)R\}\end{aligned}$$

$= +½R$

so that the standard enthalpy of reaction must **increase** with temperature.

**E3.36** (a) For the reaction

$$2\,H_2(g) + O_2(g) \rightarrow 2H_2O(g)$$

then, if we approximate the constant pressure molar heat capacities of liquid water as $9R$ and of hydrogen and oxygen as $3/2R$, then

$$\begin{aligned}\Delta_r C_p^{\ominus} &= \sum \nu\Delta_r C_{p,m}^{\ominus}(\text{products}) - \sum \nu\Delta_r C_{p,m}^{\ominus}(\text{reactants})\\ &= C_{p,m}^{\ominus}(H_2O,l) - \left(C_{p,m}^{\ominus}(H_2,g) + C_{p,m}^{\ominus}(O_2,g)\right)\\ &= 9R - \{(7/2)R + (7/2)R\}\\ &= +2R\end{aligned}$$

The difference is now positive, $+2R > 0$, so that the standard enthalpy of reaction must **increase** with temperature.

(c) For the reaction

$$CH_4(g) + 2\,O_2(g) \rightarrow CO_2(g) + 2\,H_2O(g)$$

$$\begin{aligned}\Delta_r C_p^{\ominus} &= \sum \nu\Delta_r C_{p,m}^{\ominus}(\text{products}) - \sum \nu\Delta_r C_{p,m}^{\ominus}(\text{reactants})\\ &= \left(2\times C_{p,m}^{\ominus}(H_2O,l) + C_{p,m}^{\ominus}(CO_2,g)\right) - \left(C_{p,m}^{\ominus}(CH_4,g) + 2\times C_{p,m}^{\ominus}(O_2,g)\right)\\ &= \{(2\times 9)R + (7/2)R\} - \{4R + (2\times 7/2)R\}\\ &= +21/2R\end{aligned}$$

so that the standard enthalpy of reaction must **increase** with temperature.

## Answers to projects

**P3.37** (a) A difference in the thermogram baseline at two different temperatures indicates that the sample has different heat capacities at the two temperatures. The sample may have experienced a phase transition from one crystalline, or non-crystalline, structure to another. It may have melted, evaporated, or decomposed. It may have reacted with the atmosphere or, if the sample is a mixture, components may have reacted. In all of these examples the sample has experienced either a physical or chemical change while being heated from one temperature to the other and, consequently, exhibits different heat capacities at those temperatures.

For example, the thermograms of solid polymers often often exhibit a baseline change. This results from the so-called glass transition, which occurs at a well defined temperature rather than because of any chemical reaction. Upon reaching the temperature of the glass transition the polymer appears to change from a brittle glass-like state to a more rubberlike state which allows for increased rotational motion of the polymer chain and great randomness in the positions of molecules. It is a transition from a crystalline lattice to a glassy state. The glass transition of pure polystyrene, the plastic of cheap rulers and coffee spoons, occurs at about 90 °C.

(b) Impurities lower the onset temperature observed both in the thermograms observed in the differential scanning calorimetry of organic substances and in the observed glass transition temperatures of polymers. Samples with smaller mole fractions of the major substance give lower transition temperatures. Thus, a series of samples that are prepared with a range of mole fractions of the major constituent can be examined with differential scanning calorimetry and a standard curve of mole fraction against onset temperatures, which are provided by the thermograms, can be prepared. The differential scanning calorimetry of a chemical reactor sample of unknown purity gives the sample onset temperature that is checked against the standard curve to determine the purity mole fraction. Peak temperatures of differential scanning calorimetry melting curves are used similarly.

**P3.38** For a reaction of the form

$$\nu_A A + \nu_B B + \cdots\cdots \rightarrow \nu_P P + \nu_Q Q + \qquad \Delta_r U(T)$$

let $dU_m(i)$ be the infinitesimal molar internal energy change of the $i^{th}$ chemical species due to the infinitesimal temperature change $dT$. The infinitesimal reaction internal energy change due to the temperature change is thus

$$\begin{aligned} d\{\Delta_r U(T)\} &= \{\nu_P dU_m(P) + \nu_Q dU_m(Q) + \cdots\} - \{\nu_A dU_m(A) + \nu_B dU_m(B) + \cdots\} \\ &= \sum \nu\, dU_m(\text{products}) - \sum \nu\, dU_m(\text{reactants}) \end{aligned}$$

But,

$$C_{V,m} = \frac{dU_m}{dT}$$

so that

$$dU_m = C_{V,m} dT$$

Substitution of this relationship gives

$$d\{\Delta_r U(T)\} = \sum \nu\, C_{V,m}(\text{products})dT - \sum \nu\, C_{V,m}(\text{reactants})dT$$

or

$$d\{\Delta_r U(T)\} = \Delta_r C_V\, dT$$

with

$$\Delta_r C_V = \sum \nu \Delta_r C_{V,m}(\text{products}) - \sum \nu \Delta_r C_{V,m}(\text{reactants})$$

Integration between $T$ and $T'$ gives

$$\int_T^{T'} d\{\Delta_r U(T)\} = \int_T^{T'} \Delta_r C_V \, dT$$
$$\Delta_r U(T') - \Delta_r U(T) = \Delta_r C_V \times (T' - T)$$

if we assume that the difference in the molar heat capacities at constant volume, $\Delta_r C_m$ does not change with temperature. Rearranging gives

$$\Delta_r U(T') = \Delta_r U(T) + \Delta_r C_V \times (T' - T)$$

which is similar to Kirchoff's law, eqn 3.6.

(b) Following the same approach as used in part (a), but considering enthalpy rather than internal energy, we can show that

$$\int_T^{T'} d\{\Delta_r H(T)\} = \int_T^{T'} \Delta_r C_p \, dT$$

Then, substituting

$$\Delta_r C_p = a + bT + \frac{c}{T^2}$$

so that

$$\int_T^{T'} d\{\Delta_r H(T)\} = \int_T^{T'} \left\{a + bT + \frac{c}{T^2}\right\} dT$$
$$\Delta_r H(T') - \Delta_r H(T) = [aT + ½bT^2 - cT^{-1}]_T^{T'}$$
$$= a(T' - T) + ½b(T'^2 - T^2) - c\left(\frac{1}{T'} - \frac{1}{T}\right)$$

and so the reaction enthalpy is

$$\Delta_r H(T') = \Delta_r H(T) + a(T' - T) + ½b(T'^2 - T^2) - c\left(\frac{1}{T'} - \frac{1}{T}\right)$$

**P3.39** (a) Complex carbohydrates have specific enthalpies of 17 kJ $g^{-1}$ so 40 g of carbohydrates can provide 40 g × 17 kJ $g^{-1}$ = 680 kJ of energy. Given a total daily energy requirement of 2200 Cal , which is equivalent to $9.21 \times 10^3$ kJ, the percentage provided by the 40 g of carbohydrates is

$$(680 \text{ kJ})/(9.21 \times 10^3 \text{ kJ}) = 0.074 = \mathbf{7.4 \ per\ cent}$$

(b) Glucose has a specific enthalpy of 16 kJ $g^{-1}$ so the combustion enthalpy of a 2.5 g tablet is

$$(2.5 \text{ g}) \times (16 \text{ kJ g}^{-1}) = \mathbf{40 \ kJ}$$

(c) The effective energy available for work is

$$w = 0.25 \times (40\ \text{kJ}) = 10\ \text{kJ}$$

Since the work required for a climb to height $h$ is given by $w = mgh$, the glucose tablet provides the energy for a 70 kg person to climb to

$$h = w/(mg) = (10 \times 10^3\text{J})/\{(70\ \text{kg}) \times (9.81\ \text{m s}^{-2})\} = \mathbf{15\ m}$$

(d) We may predict whether the standard enthalpy of combustion increases or descrease with temperature using Kirchoff's law, eqn 3.6. If the change in the molar heat capacities at constant pressure,

$$\Delta_r C_p = \sum \nu\Delta_r C_{p,\text{m}}(\text{products}) - \sum \nu\Delta_r C_{p,\text{m}}(\text{reactants}) > 0$$

then the standard enthalpy of combustion will be higher at blood temperature, 37 °C, than at 25 °C. For the combustion of glucose,

$$C_6H_{12}O_6(s) + 6\ O_2(g) \rightarrow 6\ CO_2(g) + 6\ H_2O(l)$$

so that

$$\begin{aligned}\Delta_r C_p &= \{6 \times C_{p,\text{m}}(\text{CO}_2, \text{g}) + 6 \times C_{p,\text{m}}(\text{H}_2\text{O}, \text{g})\} \\ &\qquad - \{C_{p,\text{m}}(\text{C}_6H_{12}\text{O}_6, \text{s}) + 6 \times C_{p,\text{m}}(\text{O}_2, \text{g})\} \\ &= \{6 \times (37.11\ \text{J K}^{-1}\text{mol}^{-1}) + 6 \times (75.291\ \text{J K}^{-1}\text{mol}^{-1})\} \\ &\qquad -\{(115\ \text{J K}^{-1}\text{mol}^{-1}) + 6 \times (29.355\ \text{J K}^{-1}\text{mol}^{-1})\} \\ &= 383\ \text{J K}^{-1}\text{mol}^{-1}\end{aligned}$$

Thus, according to Kirchhoff's law, the combustion enthalpy of glucose is **higher** at blood temperature, 37 °C, than at 25 °C.

(e) Sucrose has a specific heat capacity of

$$C_s(\text{C}_6\text{H}_{12}\text{O}_6, \text{s}) = \frac{C_\text{m}(\text{C}_6\text{H}_{12}\text{O}_6, \text{s})}{M} = \frac{(5645\ \text{kJ mol}^{-1})}{342.30\ \text{g mol}^{-1}} = 16.5\ \text{kJ g}^{-1}$$

so that the combustion enthalpy of a 1.5 g tablet is

$$mC_s(\text{C}_6\text{H}_{12}\text{O}_6, \text{s}) = (1.5\ \text{g}) \times (16.5\ \text{kJ g}^{-1}) = \mathbf{25\ kJ}$$

(f) The effective energy available for work is

$$w = 0.25 \times (25\ \text{kJ}) = 6.25\ \text{kJ}$$

Since the work required for a climb to height $h$ is given by $w = mgh$, the sucrose tablet provides the energy for a 70 kg person to climb to

$$h = w/(mg) = (6.25 \times 10^3\text{J})/\{(70\ \text{kg}) \times (9.81\ \text{m s}^{-2})\} = \mathbf{9.1\ m}$$

# Chapter 4

# Thermodynamics: the Second Law

## Answers to discussion questions

**D4.1** The apparent driving force of spontaneous change is the tendency of energy to disperse and matter to become disordered. The probability of a configuration, or state of a system, depends upon the number of ways, $W$, in which it may be achieved. For a system with constant energy, the dispersal of energy or disordering of matter leads to an increase in the number of ways in which a configuration may be achieved. The configuration with the most disorder therefore has the highest probability because it may be achieved in the most ways. We find that although many configurations may be possible, this configuration dominates all others. Spontaneous change therefore favours the formation of the most dispersed or disordered configuration.

The extent of the dispersal or disorder is measured through the thermodynamic property entropy, symbol $S$. Entropy is related to the number of ways that the molecules of the sample can be arranged through the Boltzmann formula

$$S = k \ln W$$

In a spontaneous process in a closed system, the entropy is maximised. In general, however, for open systems, in which energy and matter may be exchanged with the surroundings, spontaneous change leads to the largest increase in the combined entropy of the system and the surroundings must increase.

$$\Delta S_{\text{sys}} + \Delta S_{\text{surr}} > 0$$

This expression may be reformulated by the introduction of the Second Law of thermodynamics to give a more convenient condition for spontaneous change expressed in terms of the Gibbs energy $G$,

$$\mathrm{d}G < 0$$

**D4.2** (a) Ceaseless disorderly motion of gas-phase molecules ensures that they spread throughout the entire, available volume. There is a negligibly small probability that all molecules spontaneously move into a volume that is smaller than the total available space because to do so would be a move to greater order. The natural direction of change corresponds to the dispersal of matter. By occupying the total available space, and expanding when the container volume increases, the gas molecules maximize molecular disorder and entropy, the measure of the current state of disorder, within the constraints of volume and total energy. Eqn 4.2 quantifies the entropy change when a perfect gas expands isothermally form $V_i$ to $V_f$.

$$\Delta S = nR\ln(V_f/V_i)$$

Ludwig Boltzmann's fundamental equation $S = k\ln W$, where $W$ is the number of ways that molecules of the system can be arranged yet correspond to the same total energy, gives insight into the spontaneous spread of molecules into an expanding volume. As the volume expands, the quantum energy levels occupied by the molecules get closer together, and there are more ways of arranging the molecules for a given total energy. That is, as the container expands, $W$ increases, and therefore $S$ increases too.

(b) Entropy of a sample increases as the temperature is raised from $T_i$ to $T_f$, because the thermal disorder of the system is greater at the higher temperature due to the more vigorous molecular motion. Eqn 4.3 quantifies the entropy change when the heat capacity is constant over the range of temperatures:

$$\Delta S = C\ln(T_f/T_i)$$

where $C$ is the heat capacity of the system; if the pressure is constant during heating, we use $C_p$, and if the volume is constant, we use $C_V$. As temperature increases, a greater number of molecular quantum states become available to molecules. This increases $W$ and makes $S$ larger.

**D4.3** A liquid and its vapour are in equilibrium at the boiling point. Since the process is reversible under this condition,

$$\Delta S = \frac{\overbrace{q_{rev}}^{\text{eqn 4.1}}}{T} = \frac{\overbrace{\Delta H}^{\text{eqn 2.15}}}{T}$$

and the entropy of vaporization is given by

$$\Delta_{vap}H = \frac{\Delta_{vap}H_m}{T_b}$$

**Trouton's rule** states that the ratio $\Delta_{vap}H/T_b$, and thus the vaporization entropy, is a constant. We may explore the origin of the constancy by considering that the vaporization entropy has two components, only one of which depends upon liquid phase properties. They are the molar entropy of the liquid and the molar entropy of the gas:

$$\Delta_{vap}S_m = S_m(g) - S_m(l)$$

Under ordinary conditions the value of $S_m(g)$ is expected to be identical for all gases and relatively large with respect to $S_m(l)$ because gases behave as perfect gases for which molecular volume and intermolecular forces are negligibly small. This allows completely random, very high entropy molecular motion, which is independent of molecular properties. In addition to the large $S_m(g)$ value, should the value of $S_m(l)$ be either negligibly small or a constant value for a series of compounds, $\Delta_{vap}S_m$, and the ratio $\Delta_{vap}H/T_b$, will be a constant: Trouton's rule is followed. Small, non-polar molecules provide examples that meet these conditions. The relative absence of molecular order in their liquid states gives relatively small and constant $S_m(l)$ values. Thus, bromine, carbon tetrachloride, and cyclohexane have approximate identical vaporization entropies (~85 J K$^{-1}$ mol$^{-1}$, Table 4.1).

Exceptions to Trouton's rule include liquids in which the interactions between molecules result in the liquid being less disordered than the random jumble of molecules in something like carbon tetrachloride. This includes liquids in which hydrogen bonding creates local order as in water and small alcohols. It also includes liquid metals in which the metallic bond creates atomic organization as in mercury.

It is also interesting to explore the origin of Trouton's rule with a careful analysis of the enthalpy of vaporization. Energy in the form of heat supplied to a liquid manifests itself as an increase in thermal motion. This is an increase in the kinetic energy of molecules. When the kinetic energy of the molecules is sufficient to overcome the attractive energy that holds them together the liquid vaporizes. The enthalpy of vaporization is the heat required to accomplish this at constant pressure. It seems reasonable that the greater the enthalpy of vaporization, the greater the kinetic energy required, and the greater the temperature needed to achieve this kinetic energy. Hence, we expect that $\Delta_{vap}H$ is proportional to $T_b$, which implies that their ratio is a constant.

**D4.4** Boltzmann's equation $S = k \ln W$, where $W$ is the number of ways that molecules of the system can be arranged, whilst still corresponding to the same total energy, provides the statistical definition of entropy that associates molecular motion and molecular quantum states with the thermodynamic entropy. We justify its identification with the thermodynamic entropy $\Delta S = q_{rev}/T$ (eqn 4.1) by the finding that the entropy calculated with the Boltzmann equation matches the entropy value found by thermodynamically based experiments. This includes the entropy values at the absolute zero of temperature, residual entropies, the variation of entropy with temperature and volume, and the entropy changes of phase transitions.

**D4.5** The Gibbs energy, $G$, is the system property that is used to identify the direction of spontaneity under the conditions of constant temperature and pressure. Under these conditions:

$$\Delta G = -T\Delta S_{\text{total}}$$

and, since the **Second Law of thermodynamics** summarizes evidence that spontaneity occurs when $\Delta S_{total} > 0$, we conclude that the direction for which $\Delta G < 0$ is the spontaneous direction.

**D4.6** We must remember that the **Second Law of thermodynamics** states only that the total entropy of both the system (here, the molecules organizing themselves into cells) and the surroundings (here, the medium) must increase in a naturally occurring process. It does not state that entropy must increase in a portion of the universe that interacts with its surroundings. In this case, the cells grow by using chemical energy from their surroundings (the medium) and in the process the increase in the entropy of the medium outweighs the decrease in entropy of the system. Hence, the Second Law is not violated.

## Solutions to exercises

**E4.1** From eqn 4.8,

$$\Delta S_{\text{sur}} = \frac{q_{\text{sur}}}{T} = \frac{120\ \text{J}}{(273.15 + 20\ \text{K})} = \mathbf{+0.410\ J\ K^{-1}}$$

**E4.2** (a) We assume that the ice melts reversibly under the conditions described, therefore, from eqn 4.1

$$\Delta S_{\text{ice}} = \frac{q_{\text{rev}}}{T} = \frac{33 \times 10^3\text{J}}{(273.15 + 0)\ \text{K}} = \mathbf{+120\ J\ K^{-1}}$$

(b) From eqn 4.8, the entropy change in the surroundings is

$$\Delta S_{\text{sur}} = \frac{q_{\text{sur}}}{T} = \frac{-q_{\text{rev}}}{T} = \frac{-33 \times 10^3\text{J}}{(273.15 + 0)\ \text{K}} = \mathbf{-120\ J\ K^{-1}}$$

Because this process is reversible, the total entropy change

$$\Delta S_{\text{total}} = \Delta S_{\text{ice}} + \Delta S_{\text{sur}} = 0$$

**E4.3** The energy that must be removed as heat may be calculated from the constant-pressure heat capacity and the change in temperature using eqn 2.3

$$q = nC_{p,\text{m}}\Delta T$$

We may determine the amount of aluminium from the mass, $m$, ansd the molar mass, $M$, so that

$$\begin{aligned} q &= (m/M)C_{p,\text{m}}\Delta T \\ &= \frac{(1.00\ \text{kg})}{(26.98 \times 10^{-3}\ \text{kg mol}^{-1})} \times (24.35\ \text{J K}^{-1}\text{mol}^{-1}) \times (250\ \text{K} - 300\ \text{K}) \\ &= -45.1 \times 10^3\text{J} = \mathbf{-45.1\ kJ} \end{aligned}$$

The heat transferred is negative because energy is removed from the sample as it cools.

The entropy change of the sample follows from eqn 4.3

$$\begin{aligned} \Delta S &= nC_{p,\text{m}} \ln(T_\text{f}/T_\text{i}) \\ &= (m/M)C_{p,\text{m}} \ln(T_\text{f}/T_\text{i}) \\ &= \frac{(1.00\ \text{kg})}{(26.98 \times 10^{-3}\ \text{kg mol}^{-1})} \times (24.35\ \text{J K}^{-1}\text{mol}^{-1}) \ln\frac{(250\ \text{K})}{(300\ \text{K})} \end{aligned}$$

$$= -\mathbf{165\ J\ K^{-1}}$$

The negative sign indicates that the entropy of the aluminium block falls as it cools. The process is spontaneous because the change is accompanied by a larger increase in the entropy of the surroundings.

**E4.4** (a) The entropy change of the ice on melting is given by eqn 4.1

$$\Delta S = \frac{q_{\text{rev}}}{T}$$

For the first step, melting 100 g ice, the heat that is transferred at constant pressure may be calculated from the standard enthalpy of fusion

$$q_{\text{rev}} = n\Delta_{\text{fus}}H = (m/M)\Delta_{\text{fus}}H$$

so that

$$\Delta S = \overbrace{\frac{(100\ \text{g}) \times (6.01 \times 10^3\ \text{J mol}^{-1})}{(18.02\ \text{g mol}^{-1})}}^{q_{\text{rev}}} \times \overbrace{\frac{1}{(273\ \text{K})}}^{1/T} = \mathbf{+122\ J\ K^{-1}}$$

(b) For the second step, heating the water, the entropy change follows from eqn 4.3. Substituting for the constant-pressure specific heat capacity $C_{p,\text{s}} = C_{p,\text{m}} / M$

$$\begin{aligned}\Delta S &= nC_{p,\text{m}} \ln(T_\text{f}/T_\text{i}) = (m/M)C_{p,\text{m}} \ln(T_\text{f}/T_\text{i}) = mC_{p,\text{s}} \ln(T_\text{f}/T_\text{i}) \\ &= (100\ \text{g}) \times (4.18\ \text{J K}^{-1}\text{g}^{-1}) \times \ln\{(273.15 + 100)\text{K}/(273.15 + 0)\text{K}\} \\ &= \mathbf{+130\ J\ K^{-1}}\end{aligned}$$

(c) The calculation of the entropy change for the third step, vaporization, follows that for the first

$$\Delta S = (m/M)\frac{\Delta_{\text{vap}}H}{T} = \frac{(100\ \text{g})}{(18.02\ \text{g mol}^{-1})} \times \frac{(40.7 \times 10^3\ \text{J mol}^{-1})}{(373\ \text{K})} = \mathbf{+606\ J\ K^{-1}}$$

The total entropy change of the system when ice at 0 °C is transformed to water vapour at 100 °C is thus the sum of the individual entropy changes for each of these steps

$$\Delta S = 122\ \text{J K}^{-1} + 130\ \text{J K}^{-1} + 606\ \text{J K}^{-1} = \mathbf{+858\ J\ K^{-1}}$$

The change in temperature with time is shown in Figure 4.1. Initially, the temperature remains constant at 273 K temperature until all the ice is melted. The temperature then increases until the boiling point, 373 K, is reached. The temperature again remains constant until all the liquid is vaporized.

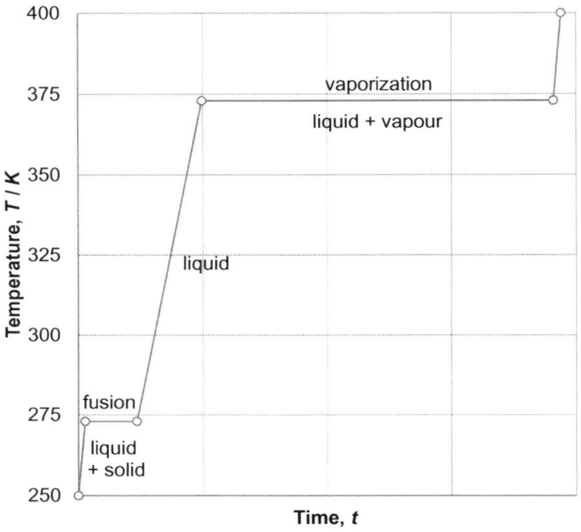


**Figure 4.1**

(b) A sketch of enthalpy as a function of time is shown in Figure 4.2. The gradient is constant because the heat is supplied at a constant rate. Note that absolute values of enthalpy are indeterminate.

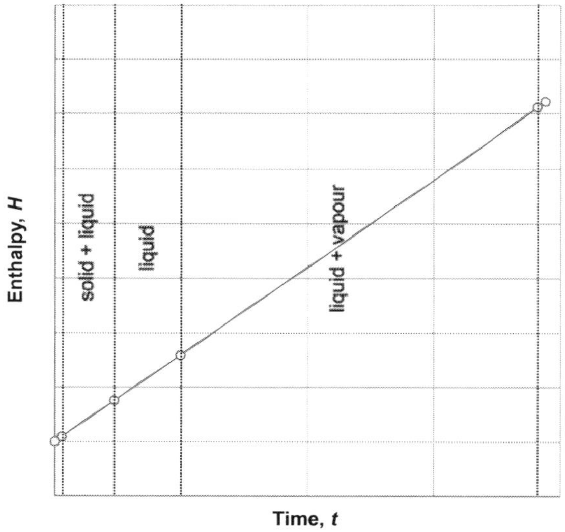


**Figure 4.2**

(c) A sketch of entropy as a function of time is shown in Figure 4.3.

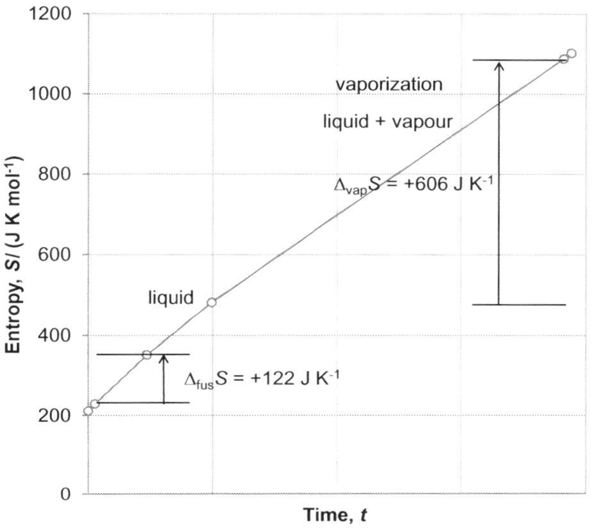


**Figure 4.3**

Note that the gradient of the graph decreases slightly as the temperature increases. This is because the effect of transferring energy on the entropy of the system decreases as temperature increases

$$\Delta S \propto \frac{1}{T}$$

**E4.5** From eqn 4.2, the change in molar entropy is

$$\begin{aligned}\Delta S_m = \Delta S/n &= R\ln(V_f/V_i)\\ &= (8.3145\ \mathrm{J\,K^{-1}mol^{-1}}) \times \ln\{(5.5\ \mathrm{dm^3})/(1.0\ \mathrm{dm^3})\}\\ &= \mathbf{+14\ J\,K^{-1}mol^{-1}}\end{aligned}$$

**E4.6** From eqn 4.2, the change in entropy on compression is

$$\Delta S = nR\ln(V_f/V_i) = -10.0\ \mathrm{J\,K^{-1}mol^{-1}}$$

We may derive an expression for the amount of gas, $n$, using the perfect gas law to substitute for $R$, because $pV = nRT$, so that, rearranging

$$\ln(V_f/V_i) = \frac{\Delta S}{nR} = \frac{\Delta S}{(p_i V_i/T)}$$

Using the rules for the manipulation of logarithms, we may write

$$\begin{aligned}\ln(V_f/\mathrm{dm}^3) &= \ln V_i + \frac{\Delta S}{(p_i V_i/T)}\\ &= \ln(15\ \mathrm{dm}^3) + \frac{(-10.0\ \mathrm{J\ K^{-1}mol^{-1}})}{\underbrace{(1.013\times10^5\ \mathrm{Pa})}_{1\ \mathrm{atm}=1.013\times10^5\mathrm{Pa}}\times(15\times10^{-3}\mathrm{m}^3)/(250\ \mathrm{K})}\\ &= 1.07\end{aligned}$$

and so

$$\begin{aligned}V_f/\mathrm{dm}^3 &= \mathrm{e}^{1.07}\\ V_f &= \mathbf{2.91\ dm^3}\end{aligned}$$

**E4.7** Entropy is a state function; the change in entropy depends only upon the final and initial states. It therefore does not matter whether the change in state occurs reversibly or irreversibly. Thus, the entropy change will be the same for the (a) reversible and (b) irreversible expansion.

If we assume that methane behaves as a perfect gas, then we may substitute for the volume, $V = nRT/p$, in eqn 4.2

$$\begin{aligned}\Delta S &= nR\ln(V_f/V_i) = nR\ln\{(nRT/p_f)/(nRT/p_i)\} = (m/M)R\ln(p_i/p_f)\\ &= \frac{(15\ \mathrm{g})}{(16.04\ \mathrm{g\ mol^{-1}})}\times(8.3145\ \mathrm{J\ K^{-1}mol^{-1}})\times\ln\frac{(105\ \mathrm{kPa})}{(1.50\ \mathrm{kPa})}\\ &= \mathbf{+33\ J\ K^{-1}}\end{aligned}$$

**E4.8** The entropy change follows from eqn 4.3

$$\begin{aligned}\Delta S &= C_p\ln(T_f/T_i) = nC_{p,\mathrm{m}}\ln(T_f/T_i) = \left(\overbrace{m/M}^{n=m/M}\right)C_{p,\mathrm{m}}\ln(T_f/T_i)\\ &= \left\{\overbrace{(100\ \mathrm{g})}^{\mathrm{mass},m}/\overbrace{(18.02\ \mathrm{g\ mol^{-1}})}^{\mathrm{molar\ mass},M}\right\}\times 75.5\ \mathrm{J\ K^{-1}mol^{-1}}\times\ln\{(310\ \mathrm{K})/(293\ \mathrm{K})\}\\ &= \mathbf{+23.6\ J\ K^{-1}}\end{aligned}$$

**E4.9** The entropy change follows from eqn 4.3

$$\begin{aligned}\Delta S &= C_p\ln(T_f/T_i) = nC_{p,\mathrm{m}}\ln(T_f/T_i) = \overbrace{(m/M)}^{n=m/M}C_{p,\mathrm{m}}\ln(T_f/T_i)\\ &= \frac{\overbrace{(1\ \mathrm{kg})}^{\mathrm{mass},m}}{\underbrace{(207.2\ \times10^{-3}\mathrm{kg\ mol^{-1}})}_{\mathrm{molar\ mass},M}}\times 26.44\ \mathrm{J\ K^{-1}mol^{-1}}\times\ln\left\{\frac{(100+273.15)\mathrm{K}}{(500+273.15\ \mathrm{K})}\right\}\\ &= \mathbf{-93.0\ J\ K^{-1}}\end{aligned}$$

**E4.10** Entropy is a state function: the change in entropy depends only upon the final and initial states of the system and not upon the way in which the change occurs. We may therefore imagine that the heating and compression are carried out sequentially rather than simultaneously. The total molar entropy change then follows as the sum of the changes for the two separate processes.

$$\begin{aligned}\Delta S_m &= S_m(0.5\ \text{dm}^3, 400\ \text{K}) - S_m(2.0\ \text{dm}^3, 300\ \text{K})\\ &= \overbrace{\{S_m(0.5\ \text{dm}^3, 400\ \text{K}) - S_m(0.5\ \text{dm}^3, 300\ \text{K})\}}^{\text{heating at a volume of } 0.5\ \text{dm}^3}\\ &\qquad + \underbrace{\{S_m(0.5\ \text{dm}^3, 300\ \text{K}) - S_m(2.0\ \text{dm}^3, 300\ \text{K})\}}_{\text{compression at a temperature of } 300\ \text{K}}\end{aligned}$$

The entropy changes for the heating and compression may be calculated using eqn 4.2 and 4.3, so that

$$\begin{aligned}\Delta S_m &= C_{V,m}\ln(T_f/T_i) + R\ln(V_f/V_i)\\ &= [(3/2)\times(8.3145\ \text{J K}^{-1}\text{mol}^{-1})\times\ln\{(400\ \text{K})/(300\ \text{K})\}]\\ &\qquad + [(8.3145\ \text{J K}^{-1}\text{mol}^{-1})\times\ln\{(0.5\ \text{dm}^3)/(2.0\ \text{dm}^3)\}]\\ &= \mathbf{-7.9\ J\ K^{-1}mol^{-1}}\end{aligned}$$

The overall entropy change is negative. The increase in entropy caused by heating is more than balanced by the decrease in entropy as a result of the compression.

**E4.11** If there is no overall entropy change, then the entropy change on the expansion, which is given by eqn 4.2, must balance that on heating, which is given by eqn 4.3. Thus,

$$nR\ln(V_f/V_i) = -nC_{V,m}\ln(T_f/T_i)$$

Rearranging,

$$\begin{aligned}\ln(T_f/T_i) &= -(R/C_{V,m})\ln(V_f/V_i)\\ &= -\{R/(3R/2)\}\ln(2)\\ &= -2/3\ln(2)\\ &= \ln(2)^{-(2/3)}\end{aligned}$$

Thus,

$$\begin{aligned}T_f &= 2^{-(2/3)}T_i\\ &= \mathbf{0.63\ T_i}\end{aligned}$$

**E4.12** The variation in entropy against temperature is shown in Figure 4.4. In the first step, the temperature does not change because the expansion is isothermal. The entropy, however, increases as the gas expands

$$\Delta S_1 = R\ln(V_f/V_i)$$

In the second step, the entropy remains constant because for an adiabatic process, $q = 0$, and from eqn 4.1,

$$\Delta S_2 = q_{rev}/T = 0$$

The temperature, however, falls, because the internal energy decreases when the gas does work in expansion.

$$\Delta U = q + w = 0 - p_{\mathrm{ex}}\Delta V = -p_{\mathrm{ex}}\Delta V$$

The entropy and temperature changes in the third and fourth steps mirror those of the first and second

$$\Delta S_3 = -\Delta S_1$$
$$\Delta S_4 = -\Delta S_2 = 0$$

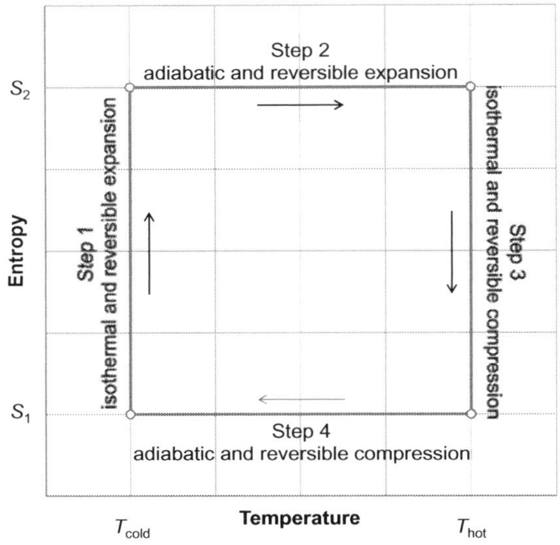


**Figure 4.4**

**E4.13** Following *Derivation 4.4*, and assuming that the heat capacity varies with temperature according to the Debye $T^3$ law, $C_{p,\mathrm{m}} = aT^3$, then

$$\Delta S_{\mathrm{m}} = \int_0^T \frac{C_{p,\mathrm{m}}}{T}\mathrm{d}T$$
$$S_{\mathrm{m}}(T) - S_{\mathrm{m}}(0) = \int_0^T \frac{aT^3}{T}\mathrm{d}T = a\int_0^T T^2\mathrm{d}T = {}^1/_3 aT^3 = {}^1/_3 C_{p,\mathrm{m}}(T)$$

We may assume that, because KCl is a pure crystalline substance, $S_{\mathrm{m}}(0) = 0$, so that

$$S_{\mathrm{m}}(T) = {}^1/_3 C_{p,\mathrm{m}}(T) = {}^1/_3 \times (1.2\times10^{-3}\ \mathrm{J\,K^{-1}\,mol^{-1}}) = \mathbf{4.0\times10^{-4}\,J\,K^{-1}mol^{-1}}$$

**E4.14** We first find the common final temperature, $T_f$, by noting that the heat lost by the hot sample is gained by the cold sample

$$-\overbrace{nC_{p,\mathrm{m}}(T_\mathrm{f}-T_\mathrm{hot})}^{\text{heat lost by hot sample}} = \overbrace{nC_{p,\mathrm{m}}(T_\mathrm{f}-T_\mathrm{cold})}^{\text{heat gained by cold sample}}$$

so that, solving for $T_f$

$$T_\mathrm{f} = \tfrac{1}{2}(T_\mathrm{hot}+T_\mathrm{cold})$$

where, converting to units of kelvin,

$$\begin{aligned} T_\mathrm{hot} &= (80+273.15)\ \mathrm{K} = 353\ \mathrm{K} \\ T_\mathrm{cold} &= (10+273.15)\ \mathrm{K} = 283\ \mathrm{K} \end{aligned}$$

The total entropy change is therefore, from eqn 4.3

$$\begin{aligned} \Delta S_\mathrm{total} &= \Delta S_\mathrm{hot} + \Delta S_\mathrm{cold} \\ &= nC_{p,\mathrm{m}}\ln(T_\mathrm{f}/T_\mathrm{hot}) + nC_{p,\mathrm{m}}\ln(T_\mathrm{f}/T_\mathrm{cold}) \\ &= nC_{p,\mathrm{m}}\ln\{T_\mathrm{f}^2/(T_\mathrm{hot}T_\mathrm{cold})\} \end{aligned}$$

We may express the amount in terms of the mass, $m$, and molar mass, $M$, as $n = m/M$, and substituting the expression for the final temperature,

$$\begin{aligned} \Delta S_\mathrm{total} &= (m/M)C_{p,\mathrm{m}}\ln\{(T_\mathrm{hot}+T_\mathrm{cold})^2/(4T_\mathrm{hot}T_\mathrm{cold})\} \\ &= \frac{\overbrace{100\ \mathrm{g}}^{\text{mass},m}}{\underbrace{18.02\ \mathrm{g\ mol^{-1}}}_{\text{molar mass},M}} \times (75.5\ \mathrm{J\ K^{-1}mol^{-1}}) \times \ln\frac{(\overbrace{353}^{T_\mathrm{hot}}+\overbrace{283}^{T_\mathrm{cold}})^2}{(4\times 353\times 283)} \\ &= \mathbf{+5.11\ J\ K^{-1}} \end{aligned}$$

The dispersal of the energy when the two samples are mixed therefore leads to an increase in entropy.

**E4.15** The general expression for the entropy change accompanying a phase transition follows from the expressions for fusion and vaporization, eqn 4.6 and 4.7

$$\Delta_\mathrm{trs}S = \frac{\Delta_\mathrm{trs}H}{T} = \frac{+1.9\times 10^3\ \mathrm{J\ mol^{-1}}}{2000\ \mathrm{K}} = \mathbf{+0.95\ J\ K^{-1}mol^{-1}}$$

**E4.16** (a) The entropy change on vaporization follows from eqn 4.7

$$\Delta_\mathrm{vap}S = \frac{\Delta_\mathrm{vap}H}{T_\mathrm{b}} = \frac{+29.4\times 10^3\ \mathrm{J\ mol^{-1}}}{334.88\ \mathrm{K}} = \mathbf{+87.8\ J\ K^{-1}mol^{-1}}$$

(b) Because the vaporization process can be accomplished reversibly, $\Delta S_\mathrm{total} = 0$; hence

$$\Delta_\mathrm{vap}S_\mathrm{surr} = -\Delta_\mathrm{vap}S_\mathrm{sys} = \mathbf{-87.8\ J\ K^{-1}mol^{-1}}$$

**E4.17** Entropy is a state function, and any change in entropy depends only upon the final and initial states. We may therefore express the melting at 25 °C as heating to its melting point at 151 °C, followed by melting, and then cooling of the liquid back to 25 °C. The entropy change for this sequence is equal to that for melting at 25 °C. The entropy of fusion at 25 °C is thus

$$\begin{aligned}\Delta S &= S(\mathrm{s}, 25\,^\circ\mathrm{C}) - S(\mathrm{l}, 25\,^\circ\mathrm{C}) \\ &= \overbrace{\{S(\mathrm{s}, 25\,^\circ\mathrm{C}) - S(\mathrm{s}, 151\,^\circ\mathrm{C})\}}^{\text{heating of solid}} + \overbrace{\{S(\mathrm{s}, 151\,^\circ\mathrm{C}) - S(\mathrm{l}, 151\,^\circ\mathrm{C})\}}^{\text{phase transition at melting temperature}} \\ &\quad + \underbrace{\{S(\mathrm{l}, 151\,^\circ\mathrm{C}) - S(\mathrm{l}, 25\,^\circ\mathrm{C})\}}_{\text{cooling of liquid}}\end{aligned}$$

Substituting eqns 4.3 and 4.6, and noting that a temperature of 25 °C corresponds to (25 + 273.15) K = 298 K, and 151 °C to (151 + 273.15) K = 424 K,

$$\begin{aligned}\Delta S &= \overbrace{C_{p,\mathrm{m}} \ln(T_\mathrm{f}/T_\mathrm{i})}^{\text{heating of solid}} + \overbrace{\Delta_\mathrm{fus}H/T_\mathrm{b}}^{\text{phase transition at melting temperature}} + \overbrace{C_{p,\mathrm{m}} \ln(T_\mathrm{i}/T_\mathrm{f})}^{\text{cooling of liquid}} \\ &= (17\,\mathrm{J\,K^{-1}mol^{-1}}) \times \ln\{(424\,\mathrm{K})/(298\,\mathrm{K})\} + \{(36 \times 10^3\,\mathrm{J\,mol^{-1}})/(424\,\mathrm{K})\} \\ &\quad + (33\,\mathrm{J\,K^{-1}mol^{-1}}) \times \ln\{(298\,\mathrm{K})/(424\,\mathrm{K})\} \\ &= \mathbf{+79\,J\,K^{-1}mol^{-1}}\end{aligned}$$

**E4.18** (a) According to Trouton's rule, which applies well to hydrocarbons such as octane,

$$\Delta_\mathrm{vap}S = \mathbf{+85\,J\,K^{-1}mol^{-1}}$$

(b) The entropy and enthalpy of vaporization are related through eqn 4.7

$$\Delta_\mathrm{vap}S = \frac{\Delta_\mathrm{vap}H}{T_\mathrm{b}}$$

so that

$$\begin{aligned}\Delta_\mathrm{vap}H &= T_\mathrm{b}\Delta_\mathrm{vap}S \\ &= \{(126 + 273.15)\,\mathrm{K}\} \times (+85\,\mathrm{J\,K^{-1}mol^{-1}}) \\ &= +34 \times 10^3\,\mathrm{J\,mol^{-1}} = \mathbf{+34\,kJ\,mol^{-1}}\end{aligned}$$

**E4.19** Applying the Boltzmann formula for entropy, $S = k \ln W$, eqn 4.11

$$\Delta S = S_\mathrm{f} - S_\mathrm{i} = k \ln W_\mathrm{f} - k \ln W_\mathrm{i} = k \ln(W_\mathrm{f}/W_\mathrm{i}) = k \ln(V_\mathrm{f}^N/V_\mathrm{i}^N)$$

Then, using the properties of logs,

$$\Delta S = k \ln(V_\mathrm{f}/V_\mathrm{i})^N = Nk \ln(V_\mathrm{f}/V_\mathrm{i})$$

When $N = N_\mathrm{A}$, we replace $kN$ with $R$ and the equation becomes

$$\Delta S_\mathrm{m} = N_\mathrm{A}k \ln(V_\mathrm{f}/V_\mathrm{i}) = R \ln(V_\mathrm{f}/V_\mathrm{i})$$

in agreement with eqn 4.2.

**E4.20** An $FClO_3$ molecule may adopt four distinct orientations, so that, for one mole, i.e. $N_A$ molecules

$$\begin{aligned} S_m &= k \ln W = k \ln 4^{N_A} = N_A k \ln 4 = R \ln 4 \\ &= (8.3145\ \mathrm{J\,K^{-1}mol^{-1}}) \times \ln 4 = \mathbf{+11.5\ J\,K^{-1}mol^{-1}} \end{aligned}$$

**E4.21** (a) **positive**: due to greater disorder in the product, although the difference may not be large.

(b) **negative**: the reaction results in a decrease in the amount of gas, so that the matter is less disordered in the product.

(c) **positive**: two new substances are formed, resulting in greater disorder in the products than the reactants

**E4.22** The standard reaction entropy follows by applying eqn 4.13

$$\Delta_r S^\ominus = \sum \nu S_m^\ominus(\text{products}) - \sum \nu S_m^\ominus(\text{reactants})$$

(a)

$$\begin{aligned} \Delta_r S^\ominus &= 2\, S_m^\ominus(\mathrm{CH_3COOH, l}) - \{2\, S_m^\ominus(\mathrm{CH_3CHO, g}) + S_m^\ominus(\mathrm{O_2, g})\} \\ &= (2 \times 159.8\ \mathrm{J\,K^{-1}mol^{-1}}) \\ &\qquad - \{(2 \times 250.3\ \mathrm{J\,K^{-1}mol^{-1}}) + (205.14\ \mathrm{J\,K^{-1}mol^{-1}})\} \\ &= \mathbf{-386.1\ J\,K^{-1}mol^{-1}} \end{aligned}$$

(b)

$$\begin{aligned} \Delta_r S^\ominus &= \{2\, S_m^\ominus(\mathrm{AgBr, s}) + 2\, S_m^\ominus(\mathrm{Cl_2, g})\} - \{2\, S_m^\ominus(\mathrm{AgCl, s}) + S_m^\ominus(\mathrm{Br_2, l})\} \\ &= \{(2 \times 107.1\ \mathrm{J\,K^{-1}mol^{-1}}) + (223.07\ \mathrm{J\,K^{-1}mol^{-1}})\} \\ &\qquad - \{(2 \times 96.2\ \mathrm{J\,K^{-1}mol^{-1}}) + (152.23\ \mathrm{J\,K^{-1}mol^{-1}})\} \\ &= \mathbf{+92.6\ J\,K^{-1}mol^{-1}} \end{aligned}$$

(c)

$$\begin{aligned} \Delta_r S^\ominus &= S_m^\ominus(\mathrm{HgCl_2, s}) - \{S_m^\ominus(\mathrm{Hg, l}) + S_m^\ominus(\mathrm{Cl_2, l})\} \\ &= (146.0\ \mathrm{J\,K^{-1}mol^{-1}}) - \{(76.02\ \mathrm{J\,K^{-1}mol^{-1}}) + (223.07\ \mathrm{J\,K^{-1}mol^{-1}})\} \\ &= \mathbf{-153.1\ J\,K^{-1}mol^{-1}} \end{aligned}$$

(d)

$$\begin{aligned} \Delta_r S^\ominus &= \{S_m^\ominus(\mathrm{Zn^{2+}, aq}) + S_m^\ominus(\mathrm{Cu, s})\} - \{S_m^\ominus(\mathrm{Zn, s}) + S_m^\ominus(\mathrm{Cu^{2+}, aq})\} \\ &= \{(-112.1\ \mathrm{J\,K^{-1}mol^{-1}}) + (33.15\ \mathrm{J\,K^{-1}mol^{-1}})\} \\ &\qquad - \{(41.63\ \mathrm{J\,K^{-1}mol^{-1}}) + (-99.6\ \mathrm{J\,K^{-1}mol^{-1}})\} \\ &= \mathbf{-21.0\ J\,K^{-1}mol^{-1}} \end{aligned}$$

(e)

$$\Delta_r S^\ominus = \{12\, S_m^\ominus(\mathrm{CO_2, g}) + 11\, S_m^\ominus(\mathrm{H_2O, l})\} - \{S_m^\ominus(\mathrm{C_{12}H_{22}O_{11}, s}) - 12\, S_m^\ominus(\mathrm{O_2, g})\}$$

$$= \{(12 \times 213.74\ \mathrm{J\,K^{-1}mol^{-1}}) + (11 \times 69.91\ \mathrm{J\,K^{-1}mol^{-1}})\} - \{(360.2\ \mathrm{J\,K^{-1}mol^{-1}}) + (12 \times 205.14\ \mathrm{J\,K^{-1}mol^{-1}})\}$$
$$= \mathbf{+512.0\ J\,K^{-1}mol^{-1}}$$

**E4.23** The standard reaction entropy depends upon the heat transferred through eqn 4.1

$$\Delta S^{\ominus} = q_{\mathrm{body}}/T$$

The heat transferred may be calculated from the standard enthalpy of reaction for the combustion of glucose,

$$q_{\mathrm{body}} = -n\Delta_c H^{\ominus} = -(m/M)\Delta_c H^{\ominus}$$

If we assume that the enthalpy of combustion varies little with temperature, so that we may approximate the value at 37 °C, with that given in tables for a temperature of 25 °C, then

$$\Delta S^{\ominus} = -(m/M)\Delta_c H^{\circ}/T$$
$$= -(100\ \mathrm{g})/(180.02\ \mathrm{g\,mol^{-1}}) \times (-2808\ \mathrm{kJ\,mol^{-1}})/(37 + 273.15)\ \mathrm{K}$$
$$= +5.03 \times 10^3\ \mathrm{J\,K^{-1}} = \mathbf{+5.03\ kJ\,K^{-1}}$$

**E4.24** The standard reaction entropy follows by applying eqn 4.13

$$\Delta_r S^{\ominus} = \sum \nu S_m^{\ominus}(\text{products}) - \sum \nu S_m^{\ominus}(\text{reactants})$$
$$= 2\,S_m^{\ominus}(\mathrm{NH_3, g}) - \{S_m^{\ominus}(\mathrm{N_2, g}) + 3\,S_m^{\ominus}(\mathrm{H_2, g})\}$$
$$= (2 \times 192.45\ \mathrm{J\,K^{-1}mol^{-1}}) - \{(191.61\ \mathrm{J\,K^{-1}mol^{-1}}) + (3 \times 130.684\ \mathrm{J\,K^{-1}mol^{-1}})\}$$
$$= \mathbf{-198.72\ J\,K^{-1}}$$

The corresponding entropy change in the surroundings follows from eqn 4.9

$$\Delta S_{\mathrm{surr}} = -\frac{\Delta_r H^{\ominus}}{T}$$

The standard enthalpy of reaction is twice the enthalpy of formation of ammonia,

$$\Delta_r H^{\ominus} = \sum \nu\Delta_f H^{\ominus}(\text{products}) - \sum \nu\Delta_f H^{\ominus}(\text{reactants})$$
$$= 2\Delta_f H^{\ominus}(\mathrm{NH_3, g}) - \{\Delta_f H^{\ominus}(\mathrm{N_2, g}) + 3\,\Delta_f H^{\ominus}(\mathrm{H_2, g})\}$$
$$= (2 \times -46.11\ \mathrm{kJ\,mol^{-1}}) - (0\ \mathrm{kJ\,mol^{-1}}) - (3 \times 0\ \mathrm{kJ\,mol^{-1}})$$
$$= -92.22\ \mathrm{kJ\,mol^{-1}}$$

because the standard enthalpies of formation of nitrogen and hydrogen are both zero, because they are in their standard states. Thus,

$$\Delta S_{\mathrm{surr}} = -\frac{-92.22 \times 10^3\ \mathrm{J\,mol^{-1}}}{298\ \mathrm{K}} = \mathbf{+309\ J\,K^{-1}\,mol^{-1}}$$

**E4.25** We may calculate the standard reaction entropy at a particular temperature from the molar entropies of the products and reactants using eqn 4.13

$$\Delta_r S^\ominus(T) = \sum \nu S_m^\ominus(\text{products}, T) - \sum \nu S_m^\ominus(\text{reactants}, T)$$

The change in standard reaction entropy when the temperature is increased is therefore

$$\Delta_r S^\ominus(T') - \Delta_r S^\ominus(T) = \sum \nu\{S_m^\ominus(\text{products}, T') - S_m^\ominus(\text{products}, T)\}$$
$$- \sum \nu S_m^\ominus(\text{reactants}, T') - \nu S_m^\ominus(\text{reactants}, T)$$

The change in the molar entropy of a component depends upon the constant-pressure heat capacity, according to eqn 4.3,

$$S_m^\ominus(T') - S_m^\ominus(T) = C_{p,m}^\ominus \ln(T'/T)$$

so that

$$\begin{aligned}\Delta_r S^\ominus(T') - \Delta_r S^\ominus(T) &= \left\{\sum \nu C_{p,m}^\ominus(\text{products}) - \sum \nu C_{p,m}^\ominus(\text{reactants})\right\}\ln(T'/T)\\ &= \Delta_r C_{p,m}^\ominus \ln(T'/T)\end{aligned}$$

(a) For the reaction

$$2\,H_2(g) + O_2\,(g) \rightarrow 2\,H_2O(g)$$

$$\begin{aligned}\Delta_r C_{p,m}^\ominus &= 2C_{p,m}^\ominus(H_2O, g) - \{2C_{p,m}^\ominus(H_2, g) + C_{p,m}^\ominus(O_2, g)\}\\ &= \{2 \times (4R)\} - \{(2 \times 7R/2) + (7R/2)\}\\ &= -5R/2\end{aligned}$$

so that, if we assume an initial temperature of 298 K,

$$\begin{aligned}\Delta_r S^\ominus(308\text{ K}) - \Delta_r S^\ominus(298\text{ K}) &= -(5R/2)\ln\{(308\text{ K})/(298\text{ K})\}\\ &= \mathbf{-0.69\ J\ K^{-1}mol^{-1}}\end{aligned}$$

(b) For the reaction

$$CH_4(g) + 2\,O_2(g) \rightarrow CO_2(g) + 2\,H_2O(g)$$

$$\begin{aligned}\Delta_r C_{p,m}^\ominus &= \{C_{p,m}^\ominus(CO_2, g) + 2C_{p,m}^\ominus(H_2O, g)\} - \{C_{p,m}^\ominus(CH_4, g) + 2C_{p,m}^\ominus(O_2, g)\}\\ &= \{(7R/2) + (2 \times 4R)\} - \{4R + (2 \times 7R/2)\}\\ &= +3R/2\end{aligned}$$

so that, if we assume an initial temperature of 298 K,

$$\begin{aligned}\Delta_r S^\ominus(308\text{ K}) - \Delta_r S^\ominus(298\text{ K}) &= +(3R/2)\ln\{(308\text{ K})/(298\text{ K})\}\\ &= \mathbf{+0.41\ J\ K^{-1}mol^{-1}}\end{aligned}$$

**E4.26** The standard Gibbs energy of reaction may be calculated, using eqn 4.16, from the standard enthalpy and standard entropy of reaction

$$\Delta_r G^\ominus = \Delta_r H^\ominus - T\Delta_r S^\ominus$$

$$= (-92.22 \times 10^3 \text{ J mol}^{-1}) - (298 \text{ K}) \times (-198.72 \text{ J K}^{-1})$$
$$= -32.99 \times 10^3 \text{ J mol}^{-1} = \mathbf{-32.99 \text{ kJ mol}^{-1}}$$

**E4.27** (a) The standard Gibbs energy of reaction may be calculated, using eqn 4.16, from the standard enthalpy and standard entropy of reaction

$$\begin{aligned}\Delta_r G^\ominus &= \Delta_r H^\ominus - T\Delta_r S^\ominus \\ &= (-135 \times 10^3 \text{ J mol}^{-1}) - \{(37 + 273.15)\text{K}\} \times (-136 \text{ J K}^{-1}) \\ &= -93 \times 10^3 \text{ J mol}^{-1} = \mathbf{-93 \text{ kJ mol}^{-1}}\end{aligned}$$

(b) **Yes**, the reaction is spontaneous because $\Delta_r G^\ominus < 0$.

(c) Rearranging eqn 4.17,

$$\Delta S_{\text{total}} = -\frac{\Delta G}{T} = -\frac{93 \times 10^3 \text{ J mol}^{-1}}{(37 + 273.15)\text{K}} = \mathbf{+300 \text{ J K}^{-1}\text{mol}^{-1}}$$

**E4.28** The maximum non-expansion work, such as that done in lifting a weight, is equal to the change in Gibbs energy, eqn 4.18, $w' = n\Delta_r G$. The work done in raising a mass $m$ through a height $h$ is $w' = mgh$. Combining these two equations and rearranging allows us to calculate the amount of glucose required

$$\begin{aligned}n &= mgh/\Delta_r G \\ &= \{(65 \text{ kg}) \times (9.81 \text{ ms}^{-2}) \times (10 \text{ m})\}/(-2828 \times 10^3 \text{J mol}^{-1}) \\ &= 2.3 \times 10^{-3} \text{ mol}\end{aligned}$$

The mass of glucose required is thus

$$nM = (2.3 \times 10^{-3} \text{ mol}) \times (180 \text{ g mol}^{-1}) = \mathbf{0.41 \text{ g}}$$

**E4.29** The metabolism of sucrose corresponds to the combustion reaction

$$C_{12}H_{22}O_{11}(s) + 12\, O_2(g) \rightarrow 12\, CO_2(g) + 11\, H_2O(l)$$

The maximum non-expansion work that may be extracted is, from eqn 4.18, equal to the change in Gibbs energy. We may calculate the Gibbs energy of reaction from the Gibbs energies of formation for the products and reactants, because, by analogy with the expression for the enthalpy of reaction, eqn 3.5

$$\begin{aligned}\Delta_c G^\ominus &= \sum \nu\Delta_f G^\ominus(\text{products}) - \sum \nu\Delta_f G^\ominus(\text{reactants}) \\ &= \overbrace{\{(12 \times \Delta_f G^\ominus(CO_2, g)) + (11 \times \Delta_f G^\ominus(H_2O, l))\}}^{\text{products}} \\ &\qquad - \underbrace{\{(\Delta_f G^\ominus(C_{12}H_{22}O_{11}, s)) + (12 \times \Delta_f G^\ominus(O_2, g))\}}_{\text{reactants}} \\ &= \{12 \times (-394.36 \text{ kJ mol}^{-1}) + 11 \times (-237.13 \text{ kJ mol}^{-1})\} \\ &\qquad -\{(-1543 \text{ kJ mol}^{-1}) + 12 \times 0\} \\ &= -5798 \text{ kJ mol}^{-1}\end{aligned}$$

Thus,

$$w' = -n\Delta_c G = -(m/M)\Delta_c G$$
$$= -\frac{(1.0\times10^{-3}\,\text{g})}{(342.30\ \text{g mol}^{-1})}\times(-5798\ \text{kJ mol}^{-1}) = \mathbf{+17\ J}$$

**E4.30** (a) **Yes**, coupling the two reactions can give a net change in the Gibbs energy that is negative, $\Delta G < 0$, so that the the overall process is spontaneous. For example, for one mole of glutamate and one mole of ATP,

$$\Delta G = \overbrace{(14.2\ \text{kJ mol}^{-1})}^{\text{formation of glutamine}} + \overbrace{(-31\ \text{kJ mol}^{-1})}^{\text{hydrolysis of ATP}} = -17\ \text{kJ mol}^{-1}$$

(b) For the minimum amount of ATP, the energy released by the hydrolysis of ATP exactly balances that required for the formation of glutamine

$$\Delta G = \{\overbrace{n_{\text{glutamine}}}^{\text{amount of glutamine}}\times(14.2\ \text{kJ mol}^{-1})\} + \{\overbrace{n_{\text{ATP}}}^{\text{amount of ATP}}\times(-31\ \text{kJ mol}^{-1})\} = 0$$

so that the amount of ATP required for the formation of 1 mol of glutamine is

$$n_{\text{ATP}} = \{(1\ \text{mol})\times(14.2\ \text{kJ mol}^{-1})\}/(31\ \text{kJ mol}^{-1}) = \mathbf{0.46\ mol}$$

**E4.31** For the synthesis, $\Delta G = +42\ \text{kJ mol}^{-1}$; hence at least $-42$ kJ would need to be provided by the ATP in order to make $\Delta G$ overall negative and the reaction spontaneous. Given that the Gibbs energy of reaction for the hydrolysis of ATP is $-31\ \text{kJ mol}^{-1}$, then the number of ATP molecules required is

$$n_{\text{ATP}}N_{\text{A}} = \frac{\{(1\ \text{mol})\times(42.1\ \text{kJ mol}^{-1})\}}{(31\ \text{kJ mol}^{-1})}\times(6.022\times10^{23}\text{mol}^{-1})$$
$$= \mathbf{8.1\times10^{23}\,molecules}$$

**E4.32** Assuming that the work done by the cell is equivalent to the Gibbs energy released by the hydrolysis of ATP, then the power density is given by the ratio of the non-expansion work, $w'$, to the volume, $V$

$$\frac{w'}{V} = -\frac{n\Delta_r G}{V} = \frac{\overbrace{(N/N_A)}^{n}\Delta_r G}{\underbrace{(4/3)\pi r^3}_{V}}$$
$$= \frac{\{10^6/(6.022\times10^{23}\text{mol}^{-1})\}\times(-31\ \text{kJ mol}^{-1})}{\{(4/3)\times\pi\times(10\times10^{-6}\ \text{m})^3\}}$$
$$= \overbrace{13\ \text{J s}^{-1}\text{m}^{-3}}^{1\ \text{W}=1\ \text{J s}^{-1}} = \mathbf{13\ W\ m^{-3}}$$

In the same way, the power density of the battery is

$$\frac{15\ \text{W}}{100\times\ 10^{-6}\ \text{m}^3} = 150\times10^3\ \text{W m}^3 = \mathbf{150\ kW\ m^{-3}}$$

demonstrating that the battery has a much higher power density.

## Answers to projects

**P4.33** If

$$\Delta S = \int_{T_\text{i}}^{T_\text{f}} \frac{C}{T}\,\text{d}T$$

then, substituting the expression for the heat capacity

$$\Delta S = \int_{T_\text{i}}^{T_\text{f}} \frac{(a+bT+cT^{-2})}{T}\text{d}T = \int_{T_\text{i}}^{T_\text{f}} (aT^{-1}+b+cT^{-3})\,\text{d}T$$
$$= [a\ln T + bT - ½cT^{-2}]_{T_\text{i}}^{T_\text{f}} = \boldsymbol{a\ln(T_\text{f}/T_\text{i}) + b(T_\text{f}-T_\text{i}) - ½c(T_\text{f}{}^{-2}-T_\text{i}{}^{-2})}$$

**P4.34** (a) Let $|q|$ be the heat extracted from the refrigerator at $T_\text{cold}$ and $|q'|$ be the heat delivered to environment at $T_\text{hot}$. The work needed to accomplish this is $w = |q'| - |q|$. The heat transfer occurs most efficiently when

$$\Delta S_\text{total} = \frac{|q'|}{T_\text{hot}} - \frac{|q|}{T_\text{cold}} = 0$$

so that

$$\frac{|q|}{|q'|} = \frac{T_\text{cold}}{T_\text{hot}}$$

The best coefficient of cooling performance is

$$c_\text{cool} = \frac{|q|}{w} = \frac{|q|}{|q'|-|q|} = \frac{(|q|/|q'|)}{1-(|q|/|q'|)} = \frac{(T_\text{cold}/T_\text{hot})}{1-(T_\text{cold}/T_\text{hot})} = \frac{T_\text{cold}}{T_\text{hot}-T_\text{cold}}$$

The rate of extraction of heat is simply the coefficient of cooling multiplied by the refrigerator power rating,

$$c_\text{cool}\times 200\ \text{W} = \frac{(15+273.15)\text{K}}{(15+273.15)\text{K}-(15+273.15)\text{K}}$$
$$= 3.27\times10^3\ \text{W} = \mathbf{3.27\ kW}$$

(b) The best coefficient of heating performance is

$$c_\text{warm} = \frac{|q'|}{w} = \frac{|q'|}{|q'|-|q|} = \frac{1}{1-(|q|/|q'|)} = \frac{1}{1-(T_\text{cold}/T_\text{hot})} = \frac{T_\text{hot}}{T_\text{hot}-T_\text{cold}}$$

Thus, the rate of heat delivery is simply the coefficient of warming multiplied by the heat pump power rating,

$$c_{\text{warm}} \times (2.5 \times 10^3\ \text{W}) = \frac{(22 + 273.15)\text{K}}{(18 + 273.15)\text{K} - (22 + 273.15)\text{K}} \times (2.5 \times 10^3\ \text{W})$$
$$= 184 \times 10^3\ \text{W} = \mathbf{184\ kW}$$

Practical heat pumps are not reversible so the heat gain is less.

**P4.35** (a) Following Derivation 4.4, and assuming that the heat capacity varies with temperature according to the Debye $T^3$ law, $C_{p,\text{m}} = aT^3$, then

$$\Delta S_{\text{m}} = S_{\text{m}}(T) - S_{\text{m}}(0) = \int_0^T \frac{C_{p,\text{m}}}{T}\text{d}T$$
$$= \int_0^T \frac{aT^3}{T}\text{d}T = a\int_0^T T^2\text{d}T = {}^1\!/_3 aT^3 = {}^1\!/_3 C_{p,\text{m}}(T)$$

(b) We may assume that, because nitrogen is a pure crystalline substance, $S_{\text{m}}(0) = 0$, then

$$S_{\text{m}}(T) = {}^1\!/_3 aT^3$$
$$= {}^1\!/_3 \times (6.15 \times 10^{-3}\ \text{J K}^{-1}\ \text{mol}^{-1}) \times (5\ \text{K})^3 = \mathbf{0.256\ J\ K^{-1}mol^{-1}}$$

# Chapter 5

# Physical equilibria: pure substances

## Answers to discussion questions

**D5.1** (a) For a one-component system the **chemical potential**, $\mu$ (mu), is equivalent to the molar Gibbs energy, $G_m$: $\mu = G_m = H_m - TS_m$. Eqn 5.2 tells us that

$$d\mu = dG_m = V_m dp - S_m dT$$

so that at constant $p$ (i.e., $dp = 0$) we see that

$$d\mu = -S_m dT$$

Our interpretation is that as temperature increases, the chemical potential varies as $-S_m$. The chemical potential varies with temperature because of the entropy of the system. Since the entropy is always positive, the chemical potential decreases with increasing temperature.

(b) At constant temperature (i.e., $dT = 0$) the expression $d\mu = V_m dp - S_m dT$ reduces to

$$d\mu = V_m dp$$

As pressure increases, the chemical potential varies as $V_m$. The chemical potential varies with pressure because of the molar volume of the system. Since the molar volume is always positive, the chemical potential increases with increasing pressure.

**D5.2** Consider two phases of a system, labeled α and β. The phase with the lower molar Gibbs energy under the given set of conditions is the more stable phase.

First, consider the variation of the molar Gibbs energy of each phase with temperature at a fixed pressure by rearranging eqn 5.4:

$$\frac{\Delta G_\alpha}{\Delta T} = -S_\alpha, \quad \frac{\Delta G_\beta}{\Delta T} = -S_\beta, \quad \text{at constant } p$$

These expressions clearly show that, if $S_\beta$ is larger in magnitude than $S_\alpha$, then $\Delta G_\beta$ decreases to a greater extent than $\Delta G_\alpha$ as temperature increases. Phase β will therefore become the more stable phase at higher temperature.

Second, consider the variation of the molar Gibbs energy of each phase with pressure at a fixed temperature by comparing the expressions, derived from eqn 5.1:

$$\frac{\Delta G_\alpha}{\Delta p} = V_\alpha, \quad \frac{\Delta G_\beta}{\Delta p} = V_\beta, \quad \text{at constant } T$$

These equations clearly show that, if $V_\beta$ is larger in magnitude than $V_\alpha$, then $\Delta G_\beta$ increases to a greater extent than $\Delta G_\alpha$ as pressure increases. Phase $\beta$ thus becomes the unstable phase at higher pressure; phase $\alpha$ becomes the stable phase.

**D5.3** From eqn 5.1,

$$\Delta G_\text{m} \propto \Delta p$$

so that a decrease in pressure causes a decrease in molar Gibbs energy, and an increase in pressure an increase in molar Gibbs energy.

(a) Attractive interactions decrease the pressure of a gas relative to its perfect value for the same volume. so that the molar Gibbs energy is lowered relative to its perfect value.

(b) Repulsive interactions increase the pressure of a gas above its perfect value raising the molar Gibbs energy relative to its perfect value.

**D5.4** The Clapeyron equation, which is written in differential format as eqn 5.5b,

$$\mathrm{d}p = \frac{\Delta_\text{trs} H}{T\Delta_\text{trs} V}\mathrm{d}T$$

is exact and applies rigorously to all first-order phase transitions. It shows how pressure and temperature vary with respect to each other for two phases in equilibrium. The Clapeyron equation therefore defines the phase boundary line.

The Clausius–Clapeyron equation, eqn 5.6

$$\mathrm{d}(\ln p) = \frac{\Delta_\text{trs} H}{RT^2}\mathrm{d}T$$

applies only to phase transitions between the gaseous state and condensed phases. It is not exact; its derivation involves approximations, in particular the assumptions that the perfect gas law holds and that the volume of condensed phases can be neglected in comparison to the volume of the gaseous phase.

**D5.5** The phase diagram for sulfur is shown as Figure 5.1. For a one-component system, $C = 1$, so that the phase rule may be written

$$F = C - P + 2 = 3 - P$$

In the areas labelled Solid 1, Solid 2, Liquid, and Gas, there is one phase, so $P = 1$ so that $F = 2$, meaning that there are two degrees of freedom. Both $T$ and $p$ may be independently varied within these regions.

Curve segments A and B are sublimation curves between crystal form 1 of sulfur and the gas phase, and crystal form 2 of sulfur and the gas phase, respectively. On these curves, because two phases coexist in equilibrium, $P = 2$ and therefore $F = 1$. There is thus only one independent variable, which means that once either temperature or pressure is set the other variable has a unique value determined by the equilibrium criteria. For identical reasons curve segments C, D, E, and F also have only one independent variable. Curves C and D are fusion curves in which the liquid is in equilibrium with either crystal form 2 or crystal form 1, respectively. Curve E is the vapour pressure curve. Curve F represents the points at which the two crystal forms are in equilibrium.

Point I, II, and III are triple points at which three phases co-exist in equilibrium, so that $P = 3$ and therefore $F = 0$. There is no independent variable at these points because triple points are fixed by equilibrium criteria.

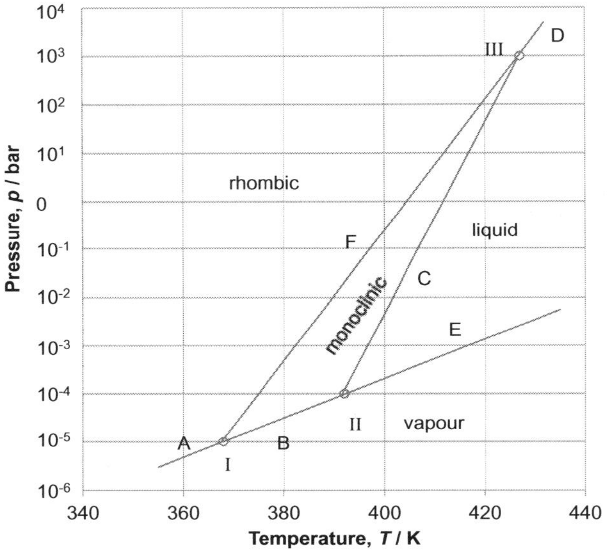


Figure 5.1

**D5.6** Molecules are in continual, random motion but on the average there is considerable **short-range order** in which molecules, even in a liquid, are positioned with some degree of crystalline structure even though the molecules can slip past one another. The order is due largely to intermolecular forces that exert their influence over short distances. As in crystals, specific intermolecular distances are preferred. However, in contrast to crystals there is no **long-range order** within a liquid. Intermolecular forces in liquids are not strong enough at large distances to overcome the randomizing effect of vigorous molecular motions and one intermolecular distance is as probable as another.

**D5.7** The supercritical fluid (SCF) extractor consists of a pump to pressurize the solvent (e.g., $CO_2$), an oven with extraction vessel, and a trapping vessel. Extractions are performed dynamically or statically. Supercritical fluid flows continuously through the sample within the extraction vessel when operating in dynamic mode. Analytes extracted into the fluid are released through a pressure maintaining restrictor into a trapping vessel. In static mode the supercritical fluid circulates repetitively through the extraction vessel until being released into the trapping vessel after a period of time. Supercritical carbon dioxide volatilizes when decompression occurs upon release into the trapping vessel.

**Advantages** of using supercritical fluid extraction technology include: the dissolving power of SCF can be adjusted with selection of tempareture and pressure; certain SCF's are inexpensive and non-toxic, so reducing pollution; thermally unstable analytes may be extracted at low temperature; the high volatility of SCF's such as $CO_2$ makes it easy to isolate analyte; SCF's have high diffusion rates, low viscosity, and low surface tension; $O_2$ and $H_2$ are completely miscible with $scCO_2$ , so reducing multi-phase reaction problems.

**Disadvantages** include: elevated pressures are required and the necessary apparatus expensive; cost may prohibit large scale applications; modifiers like methanol (1–10%) may be required to increase solvent polarity; $scCO_2$ is toxic to whole cells in biological applications.

Supercritical fluid extraction is currently used for: the extraction of caffeine, fatty acids, spices, aromas, flavors, and biological materials from natural sources; the extraction of toxic salts (with a suitable chelation agent) and organics from contaminated water; the extraction of herbicides from soil; the oxidation of toxic, intractable organic waste during water treatment; synthetic chemistry, polymer synthesis and crystallization, textile processing; heterogeneous catalysis for green chemistry processes

## Solutions to exercises

**E5.1** The substance with the lower molar Gibbs energy is the more stable; therefore, **rhombic sulfur** is the more stable.

**E5.2** The standard molar Gibbs energy of formation of graphite is lower than that of diamond by 2.900 kJ mol$^{-1}$. Thus, **graphite** is the more stable allotrope.

**E5.3** **No**, the application of pressure tends to favour the substance with the smaller molar volume, because, from eqn 5.1

$$\Delta G_m = V_m \Delta p$$

The increase in Gibbs energy with pressure is lower for the more dense material because the molar volume is smaller. Thus, the Gibbs energy of rhombic sulfur increases less with pressure than that of monoclinic sulfur. Therefore, rhombic sulfur becomes even more stable relative to monoclinic sulfur as the pressure increases.

**E5.4** The Gibbs energy of a gas varies with pressure according to eqn 5.3b

$$\Delta G_m = G_m(p_f) - G_m(p_i) = RT\ln(p_f/p_i)$$

(a) Thus, for a compression from a pressure of 1.0 bar to 3.0 bar,

$$\begin{aligned}\Delta G_m &= (8.3145\ \text{J K}^{-1}\text{mol}^{-1}) \times \{(20 + 273.15)\ \text{K}\} \times \ln(3.0\ \text{bar})/(1.0\ \text{bar}) \\ &= +2.7 \times 10^3\ \text{J mol}^{-1} = \mathbf{+2.7\ kJ\ mol^{-1}}\end{aligned}$$

(b) A pressure of 1 atm is equivalent to 1.01325 bar, so that for an expansion from 1.0 bar to $2.7 \times 10^{-4}$ atm,

$$\begin{aligned}\Delta G_m &= (8.3145\ \text{J K}^{-1}\text{mol}^{-1}) \times \{(20 + 273.15)\ \text{K}\} \\ &\qquad \times \ln\{((2.7 \times 10^{-4}\text{atm}) \times (1.01352\ \text{bar/atm}))/(1.0\ \text{bar})\} \\ &= -20 \times 10^3\ \text{J mol}^{-1} = \mathbf{-20\ kJ\ mol^{-1}}\end{aligned}$$

**E5.5** If we assume that the water vapour behaves as if a perfect gas, then, from Boyle's law, eqn 1.3,

$$p_iV_i = p_fV_f$$

so that we may rewrite eqn 5.3b as

$$\begin{aligned}\Delta G_m &= RT\ln(V_i/V_f) \\ &= (8.3145\ \text{J K}^{-1}\text{mol}^{-1}) \times (200 + 273.15)\ \text{K} \times \ln\{(350\ \text{cm}^3)/(120\ \text{cm}^3)\} \\ &= +4.2 \times 10^3\ \text{J mol}^{-1} = \mathbf{+4.2\ kJ\ mol^{-1}}\end{aligned}$$

**E5.6** (a) The variation in Gibbs energy with temperature at constant pressure is given by eqn 5.4,

$$\begin{aligned}\Delta G_m &= -S_m\Delta T \\ G_m(T_f) - G_m(T_i) &= -S_m(T_f - T_i)\end{aligned}$$

The difference in the molar Gibbs energy of rhombic and monolcinic sulfur at temperature $T_f$ is therefore

$$\begin{aligned}&G_m(\text{S, monoclinic}, T_f) - G_m(\text{S, rhombic}, T_f) \\ &= \overbrace{G_m(\text{S, monoclinic}, T_i) - \{S_m(\text{S, monoclinic}) \times (T_f - T_i)\}}^{G_m(\text{S,monoclinic},T_f)} \\ &\qquad - \overbrace{G_m(\text{S, rhombic}, T_i) - \{S_m(\text{rhombic}) \times (T_f - T_i)\}}^{G_m(\text{S,rhombic},T_f)} \\ &= \{G_m(\text{S, monoclinic}, T_i) - G_m(\text{S, rhombic}, T_i)\} \\ &\qquad - \{S_m(\text{monoclinic}) - S_m(\text{rhombic})\} \times (T_f - T_i)\end{aligned}$$

At $T_i = 298$ K,

$$S_m(\text{S, monoclinic}) - S_m(\text{S, rhombic}) = (32.6\ \text{J K}^{-1}\text{mol}^{-1}) - (31.8\ \text{J K}^{-1}\text{mol}^{-1})$$

$$= +0.8\ \mathrm{J\ K^{-1}mol^{-1}}$$

so that

$$\begin{aligned}&G_\mathrm{m}(\mathrm{S, monoclinic}, T_\mathrm{f}) - G_\mathrm{m}(\mathrm{S, rhombic}, T_f)\\&= \{G_\mathrm{m}(\mathrm{S, monoclinic, 298\ K}) - G_\mathrm{m}(\mathrm{S, rhombic, 298\ K})\}\\&\qquad - \{(0.8\ \mathrm{J\ K^{-1}\ mol^{-1}}) \times (T_\mathrm{f} - 298\ K)\}\end{aligned}$$

The negative sign before the temperature-dependent term indicates that the difference between the molar Gibbs energy of the monoclinic and rhombic allotropes decreases with temperature $T_\mathrm{f}$. Thus, there will be a temperature above 298 K for which the molar Gibbs energy of monoclinic sulfur is lower than that of rhombic sulfur; above this temperature, monoclinic sulfur will then become the most stable form.

(b) At the temperature at which the monoclinic form becomes more stable than the rhombic form,

$$G_\mathrm{m}(\mathrm{S, monoclinic}, T_\mathrm{f}) - G_\mathrm{m}(\mathrm{S, rhombic}, T_\mathrm{f}) = 0$$

The difference in the molar Gibbs energy of monoclinic and rhombic sulfur at 298 K and 1 bar is, from Exercise 5.1,

$$G_\mathrm{m}(\mathrm{S, monoclinic, 298\ K}) - G_\mathrm{m}(\mathrm{S, rhombic, 298\ K}) = +0.33 \times 10^3\ \mathrm{J\ K^{-1}mol^{-1}}$$

so that

$$(0.33 \times 10^3\ \mathrm{J\ K^{-1}mol^{-1}}) - \{(0.8\ \mathrm{J\ K^{-1}\ mol^{-1}}) \times (T_\mathrm{f} - 298\ \mathrm{K})\} = 0$$

Rearranging, gives

$$T_\mathrm{f} = \frac{(0.33 \times 10^3\ \mathrm{J\ K^{-1}mol^{-1}})}{(0.8\ \mathrm{J\ K^{-1}\ mol^{-1}})} + 298\ \mathrm{K} = \mathbf{711\ K}$$

**E5.7** For small temperature changes at constant pressure, we may use eqn 5.4

$$\begin{aligned}\Delta G_\mathrm{m} &= -S_\mathrm{m}\Delta T\\&= -(173.3\ \mathrm{J\ K^{-1}mol^{-1}}) \times (20\ \mathrm{K}) = -3.5 \times 10^3\ \mathrm{J\ mol^{-1}} = \mathbf{-3.5\ kJ\ mol^{-1}}\end{aligned}$$

**E5.8** Absolute values of the molar Gibbs energy, $G_\mathrm{m}$, are not known, but the magnitude of the slope of a graph of $G_\mathrm{m}$, against temperature, $T$, is given by the molar entropy, $S_\mathrm{m}$, because, from eqn 5.4

$$\frac{\Delta G_\mathrm{m}}{\Delta T} = -S_\mathrm{m}$$

The slopes in all phases are negative, because $S_\mathrm{m}$ is always positive, but

$$\left|\frac{\Delta G_\mathrm{m}(\mathrm{g})}{\Delta T}\right| > \left|\frac{\Delta G_\mathrm{m}(\mathrm{l})}{\Delta T}\right| > \left|\frac{\Delta G_\mathrm{m}(\mathrm{s})}{\Delta T}\right|$$

because $S_\mathrm{m}(\mathrm{g}) > S_\mathrm{m}(\mathrm{l}) > S_\mathrm{m}(\mathrm{s})$. Therefore, a graph of $G_\mathrm{m}$ against $T$ appears as in Figure 5.2. The values for the gradients given are taken from the values for the molar entropy for each phase, taken from data tables. Note the discontinuities in the slopes corresponding to the phase transitions at 273 and 373 K.

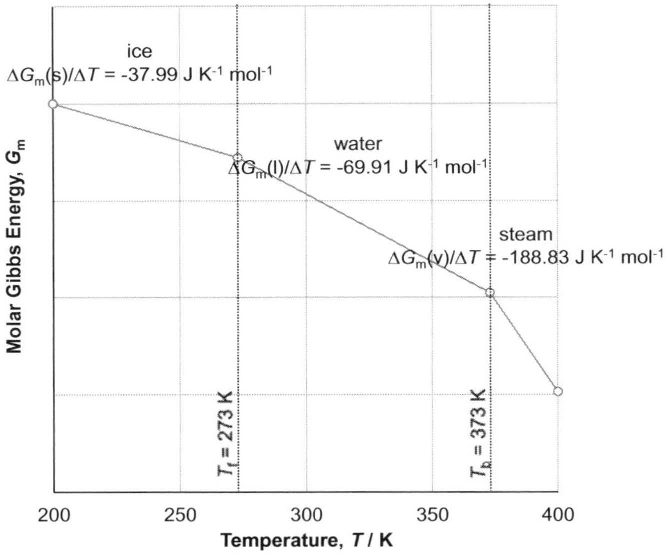


Figure 5.2

**E5.9** We may use the perfect gas law to calculate the amount, $n$, and therefore the mass, $m$, from the molar mass, $M$:

$$m = nM = \left(\overbrace{pV/RT}^{n}\right) \times M$$

(a)

$$m = \frac{(3.2 \times 10^3 \text{ Pa}) \times (5.0 \text{ m} \times 4.3 \text{ m} \times 2.2 \text{ m})}{(8.3145 \text{ J K}^{-1}\text{mol}^{-1}) \times (25 + 273.15) \text{ K}} \times 18.02 \text{ g mol}^{-1}$$
$$= 1.1 \times 10^3 \text{ g} = \mathbf{1.1\ kg}$$

(b)

$$m = \frac{(3.2 \times 10^3 \text{ Pa}) \times (5.0 \text{ m} \times 4.3 \text{ m} \times 2.2 \text{ m})}{(8.3145 \text{ J K}^{-1}\text{mol}^{-1}) \times (25 + 273.15) \text{ K}} \times 78.11 \text{ g mol}^{-1}$$
$$= 1.5 \times 10^4 \text{ g} = \mathbf{15\ kg}$$

(c)

$$m = \frac{(3.2 \times 10^3 \text{ Pa}) \times (5.0 \text{ m} \times 4.3 \text{ m} \times 2.2 \text{ m})}{(8.3145 \text{ J K}^{-1}\text{mol}^{-1}) \times (25 + 273.15) \text{ K}} \times 200.59 \text{ g mol}^{-1}$$
$$= \mathbf{1.1\ g}$$

**E5.10** (a) The Clapeyron equation for the solid-liquid phase boundary is, from eqn 5.5a

$$\Delta p = \frac{\Delta_{\text{trs}}H}{T\Delta_{\text{trs}}V} \times \Delta T$$

But, for the melting of ice,

$$\Delta_{\text{trs}}V = \Delta_{\text{fus}}V = V_{\text{m}}(\text{l}) - V_{\text{m}}(\text{s}) = M/\rho_l - M/\rho_s = M(1/\rho_l - 1/\rho_s)$$

so that the slope of the line is

$$\begin{aligned}\frac{\Delta p}{\Delta T} &= \frac{\Delta_{\text{trs}}H}{TM(1/\rho_l - 1/\rho_s)} \\ &= \frac{6.008 \times 10^3\ \text{J mol}^{-1}}{(273.15\ \text{K}) \times (18.02\ \text{g mol}^{-1}) \times \{(999.84\ \text{kg m}^{-3})^{-1} - (167.1\ \text{kg m}^{-3})^{-1}\}} \\ &= -13.46 \times 10^6\ \text{Pa K}^{-1} = \mathbf{-134.6\ bar\ K^{-1}}\end{aligned}$$

The slope is very steep with an unusual negative slope that is caused by the decrease in volume that occurs when ice melts. The melting process destroys some of the hydrogen bond scaffolding that holds ice in a larger molar volume.

(b) The pressure required to lower the melting point of ice by 1 °C is

$$\begin{aligned}p_{\text{f}} &= \left\{\overbrace{\frac{\Delta p}{\Delta T}}^{\text{slope}} \times \overbrace{\Delta T}^{-1\ \text{K}}\right\} + p_{\text{i}} \\ &= \{(-134.6\ \text{bar K}^{-1}) \times (-1\ \text{K})\} + (1\ \text{bar}) = \mathbf{+135.6\ bar}\end{aligned}$$

**E5.11** The vapour pressure at the normal boiling temperature, $T_{\text{b}}$, is, by definition, 1 bar, so that, applying the integrated form of the Clausius–Clapeyron equation, eqn 5.7,

$$\begin{aligned}\ln p' &= \ln p + \frac{\Delta_{\text{vap}}H}{R}\left\{\frac{1}{T} - \frac{1}{T'}\right\} \\ \ln(p'/\text{bar}) &= \ln(1\ \text{bar}) + \frac{\Delta_{\text{vap}}H}{R}\left\{\frac{1}{T_{\text{b}}} - \frac{1}{T'}\right\} \\ &= 0 + \frac{(24.7 \times 10^3\ \text{J mol}^{-1})}{(8.3145\ \text{J K}^{-1}\text{mol}^{-1})} \times \left\{\frac{1}{(307.7\ \text{K})} - \frac{1}{(298.15\ \text{K})}\right\} \\ &= -0.309\end{aligned}$$

Thus,

$$p = \text{e}^{-0.309} = \mathbf{0.734\ bar}$$

**E5.12** Rearranging the integrated form of the Clausius–Clapeyron equation, eqn 5.7,

$$\ln p' = \ln p + \frac{\Delta_{\text{vap}}H}{R}\left\{\frac{1}{T} - \frac{1}{T'}\right\}$$

then

$$\frac{1}{T'} = \left\{\frac{R}{\Delta_{\mathrm{vap}}H} \times (\ln p - \ln p')\right\} + \frac{1}{T}$$
$$= \left\{\frac{R}{\Delta_{\mathrm{vap}}H} \times \ln(p/p')\right\} + \frac{1}{T}$$

and remembering that the vapour pressure at the normal boiling temperature, $T_b$, is, by definition, 1.01325 bar,

$$\frac{1}{T_b} = \frac{R}{\Delta_{\mathrm{vap}}H} \times \{\ln(p/(1.01325\ \mathrm{bar})\} + \frac{1}{T}$$
$$= \left[\frac{(8.3145\ \mathrm{J\ K^{-1}mol^{-1}})}{(30.2 \times 10^3\ \mathrm{J\ mol^{-1}})} \times \overbrace{\ln\{(0.306\ \mathrm{bar})/(1.01325\ \mathrm{bar})\}}^{1\ \mathrm{kPa}=10^{-2}\ \mathrm{bar}}\right] + \frac{1}{(298.15\ \mathrm{K})}$$
$$= 3.03 \times 10^{-3}\mathrm{K^{-1}}$$

so that the normal boiling temperature is

$$T_b = \mathbf{330\ K}$$

**E5.13** (a) The integrated form of the Clausius Clapeyron equation may be written in terms of parameters $A$ and $B$

$$\ln(p/\mathrm{kPa}) = A - (B/T)$$

where

$$A = \ln p' + \frac{\Delta_{\mathrm{vap}}H}{RT'}, \quad B = \frac{\Delta_{\mathrm{vap}}H}{R}$$

Thus, using the values for hexane given in Table 5.1,

$$\Delta_{\mathrm{vap}}H = BR$$
$$= (3811\ \mathrm{K}) \times (8.3145\ \mathrm{J\ K^{-1}mol^{-1}})$$
$$= 31.69 \times 10^3\ \mathrm{J\ mol^{-1}} = \mathbf{31.69\ kJ\ mol^{-1}}$$

This value is about 10% different from the value for hexane at its boiling point, which is 28.85 kJ $\mathrm{mol^{-1}}$.

(b) Rearranging, the parameterized expression becomes

$$T = B/\{A - \ln(p/\mathrm{kPa})\}$$

At the normal boiling temperature, the vapour pressure $p = 1.01325 \times 10^2$ kPa, so that, using the values listed in Table 5.1,

$$T_b = (3811\ \mathrm{K})/\{15.77 - \ln(1.01325 \times 10^2)\} = \mathbf{341.7\ K}$$

**E5.14** Using the conversion factors listed in Table 0.1, 760 Torr = 101.325 kPa. Thus,

$$\begin{aligned}\ln(p/\text{torr}) &= \overbrace{\ln[(p/\text{kPa}) \times \{(101.325\ \text{kPa})/(760\ \text{torr})\}]}^{\ln xy = \ln x + \ln y} \\ &= \ln(p/\text{kPa}) + \ln\big((101.325\ \text{kPa})/(760\ \text{torr})\big) \\ &= \{A - (B/T)\} + \ln\big((101.325\ \text{kPa})/(760\ \text{torr})\big) \\ &= \big\{A + \ln\big((101.325\ \text{kPa})/(760\ \text{torr})\big)\big\} - (B/T) \\ &= A' - (B/T)\end{aligned}$$

Hence, if the vapour pressure is expressed in torr, the value of the parameter $A$ becomes

$$\begin{aligned}A' &= A + \ln\{(101.325\ \text{kPa})/(760\ \text{torr})\} \\ &= 17.17 + \ln\{(101.325\ \text{kPa})/(760\ \text{torr})\} = \mathbf{15.15}\end{aligned}$$

with the value of $B$ unchanged.

**E5.15** Using the integrated form of the Clausius–Clapeyron equation, eqn 5.7,

$$\ln p' = \ln p + \frac{\Delta_{\text{vap}}H}{R}\left\{\frac{1}{T} - \frac{1}{T'}\right\}$$

and substituting the value for the vapour pressure $p$ at temperature $T$

$$\begin{aligned}\ln(p'/\text{mPa}) &= \ln(160) + \frac{(59.30 \times 10^3\ \text{J mol}^{-1})}{(8.3145\ \text{J K}^{-1}\text{mol}^{-1})}\left\{\frac{1}{(20+273)\ \text{K}} - \frac{1}{(40+273)\ \text{K}}\right\} \\ &= 6.631\end{aligned}$$

Thus,

$$p/\text{mbar} = e^{6.631} = 758$$

so that the vapour pressure is **758 mbar**.

**E5.16** Rearranging the integrated form of the Clausius–Clapeyron equation, eqn 5.7,

$$\ln p' = \ln p + \frac{\Delta_{\text{vap}}H}{R}\left\{\frac{1}{T} - \frac{1}{T'}\right\}$$

and substituting

$$\Delta_{\text{vap}}H = R\frac{(\ln p' - \ln p)}{(T^{-1} - T'^{-1})}$$

At the normal boiling temperature, $T_b$, the vapour pressure $p$ = 101.325 kPa

$$\begin{aligned}\Delta_{\text{vap}}H &= R\frac{\{\ln(101.325\ \text{kPa}) - \ln p\}}{(T^{-1} - T_b^{-1})} \\ &= (8.3145\ \text{J K}^{-1}\text{mol}^{-1}) \times \frac{\{\ln(101.325\ \text{kPa}) - \ln(50.0\ \text{kPa})\}}{\{(365.7\ \text{K})^{-1} - (388.4\ \text{K})^{-1}\}} \\ &= 36.7 \times 10^3\ \text{J mol}^{-1} = \mathbf{36.7\ kJ\ mol^{-1}}\end{aligned}$$

**E5.17** We first use the Clausius–Clapeyron equation, eqn 5.7,

$$\ln p' = \ln p + \frac{\Delta_{vap}H}{R}\left\{\frac{1}{T} - \frac{1}{T'}\right\}$$

and the data provided to find $\Delta_{vap}H$. Thus, rearranging, and noting that 35 °C corresponds to (35 + 273.15) = 308.15 K, and 58.8 °C corresponds to (58.8 + 273.15) = 331.95 K

$$\begin{aligned}\Delta_{vap}H &= R\frac{\{\ln(p'/p)\}}{(T^{-1} - T'^{-1})}\\ &= (8.3145\ \mathrm{J\ K^{-1}mol^{-1}}) \times \frac{\{\ln(20.0\ \mathrm{kPa})/(50.0\ \mathrm{kPa})\}}{\{(331.95\ \mathrm{K})^{-1} - (308.15\ \mathrm{K})^{-1}\}}\\ &= 32.7 \times 10^3\ \mathrm{J\ mol^{-1}} = 32.7\ \mathrm{kJ\ mol^{-1}}\end{aligned}$$

At the normal boiling point, the vapour pressure is, by definition, 1.01325 kPa. Thus, rearranging to give an expression for temperature

$$\frac{1}{T'} = \left\{\frac{R}{\Delta_{vap}H} \times (\ln p - \ln p')\right\} + \frac{1}{T} = \left\{\frac{R}{\Delta_{vap}H} \times \ln(p/p')\right\} + \frac{1}{T}$$

and substituting,

$$\begin{aligned}\frac{1}{T_b} &= \left\{\frac{R}{\Delta_{vap}H} \times \ln(p/(101.325\ \mathrm{kPa})\right\} + \frac{1}{T}\\ &= \left\{\frac{(8.3145\ \mathrm{J\ K^{-1}mol^{-1}})}{(32.7 \times 10^3\mathrm{J\ mol^{-1}})} \times \ln(50/1.01325)\right\} + \frac{1}{(331.95\ \mathrm{K})}\\ &= 2.83 \times 10^{-3}\ \mathrm{K^{-1}}\end{aligned}$$

so that

$$T_b = \mathbf{353\ K}$$

**E5.18** (a) The two components are $Na_2SO_4$ and $H_2O$ (proton transfer equilibria to give $HSO_4^-$ etc. do not change the number of independent components) so $C = 2$. There are three phases present: solid salt, liquid solution, vapour. Thus $P = \mathbf{3}$.

(b) Applying the phase rule, eqn 5.9, the number of degrees of freedom is

$$F = C - P + 2 = 2 - 3 + 2 = \mathbf{1}$$

Either pressure or temperature may be considered the independent variable, but not both as long as the equilibrium is maintained. For example, if the pressure is changed, the temperature must be changed to maintain the equilibrium.

**E5.19** (a) If the solution is not saturated, so that no solid is present, there will only be two phases present. Thus, $P = 2$. The number of components, however, remains the same, so that $C = \mathbf{2}$.

(b) Applying the phase rule, eqn 5.9, the number of degrees of freedom is

$$F = C - P + 2 = 2 - 2 + 2 = \mathbf{2}$$

We are free to change any two of the three variables, amount of dissolved salt, pressure, or temperature, but not the third. If we change the temperature and the pressure, the amount of dissolved salt will change because it is fixed by the equilibrium condition between the two phases.

**E5.20** The vapour pressure of ice at –5 °C is $3.9 \times 10^{-3}$ atm, or 3.0 torr (*CRC Handbook of Chemistry and Physics*). Since the partial pressure of water is lower (2 torr), the frost will sublime. A partial pressure of **3.0 torr** or more will ensure that the frost remains.

**E5.21** (a) The volume decreases as the vapour is cooled from 400 K, at constant pressure, in a manner described by the perfect gas equation $V = nRT/p$. That is, $V$ is a linear function of $T$. This continues until 373 K is reached where the vapour condenses to a liquid and there is a large decrease in volume. As the temperature is lowered further to 273 K, liquid water freezes to ice. Only a small decrease in volume occurs in the liquid as temperature is decreased; a small (~9%) increase in volume occurs when the liquid freezes because ice is less dense than liquid water at 273 K. The water remains as a solid as the tenperature is decreased to 260 K. The volume of the ice decreases only very slightly as the temperature is reduced.

(b) The cooling curve appears roughly as sketched in Figure 5.3. The vapour and solid phases show a steeper rate of decline than for the liquid phase due to their smaller heat capacities. The temperature halt in the liquid plus vapour region is longer than for the liquid plus solid region due to its larger heat of transition.

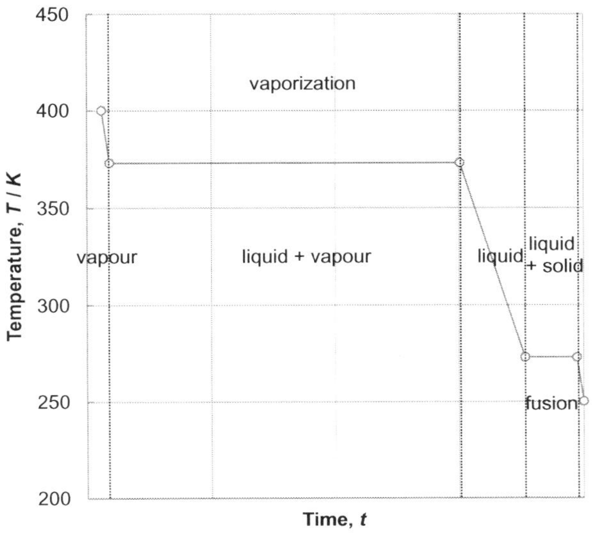


**Figure 5.3**

**E5.22** Cooling from, say, 400 K at 0.006 bar will cause a decrease in the volume of gaseous water until 273.16 K is reached, at which temperature liquid and solid water will appear. All three phases will remain in equilibrium until the constant cooling completely transforms the gas and liquid phases to ice. Then, cooling drops the temperature below 273.16 K.

**E5.23** (a) The gaseous sample expands. (b) The sample contracts but remains gaseous because 320 K is greater than the critical temperature. (c) The gas contracts and forms a liquid-like substance without the appearance of a discernible surface. As the temperature lowers further to the solid phase boundary line, solid carbon dioxide forms in equilibrium with the liquid. At 210 K the sample has become all solid. (d) The solid expands slightly as the pressure is reduced and sublimes when the pressure reaches about 5 atm. (e) The gas expands as it is heated at constant pressure.

**E5.24** The slope of the He-II/He-I phase boundary line appears to be negative everywhere. That is

$$\frac{\Delta p}{\Delta T} = \frac{\Delta_{\mathrm{trs}} H_{\mathrm{m}}}{T_{\mathrm{trs}} \Delta_{\mathrm{trs}} V_{\mathrm{m}}} < 0$$

If we assume that $\Delta_{\mathrm{trs}}H_{\mathrm{m}}$ for He-II $\rightarrow$ He-I is positive, it implies that $\Delta_{\mathrm{trs}}V_{\mathrm{m}}$ is negative, so He-I is expected to be more dense than He-II. This argument, which would work well for normal fluids, fails in the case of He. The transition to the superfluid shows no measurable $\Delta_{\mathrm{trs}}H_{\mathrm{m}}$ or $\Delta_{\mathrm{trs}}V_{\mathrm{m}}$. So at the transition, there is no difference in the density between the two forms of He.

## Answers to projects

**P5.24** The van der Waals equation of state, eqn 1.26a, is

$$(p + a/V_{\mathrm{m}}^2)(V_{\mathrm{m}} - b) = RT$$

where $V_{\mathrm{m}} = V/n$ is the molar volume. After neglecting attractive effects, the equation becomes

$$p(V_{\mathrm{m}} - b) = RT$$

(a) Solving for $V_m$ we get

$$V_{\mathrm{m}} = (RT/p) - b$$

where the first term is the molar volume of a perfect gas. Following *Derivation 5.2* with temperature constant gives

$$\Delta G_{\mathrm{m}}^{\mathrm{vdW}} = \int_{p_{\mathrm{i}}}^{p_{\mathrm{f}}} V_{\mathrm{m}}\,\mathrm{d}p = \int_{p_{\mathrm{i}}}^{p_{\mathrm{f}}} \{(RT/p) - b\}\,\mathrm{d}p = \int_{p_{\mathrm{i}}}^{p_{\mathrm{f}}} \frac{RT}{p}\,\mathrm{d}p + \int_{p_{\mathrm{i}}}^{p_{\mathrm{f}}} b\,\mathrm{d}p$$
$$= [RT \ln p + bp]_{p_{\mathrm{i}}}^{p_{\mathrm{f}}} = RT \ln(p_{\mathrm{f}}/p_{\mathrm{i}}) + b(p_{\mathrm{f}} - p_{\mathrm{i}})$$

(b) The change in molar Gibbs energy for a perfect gas is, from eqn 5.3b,

$$\Delta G_m^{ideal} = RT\ln(p_f/p_i)$$

Thus, for $p_f > p_i$, and because the parameter $b$ is positive, the change is greater for a real gas that obeys the van der Waals equation of state than a perfect gas by the amount $b(p_f - p_i)$.

(c) The relative change is given by

$$\frac{\Delta G_m^{vdW} - \Delta G_m^{real}}{\Delta G_m^{real}} = \frac{\{RT\ln(p_f/p_i) + b(p_f - p_i)\} - RT\ln(p_f/p_i)}{RT\ln(p_f/p_i)} = \frac{b(p_f - p_i)}{RT\ln(p_f/p_i)}$$

so that using the value $b = 0.0429\ \mathrm{dm^3\,mol^{-1}} = 0.0429 \times 10^{-3}\ \mathrm{m^3\,mol^{-1}}$ from Table 1.6, and assuming a temperature of 298.15 K,

$$\frac{\Delta G_m^{vdW} - \Delta G_m^{real}}{\Delta G_m^{real}}$$
$$= \frac{(0.0429 \times 10^{-3}\ \mathrm{m^3mol^{-1}}) \times \{(10.0\ \mathrm{atm} - 1.0\ \mathrm{atm}) \times (1.01325 \times 10^5\ \mathrm{Pa\,atm^{-1}})\}}{(8.3145\ \mathrm{J\,K^{-1}mol^{-1}}) \times (298.15\ \mathrm{K}) \times \ln\{(10.0\ \mathrm{atm})/(1.0\ \mathrm{atm})\}}$$
$$= 6.9 \times 10^{-3} = \mathbf{0.69\ per\ cent}$$

(d) If

$$p = \frac{nRT}{V} - \frac{an^2}{V^2} + \frac{bn^3}{V^3} = \frac{RT}{V_m} - \frac{a}{V_m^{\ 2}} + \frac{b}{V_m^{\ 3}}$$

then,

$$\frac{dp}{dV} = \frac{d}{dV}\left(\frac{RT}{V_m} - \frac{a}{V_m^{\ 2}} + \frac{b}{V_m^{\ 3}}\right) = -\frac{RT}{V_m^{\ 2}} + \frac{2a}{V_m^{\ 3}} - \frac{3b}{V_m^{\ 4}}$$

$$\frac{d^2p}{dV^2} = \frac{d}{dV}\left(\frac{dp}{dV}\right) = \frac{d}{dV}\left(-\frac{RT}{V_m^{\ 2}} + \frac{2a}{V_m^{\ 3}} - \frac{3b}{V_m^{\ 4}}\right) = \frac{2RT}{V_m^{\ 3}} - \frac{6a}{V_m^{\ 4}} + \frac{12b}{V_m^{\ 5}}$$

For a point of inflexion,

$$\frac{dp}{dV} = 0, \frac{d^2p}{dV^2} = 0$$

and, multiplying the first equation by $-V_m^{\ 4}$ and the second equation by $V_m^{\ 5}$, these two equations may be written as

$$RT_c - 2aV_{m,c} + 3b = 0$$
$$2RT_c - 6aV_{m,c} + 12b = 0$$

These two independent equations describe a critical point if they have a real solution. Solving these simultaneous equations for $V_c$ and $T_c$ gives

$$V_{m,c} = \boldsymbol{3b/a}$$

and

$$T_c = \boldsymbol{a^2/3Rb}$$

We may now use the equation of state to find an expression for the pressure at the critical point, $p_c$

$$p_c = \frac{RT_c}{V_{m,c}} - \frac{a}{V_{m,c}{}^2} + \frac{b}{V_{m,c}{}^3} = \frac{R(a^2/3Rb)}{(3b/a)} - \frac{a}{(3b/a)^2} + \frac{b}{(3b/a)^3}$$
$$= \frac{a^3}{9b^2} - \frac{a^3}{3b^2} + \frac{a^3}{27b^2} = \boldsymbol{\frac{a^3}{27b^2}}$$

Having found a real inflection point, we conclude that this equation of state does describe a critical point and that the critical constants are related to the parameters $a$ and $b$ by the above equations.

**P5.25** (a) Applying eqn 5.7, and remembering that the vapour pressure is 1.01325 bar at the normal boiling temperature

$$\ln p' = \ln p + \frac{\Delta_{vap}H}{R}\left\{\frac{1}{T} - \frac{1}{T'}\right\}$$
$$= \ln(1.01325\ \text{bar}) + \frac{(40.656\times 10^3\ \text{J mol}^{-1})}{(8.3145\ \text{J K}^{-1}\text{mol}^{-1})} \times \left\{\frac{1}{373\ \text{K}} - \frac{1}{308\ \text{K}}\right\}$$
$$= -2.75$$

Thus,

$$p/\text{bar} = e^{-2.75}$$

so that

$$p = \overbrace{0.064\ \text{bar}}^{1\ \text{bar}=10^2\ \text{kPa}} = \mathbf{6.4\ kPa}$$

(b) Starting with the differential form of the Clausius–Clapeyron equation given in Derivation 5.5,

$$\frac{d\ln p}{dT} = \frac{\Delta_{vap}H}{RT^2}$$

then, integrating between the points $(p,T)$ and $(p',T')$

$$\int_{\ln p}^{\ln p'} d\ln p = \int_T^{T'} \frac{\Delta_{vap}H}{RT^2}dT = \int_T^{T'} \frac{a+bT}{RT^2}dT = \frac{1}{R}\left\{a\int_T^{T'}\frac{1}{T^2}dT + b\int_T^{T'}\frac{1}{T}dT\right\}$$
$$[\ln p]_p^{p'} = \frac{1}{R}\left\{\left[a\left(-\frac{1}{T}\right)\right]_T^{T'} + [b\ln T]_T^{T'}\right\}$$
$$\ln p' - \ln p = \frac{1}{R}\left\{a\left(\frac{1}{T} - \frac{1}{T'}\right) + b\ln(T/T')\right\}$$

(c) Thus, if $a = 57.373\ \text{kJ mol}^{-1}$ and $b = -44.801\ \text{J K}^{-1}\ \text{mol}^{-1}$, then

$$\ln(p'/\ \text{bar}) = \ln(1.01325\ \text{bar}) + \left[\frac{(57.373\times10^{3}\ \text{J mol}^{-1})}{(8.3145\ \text{J K}^{-1}\text{mol}^{-1})}\times\left\{\frac{1}{373\ \text{K}}-\frac{1}{308\ \text{K}}\right\}\right] + \frac{(44.801\ \text{J K}^{-1}\text{mol}^{-1})}{(8.3145\ \text{J K}^{-1}\text{mol}^{-1})}\times\ln\left\{\frac{(373\ \text{K})}{(308\ \text{K})}\right\}$$

$$= -2.859$$

so that

$$p'/\text{bar} = \text{e}^{-2.859} = 0.057$$

so that

$$p' = 0.057\ \text{bar} = \mathbf{5.7\ kPa}$$

# Chapter 6

# The properties of mixtures

## Answers to discussion questions

**D6.1** A partial molar property is the contribution (per mole) that a substance makes to an overall property of a mixture. In general, the partial molar property $X_A$ (e.g., $V_A$ and $G_A$) is the slope of the plot of $X$ against $n_A$ at constant $p$, $T$, and $n_B$. This slope has the mathematical form of a partial derivative:

$$X_A = \left(\frac{\partial X}{\partial n_A}\right)_B, \quad X_B = \left(\frac{\partial X}{\partial n_B}\right)_A$$

so that we may write

$$dX = \left(\frac{\partial X}{\partial n_A}\right)_{n_B} dn_A + \left(\frac{\partial X}{\partial n_B}\right)_{n_A} dn_B = X_A dn_A + X_B dn_B$$

A substance with a high partial molar property contributes greatly to the property and values depend upon interactions between atoms, ions, and molecules. As interactions between substances are generally different than those between particles of a pure substance, partial molar properties depend upon mixture composition.

Two important partial molar properties of substance J are the **partial molar volume, $V_J$**, and the **partial molar Gibbs energy, $G_J$**. The total property is given by the sum of the partial molar property for all substances in the mixture weighted by the amount of each. For a binary mixture consisting of substances A and B, the molar volume and Gibbs energy are given by eqns 6.4 and 6.5a

$$V = n_A V_A + n_B V_B$$
$$G = n_A G_A + n_B G_B$$

**D6.2** The partial molar Gibbs energy of substance J, $G_J$, is given a special name and symbol. It is the **chemical potential, $\mu_J$** (mu), and for a mixture of A and B, eqn 6.5a is written as eqn 6.5b

$$G = n_A \mu_A + n_B \mu_B$$

where

$$\mu_A = \left(\frac{\partial G}{\partial n_A}\right)_{p,T,n_B}, \quad \mu_B = \left(\frac{\partial G}{\partial n_B}\right)_{p,T,n_A}$$

A substance with a high chemical potential contributes greatly to the total Gibbs energy $G$ of a mixture and, consequently, has a high ability to drive a reaction or some other process forward. The chemical potential of a substance within a mixture depends on interactions with neighboring atoms, ions, and molecules and, consequently, it depends upon mixture composition. Chemical potentials are especially important when discussing the direction of spontaneity of constant temperature and pressure processes because spontaneity occurs in the direction for which $G$ decreases. Should the difference between the Gibbs energy of two possible states equal zero, the two states are present in equilibrium with neither state preferred by spontaneous changes in physical or chemical properties. Applications include help in understanding the thermodynamic basis and relations of spontaneous mixing, partial vapour pressures of liquid mixtures, Raoult's law, Henry's constant, boiling point elevation and the ebullioscopic constant, freezing point depression and the cryoscopic constant, osmosis, and phase diagrams of mixtures.

**D6.3** At equilibrium, the chemical potentials of any component in both the liquid and vapour phases must be equal. This is justified with the equilibrium criteria that under constant temperature and pressure conditions, with no additional work, $\Delta G = 0$ . Consider the relationships

$$
\begin{aligned}
\mathrm{d}G_{\mathrm{m,J(l)}} &= \mathrm{d}V_{\mathrm{m,J(l)}}\,\mathrm{d}p - \mathrm{d}S_{\mathrm{m,J(l)}}\,\mathrm{d}T \\
\mathrm{d}G_{\mathrm{m,J(g)}} &= dV_{\mathrm{m,J(g)}}\,\mathrm{d}p - dS_{\mathrm{m,J(g)}}\,\mathrm{d}T
\end{aligned}
$$

for a chemical species J that is present in the liquid and vapour phases, J(l) and J(g) (see *Derivations 5.1* and *6.2*). The terms with $\mathrm{d}p$ and $\mathrm{d}T$ on the right side of these expressions equal zero for constant $p$ and constant $T$ processes, and the near equilibrium transformation

$$\mathrm{J(l)} \rightleftharpoons \mathrm{J(g)}$$

is such a process. We may express the change in the molar Gibbs energy of J in each phase using the chemical potential

$$dG_{\mathrm{m,J(l)}} = \left(\frac{\partial G_{\mathrm{m,J(l)}}}{\partial n_{\mathrm{A}}}\right)_{p,T,n_{\mathrm{B}}} \mathrm{d}n_{\mathrm{A}} = \mu_{\mathrm{J}}(\mathrm{l})\,\mathrm{d}n_{\mathrm{J}}$$

Subtraction and application of the equilibrium criteria gives

$$\mathrm{d}G_{\mathrm{J}} = \mathrm{d}G_{\mathrm{m,J(l)}} - \mathrm{d}G_{\mathrm{m,J(g)}} = \mu_{\mathrm{J}}(\mathrm{l})\mathrm{d}n_{\mathrm{J}} - \mu_{\mathrm{J}}(\mathrm{g})\mathrm{d}n_{\mathrm{J}} = \{\mu_{\mathrm{J}}(\mathrm{l}) - \mu_{\mathrm{J}}(\mathrm{g})\}\mathrm{d}n_{\mathrm{J}} = 0$$

Thus, because a equilibrium $\mathrm{d}G_{\mathrm{J}} = 0$,

$$\mu_{\mathrm{J}}(\mathrm{l}) - \mu_{\mathrm{J}}(\mathrm{g}) = 0$$

The chemical potential of each chemical species must be equal in the liquid and vapour phases, or indeed, in any two phases that are at equilibrium:

$$\mu_{\mathrm{J}}(\mathrm{l}) = \mu_{\mathrm{J}}(\mathrm{g})$$

**D6.4** **Raoult's law**, $p_J = x_J\, p_J{}^*$, describes the partial pressure of volatile component J above a solution for which the mole fraction of J is $x_J$. $p_J{}^*$ is the vapour pressure of pure J. The law is most reliable when the solution components have similar molecular shapes and are held together in the liquid by similar types and strengths of intermolecular forces. An **ideal** solution is a hypothetical solution of a solute B in a solvent A that obeys Raoult's law throughout the composition range from pure A to pure B. No mixture is perfectly ideal and all real mixtures show deviations from Raoult's law. Deviations are small for the solvent when the solution is very dilute and the law becomes exact in the limit of zero concentration of solute. It is a **limiting law**.

**Henry's law**, $p_B = x_B K_H$, describes the partial pressure of volatile solute B above a solution for which the mole fraction of B is $x_B$. Henry's law constant, $K_H$, is characteristic of the solute and chosen to equal the slope $(dp_B/dx_B)$ at $x_B = 0$ of the empirical $p_B$ against $x_B$ data plot. This law is also a limiting law in that it is usually obeyed only at low concentrations of solute in ideal-dilute solutions. It is an especially useful relation between the solubility and partial pressure of low-solubility gases. In ideal–dilute solutions solvent molecules are in an environment very much like the one they have in the pure liquid. However, the solute molecules are surrounded by solvent molecules, which is entirely different from their environment when pure. Thus, the solvent behaves like a slightly modified pure liquid, but the solute behaves entirely differently from its pure state unless the solvent and solute molecules happen to be very similar. In the latter case, the solute also obeys Raoult's law.

**D6.5** All the colligative properties (properties that depend only on the number of solute particles present, not their chemical identity) are a result of the lowering of the chemical potential of the solvent due to the presence of the solute. This reduction takes the form $\mu_A = \mu_A^* + RT\ln x_A$ or $\mu_A = \mu_A^* + RT\ln a_A$, depending on whether or not the solution can be considered ideal. The lowering of the chemical potential results in a freezing point depression and a boiling point elevation as illustrated in Figures 6.16 and 6.17 of the text. Both of these effects can be explained by the lowering of the vapour pressure of the solvent in solution due to the presence of the solute. The solute molecules get in the way of the solvent molecules, reducing their tendency to escape.

**D6.6** The activity of a solute is that property which determines how the chemical potential of the solute varies from its value in a specified standard state. This is seen from the general definition, eqn 6.18

$$\mu_J = \mu_J^\ominus + RT\ln a_J$$

where $\mu_J^\ominus$ is the value of the chemical potential of J in the standard state for which $a_J = 1$. The relation is true at all concentrations and for both the solvent and the solute. It is well worth remembering several useful activity forms.

Ideal solutions: $a_J = x_J$

Solute B of an ideal-dilute solution: $a_B = [B]/c^\ominus$ where $c^\ominus = 1\ \text{mol dm}^{-3}$

Solvent A of a non-ideal solution: $a_A = \gamma x_A$

Solute B of a non-ideal solution: $a_B = \gamma[B]/c^\ominus$ where $c^\ominus = 1 \text{ mol dm}^{-3}$

The dimensionless activity coefficients, $\gamma_J$, of non-ideal solutions must be deduced from experimental data. Also, the activity of a pure solid or a pure liquid at 1 bar always equals 1 as these are standard states.

Osmosis, the passage of a pure solvent into a solution separated from it by a semipermeable membrane through which solute cannot pass, is spontaneously driven by a diminishing total Gibbs energy until the solvent chemical potentials on each side of the membrane are equal:

$$\mu_A(\text{pure solvent at pressure } p) = \mu_A(\text{solvent in solution at pressure } p + \Pi)$$

where $\Pi$ is the osmotic pressure. Entropy increases as the solution becomes dilute.

Vigorous molecular motion causes molecules of the pure solvent to flow through microscopic holes of the membrane into the solution. Solvent molecules also flow from the solution side to the pure solvent side. However, the rate of the latter flow is reduced by the blocking action of solute with their bulky solvent cages. This results in a net flow from the pure solvent side to the solution side. The osmotic pressure is the pressure that must be applied to the solution side of the membrane in order to stop the net flow of solvent. The blocking action of solute ions or molecules is proportional to the number of solute particles present and, consequently, osmosis is a colligative property.

**D6.7** The osmotic pressure, $\Pi$, method (see *Example 6.6*) for determination of the molar mass of a polymer B involves measurement of $\Pi$ for a series of successively more dilute mass concentrations, [B]. Comparison of eqn 6.22 b, with the equation for a linear plot,

$$\overbrace{\frac{\Pi}{[B]}}^{y} = \overbrace{RT}^{\text{intercept},b} + \overbrace{BRT}^{\text{slope},m}\ \overbrace{[B]}^{x}$$

shows that for a plot of $(\Pi/[B])$ against [B], the extrapolated intercept at $[B] = 0$ equals $(RT/M_{\text{polymer}})$. Consequently, $M_{\text{polymer}} = RT/\text{intercept}$.

## Solutions to exercises

**E6.1** From eqn 6.1, the amount of sodium chloride required is related to the molar concentration and volume

$$n_{\text{NaCl}} = c_{\text{NaCl}}V$$

But, from eqn 0.2,

$$n_{\text{NaCl}} = m_{\text{NaCl}}/M_{\text{NaCl}}$$

so that

$$\begin{aligned} m_{\text{NaCl}} &= c_{\text{NaCl}} M_{\text{NaCl}} V \\ &= 1.00\ \text{mol dm}^{-3} \times (22.99 + 35.45)\ \text{g mol}^{-1} \times 0.300\ \text{dm}^3 \\ &= \mathbf{17.5\ g} \end{aligned}$$

**E6.2** The molality of the solute is, from eqn 6.2

$$b_{\text{solute}} = n_{\text{solute}}/m_{\text{solvent}}$$

Using the definition of molar mass, eqn 0.2, and mass density, eqn. 0.3, and noting that the molar mass of $Na_2HPO_4.7H_2O$ is 268.07 g mol$^{-1}$ then

$$b_{solute} = \frac{m_{\text{solute}}/M_{\text{solute}}}{\rho_{\text{solvent}} V_{\text{solvent}}} = \frac{5.96\ \text{g}/268.07\ \text{g mol}^{-1}}{0.997\ \text{g cm}^{-3} \times 250\ \text{cm}^3} = \mathbf{8.92 \times 10^{-5} mol\ kg^{-1}}$$

**E6.3** The molar concentration is, from eqn 6.1

$$c_{\text{sucrose}} = n_{\text{sucrose}}/V_{\text{solution}}$$

where $n_{\text{sucrose}}$ is the amount of sucrose molecules in solution and $V_{\text{solution}}$ is the volume of the solution. The amount of sucrose molecules is given by

$$n_{\text{sucrose}} = m_{\text{sucrose}}/M_{\text{sucrose}}$$

so that, substituting,

$$\begin{aligned} c_{\text{sucrose}} &= \frac{m_{\text{sucrose}}}{(M_{\text{sucrose}} V_{\text{solution}})} \\ &= \frac{34.5\ \text{g}}{\{(12 \times 12.01) + (22 \times 1.01) + (11 \times 16.00)\}\ \text{g mol}^{-1} \times (250 \times 10^{-3} \text{dm}^3)} \\ &= 0.403\ \text{mol dm}^{-3} \end{aligned}$$

The molality of the sucrose is given by eqn 6.3

$$b_{\text{sucrose}} = n_{\text{sucrose}}/m_{\text{water}}$$

and $m_{\text{water}}$ is the mass of the solvent which depends, according to eqn 0.3, upon the mass density

$$m_{\text{water}} = \rho_{\text{water}} V_{\text{water}}$$

so that

$$\begin{aligned} b_{\text{sucrose}} &= \frac{(m_{\text{sucrose}}/M_{\text{sucrose}})}{\rho_{\text{solution}} V_{\text{solution}}} \\ &= \frac{(34.5\ \text{g})/[\{(12 \times 12.01) + (22 \times 1.01) + (11 \times 16.00)\}\ \text{g mol}^{-1}]}{(1040\ \text{kg m}^{-3}) \times (250 \times 10^{-6} \text{m}^3)} \\ &= \mathbf{0.443\ mol\ kg^{-1}} \end{aligned}$$

**E6.4** The mole fractions of the two components are given by

$$x_B = \frac{n_B}{n_B + n_T}$$

and

$$x_T = 1 - x_B = \frac{n_T}{n_B + n_T}$$

The amount of benzene molecules is, from eqn 0.2

$$n_B = \overbrace{m_B}^{\text{mass of benzene}} \;/\; \overbrace{M_B}^{\text{molar mass of benzene}} = 56\text{ g}/\{(6 \times 12.01) + (6 \times 1.01)\}\text{ g mol}^{-1} = 0.717$$

and the amount of toluene molecules is

$$n_T = \overbrace{m_T}^{\text{mass of toluene}} \;/\; \overbrace{M_T}^{\text{molar mass of toluene}} = 120\text{ g}/\{(7 \times 12.01) + (8 \times 1.01)\}\text{ g mol}^{-1} = 1.302$$

so that

$$x_B = \frac{0.717}{0.717 + 1.302} = 0.355$$

and

$$x_T = 1 - 0.355 = 0.645$$

**E6.5** Consider a mass of air of exactly 1 g. The amount of each component in such a sample is given by eqn 0.2, so that

$$n_{N_2} = \frac{\overbrace{m_{N_2}}^{\text{mass of }N_2}}{\underbrace{M_{N_2}}_{\text{molar mass of }N_2}} = \frac{0.7553 \times 1\text{ g}}{(2 \times 14.01)\text{g mol}^{-1}} = 26.96 \times 10^{-3}\text{mol}$$

and in the same way,

$$n_{O_2} = \frac{0.2314 \times 1\text{ g}}{(2 \times 16.01)\text{g mol}^{-1}} = 7.227 \times 10^{-3}\text{ mol}$$

$$n_{Ar} = \frac{(1 - 0.7553 - 0.2314) \times 1\text{ g}}{(39.95\text{ g mol}^{-1})} = 0.3329 \times 10^{-3}\text{mol}$$

The mole fractions of the components are thus

$$x_{N_2} = \frac{x_{N_2}}{x_{N_2} + x_{O_2} + x_{Ar}} = \frac{26.96\text{ mmol}}{(26.96 + 7.227 + 0.3329)\text{ mmol}} = \mathbf{0.7810}$$

and in the same way, $x_{O_2} = \mathbf{0.2094}$ and $x_{Ar} = \mathbf{0.0096}$.

**E6.6** Following the method used in Example 6.2, the amount of glycine molecules in exactly 1 kg of water is

$$n_G = \overbrace{b_G}^{\text{molality of glycine}} \times \overbrace{m_W}^{\text{mass of water}} = (0.100 \text{ mol kg}^{-1}) \times (1 \text{ kg}) = 0.100 \text{ mol}$$

The amount of water molecules in exactly 1 kg of water is

$$n_W = \frac{\overbrace{m_W}^{\text{mass of water}}}{\underbrace{M_W}_{\text{molar mass of water}}} = \frac{10^3 \text{g}}{18.02 \text{ g mol}^{-1}} = \frac{10^3}{18.02} \text{mol}$$

The total amount of molecules present is therefore

$$n = n_G + n_W = 0.100 \text{ mol} + \frac{10^3}{18.02} \text{mol}$$

The mole fraction of glycine molecules is therefore

$$x_G = \frac{n_G}{n} = \frac{0.100 \text{ mol}}{0.100 + (10^3/18.02)\text{mol}} = \mathbf{1.80 \times 10^{-3}}$$

**E6.7** Knowing the partial molar volumes, we calculate the solution volume with eqn 6.4

$$V = n_P V_P + n_T V_T$$

where the subscripts P and T denote propanone (molar mass, $M_P = 58.08$ g mol$^{-1}$) and trichloromethane ($M_T = 119.37$ g mol$^{-1}$). The amount of each component may be calculated from our knowledge of total mass $m$ and mole fractions. The definition of mole fraction tells us that $n_P = x_P n$ and $n_T = x_T n$. Therefore,

$$n_P = (x_P/x_T) \times n_T \quad (1)$$

Thus, the total mass of the solution is

$$m = m_P + m_T = n_P M_P + n_T M_T = (x_P/x_T) n_T M_P + n_T M_T = \{(x_P/x_T) M_P + M_T\} n_T$$

so that

$$\begin{aligned} n_T &= \frac{m}{\{(x_P/x_T)M_P + M_T\}} = \frac{m x_T}{\{x_P M_P + x_T M_T\}} = \frac{m x_T}{\{(1 - x_T)M_P + x_T M_T\}} \\ &= \frac{(0.4693) \times (10^3 \text{ g})}{\{0.5307 \times \underbrace{(58.08 \text{ g mol}^{-1})}_{\text{molar mass of propanone}}\} + \{0.4693 \times \underbrace{(119.37 \text{ g mol}^{-1})}_{\text{molar mass of trichloromethane}}\}} \\ &= 5.404 \text{ mol} \end{aligned}$$

Substitution of this result gives $n_P$

$$n_P = \frac{0.5307}{0.4693} \times 5.404 \text{ mol} = 6.111 \text{ mol}$$

Finally,

$$V = \left\{\overbrace{(6.111\text{ mol})}^{n_P} \times \overbrace{(74.166\text{ cm}^3\text{mol}^{-1})}^{V_P}\right\} + \left\{\overbrace{(5.404\text{ mol})}^{n_T} \times \overbrace{(80.235\text{ cm}^3\text{mol}^{-1})}^{V_T}\right\}$$
$$= \mathbf{886.8\ cm^3}$$

**E6.8** Let the subscripts E and W denote ethanol and water. The amount of each component may be calculated from the mass density, molar mass and volume

$$n_E = V_E \times (\rho_E/M_E)$$
$$n_W = V_W \times (\rho_W/M_W)$$

allowing us to derive an expression for the mole fraction of ethanol

$$x_E = \frac{n_E}{n_E + n_W} = \frac{V_E(\rho_E/M_E)}{V_E(\rho_E/M_E) + V_W(\rho_W/M_W)}$$

The volumes of ethanol and water are the same, $V_E = V_W$, so that the expression may be simplified

$$x_E = \frac{(\rho_E/M_E)}{(\rho_E/M_E) + (\rho_W/M_W)} = \frac{1}{1 + \{(\rho_W M_E)/((\rho_E M_W\}}$$
$$= \frac{1}{1 + \left[\frac{\{(1.009\text{ g cm}^{-3}) \times (46.07\text{ g mol}^{-1})\}}{\{(0.789\text{ g cm}^{-3}) \times (18.02\text{ g mol}^{-1})\}}\right]}$$
$$= 0.234$$

From Figure 6.1 of the text, we roughly estimate the partial molar volumes as $V_E = 55.8$ cm$^3$ mol$^{-1}$ and $V_W = 17.7$ cm$^3$ mol$^{-1}$ when $x_E = 0.234$. Then, from eqn 6.4,

$$V = n_E V_E + n_W V_W$$
$$= \{(0.856\text{ mol}) \times (55.8\text{ cm}^3\text{mol}^{-1})\} + \{(2.775\text{ mol}) \times (17.7\text{ cm}^3\text{mol}^{-1})\}$$
$$= \mathbf{96.9\ cm^3}$$

**E6.9** From eqn 6.7a,

$$\mu_{CO_2(g)} - \mu^{\ominus}_{CO_2(g)} = RT\ln(p_{CO_2(g)}/p^{\ominus})$$
$$= (8.3145\text{ J K}^{-1}\text{mol}^{-1}) \times (310\text{ K}) \times \ln\{(2.0\text{ bar})/(1.0\text{ bar})\}$$
$$= +1.8 \times 10^3\text{ J mol}^{-1} = \mathbf{+1.8\ kJ\ mol^{-1}}$$

**E6.10** From eqn 6.7a, and noting that 1 atm = 1.01325 bar,

$$\mu - \mu^{\ominus} = RT\ln(p/p^{\ominus})$$
$$= (8.3145\text{ J K}^{-1}\text{mol}^{-1}) \times (298.15) \times \ln\{(1.01325\text{ bar})/(1.0\text{ bar})\}$$
$$= \mathbf{+32.631\ J\ mol^{-1}}$$

**E6.11** (a) Assuming the two components to behave as perfect gases, then the molar Gibbs energy of mixing is given by eqn 6.8

$$\begin{aligned}\Delta G_{\mathrm{m}} &= RT\{x_{\mathrm{O_2}}\ln x_{\mathrm{O_2}} + x_{\mathrm{N_2}}\ln x_{\mathrm{N_2}}\}\\ &= (8.3145\ \mathrm{J\,K^{-1}mol^{-1}}) \times (298\ \mathrm{K}) \times \{0.78\ln(0.78) + 0.22\ln(0.22)\}\\ &= -1.31\times 10^{3}\ \mathrm{J\,mol^{-1}} = \mathbf{-1.31\ kJ\ mol^{-1}}\end{aligned}$$

Mixing is spontaneous, because the change in molar Gibbs energy on mixing is negaitive.

(b) In the same, way, using eqn 6.9b

$$\begin{aligned}\Delta S_{\mathrm{m}} &= R\{x_{\mathrm{O_2}}\ln x_{\mathrm{O_2}} + x_{\mathrm{N_2}}\ln x_{\mathrm{N_2}}\}\\ &= (8.3145\ \mathrm{J\,K^{-1}mol^{-1}}) \times \{0.78\ln(0.78) + 0.22\ln(0.22)\}\\ &= \mathbf{+4.38\ J\ K^{-1}mol^{-1}}\end{aligned}$$

**E6.12** The change in molar Gibbs energy on the formation of the tertiary mixture is

$$\begin{aligned}\Delta G_{\mathrm{m}} &= RT\{x_{\mathrm{O_2}}\ln x_{\mathrm{O_2}} + x_{\mathrm{N_2}}\ln x_{\mathrm{N_2}} + x_{\mathrm{Ar}}\ln x_{\mathrm{Ar}}\}\\ &= (8.3145\ \mathrm{J\,K^{-1}mol^{-1}}) \times (298\ \mathrm{K})\\ &\qquad \times \{0.780\ln(0.780) + 0.210\ln(0.210) + 0.0096\ln(0.0096)\}\\ &= -1.40\times 10^{3}\ \mathrm{J\,mol^{-1}} = \mathbf{-1.40\ kJ\ mol^{-1}}\end{aligned}$$

Mixing is, once again, spontaneous, because the change in molar Gibbs energy on mixing is negaitive.

The molar entropy of mixing is

$$\begin{aligned}\Delta S_{\mathrm{m}} &= R\{x_{\mathrm{O_2}}\ln x_{\mathrm{O_2}} + x_{\mathrm{N_2}}\ln x_{\mathrm{N_2}} + x_{\mathrm{Ar}}\ln x_{\mathrm{Ar}}\}\\ &= (8.3145\ \mathrm{J\,K^{-1}mol^{-1}})\\ &\qquad \times \{0.780\ln(0.780) + 0.210\ln(0.210) + 0.0096\ln(0.0096)\}\\ &= \mathbf{+4.71\ J\ K^{-1}mol^{-1}}\end{aligned}$$

The addition of argon causes a change in the molar Gibbs energy of mixing of $-0.09$ kJ mol$^{-1}$ and the entropy of mixing of $+0.33$ J K$^{-1}$ mol$^{-1}$. By adding to the mixture of Exercise 6.11 a third gas as about 1% of the whole, the Gibbs energy is lowered by about 10% and the entropy of mixing is increased by about 10%.

**E6.13** For a binary mixture of two components A and B, the chemical potential for each componentsin the mixture is given by eqn 6.11

$$\begin{aligned}\mu_{\mathrm{A}} &= \mu_{\mathrm{A}}^{*} + RT\ln x_{A}\\ \mu_{\mathrm{B}} &= \mu_{\mathrm{B}}^{*} + RT\ln x_{\mathrm{B}}\end{aligned}$$

The Gibbs energy of the mixture is therefore

$$G_{\mathrm{A}} + G_{\mathrm{B}} = n_{\mathrm{A}}\mu_{\mathrm{A}} + n_{\mathrm{B}}\mu_{\mathrm{B}} = n_{\mathrm{A}}(\mu_{\mathrm{A}}^{*} + RT\ln x_{\mathrm{A}}) + n_{\mathrm{B}}(\mu_{\mathrm{B}}^{*} + RT\ln x_{\mathrm{B}})$$

so that the change on mixing is

$$\begin{aligned}\Delta G &= \overbrace{(G_A + G_B)}^{\text{Gibbs energy of mixture}} - \overbrace{(G_A^* + G_B^*)}^{\text{Gibbs energy of pure components}} \\ &= \{n_A(\mu_A^* + RT\ln x_A) + n_B(\mu_B^* + RT\ln x_B)\} - (n_A\mu_A^* + n_B\mu_B^*) \\ &= n_A RT\ln x_A + n_B RT\ln x_B\end{aligned}$$

Then, because $x_A = n_A/(n_A + n_B) = n_A/n$

$$\begin{aligned}\Delta G &= x_A nRT\ln x_A + x_B nRT\ln x_B \\ &= nRT(x_A\ln x_A + x_B\ln x_B)\end{aligned}$$

**E6.14** Assuming that the solution is ideal, then we may calculate the vapour pressure of toluene using Raoult's law, eqn 6.10

$$\begin{aligned}p_T &= x_T p_T^* = \frac{\overbrace{n_T}^{n_J = m_J/M_J}}{n_T + n_{C_{60}}} p_T^* = \frac{1}{1 + [\{m_T/M_T\}/\{(m_{C_{60}}/M_{C_{60}})\}]} p_T^* \\ &= \frac{1}{1 + [\{(100\ \text{g})/(92.14\ \text{g mol}^{-1})\}/\{(2.33\ \text{g})/(720.6\ \text{g mol}^{-1})\}]} \times 5.00\ \text{kPa} \\ &= \mathbf{4.99\ kPa}\end{aligned}$$

**E6.15** We may assume that, because the sea water behave as an ideal solution that follows Raoult's law, eqn 6.11

$$p_{\text{water}} = x_{\text{water}} p_{\text{water}}^* = \frac{n_{\text{water}}}{n_{\text{water}} + n_{\text{Na}^+} + n_{\text{Cl}^-}} p_{\text{water}}^*$$

But

$$n_{\text{Na}^+} = n_{\text{Cl}^-} = Vc_{\text{NaCl}}$$

so that

$$p_{\text{water}} = \frac{n_{\text{water}}}{n_{\text{water}} + 2Vc_{\text{NaCl}}} p_{\text{water}}^* = \frac{1}{1 + (2Vc_{\text{NaCl}}/n_{\text{water}})} p_{\text{water}}^*$$

For the sake of convenience we consider 1.000 $\text{dm}^3$ of seawater. This approach quickly gives us the mole fraction (an intensive property that is independent of the volume of solution used in the calculation) of water in the solution. Furthermore, being a dilute solution, we assume that 1.000 $\text{dm}^3$ of seawater contains roughly 1000 g of water. Thus,

$$n_{\text{water}} = m_{\text{water}}/M_{\text{water}}$$

so that

$$p_{\text{water}} = \frac{1}{1 + \{(2Vc_{\text{NaCl}})/(m_{\text{water}}/M_{\text{water}})\}} p_{\text{water}}^*$$

$$= \frac{1}{1+\{(2\times 1.000\ \mathrm{dm^3}\times 0.50\ \mathrm{mol\ dm^{-3}})/(1000\ \mathrm{g}/18.02\ \mathrm{g\ mol^{-1}})\}} \times 2.338\ \mathrm{kPa}$$
$$= \mathbf{2.30\ kPa}$$

**E6.16** Following the method outlines in *Example 6.2*, and considering a solution that contains exactly 1 kg = $10^3$ g of solvent the mole fraction of solute is

$$x_{\mathrm{solute}} = \frac{n_{\mathrm{solute}}}{n_{\mathrm{solute}}+n_{\mathrm{solvent}}}$$
$$= \frac{0.100\ \mathrm{mol}}{0.100\ \mathrm{mol}+(10^3\mathrm{g}/153.81\ \mathrm{g\ mol^{-1}})}$$
$$= 0.0151$$

and hence

$$x_{\mathrm{solvent}} = 1 - x_{\mathrm{solute}} = 0.985$$

Thus, the change in the chemical potential of the solvent is, from eqn 6.11,

$$\mu_{\mathrm{solvent}} - \mu^*_{\mathrm{solvent}} = RT\ln x_{\mathrm{solvent}}$$
$$= 8.3145\ \mathrm{J\ K^{-1}mol^{-1}} \times 298\ \mathrm{K}\times \ln 0.985$$
$$= \mathbf{-37\ J\ mol^{-1}}$$

**E6.17** If Henry's law, eqn 6.14, $p_B = K'_H x_B$, is obeyed, a graph of vapour pressure against mole fraction of HCl should be a constant, with a slope equal to the Henry's law constant $K_H'$.

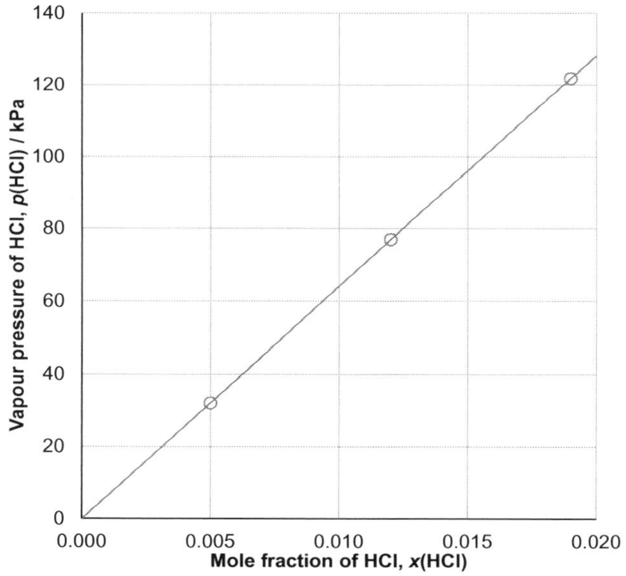


**Figure 6.1**

Figure 6.1 shows that this is indeed the case. Measuring the gradient of the line allows the value of the Henry's law constant at 300 K to be determined to be

$$K'_H = \mathbf{6.41 \times 10^3\ kPa}$$

**E6.18** The Henry's law constant is expressed in units of pressure, so we should use the form of the law given in eqn 6.14. Rearranging, and using the conversion factors for pressure given in Table 0.1,

$$x_{CO_2} = p_{CO_2}/K'_{CO_2/\text{lipid}}$$
$$= \frac{(55\ \text{kPa})}{(8.6 \times 10^4\ \text{torr}) \times \{(101.325\ \text{kPa})/(760\ \text{torr})\}} = \mathbf{4.8 \times 10^{-3}}$$

**E6.19** Using eqn 6.15, in which Henry's law is expressed in terms of concentration rather than mole fraction, and substituting the value for the Henry's law constant for a solution of hydrogen gas in water at 25 °C from Table 6.1,

$$p_{H_2} = [H_2]/K_{H_2/H_2O} = \overbrace{(1.0\ \text{mol m}^{-3})}^{1\ \text{mmol dm}^{-3} = 1\ \text{mol m}^{-3}} /(7.78 \times 10^{-3}\text{mol m}^{-3}\ \text{kPa}^{-1})$$
$$= \mathbf{129\ kPa}$$

**E6.20** (a) Using Henry's law, eqn 6.15,

$$[CO_2] = K_{CO_2/H_2O}p_{CO_2}$$
$$= (3.39 \times 10^{-1}\ \text{mol m}^{-3}\ \text{kPa}^{-1}) \times (3.8\ \text{kPa})$$
$$= 1.3\ \text{mol m}^{-3} = \mathbf{1.3\ mmol\ dm^{-3}}$$

(b)

$$[CO_2] = (3.39 \times 10^{-1}\ \text{mol m}^{-3}\ \text{kPa}^{-1}) \times (50.0\ \text{kPa})$$
$$= 17.0\ \text{mol m}^{-3} = \mathbf{17.0\ mmol\ dm^{-3}}$$

**E6.21** We may determine the molar concentrations using eqn 6.15, and by remembering that we may express the partial pressure of a component in terms of the mole fraction and total pressure, $p_J = x_J p$,

$$[J] = K_J p_J = K_J x_J p$$

Taking $p = 1.01325$ bar $= 101.325$ kPa,

$$[N_2] = (6.48 \times 10^{-3}\ \text{mol m}^{-3}\ \text{kPa}^{-1}) \times 0.78 \times (101.325\ \text{kPa})$$
$$= 0.50\ \text{mol m}^{-3} = 0.50\ \text{mmol dm}^{-3}$$

$$[O_2] = (1.30 \times 10^{-2}\ \text{mol m}^{-3}\ \text{kPa}^{-1}) \times 0.21 \times (101.325\ \text{kPa})$$
$$= 0.28\ \text{mol m}^{-3} = 0.28\ \text{mmol dm}^{-3}$$

The magnitudes of molality and molar concentration are approximately equal for very dilute aqueous solutions, so that

$$b_{N_2} = \mathbf{0.50\ mmol\ kg^{-1}}$$
$$b_{O_2} = \mathbf{0.28\ mmol\ kg^{-1}}$$

**E6.22** Applying eqn 6.15, and using the value for the Henry's law constant from Table 6.1,

$$\begin{aligned}[CO_2] &= K_{CO_2}p_{CO_2}\\ &= (3.39 \times 10^{-1}\ \text{mol m}^{-3}\text{kPa}^{-1}) \times (101.325\ \text{kPa})\\ &= 34.3\ \text{mol m}^{-3} = \mathbf{34.3\ mmol\ dm^{-3}}\end{aligned}$$

**E6.23** The partial pressure of toluene in the vapour is given in terms of the mole fraction of toluene in the vapour, $y_T$, by Dalton's law, eqn 1.1,

$$p_T = y_T p$$

and in terms of the mole fraction of toluene in the liquid, $x_T$, by Raoult's law, eqn 6.10,

$$p_T = x_T p_T^*$$

so that, combining the two expressions and rearranging,

$$y_T = p_T/p = x_T p_T^*/p$$

The vapour pressure is given by the sum of the partial pressures of the two components, and may be expressed in terms of the mole fractions in the liquid, $x_T$ and $x_X$, and pressure of the pure components, $p_T^*$ and $p_X^*$, using Raoult's law, eqn 6.10

$$\begin{aligned}p &= p_T + p_X\\ &= x_T p_T^* + x_X p_X^* = x_T p_T^* + (1 - x_T)p_X^* = x_T p_T^* - x_T p_X^* + p_X^* = x_T(p_T^* - p_X^*) + p_X^*\end{aligned}$$

so that, rearranging,

$$x_T = \frac{p - p_X^*}{p_T^* - p_X^*}$$

Using the conversion factor from Table 0.1,

$$p = (0.50\ \text{atm} \times 101.325\ \text{kPa atm}^{-1}) = 50.7\ \text{kPa}$$

Hence, substituting, the mole fraction of toluene in the vapour is

$$y_T = \overbrace{\left\{\frac{(p - p_X^*)}{(p_T^* - p_X^*)}\right\}}^{x_T} \times \frac{p_T^*}{p} = \frac{(50.7\ \text{kPa}) - (20\ \text{kPa})}{(53\ \text{kPa}) - (20\ \text{kPa})} \times \frac{(53\ \text{kPa})}{(50.7\ \text{kPa})} = \mathbf{0.97}$$

and of *o*-xylene is,

$$y_X = 1 - y_T = 1 - 0.97 = \mathbf{0.03}$$

Note that the vapour is richer in toluene than the liquid, $y_T > x_T$, because toluene is the more volatile component, $p_T^* > p_X^*$.

**E6.24** A graph of the partial pressure of the two components, $p_A$ and $p_B$, against the mole fraction of component A in the liquid, $x_A$, is shown in Figure 6.2.

**Figure 6.2**

If Raoult's law, eqn 6.10,

$$p_J = x_J p_J^*$$

is obeyed by a component J, then the partial pressure of the component should follow the straight line from $p_J = 0$ at $x_J = 0$ to $p_J = p_J^*$ at $x_J = 1$. Figure 6.2 shows that this is indeed the case for large mole fractions of both components A and B.

For smaller mole fractions, however, the partial pressure deviates from the ideal value predicted by Raoult's law. The Henry's law constant, as defined in eqn 6.14

$$p_J = K'_H x_J$$

may be determined by drawing a tangent to the pressure–composition line at $x_J = 0$ and extrapolating to find the value of the intercept at $x_J = 1$. For component A, we find that $K_H =$ **861 Torr**, and for component B, $K_H =$ **1103 Torr**. We may confirm these values using calculus by differentiating the expressions for the the partial pressures and finding the value of the derivative at $x_A = 0$ and $x_B = (1 - x_A) = 0$. The values for the Henry's law constants are greater than the partial pressures of the pure substances for both components. This implies that the interactions destablise the liquid mixture, increasing the vapour pressure above its ideal value.

**E6.25** A graph of the partial pressure of the two components, $p_A$ and $p_B$, against the mole fraction of component A in the liquid, $x_A$, is shown in Figure 6.3.

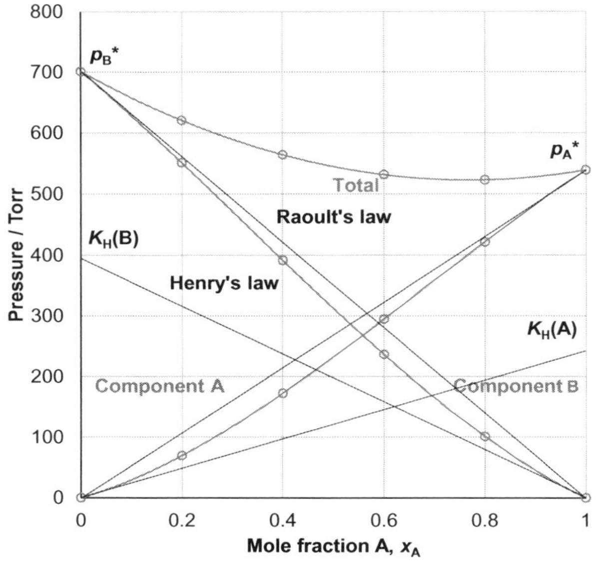


**Figure 6.3**

Just as for Exercise 6.24, it can be seen that both components obey Raoult's law when in large excess. Similarly, both components obey Henry's law when present as the minor component, with, for component A, $K_H$ = **242 Torr**, and for component B, $K_H$ = **397 Torr**. For both components, these values are lower than the partial pressures of the pure substances. This implies that the interactions stablise the liquid mixture, decreasing the vapour pressure below its ideal value.

**E6.26** The chemical potential of a solute in dilute aqueous solution is given by eqn 6. 17a

$$\mu_B = \mu_B{}^{\ominus} + RT \ln\{[B]/c^{\ominus}\}$$

The change in the chemical potential of glucose is thus

$$\begin{aligned}\Delta\mu_G &= \mu_B(0.10\ \text{mol dm}^{-3}) - \mu_B(1.0\ \text{mol dm}^{-3}) \\ &= [\mu_B{}^{\ominus} + RT \ln\{(0.10\ \text{mol dm}^{-3})/c^{\ominus}\}] \\ &\qquad - [\mu_B{}^{\ominus} + RT \ln\{(0.10\ \text{mol dm}^{-3})/c^{\ominus}\}] \\ &= (8.3145\ \text{J K}^{-1}\text{mol}^{-1}) \times \{(20+273)\text{K}\} \ln(0.10) \\ &= -5.6 \times 10^3\ \text{J mol}^{-1} = \mathbf{-5.6\ kJ\ mol^{-1}}\end{aligned}$$

**E6.27** Let B denote the benzene solvent and A the solute, then, applying Raoult's law, eqn 6.10

$$p_B = x_B p_B^* = \frac{n_B}{n_A + n_B} p_B^*$$

Rearranging,

$$n_A = \frac{n_B(p_B^* - p_B)}{p_B}$$

Then, because $n_A = m_A/M_A$, where $m_A$ is the mass of A present,

$$\begin{aligned} M_A &= \frac{m_A p_B}{n_B(p_B^* - p_B)} = \frac{m_A M_B p_B}{m_B(p_B^* - p_B)} \\ &= \frac{(0.133\ \text{g}) \times (78.11\ \text{g mol}^{-1}) \times (51.2\ \text{kPa})}{(5.00\ \text{g}) \times \{(53.0\ \text{kPa}) - (51.2\ \text{kPa})\}} = \mathbf{59.1\ g\ mol^{-1}} \end{aligned}$$

**E6.28** Assuming 200 $cm^3$ of water has a mass of 0.200 kg, then, from eqn 6.20b, and using the value for the cryoscopic constant, $K_f$, from Table 6.3, the freezing point will be depressed by

$$\begin{aligned} \Delta T_f &= K_f b_S = K_f \times \{n_S/m_W\} = K_f \times \{((m_S/M_S))/m_W\} = (K_f m_S)/(M_S m_W) \\ &= \{(1.68\ \text{K kg mol}^{-1}) \times (2.5\ \text{g})\}/\{(342.3\ \text{g mol}^{-1}) \times (0.200\ \text{kg})\} \\ &= \mathbf{+0.068\ K} \end{aligned}$$

**E6.29** Assuming 200 $cm^3$ of water has a mass of 0.200 kg, then, from eqn 6.20b, and using the value for the cryoscopic constant, $K_f$, from Table 6.3, the freezing point will be depressed by

$$\begin{aligned} \Delta T_f &= K_f b_{NaCl} \\ &= K_f \times \{n_{NaCl}/m_W\} = K_f \times \{((m_{NaCl}/M_{NaCl}))/m_W\} = (K_f m_{NaCl})/(M_{NaCl} m_W) \\ &= \{(1.68\ \text{K kg mol}^{-1}) \times (2.5\ \text{g})\}/\{(58.44\ \text{g mol}^{-1}) \times (0.200\ \text{kg})\} \\ &= \mathbf{+0.40\ K} \end{aligned}$$

**E6.30** Denoting the solvent as A and solute as B, then, from eqn 6.20b, and substituting for the molality of the solute, $b_B = n_B / m_A$

$$\Delta T_f = K_f b_B = K_f \overbrace{(n_B/m_A)}^{\text{molality of B},\,b_B} = K_f\{\overbrace{(m_B/M_B)}^{\text{amount of B molecules},\,n_B}/m_A\}$$

Thus, rearranging, and using the value for the cryoscopic constant for tetrachloromethane from Table 6.3

$$M_B = \frac{K_f m_B}{m_A \Delta T_f} = \frac{(30\ \text{K kg mol}^{-1}) \times (28.0\ \text{g})}{(750\ \text{g}) \times (5.40\ \text{K})} = 0.207\ \text{kg mol}^{-1} = \mathbf{207\ g}$$

**E6.31** We consider the addition of an amount $n$ of compound A to the propanone solvent to make up a solution with an initial concentration $c = n_{solute} / V$. The equilibrium constant may be written in terms of activities, and therefore concentrations as

$$K = \frac{a_{[A_2]}}{a_{[A]}^2} = \frac{[A_2]/c^{\ominus}}{[A]^2/c^{\ominus 2}} = \frac{[A_2]c^{\ominus}}{[A]^2}$$

If the fraction of A molecules that dimerise is $f$, then at equlibrium,

$$n_{A_2} = fn_{\text{solute}}$$
$$n_A = (1-2f)n_{\text{solute}}$$

so that

$$K = \frac{\overbrace{(fn_{\text{solute}}/V)}^{[A_2]=n_{A_2}/V} c^{\ominus}}{\underbrace{\{(1-2f)n_{\text{solute}}/V\}^2}_{[A]=n_A/V}} = \frac{f}{(1-2f)^2} \times \frac{\overbrace{V}^{c=n_{\text{solute}}/V}}{n_{\text{solute}}} \times c^{\ominus} = \frac{f}{(1-2f)^2} \times \frac{c^{\ominus}}{c}$$

The vapour pressure of the propanone solvent is, from Raoult's law, eqn 6.10,

$$p = x_{\text{solvent}}p^*$$

so that vapour pressure after the addition of compound A, is

$$\begin{aligned} p = x_{\text{solvent}}p^* &= \left(\frac{n_{\text{solvent}}}{n_{\text{solvent}} + n_A + n_{A_2}}\right)p^* \\ &= \left\{\frac{n_{\text{solvent}}}{n_{\text{solvent}} + (1-2f)n_{\text{solute}} + fn_{\text{solute}}}\right\}p^* \\ &= \left\{\frac{n_{\text{solvent}}}{n_{\text{solvent}} + (1-f)n_{\text{solute}}}\right\}p^* \end{aligned}$$

Rearranging,

$$f = 1 - \frac{n_{\text{solute}}}{n_{\text{solvent}}} \times \frac{p-p^*}{p} = 1 - \frac{n_{\text{solvent}}}{n_{\text{solute}}} \times \frac{\Delta p}{p}$$

Substituting,

$$\begin{aligned} K &= \frac{f}{(1-2f)^2} \times \frac{c^{\ominus}}{c} \\ &= \frac{1 - \{(n_{\text{solute}}/n_{\text{solvent}})(\Delta p/p)\}}{[1 - 2\times[1-\{(n_{\text{solute}}/n_{\text{solvent}})(\Delta p/p)\}]]^2} \times \frac{c^{\ominus}}{c} \\ &= \frac{1 - \{(n_{\text{solute}}/n_{\text{solvent}})(\Delta p/p)\}}{[\{2(n_{\text{solute}}/n_{\text{solvent}})(\Delta p/p)\} - 1]^2} \times \frac{c^{\ominus}}{c} \end{aligned}$$

**E6.32** For very dilute aqueous solutions, the magnitude of the molar concentration is equivalent to the molality, because $[B] = \rho b_B$, with the mass density $\rho = 1.00\ \text{kg dm}^{-3}$. We may determine the molality from the depression of the freezing point and the cryoscopic constant, by rearranging eqn 6.20b

$$b_B = \Delta T_f/K_f$$

Thus, the osmotic pressure

$$\Pi = [B]RT \approx \rho b_B RT = \rho(\Delta T_f/K_f)RT$$

so that, rearranging, and using the value for the cryoscopic constant from Table 6.3,

$$\Delta T_f = \frac{K_f \Pi}{\rho RT} = \frac{(1.86\ \mathrm{K\ kg\ mol^{-1}}) \times (150 \times 10^3\ \mathrm{Pa})}{\underbrace{(1.00\ \mathrm{kg\ dm^{-3}})}_{\text{mass density of water}} \times (8.3145\ \mathrm{J\ K^{-1}mol^{-1}}) \times (300\ \mathrm{K})} = 0.112\ \mathrm{K}$$

The freezing point of the solution will therefore be **–0.11 °C**.

**E6.33** If we assume that the solution is sufficiently dilute that it may be considered to behave as an ideal–dilute solution, we may apply the truncated form of the van 't Hoff equation, eqn 6.21b, $\Pi = [\mathrm{B}]RT$. The equation may be expressed in terms of the mass concentration, $c_\mathrm{B}$; and molar mass, $M$, as

$$\Pi = \overbrace{(c_\mathrm{B}/M)}^{[\mathrm{B}]=c_\mathrm{B}/M} RT$$

Figure 6.3 shows a plot of osmotic pressure, $\Pi$, against mass concentration, $c_\mathrm{B}$. The plot is a straight line, confirming that the system may indeed be treated as an ideal–dilute solution. The molar mass follows from the slope of the line

$$\text{slope} = RT/M = 28.11\ \mathrm{Pa/(g\ dm^{-3})} = \overbrace{28.11\ \mathrm{Pa}}^{1\ \mathrm{Pa}=1\ \mathrm{J\ m^{-3}}}\ \mathrm{/(kg\ m^{-3})} = 28.11\ \mathrm{J\ kg^{-1}}$$

so that the molar mass

$$\begin{aligned} M &= \{(8.3145\ \mathrm{J\ K^{-1}mol^{-1}}) \times (25 + 273.15)\ \mathrm{K}\}/(28.11\ \mathrm{J\ kg^{-1}}) \\ &= \mathbf{88.19\ kg\ mol^{-1}} \end{aligned}$$

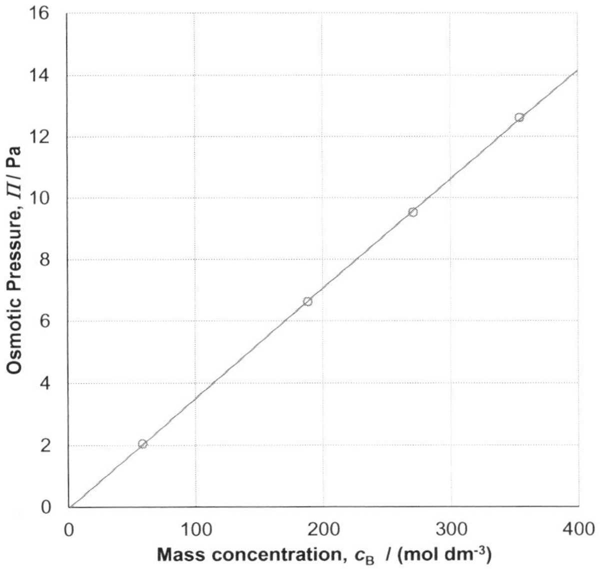


Figure 6.3

**E6.34** From the van 't Hoff equation, eqn 6.21b, for an ideal–dilute solution, the osmotic pressure depends upon the molar concentration

$$\Pi = [\mathrm{B}]RT$$

The molar concentration is related to the mass concentration, and the osmotic pressure to the height of the water drawn up the capilliary tube, so that

$$h\rho g = (c_{\mathrm{B}}/M)RT$$

Rearranging,

$$h = (RT/M\rho g)c_{\mathrm{B}}$$

so that we should expect a plot of height, $h$, against mass concentration, $c_{\mathrm{B}}$, to be a straight line with a slope equal to $(RT/M\rho g)$. Figure 6.4 shows that this is indeed the case and that it is not necessary to consider additional terms in the van 't Hoff equation.

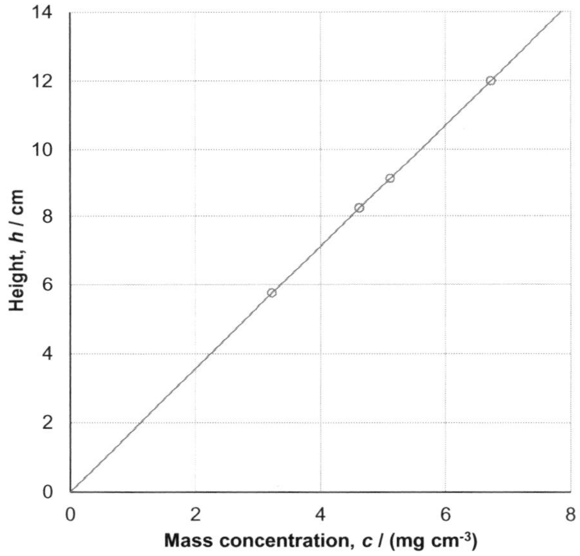


**Figure 6.4**

The slope of the graph is

$$\text{slope} = \{1.7838\ \mathrm{cm}/(\mathrm{mg\ cm^{-3}})\} = (RT/M\rho g)$$

Thus, rearranging, and paying careful attention to the units in the denominator to ensure that as many terms as possible cancel, allows us to determine the molar mass of the enzyme as

$$M = \frac{RT}{\rho g \times \{1.7838\ \mathrm{cm}/(\mathrm{mg\ cm^{-3}})\}}$$

$$= \frac{(8.3145\ \mathrm{J\ K^{-1}mol^{-1}}) \times \{(20 + 273.15)\ \mathrm{K}\}}{(1.00 \times 10^{3}\mathrm{mg\ cm^{-3}}) \times (9.81\ \mathrm{m\ s^{-2}}) \times \{1.7838 \times 10^{-2}\mathrm{m/(mg\ cm^{-3})}\}}$$
$$= 13.9\ \underbrace{\mathrm{J\ m^{-1}s^{-2}mol^{-1}}}_{1\ \mathrm{J}=1\ \mathrm{kg\ m^{2}s^{-2}}} = \mathbf{13.9\ kg\ mol^{-1}}$$

**E6.35** The data are plotted in Figure 6.5.

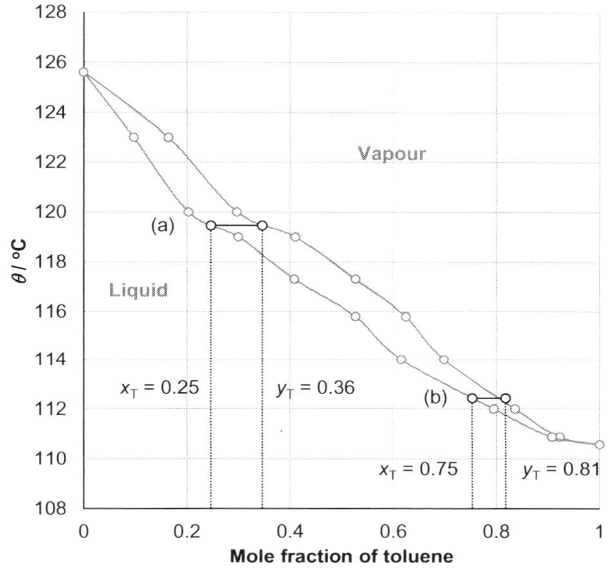


**Figure 6.5**

From tie line (a) on the graph, the vapour in equilibrium with liquid of composition $x_T$ = 0.250 has $y_T$ = **0.36**. From tie line (b), for $x_O$ = 0.250, $x_T = (1 - x_O) = 1 - 0.250 = 0.750$ and so $y_T$ = **0.81**.

**E6.36** Referring to Figure 6.39 of the text, at $b_3$ there are two partially miscible liquids at equilibrium with compositions $x_B = 0.34$ and $x_B = 0.62$; the lever rule may be used to show that their abundances are in the ratio 1.5. Because there are two components, $C = 2$, and two phases, $P = 2$, from the phase rule we have $F = 2$ and therefore two degrees of freedom, such as pressure and composition. On heating, the phases merge, and the single-phase liquid region is encountered near an upper critical point. Then, $P = 1$, and so $F = 3$ and there are three degrees of freedom, such as pressure, temperature and composition. The liquid comes into equilibrium with its vapour (i.e, boils) when the isopleth cuts the phase line at $b_2$; the vapour composition is $x_B = 0.29$ and subsequent condensation and vaporization quickly leads to the low-boiling azeotrope at $x_B = 0.21$.

If heating begins in the single liquid phase region at point $a_1$ ($x_B = 0.73$), boiling occurs at $a_2$ with a vapour phase composition of $x_B = 0.51$. Once again, subsequent condensation and vaporization (in a fractionating column) leads to the low-boiling azeotrope at $x_B = 0.21$.

**E6.37** The phase diagram of the $NH_3/N_2H_4$ system is sketched in Figure 6.6.

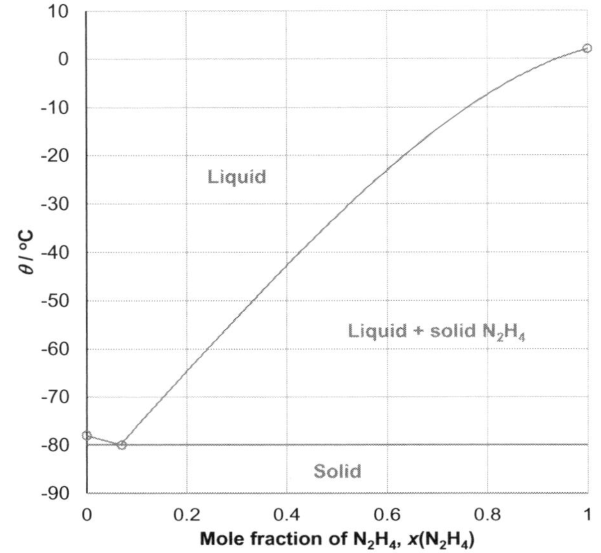


Figure 6.6

**E6.38** The phase diagrams and cooling curves are shown in Figure 6.7. (*a*) Solid silver with dissolved tin begins to precipitate at $a_1$, and the sample solidifies completely at $a_2$. (*b*) Solid silver with dissolved tin begins to precipitate at $b_1$, and the liquid becomes richer in Sn. The peritectic reaction occurs at $b_2$, and as cooling continues $Ag_3Sn$ is precipitated and the liquid becomes richer in tin. At $b_3$ the system has its eutectic composition (e) and freezes without further change.

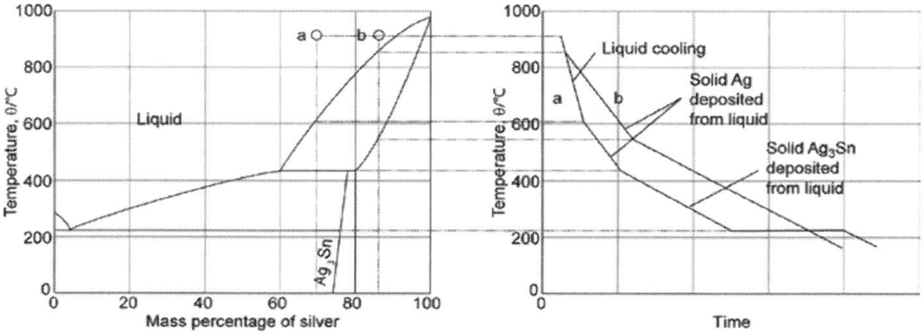


Figure 6.7

**E6.39** The curves are shown in part (b) of Figure 6.7. Upon cooling from point *a*, a single liquid is observed until a solid of about 89% silver condenses at about 610 °C. $Ag_3Sn(s)$ begins to appear in the liquid at about 430°C. Upon cooling from point *b*, a single liquid is observed until a solid of about 97% silver condenses at about 860 °C. Note the eutectic halt for the isopleth b.

**E6.40** (a) Reading the silver composition from the 800 °C solid-phase line of text Figure 6.40, we find the solid to be 95% silver by mass. Thus, the solubility is 5% tin by mass. Furthermore, at this temperature the solid is in equilibrium with liquid that is 83% silver.

(b) Reading the silver composition from the 460 °C solid-phase line, we find the solid to be 82% silver by mass. Furthermore, at this temperature the solid is in equilibrium with liquid that is 62% silver. There is no $Ag_3Sn$ in the solid at this temperature because the compound $Ag_3Sn$ decomposes at this temperature.

(c) At 300 °C the solid is 80% silver. Thus, the solubility is 20% $Ag_3Sn$ by mass.

**E6.41** The phase diagram of an alloy of copper and aluminium, is shown as Figure 6.8.

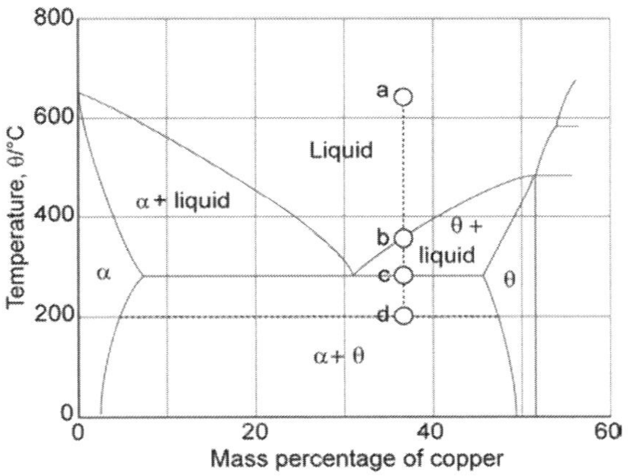


**Figure 6.8**

When lowering the temperature from point a toward point *b*, a two-component liquid of about 37% Cu is present. Upon reaching point b (~350 °C) the solid θ, which is a 48% Cu alloy at this temperature, begins to come out of solution and the remaining liquid becomes richer in aluminium.

Upon reaching the temperature of point *c* (~300 °C) the liquid composition has dropped to about 32% copper and the composition of solid θ has also dropped slightly to about 45% Cu. A second solid phase begins to come out of solution at this temperature. This is solid α, an aluminium alloy that is about 7% Cu.

Lowering the temperature below point *c* completely freezes the liquid into a heterogeneous mixture of θ and α phases. At point d (~200 °C) the lever rule indicates that the mole ratio $n_\theta/n_\alpha$ is about 3.4.

**E6.42** We follow the vertical line from point *a* to point *e* in the Figure 6.9 phase diagram of a simple steel.

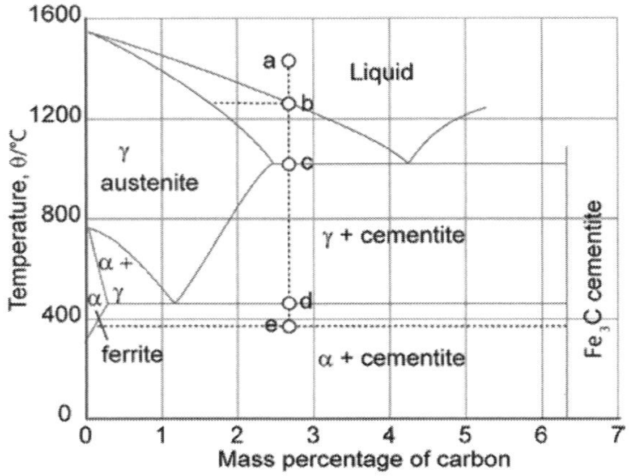


**Figure 6.9**

When lowering the temperature from point a toward point *b*, a two-component liquid of about 2.7% C and 97.3% Fe is present. Upon reaching point b (~1300 °C) the solid γ (the mineral austenite), which is a 1.6% C alloy at this temperature, begins to come out of solution and the remaining liquid becomes richer in carbon.

Just before reaching the temperature of point *c* (~1000 °C) the liquid composition has increased to about 4.2% C and the composition of solid γ has increased to about 2.3% C. Upon reaching point *c*, a second solid phase begins to come out of solution. This is solid $Fe_3C$ (the mineral cementine), an iron alloy that is about 6.3% C. The liquid completely freezes below point *c*. At temperatures between points *c* and *d*, there is a heterogeneous mixture of γ and $Fe_3C$ phase with a predominance of the γ phase.

Solid α (the mineral ferrite) appears in the equilibrium mixture at point *d* (~500°C). Below point *d*, γ is not present in the heterogeneous mixture and at room temperature (point *e*) only α and $Fe_3C$ are observed.

**E6.43** The temperature–composition diagram for hexane and perfluorohexane is sketched in Figure 6.10.

(a) The mixture has a single liquid phase at all compositions above 22.7 °C. (b) Upon adding perfluorohexane to hexane at 22.0 °C, the perfluorohexane dissolves in the hexane until the mole fraction of perfluorohexane reaches 0.24. When the composition reaches

$x(C_6F_{10}) = 0.24$, the mixture separates into two liquid phases of composition $x(C_6F_{10}) = 0.24$ and 0.48. The relative amounts of the two phases change as more perfluorohexane is added until the composition reaches $x(C_6F_{10}) = 0.48$. At all mole fractions greater than 0.48 in $C_6F_{14}$ the mixture forms a single liquid phase.

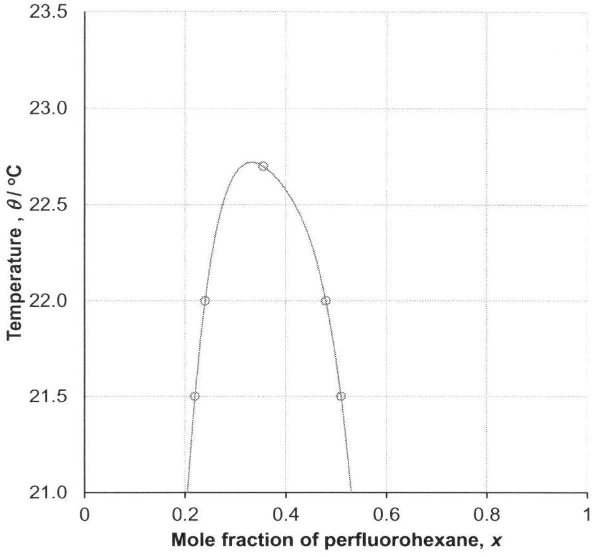


Figure 6.10

**E6.44** (a) No, the region of stability of the molten-globule form does not extend below 0.1 concentration of denaturant.

(b) The native form converts to the molten-globule form at $T \approx 0.65$ and finally to the unfolded form at $T \approx 0.85$.

**E6.45** At roughly 28 °C, solid begins to form as the state point enters the two-phase region. Within the two-phase region, the proportion of liquid and solid can be determined by the lever rule. As the temperature is lowered through the two-phase region, the proportion of solid increases until, at roughly 23 °C, the system becomes totally solid.

**E6.46** The Nernst distribution law, eqn 6.24, tells us that the ratio of mole fractions of aspirin in the two immiscible liquids is constant

$$K = \frac{x_{\text{aspirin}}(2)}{x_{\text{aspirin}}(1)} = \frac{0.18}{0.11}$$

Thus, when the amounts are changed so that $x_{\text{aspirin}} = 0.15$, the mole fraction in liquid 2 becomes

$$x_{\text{aspirin}}(2) = Kx_{\text{aspirin}}(1) = \frac{0.18}{0.11} \times 0.15 = \mathbf{0.25}$$

# Answers to projects

**P6.47** Figure 6.11 is a plot of the partial molar volume of ethanol in solution at 25 °C.

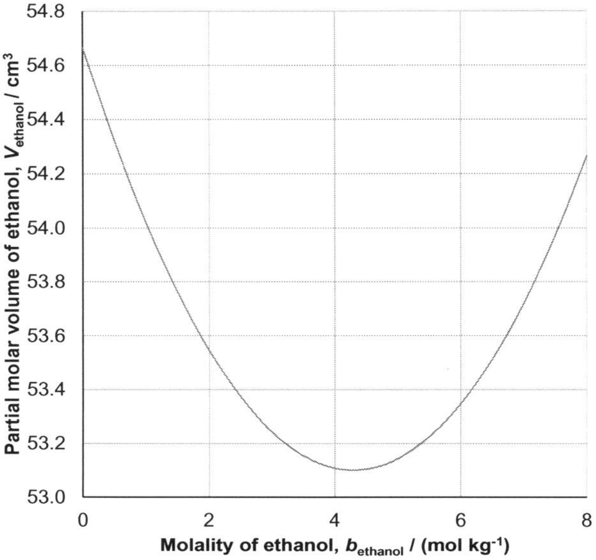


**Figure 6.11**

Examination of the plot shows that the minimum occurs at $b_{\min} \approx 4.3$ mol kg$^{-1}$ with $V_{\text{ethanol}} = 53.0$ cm$^3$ mol$^{-1}$. We may calculate the corresponding mole fraction in terms of the molality of the ethanol and water

$$x_{\text{ethanol}} = \frac{n_{\text{ethanol}}}{n_{\text{ethanol}} + n_{\text{water}}} = \frac{b_{\text{ethanol}} m_{\text{solvent}}}{b_{\text{ethanol}} m_{\text{solvent}} + b_{\text{water}} m_{\text{solvent}}}$$
$$= \frac{b_{\text{ethanol}}}{b_{\text{ethanol}} + b_{\text{water}}}$$

where we have written the molality of ethanol explicitly as $b_{\text{ethanol}}$ rather than just $b$. For water, from eqn 6.3,

$$b_{\text{water}} = n_{\text{water}}/m_{\text{water}} = (m_{\text{water}}/M_{\text{water}})/m_{\text{water}} = 1/M_{\text{water}}$$
$$= \{1/(18.02 \times 10^{-3}\,\text{g mol}^{-1})\} = 55.51\ \text{mol kg}^{-1}$$

so that

$$x_{\text{ethanol}} = \frac{4.3\ \text{mol kg}^{-1}}{4.3\ \text{mol kg}^{-1} + 55.51\ \text{mol kg}^{-1}} = \mathbf{0.072}$$

(b) Writing the expression for simplicity as

$$V_{\text{ethanol}} = c_0 + c_1 b + c_2 b^2$$

and differentiating,

$$\frac{dV_{\text{ethanol}}}{db} = c_1 + 2c_2 b$$

The minimum occurs when the value of this first derivative is zero

$$\frac{dV_{\text{ethanol}}}{db} = c_1 + 2c_2 b_{\text{min}} = 0$$

The numerical value of the molality at the minimum is therefore

$$b_{\text{min}} = -c_1/(2c_2) = +0.72788\,/(2 \times 0.084768) = 4.2934$$

so that $b_{\text{min}} = 4.2934\ \text{mol kg}^{-1}$ and therefore

$$V_{\text{ethanol}}/(\text{cm}^3\text{mol}^{-1}) = 54.664 - 0.72788 \times 4.2934 + 0.084768 \times 4.2934^2$$
$$= 53.1039$$

with $V_{\text{ethanol}} = \mathbf{53.1039\ cm^3\ mol^{-1}}$.

**P6.48** (a) The total volume of the mixture may be expressed in terms of the partial molar volumes of the two components, $V_{\text{ethanol}}$ and $V_{\text{water}}$, using eqn 6.4

$$V = n_{\text{ethanol}}V_{\text{ethanol}} + n_{\text{water}}V_{\text{water}}$$

But, we may express the amount of each component in terms of the molality and mass of solvent, because, from eqn 6.3, $b_J = n_J\,/\,m_{\text{solvent}}$ Thus

$$V_{\text{water}} = \frac{(V - n_{\text{ethanol}}V_{\text{ethanol}})}{n_{\text{water}}} = \frac{(V - b_{\text{ethanol}}m_{\text{solvent}}V_{\text{ethanol}})}{b_{\text{water}}m_{\text{solvent}}}$$
$$= \frac{\{(V/m_{\text{solvent}}) - b_{\text{ethanol}}V_{\text{ethanol}}\}}{b_{\text{water}}}$$

Substituting, and using the value for the molality of water, $b_{\text{water}} = 55.51\ \text{mol kg}^{-1}$, calculated in Exercise 6.47, and noting that $m_{\text{solvent}} = 1\ \text{kg}$,

$$V_{\text{water}}/\text{cm}^3 = \{(1002.93 + 54.6664b - 0.36394b^2 + 0.028256b^3)$$
$$-b(54.6664 - 0.72788b + 0.084768b^2)\}/55.51$$
$$= (1002.93 + 0.36394b^2 - 0.056512b^3)/55.51$$
$$= \mathbf{18.068 + 6.557 \times 10^{-3}}\boldsymbol{b}^{\mathbf{2}} \mathbf{- 1.018 \times 10^{-3}}\boldsymbol{b}^{\mathbf{3}}$$

This function is plotted as Figure 6.12. The figure shows that the maximum value for the partial molar volume of water occurs at a molality of $b_{\text{ethanol}} \approx 4.3\ \text{mol kg}^{-1}$, in agreement with the minimum found for $V_{\text{ethanol}}$.

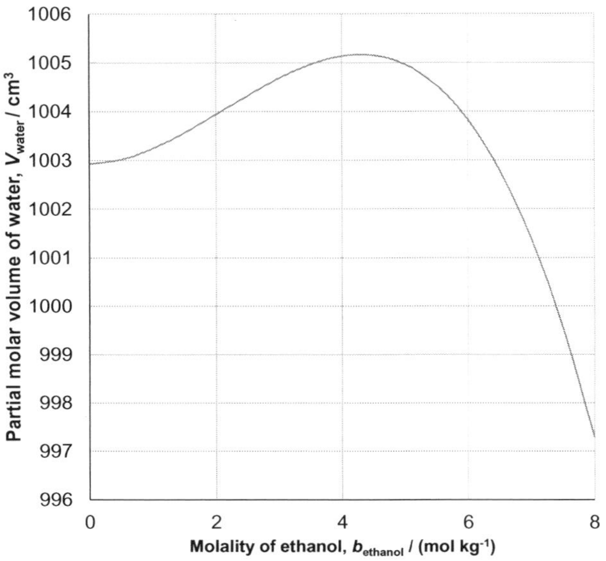


**Figure 6.12**

**P6.49** (a) The 97 per cent saturated haemoglobin (Hb) in the lungs releases oxygen in the capillary until the haemoglobin is 75 percent saturated. The difference, which is equivalent to 97 – 75 = 12 per cent, is taken up by the body tissue. For a volume of 100 cm$^3$ of blood, this is equivalent to

$$\overbrace{(0.97-0.75)}^{\text{difference in saturation}} \times \overbrace{\{1.34\ \text{cm}^3\text{O}_2/(\text{g Hb})\}}^{\text{volume of O}_2\text{ per unit mass of Hb}} \times \overbrace{\{150\ (\text{g Hb})\ /\text{dm}^3\}}^{\text{mass of Hb per unit volume of blood}} \times \overbrace{0.100\ \text{dm}^3}^{\text{volume of blood}}$$
$$= \mathbf{5\ cm^3 O_2}$$

(b) In this case, we write the Henry's law expression as

$$\begin{aligned} m_{N_2} &= p_{N_2} m_{H_2O} K_{N_2} \\ &= (x_{N_2} p) m_{H_2O} K_{N_2} \\ &= (0.78 \times 4.0\ \text{atm}) \times (100\ \text{g H}_2\text{O}) \times \{1.8 \times 10^{-4}\ \text{g N}_2/(\text{g H}_2\text{O atm})\} \\ &= 56 \times 10^{-6}\ \text{g N}_2 = \mathbf{56\ \mu g\ N_2} \end{aligned}$$

If the total pressure is 1.0 atm, then

$$\begin{aligned} m_{N_2} &= (0.78 \times 1.0\ \text{atm}) \times (100\ \text{g H}_2\text{O}) \times \{1.8 \times 10^{-4}\ \text{g N}_2/(\text{g H}_2\text{O atm})\} \\ &= 56 \times 10^{-6}\ \text{g N}_2 = \mathbf{14\ \mu g\ N_2} \end{aligned}$$

(c) In fatty tissue the increase in $N_2$ concentration from 1 atm to 4 atm is therefore

$$4 \times (56\ \mu\text{g N}_2 - 14\ \text{ug N}_2) = \mathbf{170\ \mu g\ N_2}$$

# Chapter 7

# Chemical equilibria: the principles

## Answers to discussion questions

**D7.1** The position of equilibrium is always determined by the condition that the reaction Gibbs energy equals zero at equilibrium:

$$\Delta_r G = 0 \text{ at equilibrium}$$

and therefore, from eqn 7.8,

$$\Delta_r G^{\ominus} = -RT \ln Q_{eq} = -RT \ln K$$

If the mixing of reactants and products gives $\Delta_r G < 0$, reactant activities will spontaneously diminish to increase product activities until $\Delta_r G = 0$. If the mixing gives $\Delta_r G > 0$, product activities will spontaneously diminish to increase reactant activities until $\Delta_r G = 0$. For the general reaction

$$a\,\mathrm{A} + b\,\mathrm{B} \rightleftharpoons c\,\mathrm{C} + d\,\mathrm{D}$$

the reaction quotient is given by eqn 7.5

$$Q = a_\mathrm{C}^c a_\mathrm{D}^d / a_\mathrm{A}^a a_\mathrm{B}^b$$

We say that, when the mixing gives $\Delta_r G < 0$, the reaction proceeds spontaneously to the right (*forward* reaction) until equilibrium is achieved but, when $\Delta_r G > 0$, the reaction proceeds spontaneously to the left (*reverse* direction). If reactant or product is added to an equilibrium mixture, the reaction spontaneously shifts in the direction that lowers the Gibbs energy of the reaction mixture (see text Figures 7.1–7.3, remembering that $\Delta_r G$ is the *slope* of $G$ plotted against composition). The reaction spontaneously shifts to the right upon addition of reactant to an equilibrium mixture; left upon addition of product. We must also remember that thermodynamics says nothing about the rate at which the reaction occurs or shifts. A spontaneous reaction may occur very rapidly, infinitely slowly, or at any intermediate speed.

**D7.2** A non-spontaneous, endergonic reaction ($\Delta_r G > 0$) may be driven forward by a spontaneous, exergonic reaction ($\Delta_r G < 0$) that can supply the requisite reaction Gibbs energy. The total Gibbs energy change for this reaction coupling must be exergonic and the coupling is accomplished in many enzyme-catalyzed biochemical reactions where the enzyme serves as the transfer agent for the Gibbs energy. The exergonic reaction gives up a portion of its Gibbs energy not as heat but to the conversion of a low-potential biochemical intermediate to a high potential one. The high-potential species carries the energy to the endergonic reaction (on the enzyme surface for example) and in the process of releasing its chemical energy to the endergonic reaction it returns to its low potential form. The energy carrying intermediate effectively couples the two reactions. Adenosine diphosphate (ADP) and adenosine triphosphate (ADP) is an example set of coupling intermediates:

$$ATP(aq) + H_2O(l) \rightarrow ADP(aq) + P_i^-(aq) + H^+(aq) \qquad \Delta_r G^\ominus = -31 \text{ kJ mol}^{-1}$$

D7.3 **Le Chatelier's principle**, is an empirical rule: when a system at equilibrium is subjected to a disturbance, the composition of the system adjusts so as to tend to minimize the effect of the disturbance.

Thermodynamics provides both understanding of the rule's origin and relations that quantify the effect of adding a catalyst, or of changing the temperatureor pressure.

(1) Response to the presence of a catalyst: Neither the quantity $\Delta_r G^\ominus$ nor the equilibrium constant $K$ is affected by a catalyst so the presence of a catalyst does not illicit a reaction response within a chemical mixture at equilibrium. The catalyst increases both the forward and backward reaction rates but these rates remain equal at dynamic equilibrium.

(2) Response to a change in temperature: The van 't Hoff equation, eqn 7.15,

$$\ln K' = \ln K + \frac{\Delta_r H^\ominus}{R}\left\{\frac{1}{T} - \frac{1}{T'}\right\}$$

shows that $K$ decreases with increasing temperature when the reaction is exothermic and $\Delta_r H^\ominus < 0$ and the point of equilibirum shifts to the left. The opposite is true for endothermic reactions $\Delta_r H^\ominus > 0$.

The reaction in which reactants and products exhibit identical standard enthalpies ($\Delta_r H^\ominus = 0$) has an equilibrium constant that is independent of temperature ($K' = K$). A simple example is provided by mixing to form an ideal solution.

(3) Response to a change in pressure. The equilibrium constant for a gas-phase reaction has no dependence upon pressure. Nonetheless, individual partial pressures and mole fractions can change as the total pressure changes. This will happen when there is a difference, $\Delta \nu_{gas}$, between the amount of gas molecules on the product and reactant sides of the chemical equation. The requirement of an unchanged equilibrium constant implies that the side with the smaller amount of gas be favoured as pressure increases.

For the general gas-phase reaction equation

$$a\,A + b\,B \rightleftharpoons c\,C + d\,D$$

the equilibrium constant is

$$K = \frac{a_C^c a_D^d}{a_A^a a_B^b} = \frac{(p_C/p^\ominus)^c\,(p_D/p^\ominus)^d}{(p_A/p^\ominus)^a\,(p_B/p^\ominus)^b} = \frac{(x_C p/p^\ominus)^c\,(x_D p/p^\ominus)^d}{(x_A p/p^\ominus)^a\,(x_B p/p^\ominus)^b}$$
$$= \frac{x_C^c x_D^d}{x_A^a x_B^b} \times (p/p^\ominus)^{[(c+d)-(a+b)]} = \frac{x_C^c x_D^d}{x_A^a x_B^b} \times (p/p^\ominus)^{\Delta\nu_{gas}}$$

Thus

$$\frac{x_C^c x_D^d}{x_A^a x_B^b} = K(p/p^\ominus)^{-\Delta\nu_{gas}}$$

If $\Delta\nu_{gas} > 0$, the ratio of the mole fractions of products to reactants must decrease with pressure. This corresponds to a shift in the point of equilibrium to the left, the side with fewer moles of gas in the balanced reaction equation. For the same reason, the shift is to the right when $\Delta\nu_{gas} < 0$. If $\Delta\nu_{gas} = 0$, there will be no reaction shift when the pressure is changed.

Our analysis assumes that the gases are perfect. Should the gases of one side of the reaction equation strongly repel while the gas molecules of the other side strongly attract, a compression may shift the reaction in the direction opposite to that expected for perfect gases.

**D7.4** For a general gas-phase reaction

$$a\,A + b\,B \rightleftharpoons c\,C + d\,D$$

we may define the equilibrium constant expressed in terms of partial pressures as

$$K_p = \frac{p_C^c p_D^d}{p_A^a p_B^b}$$

Because for a real gas, the activity depends through eqns 1.9 and 6.19, upon both the partial pressure and the activity coefficient,

$$a_J = \gamma_J x_J = \gamma_J p_J/p^\ominus$$

the thermodynamic equilibrium constant may, however, be expressed as

$$K = \frac{a_C^c a_D^d}{a_A^a a_B^b} = \frac{(\gamma_C p_C/p^\ominus)^c\,(\gamma_D p_D/p^\ominus)^d}{(\gamma_A p_A/p^\ominus)^a\,(\gamma_B p_B/p^\ominus)^b} = \frac{\gamma_C^c \gamma_D^d}{\gamma_A^a \gamma_B^b} \times \frac{p_C^c p_D^d}{p_A^a p_B^b} \times p^{\ominus-[(c+d)-(a+b)]}$$

Rearranging, we can therefore write

$$K_p = \frac{\gamma_A^a \gamma_B^b}{\gamma_C^c \gamma_D^d} p^{\ominus[(c+d)-(a+b)]} \times K$$

The temperature variation of $K_p$ thus depends, in addition to the change predicted by the van 't Hoff equation, on how the activity coefficients vary with temperature. The activity coefficient of a real gas gives an indication of the dominant intermolecular forces.

Coefficients greater than 1 are observed when repulsions dominate; coefficients less than one dominate when attractions dominate. The way that these intermolecular forces change with temperature will be different for the various products and components. We may thus expect that the exact temperature dependence of $K_p$ will be a complicated function.

**D7.5** We may see from Derivation 7.2, that the van 't Hoff equation, eqn 7.15, written as

$$\ln K' = \ln K + \frac{\Delta_r H^{\ominus}}{R}\left\{\frac{1}{T} - \frac{1}{T'}\right\}$$

is valid over small temperature ranges in which neither $\Delta_r H^{\ominus}$ nor $\Delta_r S^{\ominus}$ vary much with temperature. Kirchhoff's law, eqn 3.6,

$$\Delta_r H^{\ominus}(T') = \Delta_r H^{\ominus}(T) + \{\Delta_r C_p^{\ominus} \times (T' - T)\}$$

indicates that the former criteria is often satisfied because $\Delta_r C_p^{\ominus}$ is often small. The latter criteria is justified because, for a constant temperature and pressure process, $\Delta_r S^{\ominus} = \Delta_r H^{\ominus} / T$; the numerator of this relationship does not change much with temperature, and the large magnitude of $T$ means the $1/T$ does not change much either. Thus, there is little variation of $\Delta_r S^{\ominus}$ over a small temperature range.

## Solutions to exercises

**E7.1** For the general reaction

$$a\,\mathrm{A} + b\,\mathrm{B} \rightleftharpoons c\,\mathrm{C} + d\,\mathrm{D}$$

the reaction quotient is given by eqn 7.5

$$Q = a_C^c a_D^d / a_A^a a_B^b$$

For a specific reaction, we may substitute the expressions for the activity given in Section 6.6. These expressions vary according to the state of the component. Thus, for a pure solid or liquid, $a_J = 1$. For a solute $a_J = \gamma_J[\mathrm{J}]/c^{\ominus}$, which for an ideal mixture becomes $a_J \approx [\mathrm{J}]/c^{\ominus}$ because $\gamma_J = 1$. For a gas, $a_J = \gamma_J p_J/p^{\ominus}$, which may be simplified for a perfect gas to $a_J \approx p_J/p^{\ominus}$. We often omit the standard concentration and pressure, $c^{\ominus}$ and $p^{\ominus}$, for convenience, but must remember to include the terms during calculations. The concentrations and partial pressures of the reaction quotient change in time as the reaction occurs until equilibrium is achieved.

(a) Thus, for the reaction

$$2\,CH_3COCOOH(aq) + 5\,O_2(g) \rightleftharpoons 6\,CO_2(g) + 4\,H_2O(l)$$

$$Q=\frac{\overbrace{a^6_{CO_2(g)}}^{\text{gas}}\,\overbrace{a^4_{H_2O(l)}}^{\text{pure liquid}}}{\underbrace{a^2_{CH_3COCOOH(aq)}}_{\text{solute}}\,\underbrace{a^5_{O_2(g)}}_{\text{gas}}}$$

$$=\frac{\left(p_{CO_2(g)}/p^{\ominus}\right)^6\times 1^4}{([CH_3COCOOH]/c^{\ominus})^2\left(p_{O_2(g)}/p^{\ominus}\right)^5}=\frac{\boldsymbol{p^6_{CO_2(g)}}}{\boldsymbol{[CH_3COCOOH]^2 p^5_{O_2(g)}}}\times\left(\boldsymbol{c^{\ominus 2}/p^{\ominus}}\right)$$

(b) For

$$Fe(s) + PbSO_4\,(aq) \rightleftharpoons FeSO_4(aq) + Pb(s)$$

$$Q=\frac{\overbrace{a_{FeSO_4(aq)}}^{\text{solute}}\,\overbrace{a_{Pb(s)}}^{\text{pure solid}}}{\underbrace{a_{Fe(s)}}_{\text{pure solid}}\,\underbrace{a_{PbSO_4(aq)}}_{\text{solute}}}\approx\frac{([FeSO_4]/c^{\ominus})\times 1}{1\times([PbSO_4]/c^{\ominus})}=\frac{\boldsymbol{[FeSO_4]}}{\boldsymbol{[PbSO_4]}}$$

(c) For

$$Hg_2Cl_2(s) + H_2(g) \rightleftharpoons 2\,HCl(g) + 2\,Hg(l)$$

$$Q=\frac{\overbrace{a^2_{HCl(aq)}}^{\text{solute}}\,\overbrace{a^2_{Hg(l)}}^{\text{pure liquid}}}{\underbrace{a_{Hg_2Cl_2(s)}}_{\text{pure solid}}\,\underbrace{a_{H_2(g)}}_{\text{gas}}}\approx\frac{([HCl]/c^{\ominus})^2\times 1}{1\times\left(p_{H_2(g)}/p^{\ominus}\right)}=\frac{\boldsymbol{[HCl]^2}}{\boldsymbol{p_{H_2(g)}}}\times\frac{\boldsymbol{p^{\ominus}}}{\boldsymbol{c^{\ominus 2}}}$$

(d) For

$$2\,CuCl(aq) \rightleftharpoons Cu(s) + CuCl_2(aq)$$

$$Q=\frac{\overbrace{a_{Cu(s)}}^{\text{pure solid}}\,\overbrace{a_{CuCl_2(aq)}}^{\text{solute}}}{\underbrace{a^2_{CuCl(aq)}}_{\text{solute}}}\approx 1\times\frac{[CuCl_2]/c^{\ominus}}{([CuCl]/c^{\ominus})^2}=\frac{\boldsymbol{[CuCl_2]}}{\boldsymbol{[CuCl]^2}}\times\boldsymbol{c^{\ominus}}$$

**E7.2** Let B and I denote borneol and isoborneol, respectively. The reaction is

$$B(g) \rightarrow I(g)$$

with $\Delta_r G^{\ominus} = +9.4\ \text{kJ mol}^{-1}$ at 503 K. From eqn 7.6, and assuming that both the reactant and product may be treated as perfect gases

$$\begin{aligned}\Delta_r G &= \Delta_r G^{\ominus} + RT\ln Q\\ &= \Delta_r G^{\ominus} + RT\ln\frac{(p_I/p^{\ominus})}{(p_B/p^{\ominus})} = \Delta_r G^{\ominus} + RT\ln\frac{(x_I p/p^{\ominus})}{(x_B p/p^{\ominus})}\\ &= \Delta_r G^{\ominus} + RT\ln(x_I/x_B) = \Delta_r G^{\ominus} + RT\ln(n_I/n_B)\end{aligned}$$

$$= +9.4 \times 10^3\ \mathrm{J\ mol^{-1}} + \{(8.3145\ \mathrm{J\ K^{-1} mol^{-1}}) \times (503\ \mathrm{K}) \times \ln(0.30\ \mathrm{mol}/0.15\ \mathrm{mol})\}$$
$$= +12.3 \times 10^3\mathrm{J\ mol^{-1}} = \mathbf{+12.3\ kJ\ mol^{-1}}$$

Because the amount of gas does not change as a result of the isomerization process, $\Delta\nu_{gas} = 0$, the total pressure does not affect the position of equilibrium and therefore is not involved in the calculation.

**E7.3** The balanced equation for the hydrolysis of ATP is

$$\mathrm{ATP(aq) + H_2O(l) \rightarrow ADP(aq) + P_i^-(aq) + H^+(aq)}$$

with $\Delta_r G^{\oplus} = -30.5\ \mathrm{kJ\ mol^{-1}}$. The symbol $\oplus$ indicates that the reaction Gibbs energy quoted applies to the biological standard state where $a_{H^+} = [H^+]/c^{\ominus} = 10^{-7}$, which corresponds to pH = 7, and all other activities are 1. The reaction quotient is

$$Q^{\oplus} = \frac{\overbrace{a_{\mathrm{ADP(aq)}}}^{1}\ \overbrace{a_{\mathrm{P_i^-(aq)}}}^{1}\ \overbrace{a_{\mathrm{H^+(aq)}}}^{10^{-7}}}{\underbrace{a_{\mathrm{ATP(aq)}}}_{1}\ \underbrace{a_{\mathrm{H_2O(l)}}}_{1}} = a_{\mathrm{H^+(aq)}}$$

Applying eqn 7.6,

$$\Delta_r G^{\oplus} = \Delta_r G^{\ominus} + RT \ln Q^{\oplus}$$

so that

$$\Delta_r G^{\ominus} = \Delta_r G^{\oplus} - RT \ln Q^{\oplus}$$

Hence, for a general set of conditions,

$$\Delta_r G = \Delta_r G^{\ominus} + RT \ln Q = (\Delta_r G^{\oplus} - RT \ln Q^{\oplus}) + RT \ln Q = \Delta_r G^{\oplus} + RT \ln(Q/Q^{\oplus})$$
$$= \Delta_r G^{\oplus} + RT \ln \left( \overbrace{\frac{a_{\mathrm{ADP(aq)}} a_{\mathrm{P_i^-(aq)}} a_{\mathrm{H^+(aq)}}}{a_{\mathrm{ATP(aq)}} a_{\mathrm{H_2O(l)}}}}^{Q} \Big/ \overbrace{a_{\mathrm{H^+(aq)}}}^{Q^{\oplus}} \right)$$
$$= \Delta_r G^{\oplus} + RT \ln \left( \frac{a_{\mathrm{ADP(aq)}} a_{\mathrm{P_i^-(aq)}}}{a_{\mathrm{ATP(aq)}} a_{\mathrm{H_2O(l)}}} \right)$$

From Table 6.2, the activity of solute in an ideal solution, $a_J \approx [J]/c^{\ominus}$, and the activity of a pure liquid is $a_J = 1$, so that

$$\Delta_r G = \Delta_r G^{\oplus} + RT \ln \left( \frac{[\mathrm{ADP}][\mathrm{P_i^-}]}{[\mathrm{ATP}]c^{\ominus}} \right)$$

(a) Thus, if the concentrations of ADP, $P_i^-$ and ATP are all 1.0 mmol dm$^{-3}$

$$\left( \frac{[\mathrm{ADP}][\mathrm{P_i^-}]}{[\mathrm{ATP}]c^{\ominus}} \right) = \left[ \frac{(0.1 \times 10^{-3}\mathrm{mol\ dm^{-3}})(0.1 \times 10^{-3}\mathrm{mol\ dm^{-3}})}{(0.1 \times 10^{-3}\mathrm{mol\ dm^{-3}})(1\ \mathrm{mol\ dm^{-3}})} \right] = 10^{-4}$$

and so

$$\Delta_r G = -30.5\times10^3\ \text{J mol}^{-1} + [(8.3145\ \text{J K}^{-1}\text{mol}^{-1})\times(37+273.15)\ \text{K}]\times\ln 10^{-4}$$
$$= -48.3\times10^3\text{J mol}^{-1} = \mathbf{-48.3\ kJ\ mol^{-1}}$$

(b) In the same way, if the concentrations of ADP, $P_i^-$ and ATP are all 1.0 μmol dm$^{-3}$,

$$\Delta_r G = -30.5\times10^3\ \text{J mol}^{-1} + [(8.3145\ \text{J K}^{-1}\text{mol}^{-1})\times(37+273.15)\ \text{K}]\times\ln 10^{-7}$$
$$= -66.1\times10^3\text{J mol}^{-1} = \mathbf{-66.1\ kJ\ mol^{-1}}$$

**E7.4** Applying eqn 7.6 to the equilibrium

$$Na^+(\text{inside}) \rightleftharpoons Na^+(\text{outside})$$

and noting that the standard reaction Gibbs energy

$$\Delta_r G^\ominus = \mu^\ominus(\text{Na}) - \mu^\ominus(\text{Na}) = 0$$

then

$$\Delta_r G = \Delta_r G^\ominus + RT\ln Q = 0 + RT\ln\left(a_{\text{Na}^+(\text{outside})}/a_{\text{Na}^+(\text{inside})}\right)$$

If we treat the cell as an ideal–dilute solution, we may use the expression, $a_J \approx [J]/c^\ominus$, from Table 6.2, to replace the activities of the sodium ions by their concentrations, so that

$$\Delta_r G = RT\ln([\text{Na}^+]_{\text{outside}}/[\text{Na}^+]_{\text{inside}})$$
$$= (8.3145\ \text{J K}^{-1}\text{mol}^{-1})\times(37+273.15)\text{K} \times \ln[(140\ \text{mmol dm}^{-3})/(10\ \text{mmol dm}^{-3})]$$
$$= +6.8\times10^3\text{J mol}^{-1} = \mathbf{+6.8\ kJ\ mol^{-1}}$$

**E7.5** For the general reaction

$$a\,\text{A} + b\,\text{B} \rightleftharpoons c\,\text{C} + d\,\text{D}$$

the equilibrium constant is given by eqn 7.7

$$K = (a_C^c a_D^d / a_A^a a_B^b)_{\text{equilibrium}}$$

Using the expressions given in Section 6.6, we may write the activity of a gas as $a_J = \gamma_J p_J/p^\ominus$ , which may be simplified for a perfect gas to $a_J \approx p_J/p^\ominus$. Just as for the reaction quotient, we often omit the standard pressure, $p^\ominus$, for convenience, but must remember to include the term during calculations.

(a) Thus, for the reaction

$$CO(g) + Cl_2(g) \rightleftharpoons COCl(g) + Cl(g)$$

and treating all gases as perfect

$$K = \frac{a_{\mathrm{COCl(g)}}a_{\mathrm{Cl(g)}}}{a_{\mathrm{CO(g)}}a_{\mathrm{Cl_2(g)}}} = \frac{(p_{\mathrm{COCl(g)}}/p^{\ominus})(p_{\mathrm{Cl(g)}}/p^{\ominus})}{(p_{\mathrm{CO(g)}}/p^{\ominus})(p_{\mathrm{Cl_2(g)}}/p^{\ominus})} = \frac{\boldsymbol{p_{\mathrm{COCl(g)}}p_{\mathrm{Cl(g)}}}}{\boldsymbol{p_{\mathrm{CO(g)}}p_{\mathrm{Cl_2(g)}}}}$$

(b) In the same way for

$2\ SO_2(g) + O_2(g) \rightleftharpoons 2\ SO_3(g)$

$$K = \frac{a^2_{\mathrm{SO_3(g)}}}{a^2_{\mathrm{SO_2(g)}}a_{\mathrm{O_2(g)}}} = \frac{(p_{\mathrm{SO_3(g)}}/p^{\ominus})^2}{(p_{\mathrm{SO_2(g)}}/p^{\ominus})^2(p_{\mathrm{O_2(g)}}/p^{\ominus})} = \frac{\boldsymbol{p^2_{\mathrm{SO_3(g)}}p^{\ominus}}}{\boldsymbol{p^2_{\mathrm{SO_2(g)}}p_{\mathrm{O_2(g)}}}}$$

(c) For

$H_2(g) + Br_2(g) \rightleftharpoons 2\ HBr(g)$

$$K = \frac{a^2_{\mathrm{HBr(g)}}}{a_{\mathrm{H_2(g)}}a_{\mathrm{Br_2(g)}}} = \frac{(p_{\mathrm{HBr(g)}}/p^{\ominus})^2}{(p_{\mathrm{H_2(g)}}/p^{\ominus})(p_{\mathrm{Br_2(g)}}/p^{\ominus})} = \frac{\boldsymbol{p^2_{\mathrm{HBr(g)}}}}{\boldsymbol{p_{\mathrm{H_2(g)}}p_{\mathrm{Br_2(g)}}}}$$

(d) For

$2\ O_3(g) \rightleftharpoons 3\ O_2(g)$

$$K = \frac{a^3_{\mathrm{O_2(g)}}}{a^2_{\mathrm{O_3(g)}}} = \frac{(p_{\mathrm{O_2(g)}}/p^{\ominus})^3}{(p_{\mathrm{O_3(g)}}/p^{\ominus})^2} = \frac{\boldsymbol{p^3_{\mathrm{O_2(g)}}}}{\boldsymbol{p^2_{\mathrm{O_3(g)}}p^{\ominus}}}$$

**E7.6** The balanced equation for the formation of $NH_3$ from $H_2$ and $N_2$ may be written in many ways, with different multiples of the stoichiometric coefficients. However, the standard Gibbs energy of formation is a molar quantity, and it is therefore appropriate to write it as

$3/2\ H_2(g) + 1/2\ N_2(g) \rightleftharpoons NH_3(g)$

so that it refers to the production of 1 mol of $NH_3$. Using eqn 7.6, and assuming that the gases are perfect, so that the activities may eb expressed in terms of partial pressures as $a_J = \gamma_J p_J$, we may then write

$$\begin{aligned}
\Delta_r G &= \Delta_r G^{\ominus} + RT \ln Q \\
&= \Delta_r G^{\ominus} + RT \ln \frac{a_{\mathrm{NH_3(g)}}}{a^{3/2}_{\mathrm{H_2(g)}}a^{1/2}_{\mathrm{N_2(g)}}} \\
&= \Delta_r G^{\ominus} + RT \ln \frac{p_{\mathrm{NH_3(g)}}/p^{\ominus}}{(p_{\mathrm{H_2(g)}}/p^{\ominus})^{3/2}(p_{\mathrm{N_2(g)}}/p^{\ominus})^{1/2}} \\
&= \Delta_r G^{\ominus} + RT \ln \frac{p_{\mathrm{NH_3(g)}}p^{\ominus}}{p^{3/2}_{\mathrm{H_2(g)}}p^{1/2}_{\mathrm{N_2(g)}}} \\
&= -16.5 \times 10^3\ \mathrm{J\ mol^{-1}} \\
&\qquad + (8.3145\ \mathrm{J\ K^{-1} mol^{-1}}) \times (298\ \mathrm{K}) \times \ln\left\{\frac{(4.0\ \mathrm{bar}) \times (1.0\ \mathrm{bar})}{(1.0\ \mathrm{bar})^{3/2} \times (3.0\ \mathrm{bar})^{1/2}}\right\} \\
&= -14.4 \times 10^3\ \mathrm{J\ mol^{-1}} = \mathbf{-14.4\ kJ\ mol^{-1}}
\end{aligned}$$

The Gibbs energy of formation, $\Delta_r G < 0$, so that formation of $NH_3$ is spontaneous for this composition.

**E7.7** From, eqn 7.7, the equilibrium constant for the forward reaction A + B $\rightleftharpoons$ C is

$$K = \frac{a_C}{a_A a_B} = 0.432$$

The equilibrium constant for the reverse reaction is thus

$$K' = \frac{a_A a_B}{a_C} = \frac{1}{0.432} = \mathbf{2.31}$$

**E7.8** For the reaction A + B $\rightleftharpoons$ 2 C, the equilibrium constant is, from eqn 7.7,

$$K = \frac{a_C^2}{a_A a_B} = 7.2 \times 10^5$$

(a) If instead, the reaction is written as 2 A + 2 B $\rightleftharpoons$ 4 C, then the equilibrium constant is

$$K' = \frac{a_C^4}{a_A^2 a_B^2} = \left(\frac{a_C^2}{a_A a_B}\right)^2 = (7.2 \times 10^5)^2 = \mathbf{5.2 \times 10^{11}}$$

We may therefore infer that if we double the stoichiometric coefficients, the equilibrium constant for the new reaction is the square of the original value

$$K' = K^2$$

(b) It follows that because the stoichiometric coefficients of the reaction ½ A + ½ B $\rightleftharpoons$ C are half those of the original reaction, the equilibrium constant is the square root of the original value

$$K'' = K^{1/2} = (7.2 \times 10^5)^{1/2} = \mathbf{850}$$

**E7.9** From eqn 7.8,

$$\begin{aligned}\Delta_r G^{\ominus} &= -RT \ln K = -(8.3145\ \mathrm{J\ K^{-1} mol^{-1}}) \times (400\ \mathrm{K}) \times \ln 2.07 \\ &= -2.42 \times 10^3 \mathrm{J\ mol^{-1}} = \mathbf{-2.42\ kJ\ mol^{-1}}\end{aligned}$$

The standard Gibbs energy $\Delta_r G^{\ominus} < 0$, implying that the reaction is spontaneous. This is consistent with the value of the equilibrium constant, $K > 1$, which shows that the position of equilibrium lies in favour of the formation of products.

**E7.10** Rearranging eqn 7.8

$$K = e^{-\Delta_r G^{\ominus}/RT} = e^{-(-3.67\times 10^3 \mathrm{J\ mol^{-1}})/\{(8.3145\ \mathrm{J\ K^{-1} mol^{-1}})\times(300\ \mathrm{K})\}} = \mathbf{4.36}$$

The equilibrium constant, $K > 1$, so that the equilibrium favours reactants over products. The reaction is thus not spontaneous in the direction written.

**E7.11** From eqn 7.8,

$$K = e^{-\Delta_r G^\ominus/RT}$$

so that the ratio of two equilibrium constants is given by

$$K_{r1}/K_{r2} = e^{-\Delta_{r1}G^\ominus/RT}/e^{-\Delta_{r2}G^\ominus/RT} = e^{-(\Delta_{r1}G^\ominus-\Delta_{r2}G^\ominus)/RT}$$
$$= e^{-(320-55)\times10^3\,\mathrm{J\,mol^{-1}}/\{(8.3145\,\mathrm{J\,K^{-1}mol^{-1}})\times300\,\mathrm{K}\}} = \mathbf{1.38\times10^{46}}$$

This is an enormous difference. Because of the exponential relation between $K$ and $\Delta_r G^\ominus$ even small differences in $\Delta_r G^\ominus$ can make large differences in $K$.

**E7.12** If $K_{r1} = 8.4 \times K_{r2}$, then, from eqn 8.6 and using the rules for the manipulation of logs

$$\Delta_{r2}G^\ominus = -RT\ln K_{r2} = -RT\overbrace{\ln(K_{r1}/8.4)}^{\ln(x/y)=\ln x-\ln y} = -RT\ln K_{r1} + RT\ln 8.4$$
$$= \Delta_{r2}G^\ominus + RT\ln 8.4$$
$$= -250\times10^3\,\mathrm{J\,mol^{-1}} + \{(8.3145\,\mathrm{J\,K^{-1}mol^{-1}})\times(298\,\mathrm{K})\times(\ln 8.4)\}$$
$$= -245\times10^3\,\mathrm{J\,mol^{-1}} = \mathbf{-245\,kJ\,mol^{-1}}$$

**E7.13** From eqn 8.7,

$$K = e^{-\Delta_r G^\ominus/RT}$$

so that for a reaction for which the standard reaction Gibbs energy is zero,

$$K = e^0 = \mathbf{1}$$

**E7.14** The standard Gibbs energies given refer to the biological standard state, with pH = 7, so that using eqn 8.7, we may write

$$K = e^{-\Delta_r G^\oplus/RT}$$

so that, for the hydrolysis of glucose-1-phosphate, glucose-6-phosphate and glucose-3-phosphate, respectively,

$$K = e^{-(-21\times10^3\,\mathrm{kJ\,mol^{-1}})/\{(8.3145\,\mathrm{J\,K^{-1}mol^{-1}})\times(37+273.15)\mathrm{K}\}} = \mathbf{3.5\times10^3}$$
$$K = e^{-(-14\times10^3\,\mathrm{kJ\,mol^{-1}})/\{(8.3145\,\mathrm{J\,K^{-1}mol^{-1}})\times(37+273.15)\mathrm{K}\}} = \mathbf{2.3\times10^2}$$
$$K = e^{-(-9.2\times10^3\,\mathrm{kJ\,mol^{-1}})/\{(8.3145\,\mathrm{J\,K^{-1}mol^{-1}})\times(37+273.15)\mathrm{K}\}} = \mathbf{36}$$

**E7.15** Endergomic reactions are those for which $\Delta_r G^\ominus > 0$, and exergonic reactions are those for which $\Delta_r G^\ominus < 0$. Thus, checking the sign of $\Delta_r G^\ominus$ for each compound,

(a) –, exergonic

(b) +, endergonic

(c) +, endergonic

(d) –, exergonic

**E7.16** As the temperature of the decomposition reaction increases there comes a temperature $T$ for which the reaction becomes spontaneous. At this temperature, $\Delta_r G^\ominus = 0$, so that, from eqn 4.16

$$\Delta_r G^\ominus = \Delta_r H^\ominus - T\Delta_r S^\ominus = 0$$

and we may rearrange to give eqn 7.9

$$T = \Delta_r H^\ominus / \Delta_r S^\ominus$$

The standard reaction enthalpy may be calculated from the standard enthalpies of formation, using eqn 3.5

$$\Delta_r H^\ominus = \sum \nu \Delta_f H^\ominus(\text{products}) - \sum \nu \Delta_f H^\ominus(\text{reactants})$$

and the standard reaction entropy using eqn 4.13

$$\Delta_r S^\ominus = \sum \nu S_m^\ominus(\text{products}) - \sum \nu S_m^\ominus(\text{reactants})$$

If we assume that the standard enthalpy and standard reaction entropy vary little with temperature, we use the values given in the *Data section* for a temperature of 298 K.

(a) Thus, for

$$CaCO_3(s) \rightarrow CaO(s) + CO_2(g)$$

$$\begin{aligned}\Delta_r H^\ominus &= \overbrace{\{\Delta_f H^\ominus(CaO(s)) + \Delta_f H^\ominus(CO_2(g))\}}^{\text{products}} - \overbrace{\Delta_f H^\ominus(CaCO_3(s))}^{\text{reactant}} \\ &= (-635.09\ \text{kJ mol}^{-1} - 393.51\ \text{kJ mol}^{-1}) - (-1206.9\ \text{kJ mol}^{-1}) \\ &= +178.3\ \text{kJ mol}^{-1}\end{aligned}$$

$$\begin{aligned}\Delta_r S^\ominus &= \overbrace{\{S_m^\ominus(CaO(s)) + S_m^\ominus(CO_2(g))\}}^{\text{products}} - \overbrace{S_m^\ominus(CaCO_3(s))}^{\text{reactant}} \\ &= (39.75\ \text{J K}^{-1}\text{mol}^{-1} + 213.74\ \text{J K}^{-1}\text{mol}^{-1}) - (92.9\ \text{J K}^{-1}\text{mol}^{-1}) \\ &= +160.6\ \text{J K}^{-1}\text{mol}^{-1}\end{aligned}$$

$$T = \frac{\overbrace{+178.3 \times 10^3\ \text{J mol}^{-1}}^{\Delta_r H^\ominus}}{\underbrace{+160.6\ \text{J K}^{-1}\text{mol}^{-1}}_{\Delta_r S^\ominus}} = \mathbf{1110\ K}$$

(b) For

$$CuSO_4.5H_2O \rightleftharpoons CuSO_4(s) + 5\ H_2O(g)$$

$$\begin{aligned}\Delta_r H^\ominus &= \overbrace{\{\Delta_f H^\ominus(CuSO_4(s)) + 5 \times \Delta_f H^\ominus(H_2O(g))\}}^{\text{products}} - \overbrace{\Delta_f H^\ominus(CuSO_4.5H_2O(s))}^{\text{reactant}} \\ &= \{-771.36\ \text{kJ mol}^{-1} + (5 \times -241.82\ \text{kJ mol}^{-1})\} - (-2279.9\ \text{kJ mol}^{-1}) \\ &= +299.2\ \text{kJ mol}^{-1}\end{aligned}$$

$$\Delta_r S^\ominus = \overbrace{\{S_m^\ominus(\text{CuSO}_4(\text{s})) + 5\times S_m^\ominus(\text{H}_2\text{O}(\text{g}))\}}^{\text{products}} - \overbrace{S_m^\ominus(\text{CuSO}_4.5\text{H}_2\text{O}(\text{s}))}^{\text{reactant}}$$
$$= \{109\ \text{J K}^{-1}\text{mol}^{-1} + (5\times 188.83\ \text{J K}^{-1}\text{mol}^{-1})\} - (300.4\ \text{J K}^{-1}\text{mol}^{-1})$$
$$= +753\ \text{J K}^{-1}\text{mol}^{-1}$$

$$T = \frac{\overbrace{+299.2\times 10^3\ \text{J mol}^{-1}}^{\Delta_r H^\ominus}}{\underbrace{+753\ \text{J K}^{-1}\text{mol}^{-1}}_{\Delta_r S^\ominus}} = \mathbf{397\ K}$$

**E7.17** The equilibrium constant becomes greater than 1 at the temperature at which the standard reaction Gibbs energy is zero. This temperature is given by eqn 7.9,

$$T = \Delta_r H^\ominus/\Delta_r S^\ominus$$

Although the standard reaction Gibbs energy will vary significantly with temperature, it is reasonable to assume that the standard enthalpy and entropy of reaction are constant. The standard reaction enthalpy is given as $\Delta_r H^\ominus = +224\ \text{kJ mol}^{-1}$. We may calculate the standard reaction entropy by rearranging eqn 4.16, $\Delta_r G^\ominus = \Delta_r H^\ominus - T\Delta_r S^\ominus$, and substituting the value of the standard reaction Gibbs energy at 1280 K,

$$\Delta_r S^\ominus = (\Delta_r G^\ominus - \Delta_r H^\ominus)/T$$
$$= \{(+33\times 10^3\text{J mol}^{-1}) - (+224\times 10^3\text{J mol}^{-1})\}/1280\ \text{K} = +149\ \text{J K}^{-1}\text{mol}^{-1}$$

Consequently the temperature at which the reaction becomes spontaneous is given by

$$T = \frac{\overbrace{+224\times 10^3\text{J mol}^{-1}}^{\Delta_r H^\ominus}}{\underbrace{+149\ \text{J K}^{-1}\text{mol}^{-1}}_{\Delta_r S^\ominus}} = \mathbf{1500\ K}$$

**E7.18** In each case, we calculate $\Delta_r S^\ominus$ and $\Delta_r H^\ominus$ from information found in the text *Data section* and then calculate $\Delta_r G^\ominus$ from $\Delta_r G^\ominus = \Delta_r H^\ominus - T\Delta_r S^\ominus$.

(a)

$$\Delta_r S^\ominus = \{94.6 - (186.91 + 192.45)\}\ \text{J K}^{-1}\text{mol}^{-1} = -284.8\ \text{J K}^{-1}\text{mol}^{-1}$$
$$\Delta_r H^\ominus = \{-314.43 - (-92.31 - 46.11)\}\ \text{kJ mol}^{-1} = -176.01\ \text{kJ mol}^{-1}$$

$$\Delta_r G^\ominus = (-176.01\times 10^3\ \text{J mol}^{-1}) - \{(298\ \text{K})\times(-284.8\ \text{J K}^{-1}\text{mol}^{-1})\}$$
$$= -91.14\times 10^3\ \text{J mol}^{-1} = \mathbf{-91.14\ kJ\ mol^{-1}}$$

(b)

$$\Delta_r S^\ominus = [\{(4\times 28.33) + (3\times 41.84)\} - \{(2\times 50.92) + (3\times 18.83)\}]\ \text{J K}^{-1}\text{mol}^{-1}$$
$$= +80.51\ \text{J K}^{-1}\text{mol}^{-1}$$
$$\Delta_r H^\ominus = [\{(4\times 0) + (3\times -910.93)\} - \{(2\times 0) + (2\times -1675.7)\}]\ \text{kJ mol}^{-1}$$
$$= +618.6\ \text{kJ mol}^{-1}$$

$$\Delta_r G^\ominus = (+618.6 \times 10^3\ \text{J mol}^{-1}) - \{(298\ \text{K}) \times (+80.51\ \text{J K}^{-1}\text{mol}^{-1})\}$$
$$= +594.6 \times 10^3\ \text{J mol}^{-1} = \mathbf{+594.6\ kJ\ mol^{-1}}$$

(c)

$$\Delta_r S^\ominus = \{(60.29 + 130.684) - (27.28 + 205.79)\}\ \text{J K}^{-1}\text{mol}^{-1}$$
$$= -42.10\ \text{J K}^{-1}\text{mol}^{-1}$$
$$\Delta_r H^\ominus = \{(-100.0 + 0) - (0 - 20.63)\}\ \text{kJ mol}^{-1}$$
$$= -79.5\ \text{kJ mol}^{-1}$$

$$\Delta_r G^\ominus = (-79.5 \times 10^3\ \text{J mol}^{-1}) - \{(298\ \text{K}) \times (-42.10\ \text{J K}^{-1}\text{mol}^{-1})\}$$
$$= -66.8 \times 10^3\ \text{J mol}^{-1} = \mathbf{-66.8\ kJ\ mol^{-1}}$$

(d)

$$\Delta_r S^\ominus = [\{27.28 + (2 \times 205.79)\} - \{52.93 + (2 \times 130.684)\}]\ \text{J K}^{-1}\text{mol}^{-1}$$
$$= +124.56\ \text{J K}^{-1}\text{mol}^{-1}$$
$$\Delta_r H^\ominus = \{0 + (2 \times -20.63)\} - \{-178.2 + (2 \times 0)\}\ \text{kJ mol}^{-1}$$
$$= +136.9\ \text{kJ mol}^{-1}$$

$$\Delta_r G^\ominus = (+136.9 \times 10^3\ \text{J mol}^{-1}) - \{(298\ \text{K}) \times (+124.56\ \text{J K}^{-1}\text{mol}^{-1})\}$$
$$= +99.8 \times 10^3\ \text{J mol}^{-1} = \mathbf{+99.8\ kJ\ mol^{-1}}$$

(e)

$$\Delta_r S^\ominus = [\{156.9 + (2 \times 130.684)\} - \{205.79 + (2 \times 109.6)\}]\ \text{J K}^{-1}\text{mol}^{-1}$$
$$= -6.7\ \text{J K}^{-1}\text{mol}^{-1}$$
$$\Delta_r H^\ominus = \{-813.99 + (2 \times -187.78)\} - \{-20.63 + (2 \times 0)\}\ \text{kJ mol}^{-1}$$
$$= -417.80\ \text{kJ mol}^{-1}$$

$$\Delta_r G^\ominus = (-417.80 \times 10^3\ \text{J mol}^{-1}) - \{(298\ \text{K}) \times (-6.7\ \text{J K}^{-1}\text{mol}^{-1})\}$$
$$= -415.80 \times 10^3\ \text{J mol}^{-1} = \mathbf{-415.80\ kJ\ mol^{-1}}$$

**E7.19** In each case, we may use eqn 7.10,

$$\Delta_r G^\ominus = \sum \nu\Delta_f G^\ominus(\text{products}) - \sum \nu\Delta_f G^\ominus(\text{reactants})$$

to calculate the standard reaction Gibbs energy from the standard Gibbs energies of formation of the various products and reactants found in the text *Data section*. Reactions for which $\Delta_r G^\ominus < 0$ are spontaneous, and have $K > 1$.

(a)

$$\Delta_r G^\ominus = 2\ \Delta_f G^\ominus(CH_3COOH, l) - 2\ \Delta_f G^\ominus(CH_3CHO, g)$$
$$= \{(2 \times -889.9) - (2 \times -128.66)\}\ \text{kJ mol}^{-1} = -522.1\ \text{kJ mol}^{-1}$$

$\Delta_r G^\ominus < 0$, and therefore $\boldsymbol{K > 1}$.

(b)

$$\begin{aligned}\Delta_r G^\ominus &= \{2\,\Delta_f G^\ominus(\text{AgBr, s}) + \Delta_f G^\ominus(\text{Cl}_2,\text{g})\} - \{2\,\Delta_f G^\ominus(\text{AgCl, s}) + \Delta_f G^\ominus(\text{Br}_2,\text{g})\}\\ &= \{(2\times -96.90) + 0\} - \{(2\times -109.79) + 0\}\ \text{kJ mol}^{-1} = +25.78\ \text{kJ mol}^{-1}\end{aligned}$$

$\Delta_r G^\ominus > 0$, and therefore $\boldsymbol{K < 1}$.

(c)

$$\begin{aligned}\Delta_r G^\ominus &= \{\Delta_f G^\ominus(\text{HgCl}_2,\text{s})\} - \{\Delta_f G^\ominus(\text{Hg, l}) + \Delta_f G^\ominus(\text{Cl}_2,\text{g})\}\\ &= \{-178.6 - (0+0)\}\ \text{kJ mol}^{-1} = -178.6\ \text{kJ mol}^{-1}\end{aligned}$$

$\Delta_r G^\ominus < 0$, and therefore $\boldsymbol{K > 1}$.

(d)

$$\begin{aligned}\Delta_r G^\ominus &= \{\Delta_f G^\ominus(\text{Zn}^{2+},\text{aq}) + \Delta_f G^\ominus(\text{Cu, s})\} - \{\Delta_f G^\ominus(\text{Cu}^{2+},\text{aq}) + \Delta_f G^\ominus(\text{Zn, s})\}\\ &= \{(-147.06 + 0) - (65.49 + 0)\}\ \text{kJ mol}^{-1} = -212.55\ \text{kJ mol}^{-1}\end{aligned}$$

$\Delta_r G^\ominus < 0$, and therefore $\boldsymbol{K > 1}$.

(e)

$$\begin{aligned}\Delta_r G^\ominus &= \{12\Delta_f G^\ominus(\text{CO}_2,\text{g}) + 11\Delta_f G^\ominus(\text{H}_2\text{O, l})\}\\ &\qquad -\{\Delta_f G^\ominus(\text{C}_{12}\text{H}_{22}\text{O}_{11},\text{s}) + 12\Delta_f G^\ominus(\text{O}_2,\text{g})\}\\ &= \{(12\times -394.36) + (11\times -237.13)\} - \{-1543 + (12\times 0)\}\ \text{kJ mol}^{-1}\\ &= -5798\ \text{kJ mol}^{-1}\end{aligned}$$

$\Delta_r G^\ominus < 0$, and therefore $\boldsymbol{K > 1}$.

**E7.20** To calculate the standard Gibbs energy of formation, we need to calculate the standard entropy of formation and the standard enthalpy of formation and use eqn 4.16, $\Delta_f G^\ominus = \Delta_f H^\ominus - T\Delta_f S^\ominus$. The balanced equation for the formation reaction is

$$6\,\text{C(s)} + 3\,\text{H}_2\text{(g)} + \tfrac{1}{2}\,\text{O}_2\text{(g)} \rightarrow \text{C}_6\text{H}_5\text{OH(s)}$$

The standard entropy of formation follows from eqn 4.13, with values taken from the *Data section*,

$$\begin{aligned}\Delta_r S^\ominus &= \sum \nu S_m^\ominus(\text{products}) - \sum \nu S_m^\ominus(\text{reactants})\\ &= S_m^\ominus(\text{C}_6\text{H}_5\text{OH, s}) - \{6\,S_m^\ominus(\text{C, graphite}) + 3\,S_m^\ominus(\text{H}_2,\text{g}) + \tfrac{1}{2}\,S_m^\ominus(\text{O}_2,\text{g})\}\\ &= \{144.0 - (6\times 5.740 - 3\times 130.68 - \tfrac{1}{2}\times 205.15)\}\ \text{J K}^{-1}\text{mol}^{-1}\\ &= -385.05\ \text{J K}^{-1}\text{mol}^{-1}\end{aligned}$$

In the same way, from eqn 3.5,

$$\begin{aligned}\Delta_r H^\ominus &= \sum \nu\Delta_c H^\ominus(\text{products}) - \sum \nu\Delta_c H^\ominus(\text{reactants})\\ &= \Delta_c H^\ominus(\text{C}_6\text{H}_5\text{OH, s})\\ &\qquad - \{6\,\Delta_c H^\ominus(\text{C, graphite}) + 3\,\Delta_c H^\ominus(\text{H}_2,\text{g}) + \tfrac{1}{2}\,\Delta_c H^\ominus(\text{O}_2,\text{g})\}\end{aligned}$$

We may express the unknown enthalpies of combustion in terms of known enthalpies of formation. For example, the combustion reaction

$$C(s) + O_2(g) \rightarrow CO_2(g)$$

is equivalent to the formation of $CO_2(g)$, so that $\Delta_c H^\ominus(\text{C,graphite}) = \Delta_f H^\ominus(CO_2,g)$. In the same way, we may show that $\Delta_c H^\ominus(H_2,g) = \Delta_f H^\ominus(H_2O,l)$. By definition, $\Delta_c H^\ominus(O_2, g) = 0$. Thus,

$$\begin{aligned}\Delta_r H^\ominus &= \Delta_c H^\ominus(C_6H_5OH,s) - \{6\,\Delta_f H^\ominus(CO_2,g) + 3\,\Delta_f H^\ominus(H_2O,l)\} \\ &= -3054 - \{(6\times -393.51) + (3\times -285.83)\}\ \text{kJ mol}^{-1} \\ &= -164.55\ \text{kJ mol}^{-1}\end{aligned}$$

Hence, combining these two values,

$$\begin{aligned}\Delta_r G^\ominus &= -164.55\times 10^3\ \text{J mol}^{-1} - \{(298\ \text{K})\times(-385.05\ \text{J K}^{-1}\text{mol}^{-1})\} \\ &= -49.8\times 10^3\text{J mol}^{-1} = \mathbf{-49.8\ kJ\ mol^{-1}}\end{aligned}$$

**E7.21** The balanced equation for the hydrolysis of ATP is

$$\text{ATP(aq)} + H_2O(l) \rightarrow \text{ADP(aq)} + P_i^-(aq) + H^+(aq)$$

We may calculate the reaction Gibbs energy for any composition, using eqn 7.6,

$$\Delta_r G = \Delta_r G^\ominus + RT\ln Q$$

For the biological standard state, the activity of $H^+$ is $a_{H^+} = 10^{-pH} = 10^{-7}$, and the activities of all other components are 1. Thus,

$$\begin{aligned}\Delta_r G^\oplus &= \Delta_r G^\ominus + RT\ln\frac{\overbrace{a_{\text{ADP(aq)}}}^{1}\,\overbrace{a_{P_i^-(aq)}}^{1}\,\overbrace{a_{H^+(aq)}}^{10^{-7}}}{\underbrace{a_{\text{ATP(aq)}}}_{1}\,\underbrace{a_{H_2O(l)}}_{1}} = \Delta_r G^\ominus + RT\ln a_{H^+(aq)} \\ &= +10\times 10^3\ \text{J mol}^{-1} + \{(8.3145\ \text{J K}^{-1}\text{mol}^{-1})\times(298\ \text{K})\times\ln 10^{-7}\} \\ &= -30\times 10^3\ \text{J mol}^{-1} = \mathbf{-30\ kJ\ mol^{-1}}\end{aligned}$$

**E7.22** Applying eqn 7.6,

$$\Delta_r G = \Delta_r G^\ominus + RT\ln Q$$

and noting that for the biological standard state, the activity of $H^+$ is $a_{H^+} = 10^{-pH} = 10^{-7}$, and the activities of all other components are 1,

$$\begin{aligned}\Delta_r G^\oplus &= \Delta_r G^\ominus + RT\ln\frac{\overbrace{a_{\text{lactate}^-(aq)}}^{1}\,\overbrace{a_{\text{NAD}^+(aq)}}^{1}}{\underbrace{a_{\text{pyruvate}^-(aq)}}_{1}\,\underbrace{a_{\text{NADH(aq)}}}_{1}\,\underbrace{a_{H^+(aq)}}_{10^{-7}}} \\ &= \Delta_r G^\ominus + RT\ln\left(1/a_{H^+(aq)}\right) = \Delta_r G^\ominus - RT\ln a_{H^+(aq)} \\ &= -66.6\times 10^3\text{J mol}^{-1} - \{(8.3145\ \text{J K}^{-1}\text{mol}^{-1})\times(310\ \text{K})\times\ln 10^{-7}\} \\ &= -25.1\times 10^3\text{J mol}^{-1} = \mathbf{-25.1\ kJ\ mol^{-1}}\end{aligned}$$

**E7.23** The balanced equation for the reaction is

$$\mathrm{AMP(aq) + H_2O(l) \rightarrow A(aq) + P_i^-(aq) + H^+(aq)}$$

Denoting $Q^{\oplus}$ as the reaction quotient for the biological standard state defined with pH = 7, so that $a_{\mathrm{H^+}} = 10^{-\mathrm{pH}} = 10^{-7}$, and all other activities are 1, then, rearranging eqn 7.6, $\Delta_r G = \Delta_r G^{\ominus} + RT \ln Q$,

$$\begin{aligned}
\Delta_r G^{\ominus} &= \Delta_r G^{\oplus} - RT \ln Q^{\oplus} \\
&= \Delta_r G^{\oplus} - RT \ln \frac{\overbrace{a_{\mathrm{A(aq)}}}^{1}\,\overbrace{a_{\mathrm{P_i^-(aq)}}}^{1}\,\overbrace{a_{\mathrm{H^+(aq)}}}^{10^{-7}}}{\underbrace{a_{\mathrm{AMP(aq)}}}_{1}\,\underbrace{a_{\mathrm{H_2O(l)}}}_{1}} \\
&= \Delta_r G^{\oplus} - RT \ln a_{\mathrm{H^+}} \\
&= -14 \times 10^3\ \mathrm{J\ mol^{-1}} - \{(8.3145\ \mathrm{J\ K^{-1} mol^{-1}}) \times (298\ \mathrm{K}) \times \ln 10^{-7}\} \\
&= +26 \times 10^3 \mathrm{J\ mol^{-1}} = \mathbf{+26\ kJ\ mol^{-1}}
\end{aligned}$$

**E7.24** Rearranging,

$$\begin{aligned}
\Delta_r G^{\ominus} &= \Delta_r G^{\oplus} - RT \ln Q^{\oplus} \\
&= \Delta_r G^{\oplus} - RT \ln \frac{\overbrace{a^2_{\mathrm{CH_3COCO_2^-(aq)}}}^{1}\,\overbrace{a^2_{\mathrm{ATP(aq)}}}^{1}\,\overbrace{a^2_{\mathrm{NADH(aq)}}}^{1}\,\overbrace{a^2_{\mathrm{H^+(aq)}}}^{10^{-7}}}{\underbrace{a_{\mathrm{glucose(aq)}}}_{1}\,\underbrace{a^2_{\mathrm{NAD^+(aq)}}}_{1}\,\underbrace{a^2_{\mathrm{ADP(aq)}}}_{1}\,\underbrace{a^2_{\mathrm{P_i^-(aq)}}}_{1}\,\underbrace{a^2_{\mathrm{H_2O(aq)}}}_{1}} \\
&= \Delta_r G^{\oplus} - RT \ln a_{\mathrm{H^+}}{}^2 = \Delta_r G^{\oplus} - 2RT \ln 10^{-7} \\
&= -80.6 \times 10^3\ \mathrm{J\ mol^{-1}} - \{2 \times (8.3145\ \mathrm{J\ K^{-1} mol^{-1}}) \times (298\ \mathrm{K}) \times \ln 10^{-7}\} \\
&= -0.7 \times 10^3 \mathrm{J\ mol^{-1}} = \mathbf{-0.7\ kJ\ mol^{-1}}
\end{aligned}$$

**E7.25** For the equilibrium,

$$\mathrm{G6P \rightarrow F6P}$$

the reaction quotient may be written

$$Q = \frac{a_{\mathrm{F6P}}}{a_{\mathrm{G6P}}} = \frac{[\mathrm{F6P}]/c^{\ominus}}{[\mathrm{G6P}]/c^{\ominus}} = \frac{[\mathrm{F6P}]}{[\mathrm{G6P}]}$$

The fraction of F6P in solution is thus

$$f = \frac{[\mathrm{F6P}]}{[\mathrm{F6P}] + [\mathrm{G6P}]} = \frac{([\mathrm{F6P}]/[\mathrm{G6P}])}{([\mathrm{F6P}]/[\mathrm{G6P}]) + 1} = \frac{Q}{Q+1}$$

Rearranging gives

$$Q = \frac{1}{1-f}$$

Thus, from eqn 7.6,

$$\begin{aligned}
\Delta_r G &= \Delta_r G^{\ominus} + RT \ln Q \\
&= 1.7 \times 10^3\ \mathrm{J\ mol^{-1}} + [(8.3145\ \mathrm{J\ K^{-1} mol^{-1}}) \times (298\ \mathrm{K}) \times \ln\{1/(1-f)\}]
\end{aligned}$$

Figure 7.1 gives a plot of $\Delta_r G$ against $f$. When $\Delta_r G < 0$, the forward reaction proceeds spontaneously until $\Delta_r G = 0$ at the equilibrium value of $f$, i.e., $f_{eq} = 0.33$ (*Example 7.2*). When $\Delta_r G > 0$, the backward reaction proceeds spontaneously until $\Delta_r G = 0$ at the equilibrium value of $f$.

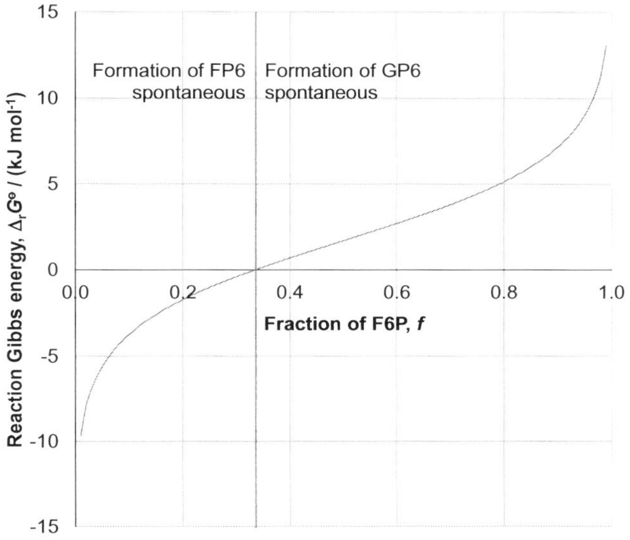


**Figure 7.1**

**E7.26** Let B and I denote borneol and isoborneol, respectively. For the reaction

$$B(g) \rightarrow I(g)$$

we may express the equilibrium constant as $K = a_I/a_B$. If we assume that both components may be treated as perfect gases, so that the activity may be expressed in terms of the partial pressure, $a_J = p_J/p^{\ominus}$, then

$$K = \frac{a_I}{a_B} = \frac{(p_I/p^{\ominus})}{(p_B/p^{\ominus})} = \frac{p_I}{p_B} = \frac{x_I p}{x_B p} = \frac{x_I}{1 - x_I}$$

Rearranging, for the mole fraction of isoborneol, $x_I$,

$$x_I = \frac{K}{1+K} = \frac{0.106}{1 + 0.106} = \mathbf{0.0958}$$
$$x_B = 1 - x_I = 1 - 0.0958 = \mathbf{0.9042}$$

**E7.27** We may write the balanced equation for the formation of $NH_3$ from $N_2$ and $H_2$ in many ways, with different multiples of the stoichiometric coefficients. Following the approach adopted in Example 7.3, and writing

$$3\,H_2(g) + N_2(g) \rightleftharpoons 2\,NH_3(g)$$

we may draw up an equilibrium table

| | $N_2(g)$ | $H_2(g)$ | $NH_3(g)$ |
|---|---|---|---|
| **Initial partial pressure / bar** | 1.00 | 4.00 | 0 |
| **Change in pressure / bar** | $-x$ | $-3x$ | $+2x$ |
| **Equilibrium partial pressure / bar** | $1.00 - x$ | $4.00 - 3x$ | $2x$ |

The equilibrium constant is thus

$$K = \frac{a_{NH_3(g)}^2}{a_{H_2(g)}^3 a_{N_2(g)}} = \frac{(p_{NH_3(g)}/p^{\ominus})^2}{(p_{H_2(g)}/p^{\ominus})^3 (p_{N_2(g)}/p^{\ominus})} = \frac{(2x)^2}{(4.00 - 3x)^3(1.00 - x)} = 89.8$$

In general, it is not possible to solve a fourth-order polynomial equation such as this algebraically. We may instead solve the equation using mathematical software, or by plotting a graph of the function and finding the roots. However, since $K >> 1$ we can estimate that the limiting reagent, which in this case is $N_2$, almost completely reacts. This means that $x \approx 1$, so that $(2x)^2 \approx 4$ and $(4.00 - 3x) \approx 1$, and therefore

$$\frac{(2x)^2}{(4.00 - 3x)^3(1.00 - x)} \approx \frac{4}{1^3(1.00 - x)} = 89.8$$

and so, rearranging,

$$x \approx (89.8 - 4)/89.8 = 0.955$$

We may now repeat this process to obtain a better estimate for $x$. Repeating this procedure until two successive iterations agree to within three significant figures, which is the precision to which the equilibrium constant is quoted, leads to $x = 0.967$. Thus,

$$\begin{aligned} p_{NH_3(g)} &= 2x\, p^{\ominus} = (2 \times 0.97)\text{ bar} = \mathbf{1.93\ bar} \\ p_{H_3(g)} &= (4.00 - 3x)\, p^{\ominus} = \{4.00 - (3 \times 0.97)\}\, p^{\ominus} = \mathbf{1.10\ bar} \\ p_{N_3(g)} &= (1.00 - x)\, p^{\ominus} = (1.00 - 0.97)\, p^{\ominus} = \mathbf{0.03\ bar} \end{aligned}$$

**E7.28** We may express the equilibrium constant for the reaction

$$SbCl_5(g) \rightleftharpoons SbCl_3(g) + Cl_2$$

in terms of partial pressures as

$$K = \frac{a_{SbCl_3(g)} a_{Cl_2(g)}}{a_{SbCl_5(g)}} = \frac{(p_{SbCl_3(g)}/p^{\ominus})(p_{Cl_2(g)}/p^{\ominus})}{(p_{SbCl_5(g)}/p^{\ominus})} = \frac{p_{SbCl_3(g)} p_{Cl_2(g)}}{p_{SbCl_5(g)} p^{\ominus}}$$

if we assume that all components may be treated as perfect gases so that the activity of each is given by the appropriate expression from Table 6.2, $a_J = p_J/p^{\ominus}$. Rearranging,

$$p_{Cl_2(g)} = K \frac{p_{SbCl_5(g)}}{p_{SbCl_3(g)}} p^{\ominus} = (3.5 \times 10^{-4}) \times \frac{0.17\text{ bar}}{0.22\text{ bar}} \times (1\text{ bar}) = \mathbf{2.7 \times 10^{-4}\ bar}$$

**E7.29** For the decomposition of $PCl_5$,

$$PCl_5(g) \rightleftharpoons PCl_3(g) + Cl_2(g)$$

the concentration of $PCl_3$ must be the same as the concentration of $Cl_2$, because the products are formed in equal amounts. Furthermore, if we denote the initial concentration of $PCl_5$ as $[PCl_5]_0$, then

$$[PCl_3] = [Cl_2] = ([PCl_5] - [PCl_5]_0)$$

Thus, the equilibrium constant may be expressed in terms of molar concentration as

$$K_c = \frac{[PCl_3][Cl_2]}{[PCl_5]} = \frac{([PCl_5] - [PCl_5]_0)^2}{[PCl_5]}$$

The initial concentration of $PCl_5$ is given by

$$[PCl_5]_0 = \frac{n_{PCl_5}}{V} = \frac{m_{PCl_5}}{M_{PCl_5}V}$$
$$= \frac{(1.5\text{ g})}{(208.24\text{ g mol}^{-1}) \times (250 \times 10^{-3}\text{ dm}^3)} = 0.029\text{ mol dm}^{-3}$$

This form of the equilibrium constant is related to the thermodynamic equilibrium constant, $K$, through eqn 7.13b. For this reaction, the difference between the stoichiometric coefficients of the gas-phase species, $\Delta\nu_{gas} = +1$ because for every molecule of gas that decomposes, two molecules of gas are formed. Thus, at 400 K, if

$$K = K_c \times \left(\frac{c^{\ominus}RT}{p^{\ominus}}\right)^{\Delta\nu_{gas}}$$

then

$$K_c = K \times \left(\frac{c^{\ominus}RT}{p^{\ominus}}\right)^{-\Delta\nu_{gas}}$$
$$= 0.36 \times \left\{\frac{(1\text{ mol dm}^{-3}) \times (8.3145\text{ J K}^{-1}\text{mol}^{-1}) \times (400\text{ K})}{(1\text{ bar})}\right\}^{-1}$$
$$= 0.0109$$

(a) Subsitituting these numerical values into the expression for $K_c$, and rearranging,

$$\frac{([PCl_5] - \overbrace{0.029}^{[PCl_5]_0})^2}{[PCl_5]} = 0.0109$$
$$[PCl_5]^2 - (2 \times 0.029 \times [PCl_5]) + 0.029^2 = 0.0109[PCl_5]$$
$$[PCl_5]^2 - [(2 \times 0.029) + 0.0109][PCl_5] + 8.30 \times 10^{-4} = 0$$
$$[PCl_5]^2 - 0.069[PCl_5] + 8.3 \times 10^{-4} = 0$$

This is a quadratic equation of the form $ax^2 + bx + c = 0$, with $a = 1$, $b = -0.069$ and $c = 8.3 \times 10^{-4}$, which has solutions, according to the method shown in *The chemist's toolkit 7.1*, of

$$
\begin{aligned}
[\mathrm{PCl_5}]/\mathrm{mol\ dm^{-3}} &= \frac{-b \pm \sqrt{b^2 - 4ac}}{2a} \\
&= \frac{0.069 \pm \sqrt{0.069^2 - 4 \times 1 \times 8.3 \times 10^{-4}}}{2 \times 1} \\
&= 0.016 \text{ or } 0.053
\end{aligned}
$$

We may disregard the second solution because this implies that the concentration of $PCl_5$at equilibrium is greater than the initial concentration. Thus,

$$
\begin{aligned}
[\mathrm{PCl_5}] &= \mathbf{0.016\ mol\ dm^{-3}} \\
[\mathrm{PCl_3}] = [\mathrm{Cl_2}] &= [\mathrm{PCl_5}]_0 - [\mathrm{PCl_5}] \\
&= (0.029 - 0.016)\ \mathrm{mol\ dm^{-3}} = \mathbf{0.013\ mol\ dm^{-3}}
\end{aligned}
$$

(b) The proportion decomposed is

$$
\frac{[\mathrm{PCl_5}]_0 - [\mathrm{PCl_5}]}{[\mathrm{PCl_5}]_0} = \frac{0.013\ \mathrm{mol\ dm^{-3}}}{0.029\ \mathrm{mol\ dm^{-3}}} = 0.45 \text{ or } \mathbf{45\ per\ cent}
$$

**E7.30** Following the approach adopted in Example 7.3 and Exercise 7.27, we may draw up an equilibrium table for the reaction

$$3\,\mathrm{H_2(g)} + \mathrm{N_2(g)} \rightleftharpoons 2\,\mathrm{NH_3(g)}$$

| | $N_2$(g) | $H_2$(g) | $NH_3$(g) |
|---|---|---|---|
| **Initial partial pressure / bar** | 0.020 | 0.020 | 0 |
| **Change in pressure / bar** | $-x$ | $-3x$ | $+2x$ |
| **Equilibrium partial pressure / bar** | $0.020 - x$ | $0.020 - 3x$ | $2x$ |

The equilibrium constant is thus

$$
\begin{aligned}
K &= \frac{a^2_{\mathrm{NH_3(g)}}}{a^3_{\mathrm{H_2(g)}} a_{\mathrm{N_2(g)}}} = \frac{\left(p_{\mathrm{NH_3(g)}}/p^{\ominus}\right)^2}{\left(p_{\mathrm{H_2(g)}}/p^{\ominus}\right)^3 \left(p_{\mathrm{N_2(g)}}/p^{\ominus}\right)} \\
&= \frac{(2x)^2}{(0.020 - x)^3(0.020 - 3x)} = \frac{(2x)^2}{(0.020 - x)^4} = 0.036
\end{aligned}
$$

Using the same iterative methods methods outlined in Exercise 7.27 leads to the solution $x = 3.8 \times 10^{-5}$. Thus, the extent of reaction is so small that the partial pressures of $H_2$ and $N_2$ remain effectively unchanged

$$
\begin{aligned}
p_{\mathrm{H_3(g)}} &= (0.20 - 3x)\, p^{\ominus} \approx \mathbf{0.20\ bar} \\
p_{\mathrm{N_3(g)}} &= (0.20 - x)\, p^{\ominus} \approx \mathbf{0.20\ bar}
\end{aligned}
$$

but

$$p_{NH_3(g)} = 2x\,p^{\ominus} = 2 \times (3.8 \times 10^{-5})\ \text{bar} = \mathbf{7.6 \times 10^{-5}\ bar}$$

**E7.31** We may write the balanced equation for the equilibrium between solid uranium hydride and solid uranium and $H_2$ gas as

$$UH_3(s) \rightleftharpoons U(s) + 3/2\ H_2(g)$$

The equilibrium constant is thus

$$K = \frac{a_{U(s)}a_{H_2(g)}^{3/2}}{a_{UH_3(s)}}$$

The activities of the solid uranium and uranium hydride are 1, and if we assume that the hydrogen behaves as a perfect gas, so that we may express the activity of hydrogen in terms of the partial pressure, then the equilibrium constant becomes

$$K = \left(p_{H_2(g)}/p^{\ominus}\right)^{3/2}$$

Using eqn 7.8,

$$\begin{aligned}\Delta_r G^{o} &= -RT\ln K \\ &= -RT\ln\left(p_{H_2(g)}/p^{\ominus}\right)^{3/2} = -(3/2)RT\ln\left(p_{H_2(g)}/p^{\ominus}\right) \\ &= -(3/2) \times (8.3145\ \text{J K}^{-1}\text{mol}^{-1}) \times (500\ \text{K}) \times \ln(1.04\ \text{Torr}/760\ \text{Torr}) \\ &= +41.1 \times 10^3\ \text{J mol}^{-1} = \mathbf{+41.1\ kJ\ mol^{-1}}\end{aligned}$$

**E7.32** The equilibrium constant expressed in terms of concentration is related to the thermodynamic equilibrium constant, $K$, through eqn 7.13b

$$K = K_c \times \left(\frac{c^{\ominus}RT}{p^{\ominus}}\right)^{\Delta\nu_{gas}}$$

For the reaction,

$$I_2(g) \rightarrow 2\ I(g)$$

the difference between the stoichiometric coefficients of the gas-phase species $\Delta\nu_{gas} = +1$ because for every molecule of $I_2$ gas that decomposes, two atoms of gaesous I atoms are formed. Thus, at 1000 K, rearranging eqn 7.13 and substituting,

$$\begin{aligned}K_c &= K \times \left(\frac{c^{\ominus}RT}{p^{\ominus}}\right)^{-\Delta\nu_{gas}} \\ &= 0.26 \times \left[\frac{\overbrace{(10^3\ \text{mol m}^{-3})}^{c^{\ominus}=1\ \text{mol dm}^{-3} = 10^3\ \text{mol m}^{-3}} \times (8.3145\ \text{J K}^{-1}\text{mol}^{-1}) \times (1000\ \text{K})}{\underbrace{10^5\ \text{Pa}}_{p^{\ominus} = 1\ \text{bar} = 10^5\ \text{Pa}}}\right]^{-1} \\ &= \mathbf{3.1 \times 10^{-3}}\end{aligned}$$

**E7.33** We may calculate the value of the equlibrium constant in terms of concentration from the standard reaction Gibbs energy by combining eqn 7.8

$$\Delta G^{\ominus} = -RT \ln K$$

which may be rewritten as

$$K = \mathrm{e}^{-\Delta_r G^{\ominus}/RT}$$

and eqn 7.13b,

$$K = K_c \times \left(\frac{c^{\ominus}RT}{p^{\ominus}}\right)^{\Delta\nu_{\mathrm{gas}}}$$

which is equivalent to

$$K_c = K \times \left(\frac{c^{\ominus}RT}{p^{\ominus}}\right)^{-\Delta\nu_{\mathrm{gas}}}$$

so that

$$K_c = \mathrm{e}^{-\Delta_r G^{\ominus}/RT} \times \left(\frac{c^{\ominus}RT}{p^{\ominus}}\right)^{-\Delta\nu_{\mathrm{gas}}}$$

For the reaction,

$$H_2(g) + \tfrac{1}{2}\,O_2(g) \rightarrow H_2O(l)$$

the difference between the stoichiometric coefficients of the gas-phase species $\Delta\nu_{\mathrm{gas}} = -3/2$. Thus, at 25 °C,

$$K_c = \mathrm{e}^{+237.13\times10^3\,\mathrm{J\,mol^{-1}}/\{(8.3145\,\mathrm{J\,K^{-1}mol^{-1}})\times(25+273.15)\mathrm{K}\}}$$
$$\times \left[\frac{(10^3\ \mathrm{mol\ m^{-3}}) \times (8.3145\ \mathrm{J\ K^{-1}mol^{-1}}) \times (25 + 273.15)\mathrm{K}}{10^5\ \mathrm{Pa}}\right]^{+3/2}$$
$$= \mathbf{4.53 \times 10^{43}}$$

**E7.34** Rearranging the van 't Hoff equation,

$$\ln K' = \ln K + \frac{\Delta_r H^{\ominus}}{R}\left(\frac{1}{T} - \frac{1}{T'}\right)$$

$$\overbrace{\ln(K'/K)}^{\ln x - \ln y = \ln(x/y)} = \frac{\Delta_r H^{\ominus}}{R}\left(\frac{T' - T}{TT'}\right)$$

$$\Delta_r H^{\ominus} = R\left(\frac{TT'}{T' - T}\right)\ln(K'/K)$$

(a) Thus, if the equilbrium constant doubles, so that $K'/K = 2$, when the temperature increases from $T = 298$ K to $T' = 308$ K,

$$\Delta_r H^{\ominus} = (8.3145\ \mathrm{J\ K^{-1}mol^{-1}}) \times \left\{\frac{(298\ \mathrm{K}) \times (308\ \mathrm{K})}{(308\ \mathrm{K}) - (298\ \mathrm{K})}\right\}\ln(2)$$
$$= 52.9 \times 10^3\ \mathrm{J\ mol^{-1}} = \mathbf{+52.9\ kJ\ mol^{-1}}$$

(b) If the equilibrium constant halves, so that $K'/K = ½$, we may state, without calculation, that

$$\Delta_r H^\ominus = \mathbf{-52.9\ kJ\ mol^{-1}}$$

because the van 't Hoff equation shows that the standard enthalpy of reaction is proportional to the logarithm of the ratio of the equilibrium constants and, from the rules for logarithms given in *The chemist's toolkit*, 2.2,

$$\ln(½) = \ln(2^{-1}) = -\ln(2)$$

**E7.35** For the reaction

$$NH_4Cl(s) \rightleftharpoons NH_3(g) + HCl(g)$$

the equilibrium constant is, from eqn 7.7

$$K = \frac{a_{NH_3(g)}a_{HCl(g)}}{a_{NH_4Cl(s)}} = (p_{NH_3(g)}/p^\ominus)(p_{HCl(g)}/p^\ominus)$$

where we have used the relationships in Table 6.2 to express the activity of the solid $NH_4Cl$, $a_J = 1$, and the activities of the gaseous $NH_3$ and HCl in terms of their partial pressures, $a_J = p_J / p^\ominus$.

(a) Writing the total pressure as $p$, because of the stoichiometry of the dissociation, $p_{NH_3} = p_{HCl} = ½p$, and so

$$K = (p/2p^\ominus)^2 = 1/4(p/p^\ominus)^2$$

At a temperature of 427 °C,

$$K = 1/4\{(608 \times 10^3\ \text{Pa})/(10^5\ \text{Pa})\}^2 = \mathbf{9.24}$$

(b) Using eqn 7.8, the standard reaction Gibbs energy at 427 °C, which is equivalent to 700 K, is

$$\begin{aligned}\Delta_r G^\ominus = -RT\ln K &= -(8.3145\ \text{J K}^{-1}\text{mol}^{-1}) \times (427 + 273.15)\ \text{K} \times \ln(9.24)\\ &= -12.9 \times 10^3\ \text{J mol}^{-1} = \mathbf{-12.9\ kJ\ mol^{-1}}\end{aligned}$$

(c) Rearranging the van 't Hoff equation, eqn 7.15, and substituting the expression for the equlibrium constant in terms of the total pressure,

$$\ln K' = \ln K + \frac{\Delta_r H^\ominus}{R}\left(\frac{1}{T} - \frac{1}{T'}\right)$$

$$\overbrace{\ln(K'/K)}^{\ln x - \ln y = \ln(x/y)} = \frac{\Delta_r H^\ominus}{R}\left(\frac{T' - T}{TT'}\right)$$

Thus,

$$\Delta_r H^{\ominus} = R\left(\frac{TT'}{T'-T}\right)\ln\left(\frac{\overbrace{K'}^{1/4(p'/p^{\ominus})^2}}{\underbrace{K}_{1/4(p/p^{\ominus})^2}}\right)$$

$$= R\left(\frac{TT'}{T'-T}\right)\ln(p'/p)^2$$

$$= (8.3145\ \mathrm{J\ K^{-1}mol^{-1}}) \times \left\{\frac{(700\ \mathrm{K}) \times (732\ \mathrm{K})}{(732\ \mathrm{K}) - (700\ \mathrm{K})}\right\} \times \ln\left(\frac{1115\ \mathrm{kPa}}{608\ \mathrm{kPa}}\right)^2$$

$$= \mathbf{+161\ kJ\ mol^{-1}}$$

(d) Rearranging eqn 7.11

$$\Delta_r S^{\ominus} = (\Delta_r H^{\ominus} - \Delta_r G^{\ominus})/T$$
$$= [\{161 - (-12.9)\} \times 10^3\ \mathrm{mol^{-1}}]/(700\ \mathrm{K}) = \mathbf{+248\ J\ K^{-1}mol^{-1}}$$

**E7.36** The van 't Hoff equation, eqn 7.15, may be rearranged into the form of a linear graph,

$$\ln K' = \ln K + \frac{\Delta_r H^{o}}{R}\left(\frac{1}{T} - \frac{1}{T'}\right)$$

$$\overbrace{\ln K'}^{y} = \overbrace{-\frac{\Delta_r H^{o}}{R}}^{\text{slope}} \times \overbrace{\frac{1}{T'}}^{x} + \overbrace{\left(\ln K - \frac{\Delta_r H^{o}}{RT}\right)}^{\text{intercept}}$$

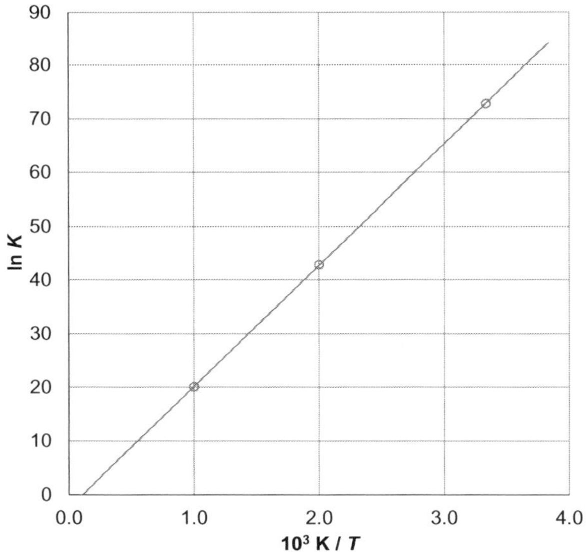


**Figure 7.2**

Figure 7.2 shows that for the data given, a graph of the log of the equilibrium constant against the reciprocal of temperature, is indeed a straight line, with a slope

$$m = -(\Delta_r H^{\ominus})/R = 22.585 \times 10^3 \text{ K}$$

Thus

$$\Delta_r H^{\ominus} = -mR = -(22.585 \times 10^3 \text{ K}) \times (8.3145 \text{ J K}^{-1}\text{mol}^{-1})$$
$$= -187.78 \times 10^3 \text{J mol}^{-1} = \mathbf{-187.78\ kJ\ mol^{-1}}$$

**E7.37** Denoting the equilibrium constant at 390 K as $K$ and at 410 K as $K'$

$$\ln K = -1.04 - \frac{1088 \text{ K}}{390 \text{ K}} + \frac{1.51 \times 10^{-2}\text{K}^2}{(390 \text{ K})^2} = -2.84$$
$$\ln K' = -1.04 - \frac{1088 \text{ K}}{410 \text{ K}} + \frac{1.51 \times 10^{-2}\text{K}^2}{(410 \text{ K})^2} = -2.80$$

Rearranging the van 't Hoff equation, eqn 7.15, and substituting,

$$\ln K' = \ln K + \frac{\Delta_r H^{\ominus}}{R}\left(\frac{1}{T} - \frac{1}{T'}\right)$$
$$\ln K' - \ln K = \frac{\Delta_r H^{\ominus}}{R}\left(\frac{T' - T}{TT'}\right)$$
$$\Delta_r H^{\ominus} = R\left(\frac{TT'}{T' - T}\right)\{\ln K' - \ln K\}$$
$$= (8.3145 \text{ J K}^{-1}\text{mol}^{-1}) \times \left\{\frac{(390 \text{ K}) \times (410 \text{ K})}{(410 \text{ K}) - (390 \text{ K})}\right\}$$
$$\times \{(-2.80) - (-2.84)\}$$
$$= +2.66 \times 10^3 \text{J mol}^{-1} = +2.66 \text{ kJ mol}^{-1}$$

But, from eqn 7.8, the standard reaction Gibbs energy at 400 K is

$$\Delta_r G^{\ominus} = -RT \ln K = -RT \times \left\{-1.04 - \frac{1088 \text{ K}}{T} + \frac{1.51 \times 10^{-2}\text{K}^2}{T^2}\right\}$$
$$= \left\{1.04\, T + 1088 \text{ K} - \frac{1.51 \times 10^{-2}\text{K}^2}{T}\right\} R$$
$$= \left\{(1.04 \times 400 \text{ K}) + 1088 \text{ K} - \frac{1.51 \times 10^{-2}\text{K}^2}{400 \text{ K}}\right\} \times (8.3145 \text{ J K}^{-1}\text{mol}^{-1})$$
$$= +9.36 \times 10^3 \text{ J mol}^{-1} = +9.36 \text{ kJ mol}^{-1}$$

Thus, rearranging eqn 7.11,

$$\Delta_r S^{\ominus} = (\Delta_r H^{\ominus} - \Delta_r G^{\ominus})/T$$
$$= \{(2.66 - 9.36) \times 10^3 \text{ mol}^{-1}\}/(400 \text{ K}) = \mathbf{-16.8\ J\ K^{-1}mol^{-1}}$$

**E7.38** For the reaction

$$N_2O_4(g) \rightleftharpoons 2\ NO_2(g)$$

if we assume that both components behave as perfect gases, so that their activities may be expressed in terms of partial pressures using the expression in Table 6.2, $a_J = p_J / p^{\ominus}$, then the equilibrium constant may be expressed as

$$K = \frac{a^2_{NO_2(g)}}{a_{N_2O_4(g)}} = \frac{\left(p_{NO_2(g)}/p^{\ominus}\right)^2}{\left(p_{N_2O_4(g)}/p^{\ominus}\right)} = \frac{p^2_{NO_2(g)}}{p_{N_2O_4(g)}} \times \frac{1}{p^{\ominus}}$$

Expressing the partial pressure in terms of the mole fraction and total pressure, using eqn 1.9, $p_J = x_J p$ then

$$K = \frac{x^2_{NO_2(g)}}{x_{N_2O_4(g)}} \times \frac{p}{p^{\ominus}}$$

If $\alpha$ is the fraction of $N_2O_4$ molecules that dissociate as equilibrium is established, then if the initial amount of $N_2O_4$ is $n_0$ the, amounts of the components at equilibrium are

$$n_{N_2O_4(g)} = (1-\alpha)n_0$$
$$n_{NO_2(g)} = 2\alpha n_0$$

so that the total amount is

$$n_{total} = n_{N_2O_4(g)} + n_{NO_2(g)} = (1-\alpha)n_0 + 2\alpha n_0 = (1+\alpha)n_0$$

giving mole fractions

$$x_{N_2O_4(g)} = \frac{n_{N_2O_4(g)}}{n_{total}} = \frac{(1-\alpha)n_0}{(1+\alpha)n_0} = \frac{(1-\alpha)}{(1+\alpha)}$$

$$x_{NO_2(g)} = \frac{n_{NO_2(g)}}{n_{total}} = \frac{2\alpha n_0}{(1+\alpha)n_0} = \frac{2\alpha}{(1+\alpha)}$$

Substituting into the expression for the equilibrium constant,

$$K = \frac{\{2\alpha/(1+\alpha)\}^2}{\{(1-\alpha)/(1+\alpha)\}} \times \frac{p}{p^{\ominus}} = \frac{4\alpha^2}{(1-\alpha)(1+\alpha)} \times \frac{p}{p^{\ominus}} = \boldsymbol{\frac{4\alpha^2}{1-\alpha^2} \times \frac{p}{p^{\ominus}}}$$

If $\alpha \ll 1$, then 1 - $\alpha^2 \ll 1$, so that

$$K \approx 4\alpha^2 \times \frac{p}{p^{\ominus}}$$

Rearranging,

$$\alpha \approx (Kp^{\ominus}/4p)^{1/2}$$

demonstrating that under these conditions, $\alpha \propto p^{-1/2}$.

# Answers to projects

**P7.39** (a) For the dissociation of $I_2$,

$$I_2(g) \rightleftharpoons 2\ I(g)$$

the equilibrium constant may be expressed as

$$K = \frac{a_{I(g)}^2}{a_{I_2(g)}} = \frac{(p_{I(g)}/p^{\ominus})^2}{(p_{I_2(g)}/p^{\ominus})} = \frac{p_{I(g)}^2}{p_{I_2(g)}} \times \frac{1}{p^{\ominus}}$$

where we have assumed that the components behave as perfect gases so that their activities may be expressed in terms of the partial pressures, $a_J = p_J / p^{\ominus}$, according to Table 6.2. The partial pressures are related to the mole fractions and the total pressure through eqn 1.9, $p_J = x_J p$, so that we may write

$$K = \frac{x_{I(g)}^2}{x_{I_2(g)}} \times \frac{p}{p^{\ominus}} = \frac{x_{I(g)}^2}{x_{I_2(g)}} \times \frac{p}{p^{\ominus}}$$

Denoting the degree of dissociation as $\alpha$, and the initial amount of $I_2$ molecules as $n_0$, then the amounts of the two components at equilibrium are

$$n_{I_2(g)} = (1-\alpha)n_0$$
$$n_{I(g)} = 2\alpha n_0$$

so that the total amount of molecules is

$$n_{\text{total}} = n_{I_2(g)} + n_{I(g)} = (1-\alpha)n_0 + 2\alpha n_0 = (1+\alpha)n_0$$

The corresponding mole fractions are given by

$$x_{I_2(g)} = n_{I_2(g)}/n_{\text{total}} = (1-\alpha)n_0/(1+\alpha)n_0 = (1-\alpha)/(1+\alpha)$$
$$x_{I(g)} = n_{I(g)}/n_{\text{total}} = 2\alpha n_0/(1+\alpha)n_0 = 2\alpha/(1+\alpha)$$

and the total pressure, using the perfect gas equation, eqn 1.2a, by

$$p = n_{\text{total}}RT/V = (1+\alpha)n_0RT/V$$

The initial amount of iodine is

$$n_{I_2(g)} = m_{I_2(g)}/M_{I_2(g)}$$

The degree of dissociation at equilibrium is given by the difference in the mass of $I_2$ initially and at equlibrium

$$\alpha = (m_{I_2(g),0} - m_{I_2(g),\text{eq}})/m_{I_2(g),0} = (1.000\text{ g} - 0.830\text{ g})\,/(1.000\text{ g}) = 0.170$$

Substituting,

$$K = \frac{\{2\alpha/(1+\alpha)\}^2}{(1-\alpha)/(1+\alpha)} \times \frac{(1+\alpha)n_0RT/V}{p^{\ominus}} = \frac{4\alpha^2}{1-\alpha} \times \frac{n_0RT}{p^{\ominus}V}$$

$$= \frac{4\alpha^2}{1-\alpha} \times \frac{m_{I_2(g)}}{M_{I_2(g)}} \times \frac{RT}{p^{\ominus}V}$$

$$= \frac{4 \times 0.170^2}{(1-0.170)} \times \frac{1.00\text{ g}}{253.8\text{ g mol}^{-1}} \times \frac{(8.3145\text{ J K}^{-1}\text{mol}^{-1}) \times (1000\text{ K})}{(10^5\text{ Pa}) \times \underbrace{(1.00 \times 10^{-3}\text{ m}^3)}_{1\text{ dm}^3 = 10^{-3}\text{m}^3}}$$

$$= \mathbf{0.0456}$$

(c) The equilibrium constant expressed in terms of concentration, $K_c$, is related to the thermodynamic equilibrium constant through eqn 7.13b

$$K = K_c \times \left(\frac{c^{\ominus}RT}{p^{\ominus}}\right)^{\Delta\nu_{\text{gas}}}$$

Thus, using the rules for manipulation of logarithms given in *The chemist's toolkit 2.2*,

$$\begin{aligned}\ln K &= \ln(K_c(c^{\ominus}RT/p^{\ominus})^{\Delta\nu_{\text{gas}}}) = \ln K_c + \ln(c^{\ominus}RT/p^{\ominus})^{\Delta\nu_{\text{gas}}} \\ &= \ln K_c + \Delta\nu_{\text{gas}}\ln(c^{\ominus}RT/p^{\ominus}) \quad = \ln K_c + \Delta\nu_{\text{gas}}\ln T + \Delta\nu_{\text{gas}}\ln(c^{\ominus}R/p^{\ominus})\end{aligned}$$

and using the thermodynamically exact form of the van 't Hoff equation,

$$\frac{\text{d}}{\text{d}T}\overbrace{\{\ln K_c + \Delta\nu_{\text{gas}}\ln T + \Delta\nu_{\text{gas}}\ln(c^{\ominus}R/p^{\ominus})\}}^{\ln K} = -\frac{\Delta_r H^{\ominus}}{RT^2}$$

$$\frac{\text{d}(\ln K_c)}{\text{d}T} + \Delta\nu_{\text{gas}}\overbrace{\frac{\text{d}}{\text{d}T}\ln T}^{1/T} + \overbrace{\frac{\text{d}}{\text{d}T}\Delta\nu_{\text{gas}}\ln(c^{\ominus}R/p^{\ominus})}^{0} = -\frac{\Delta_r H^{\ominus}}{RT^2}$$

$$\frac{\text{d}(\ln K_c)}{\text{d}T} = -\boldsymbol{\frac{\Delta_r H^{\ominus}}{RT^2} - \frac{\Delta\nu_{\text{gas}}}{T}}$$

**P7.40** (a) In order to calculate the fractional saturation at the required pressure, we need to know the value of the constant $K$ in the Hill equation. $K$ can be determined approximately from the figure shown in the Box. For $s = 0.5$, $p = p_{50}$ where $p_{50}$ is the pressure of $O_2$ at 50% saturation. Thus,

$$\begin{aligned}\log\frac{s}{1-s} &= \nu\log p - \nu\log K \\ \log\frac{0.5}{1-0.5} &= \nu\log p_{50} - \nu\log K \\ \log(0.5/0.5) &= \nu\log p_{50} - \nu\log K \\ 0 &= \nu\log p_{50} - \nu\log K\end{aligned}$$

It follows that

$$K = p_{50}$$

From the graph we estimate that for haemoglobin, $p_{50} = K =$ **30 Torr**, which is equivalent to **3.9 kPa**; for myoglobin, $p_{50} = K =$ **5 Torr**, which is equivalent to **0.66 kPa**. Rearranging the Hill equation we obtain

$$\log\frac{s}{1-s} = \nu\log(p/K)$$

$$\frac{s}{1-s} = \left(\frac{p}{K}\right)^{v}$$

$$s = \frac{(p/K)^{v}}{1+(p/K)^{v}}$$

$$s = \frac{1}{(K/p)^{v}+1}$$

Then, using the appropriate values for $K$ and $v$ for Hb and Mb, we obtain

| | **$p$ / kPa** | **1.0** | **1.5** | **2.0** | **4.0** | **8.0** |
|---|---|---|---|---|---|---|
| **Hb $v = 2.8$** | **$s / 10^6$** | 0.054 | 0.167 | 0.698 | 2.60 | 18.1 |
| **Mb $v = 1$** | **$s$** | 0.015 | 0.022 | 0.037 | 0.057 | 0.109 |

(b) In the same way, using $v = 4$,

| | **$p$ / kPa** | **1.0** | **1.5** | **2.0** | **4.0** | **8.0** |
|---|---|---|---|---|---|---|
| **Hb $v = 4$** | **$s / 10^6$** | 0.000 | 0.000 | 0.002 | 0.011 | 0.168 |
| **Mb $v = 4$** | **$s / 10^6$** | 0.054 | 0.272 | 2.10 | 13.7 | 220 |

# Chapter 8

# Chemical equilibria: solutions

## Answers to discussion questions

**D8.1** (a) Figure 8.4 of the text illustrates the typical pH curve for the titration of a weak acid with a strong base. Prior to reaching the stoichiometric point, when titrant volumes are small, the slope of the curve is positive but of small magnitude and an important inflection point is observed, which characterizes the p$K_a$ of the weak acid. pH changes are small in this region because HA can both neutralize titrant and dissociate to maintain pH. Near the stoichiometric point the curve slope is very large because each addition of even a small drop of base causes a large pH change. The remaining amount of weak acid is not sufficient to maintain pH constancy through dissociation. At the stoichiometric point, $[A^-] = [HA]_{initial}V_{initial}/V$. After the stoichiometric point the curve levels off as the mixture approaches the pH of the titrant. If the acid is extremely weak, there is no large increase in pH near the stoichiometric point.

(b) Figure 8.5 of the text illustrates the typical pH curve for the titrations of a weak base with a strong acid. Prior to reaching the stoichiometric point, when titrant volumes are small, the slope of the curve is negative but of small magnitude and an important inflection point is observed, which characterizes the p$K_b$ of the weak base. pH changes are small in this region because the base can both neutralize titrant and dissociate to maintain pH. Near the stoichiometric point the curve slope is very steep because each addition of even a small drop of acid causes a large pH change. The remaining amount of weak base is not sufficient to maintain pH constancy through dissociation. After the stoichiometric point the curve levels off as the mixture approaches the pH of the titrant. If the base is extremely weak, there is no large drop in pH near the stoichiometric point.

**D8.2** An **acid buffer** is a solution of approximately equal concentrations of a weak acid and its salt. This solution maintains some constancy in the acidic pH range through its ability to neutralize both a small amount of strong base and a small amount of strong acid. A base buffer, a solution of equal concentrations of a weak base and its salt, does much the same thing but in the base pH range.

**Indicators** are weak acids which in their undissociated acid form have one colour, and in their dissociated anion form, another. In acidic solution, the indicator exists in the predominantly acid form (one colour), in basic solution in the predominantly anion form (the other colour). The ratio of the two forms is very pH sensitive because of the small value of $pK_a$ of the indicator, so the colour change can occur very rapidly with change in pH. The indicator dye for an acid/base titration is chosen with care to match the pH at which colour change occurs with the stoichiometric point.

**D8.3** At the **stoichiometric point** (also called the **equivalence point**) of an acid–base titration, a stoichiometrically equivalent amount of acid has been added to a given amount of base. In a strong-acid–strong-base titration the pH changes sharply through several pH units around the stoichiometric point. The colour change of an indicator dye is often used to estimate the point at which the volume of titrant has provided acid–base equivalency. The titration point at which the indicator dye colour changes is called the titration **end point**. With a well-chosen indicator, the end point of the indicator coincides with the stoichiometric point of the titration. Other methods for detecting the end point include monitoring the electrical conductance of the solution and monitoring light absorption with a visible spectrophotometer.

**D8.4** Phosphoric acid is a convenient example of a triprotic acid. Like all polyprotic acids its successive acid constants are progressively smaller because of the increased charge on the dissociating anion: $pK_{a1} = 2.12$, $pK_{a2} = 7.21$, $pK_{a3} = 12.67$. The fractional composition of the protonated and deprotonated forms of a triprotic acid are illustrated in text Figure 8.3 using phosphoric acid as the example. At the lowest pH values, the fraction of the fully protonated species ($H_3PO_4$) is 1 but this fraction decreases with increasing pH. The Henderson–Hasselbalch equation, eqn 8.13, predicts that when $pH = pK_{a1}$ the fraction of the fully protonated species equals its conjugate base (diprotic $H_2PO_4^-$). As the pH changes to greater values the fraction of the diprotic species increases to a maximum at $pH = \frac{1}{2}(pK_{a1} + pK_{a2})$, eqn 8.12. At yet larger pH the diprotic species fraction diminishes while its conjugate base (monoprotic $HPO_4^{2-}$) fraction increases; the fractions of these two are equal at $pH = pK_{a2}$. The monoprotic species fraction is a maximum at $pH = \frac{1}{2}(pK_{a2} + pK_{a3})$ after which it decreases until its fraction equals the fraction of its conjugate base ($PO_4^{3-}$) when $pH = pK_{a3}$. At the highest pH values the fully deprotonated species is present alone.

The fraction of a species at any chosen pH may be calculated using equations that are analogous to eqns 8.11a–8.11c, which are appropriate for a diprotic acid. Let $D$ be the function

$$D = [H_3O^+]^3 + [H_3O^+]^2K_{a1} + [H_3O^+]K_{a2} + K_{a1}K_{a2}K_{a3}$$

which depends on the pH of the solution. Then for a triprotic acid, the fractions of each species are

$$\begin{aligned} f(H_3PO_4) &= [H_3O^+]^3/D \\ f(H_2PO_4^-) &= [H_3O^+]^2K_{a1}/D \\ f(HPO_4^{2-}) &= [H_3O^+]K_{a1}K_{a2}/D \\ f(PO_4^{3-}) &= K_{a1}K_{a2}K_{a3}/D \end{aligned}$$

**D8.5** The pH of the solution of an amphiprotic species may be estimated with the relation $pH = \frac{1}{2}(pK_{a1} + pK_{a2})$, eqn 8.12. This relation is valid when the **formal concentration** $F$ (the concentration as prepared) of the salt MHA, where $HA^-$ is an amphiprotic anion, satisfies the condition $F/c^{\ominus} \gg K_w/K_{a2}$ and $F/c^{\ominus} \gg K_{a1}$ (see Derivation 8.1). Under these conditions eqn 8.12 indicates that the formal concentration does not determine the pH because $F$ does not appear in the equation. Thus, the pH is constant over a considerable range of formal concentration. These conditions also cause $[H_2A] \approx [A^-]$.

**D8.6** The Henderson–Hasselbalch equation, eqn 8.13

$$pH = pK_a - \log\frac{[\text{acid}]}{[\text{base}]}$$

is limited to the condition that the weak acid solution has a **formal concentration** $F$ (the concentration as prepared) that is sufficiently dilute that we may replace activities with concentrations in equilibrium expressions.

Other conditions become more important when the equation is used in the form $pH \approx pK_a - \log(c_{HA}/c_{MA})$ where $c_{HA}$ and $c_{MA}$ are the formal concentrations of a solution prepared from a weak acid HA and a salt of its conjugate base A−. For example, the common 0.025 mol dm$^{-3}$ phosphate buffer is prepared with a concentration of 25.0 mmol dm$^{-3}$ of both $KH_2PO_4$ and $Na_2HPO_4$ and has pH = 6.86 at 25 °C, but the Henderson–Hasselbalch equation predicts that because the formal concentrations of acid and base are equal,

$$pH \approx pK_{a,H_2PO_4^-} - \log\left(\overbrace{c_{KH_2PO_4}}^{25.0\ \text{mmol dm}^{-3}} \; / \; \overbrace{c_{Na_2HPO_4}}^{25.0\ \text{mmol dm}^{-3}}\right) \approx pK_{a,H_2PO_4^-} = 7.21$$

To investigate the reason for this discrepancy, we draw an equilibrium table.

| | HA | $\rightleftharpoons$ | $A^-$ | $H_3O^+$ |
|---|---|---|---|---|
| Initial molar concentration / mol dm$^{-3}$ | $c_{HA}$ | | $c_{MA}$ | 0 |
| Change to reach equilibrium / mol dm$^{-3}$ | $-x$ | | $+x$ | $+x$ |
| Equilibrium concentration / mol dm$^{-3}$ | $c_{HA} - x$ | | $c_{MA} + x$ | $x$ |

For dilute solutions, we may express the activities of the components in terms only of concentrations, $a_J = \gamma_J[J]/c^{\ominus} \approx [J]/c^{\ominus}$, so that we may write the acid dissociation constant as

$$K_a = \frac{a_{H_3O^+}a_{A^-}}{a_{HA}} = \frac{[H_3O^+][A^-]}{[HA]} = \frac{[H_3O^+](c_{MA} + x)}{(c_{HA} - x)}$$

where we have neglected to include the term in the standard concentration, $c^{\ominus}$, to keep the expression simple. If $x$ is small, then $|x| \ll c_{MA}$ and $|x| \ll c_{HA}$ and therefore

$$K_a \approx \frac{[H_3O^+]c_{MA}}{c_{HA}}$$

This equation leads to our approximate version of the Henderson–Hasselbalch equation, $pH \approx pK_a - \log(c_{HA}/c_{MA})$.

The discrepancy between the actual pH and the prediction of the Henderson–Hasselbalch equation has two origins: the activity coefficients do not equal 1 exactly and the condition $|x| \ll c_{MA}, c_{HA}$ is not entirely satisfied. For the example of the phosphate buffer, we may rearrange our expression for the acidity constant to obtain an expression for $x$. Remembering that all concentrations must be in units of mol dm$^{-3}$ because of the missing term in $c^{\ominus}$, we find that

$$\begin{aligned} x &= \frac{c_{HA}K_a - c_{MA}[H^+]}{K_a + [H^+]} \\ &= \frac{(25 \times 10^{-3} \times \overbrace{10^{-7.21}}^{K_a=10^{-pK_a}}) - (25 \times 10^{-3} \times \overbrace{10^{-6.86}}^{[H^+]=10^{-pH}c^{\ominus}})}{(10^{-7.21} - 10^{-6.86})} \\ &= -9.6 \times 10^{-3}\,\text{mol dm}^{-3} = -9.6\,\text{mmol dm}^{-3} \end{aligned}$$

Thus,

$$|x|/c_{HA} = |x|/c_{MA} = (9.6\,\text{mmol dm}^{-3})/(25\,\text{mmol dm}^{-3}) = 0.38$$

Hence, our condition that $|x| \ll c_{MA}, c_{HA}$ is not satisfied, explaining the observed discrepancy with the Henderson–Hasselbalch equation.

**D8.7** The common-ion effect is the phenomenon by which the solubility of a sparingly soluble salt is reduced by a second salt when the two share a common ion. For example, the solubility of lead(II) sulfate is reduced by sodium sulfate. This is expected from Le Chatelier's principle: when the concentration of the common ion is increased, the equilibrium shifts to minimize that increase. As a result, the solubility of the original salt can be expected to decrease.

## Solutions to exercises

**E8.1** (a)

$$\overbrace{\overbrace{H_2SO_4(aq)}^{\text{acid}} + \underbrace{\underbrace{H_2O(l)}_{\text{base}} \rightleftharpoons \underbrace{H_3O^+(aq)}_{\text{acid}}}_{\text{conjugate}} + \overbrace{HSO_4^-(aq)}^{\text{base}}}^{\text{conjugate}}$$

(b)

$$\overbrace{\overbrace{HF(aq)}^{\text{acid}} + \underbrace{\underbrace{H_2O(l)}_{\text{base}} \rightleftharpoons \underbrace{H_3O^+(aq)}_{\text{acid}}}_{\text{conjugate}} + \overbrace{F^-(aq)}^{\text{base}}}^{\text{conjugate}}$$

(c)

$$\overbrace{\overbrace{C_6H_5NH_3^+(aq)}^{\text{acid}} + \underbrace{\underbrace{H_2O(l)}_{\text{base}} \rightleftharpoons \underbrace{H_3O^+(aq)}_{\text{acid}}}_{\text{conjugate}} + \overbrace{C_6H_5NH_2\,(aq)}^{\text{base}}}^{\text{conjugate}}$$

(d)

$$\overbrace{\overbrace{H_2PO_4^-(aq)}^{\text{acid}} + \underbrace{\underbrace{H_2O(l)}_{\text{base}} \rightleftharpoons \underbrace{H_3O^+(aq)}_{\text{acid}}}_{\text{conjugate}} + \overbrace{HPO_4^{2-}\,(aq)}^{\text{base}}}^{\text{conjugate}}$$

(e)

$$\overbrace{\overbrace{HCOOH(aq)}^{\text{acid}} + \underbrace{\underbrace{H_2O(l)}_{\text{base}} \rightleftharpoons \underbrace{H_3O^+(aq)}_{\text{acid}}}_{\text{conjugate}} + \overbrace{HCO_2{}^-\,(aq)}^{\text{base}}}^{\text{conjugate}}$$

(f)

$$\overbrace{\overbrace{NH_2NH_3^+(aq)}^{\text{acid}} + \underbrace{\underbrace{H_2O(l)}_{\text{base}} \rightleftharpoons \underbrace{H_3O^+(aq)}_{\text{acid}}}_{\text{conjugate}} + \overbrace{NH_2NH_2(aq)}^{\text{base}}}^{\text{conjugate}}$$

**E8.2** Writing the reactions without state symbols, for clarity,

(a)

$$\overbrace{\overbrace{CH_3CH(OH)COOH}^{\text{acid}} + \underbrace{\underbrace{H_2O}_{\text{base}} \rightleftharpoons \underbrace{H_3O^+}_{\text{acid}}}_{\text{conjugate}} + \overbrace{CH_3CH(OH)CO_2^-}^{\text{base}}}^{\text{conjugate}}$$

(b) For the diprotic glutamic acid, we may write two successive deprotonations reactions, one for each carboyxlic acid group. The carboxylic acid dissociation reactions are thus

$$\overbrace{\overbrace{HOOC(CH_2)_2CH(NH_2)COOH}^{\text{acid}} + \underbrace{\underbrace{H_2O}_{\text{base}} \rightleftharpoons \underbrace{H_3O^+}_{\text{acid}}}_{\text{conjugate}} + \overbrace{HOOC(CH_2)_2CH(NH_2)CO_2^-}^{\text{base}}}^{\text{conjugate}}$$

$$\overbrace{\overbrace{HOOC(CH_2)_2CH(NH_2)CO_2^-}^{\text{acid}} + \underbrace{H_2O \rightleftharpoons H_3O^+}_{\text{conjugate}} + \overbrace{{}^-O_2C(CH_2)_2CH(NH_2)CO_2^-}^{\text{base}}}^{\text{conjugate}}$$

The amine group ($R{-}NH_2$) is a base so proton transfer reactions can also be written that show the proton transfer from water to the amine for each of the above four species. Thus, for example, glutamic acid may also act as a base, as well as an acid

$$\underbrace{\underbrace{H_2O}_{\text{acid}} + \overbrace{\overbrace{HOOC(CH_2)_2CH(NH_2)COOH}^{\text{base}} \rightleftharpoons \overbrace{HOOC(CH_2)_2CH(NH_3^+)COOH}^{\text{acid}}}^{\text{conjugate}} + \underbrace{OH^-}_{\text{base}}}_{\text{conjugate}}$$

(c) Glycine is also amphiprotic, meaning that it too can act as both an acid

$$\overbrace{\overbrace{NH_2CH_2COOH}^{\text{acid}} + \underbrace{\underbrace{H_2O}_{\text{base}} \rightleftharpoons \underbrace{H_3O^+}_{\text{acid}}}_{\text{conjugate}} + \overbrace{NH_2CH_2CO_2^-}^{\text{base}}}^{\text{conjugate}}$$

and as a base

$$\underbrace{\underbrace{H_2O}_{\text{acid}} + \overbrace{\overbrace{NH_2CH_2COOH}^{\text{base}} \rightleftharpoons \overbrace{{}^+NH_3CH_2COOH}^{\text{acid}}}^{\text{conjugate}} + \underbrace{OH^-}_{\text{base}}}_{\text{conjugate}}$$

$$\underbrace{\underbrace{H_2O}_{\text{acid}} + \overbrace{\overbrace{NH_2CH_2CO_2^-}^{\text{base}} + \rightleftharpoons \overbrace{{}^+NH_3CH_2CO_2^-}^{\text{acid}}}^{\text{conjugate}} + \underbrace{OH^-}_{\text{base}}}_{\text{conjugate}}$$

This final form, in which the molecule is considered to have both positive and negative charges, is known as a zwitterion.

(d)

$$\overbrace{\overbrace{HOOCCOOH}^{\text{acid}} + \underbrace{\underbrace{H_2O}_{\text{base}} \rightleftharpoons \underbrace{H_3O^+}_{\text{acid}}}_{\text{conjugate}} + \overbrace{HOOCCO_2^-}^{\text{base}}}^{\text{conjugate}}$$

$$\overbrace{\overbrace{HOOCCO_2^-}^{\text{acid}} + \underbrace{\underbrace{H_2O}_{\text{base}} \rightleftharpoons \underbrace{H_3O^+}_{\text{acid}}}_{\text{conjugate}} + \overbrace{{}^-O_2CCO_2^-}^{\text{base}}}^{\text{conjugate}}$$

**E8.3** If we assume that the solutions are ideal, so that we may express activity of the $H_3O^+$ ions in terms of their concentration only, then, from eqn 8.3

$$\text{pH} = -\log a_{H_3O^+} = -\log_{10}([H_3O^+]/c^{\ominus})$$

and from eqn 8.9

$$\mathrm{pOH} = \mathrm{p}K_\mathrm{w} - \mathrm{pH} = 14 - \mathrm{pH}$$

(a)

$$\mathrm{pH} = -\log[(1.5 \times 10^{-5}\ \mathrm{mol\ dm^{-3}})/(1\ \mathrm{mol\ dm^{-3}})] = \mathbf{4.8}$$
$$\mathrm{pOH} = 14 - 4.8 = \mathbf{9.2}$$

(b)

$$\mathrm{pH} = -\log[(1.5 \times 10^{-3}\ \mathrm{mol\ dm^{-3}})/(1\ \mathrm{mol\ dm^{-3}})] = \mathbf{2.8}$$
$$\mathrm{pOH} = 14 - 2.8 = \mathbf{11.2}$$

(c)

$$\mathrm{pH} = -\log[(5.1 \times 10^{-14}\ \mathrm{mol\ dm^{-3}})/(1\ \mathrm{mol\ dm^{-3}})] = \mathbf{13.3}$$
$$\mathrm{pOH} = 14 - 13.3 = \mathbf{0.7}$$

(d)

$$\mathrm{pH} = -\log[(5.01 \times 10^{-5}\ \mathrm{mol\ dm^{-3}})/(1\ \mathrm{mol\ dm^{-3}})] = \mathbf{4.3}$$
$$\mathrm{pOH} = 14 - 4.3 = \mathbf{9.7}$$

**E8.4** (a) The amount of $H_3O^+$ and $OH^-$ ions added is

$$n_{\mathrm{H_3O^+}} = c_\mathrm{HA} \times V_\mathrm{acid}$$
$$n_{\mathrm{OH^-}} = c_\mathrm{MOH} \times V_\mathrm{base}$$

The concentration of $H_3O^+$ ions is thus given by the ratio of the amount of excess $H_3O^+$ divided by the total volume of the resulting solution,

$$[\mathrm{H_3O^+}] = \frac{n_{\mathrm{H_3O^+}} - n_{\mathrm{OH^-}}}{V_\mathrm{acid} + V_\mathrm{base}} = \frac{(c_\mathrm{HA} \times V_\mathrm{acid}) - (c_\mathrm{MOH} \times V_\mathrm{base})}{V_\mathrm{acid} + V_\mathrm{base}}$$
$$= \frac{\left(\overbrace{0.144\ \mathrm{mol\ dm^{-3}}}^{c_\mathrm{HCl}} \times 25.0 \times 10^{-3}\ \mathrm{dm^3}\right) - \left(\overbrace{0.125\ \mathrm{mol\ dm^{-3}}}^{c_\mathrm{NaOH}} \times 25.0 \times 10^{-3}\ \mathrm{dm^3}\right)}{25.0 \times 10^{-3}\ \mathrm{dm^3} + 25.0 \times 10^{-3}\ \mathrm{dm^3}}$$
$$= 9.5 \times 10^{-3}\mathrm{mol\ dm^{-3}} = \mathbf{9.5\ mmol\ dm^{-3}}$$

If we assume that the resulting solution is ideal, the pH is

$$\mathrm{pH} = -\log_{10}(a_{\mathrm{H_3O^+}}) = -\log_{10}([\mathrm{H_3O^+}]/c^\ominus)\ \mathrm{pH}$$
$$= -\log_{10}[(9.5 \times 10^{-3}\mathrm{mol\ dm^{-3}})/(1\ \mathrm{mol\ dm^{-3}})] = \mathbf{2.0}$$

(b) For the given mixture of HCl and KOH, $OH^-$ ions are in excess. Using the same approach,

$$[\mathrm{OH^-}] = \frac{\overbrace{(c_\mathrm{MOH} \times V_\mathrm{base})}^{n_{\mathrm{OH^-}}} - \overbrace{(c_\mathrm{HA} \times V_\mathrm{acid})}^{n_{\mathrm{H_3O^+}}}}{V_\mathrm{acid} + V_\mathrm{base}}$$

$$= \frac{\left(\overbrace{0.15\ \text{mol dm}^{-3}}^{c_{\text{KOH}}} \times 35.0 \times 10^{-3}\ \text{dm}^3\right) - \left(\overbrace{0.15\ \text{mol dm}^{-3}}^{c_{\text{HCl}}} \times 25.0 \times 10^{-3}\ \text{dm}^3\right)}{25.0 \times 10^{-3}\ \text{dm}^3 + 35.0 \times 10^{-3}\ \text{dm}^3}$$
$$= 21 \times 10^{-3} \text{mol dm}^{-3} = \mathbf{21\ mmol\ dm^{-3}}$$

$$\text{pOH} = -\log(a_{\text{OH}^-}) = -\log([\text{OH}^-]/c^\ominus)\ \text{pH}$$
$$= -\log[(21 \times 10^{-3} \text{mol dm}^{-3})/(1\ \text{mol dm}^{-3})] = 1.7$$

$$\text{pH} = 14.0 - \text{pOH} = 14.0 - 1.7 = \mathbf{12.3}$$

(c) For the final mixture, of $HNO_3$ and NaOH, $H_3O^+$ ions are in excess, so that

$$[\text{H}_3\text{O}^+] = \frac{n_{\text{H}_3\text{O}^+} - n_{\text{OH}^-}}{V_{\text{acid}} + V_{\text{base}}} = \frac{(c_{\text{HA}} \times V_{\text{acid}}) - (c_{\text{MOH}} \times V_{\text{base}})}{V_{\text{acid}} + V_{\text{base}}}$$
$$= \frac{\left(\overbrace{0.22\ \text{mol dm}^{-3}}^{c_{\text{HNO}_3}} \times 21.2 \times 10^{-3}\ \text{dm}^3\right) - \left(\overbrace{0.30\ \text{mol dm}^{-3}}^{c_{\text{NaOH}}} \times 10.0 \times 10^{-3}\ \text{dm}^3\right)}{21.2 \times 10^{-3}\ \text{dm}^3 + 10.0 \times 10^{-3}\ \text{dm}^3}$$
$$= 53 \times 10^{-3} \text{mol dm}^{-3} = \mathbf{53\ mmol\ dm^{-3}}$$

$$\text{pH} = -\log(a_{\text{H}_3\text{O}^+}) = -\log([\text{H}_3\text{O}^+]/c^\ominus)\ \text{pH}$$
$$= -\log[(53 \times 10^{-3} \text{mol dm}^{-3})/(1\ \text{mol dm}^{-3})] = \mathbf{1.3}$$

**E8.5** (a) From the definition of the autoprotolysis constant of water, eqn 8.7,

$$K_w = a_{\text{H}_3\text{O}^+} a_{\text{OH}^-} \approx ([\text{H}_3\text{O}^+]/c^\ominus)([\text{OH}^-]/c^\ominus)$$

For neutral water, $[H_3O^+] = [OH^-]$,

$$K_w = ([\text{H}_3\text{O}^+]/c^\ominus)^2 = 2.5 \times 10^{-14}$$

and so the molar concentration of $H_3O^+$ ions is

$$[\text{H}_3\text{O}^+] = (2.5 \times 10^{-14})^{1/2}\ \text{mol dm}^{-3} = \mathbf{1.6 \times 10^{-7}\ mol\ dm^{-3}}$$

with

$$\text{pH} = -\log(a_{\text{H}_3\text{O}^+}) = -\log([\text{H}_3\text{O}^+]/c^\ominus)\ \text{pH}$$
$$= -\log[(1.6 \times 10^{-7}\ \text{mol dm}^{-3})/(1\ \text{mol dm}^{-3})] = \mathbf{6.8}$$

(b) The molar concentration of $OH^-$ ions is the same as that of $H_3O^+$ ions in neutral solution, so that

$$[\text{OH}^-] = \mathbf{1.6 \times 10^{-7}\ mol\ dm^{-3}}$$
$$\text{pOH} = \mathbf{6.8}$$

**E8.6** (a) By analogy with the equivalent expression for autoprotolysis,

$$2\ \text{D}_2\text{O(l)} \rightleftharpoons \text{D}_3\text{O}^+\text{(aq)} + \text{OD}^-\text{(aq)}$$

(b) From eqn 8.7,

$$pK_w = -\log_{10} K_w = -\log(1.35 \times 10^{-15}) = \mathbf{14.9}$$

(c) In neutral water, $[D_3O^+] = [OD^-]$, so that

$$K_w = a_{D_3O^+}a_{OD^-} \approx ([D_3O^+]/c^\ominus)([OD^-]/c^\ominus) = ([D_3O^+]/c^\ominus)^2 = 1.35 \times 10^{-15}$$

and so the molar concentration of $D_3O^+$ and $OD^-$ ions is

$$[D_3O^+] = [OD^-] = (1.35 \times 10^{-15})^{1/2}\ \text{mol dm}^{-3} = \mathbf{3.67 \times 10^{-8}\ mol\ dm^{-3}}$$

(d) with

$$\begin{aligned} pD = pOD &= -\log(a_{H_3O^+}) = -\log([D_3O^+]/c^\circ) \\ &= -\log(3.67 \times 10^{-8}) = \mathbf{7.43} \end{aligned}$$

(e) By comparison with eqn 8.9

$$pD + pOD = pK_{D_2O} = \mathbf{14.9}$$

**E8.7** Being a strong acid, we might expect the hydrochloric acid to be fully dissociated in solution, so that $[H_3O^+] = 0.50$ mol dm$^{-3}$. From the definition of pH, eqn 8.3,

$$\begin{aligned} pH &= -\log(a_{H_3O^+}) = -\log(\gamma_{H_3O^+}[H_3O^+]/c^\ominus) \\ &= -\log[0.769 \times (0.50\ \text{mol dm}^{-3})/(1\ \text{mol dm}^{-3})] = \mathbf{0.41} \end{aligned}$$

If, instead, we assume that the solution is ideal, so that value of the activity coefficient is one,

$$\begin{aligned} pH &= -\log(a_{H_3O^+}) = -\log(\gamma_{H_3O^+}[H_3O^+]/c^\ominus) \\ &= -\log[1 \times (0.50\ \text{mol dm}^{-3})/(1\ \text{mol dm}^{-3})] = \mathbf{0.30} \end{aligned}$$

**E8.8** The van 't Hoff equation, eqn 7.15,

$$\ln K' = \ln K + \frac{\Delta_r H^\ominus}{R}\left\{\frac{1}{T} - \frac{1}{T'}\right\}$$

is expressed in terms of natural logarithms, whereas the definition of $pK_a$, eqn 8.5, is in terms of logarithms to base 10

$$pK_a = -\log K_a$$

We may convert between these forms using the relationship

$$\ln x = (\ln 10) \times (\log_{10} x)$$

The van 't Hoff equation then becomes

$$(\ln 10) \times (\log_{10} K_a') = (\ln 10) \times \overbrace{(\log_{10} K_a)}^{-pK_a} + \frac{\Delta_r H^\ominus}{R}\left\{\frac{1}{T} - \frac{1}{T'}\right\}$$

which may be rearranged into the form of a straight-line graph,

$$\overbrace{\mathrm{p}K_\mathrm{a}}^{y}=\overbrace{\frac{\Delta_\mathrm{r}H^\ominus}{R\ (\ln 10)}}^{\text{slope}}\times\overbrace{\frac{1}{T}}^{x}+\overbrace{\left\{\mathrm{p}K_\mathrm{a}{}'-\frac{\Delta_\mathrm{r}H^\ominus}{RT'(\ln 10)}\right\}}^{\text{intercept}}$$

The slope of a graph of $\mathrm{p}K_\mathrm{a}$ against $1/T$ is therefore $\Delta_\mathrm{r}H^\ominus/(R\ \ln 10)$.

**E8.9** We may determine the enthalpy of deprotonation by constructing a plot of $\mathrm{p}K_\mathrm{w}$ against $1/T$. The data are plotted in Figure 8.1.The slope of the graph is $2.99\times 10^3$ K. We demonstrated in the previous exercise that the slope is equal to $\Delta_\mathrm{r}H^\ominus/(R\ \ln 10)$, so that

$$\begin{aligned}\Delta_\mathrm{r}H^\ominus &= \text{slope}\times(R\ln 10)=(2.99\times 10^3\ \mathrm{K})\times(8.3145\ \mathrm{J\ K^{-1}mol^{-1}})\times\ln 10\\ &= +57.1\times 10^3\ \mathrm{J\ mol^{-1}} = \mathbf{+57.1\ kJ\ mol^{-1}}\end{aligned}$$

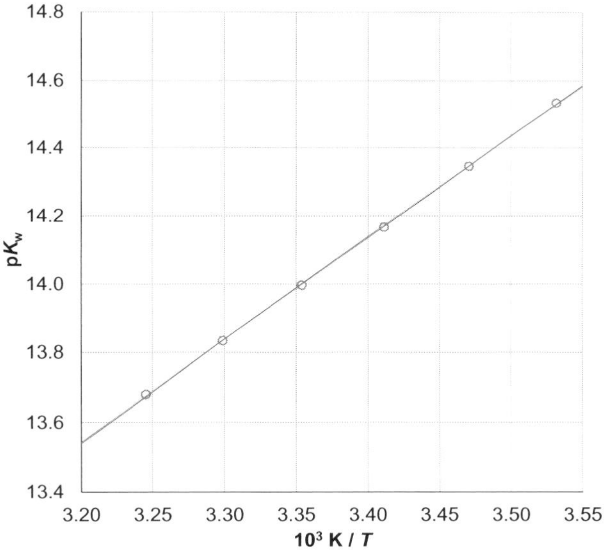


**Figure 8.1**

**E8.10** By analogy with the expression derived in the previous exercise, we may expect $\mathrm{p}K_\mathrm{b}$ to vary with temperature according to the relationship

$$\overbrace{\mathrm{p}K_\mathrm{b}}^{y}=\overbrace{\frac{\Delta_\mathrm{r}H^\ominus}{R\ (\ln 10)}}^{\text{slope}}\times\overbrace{\frac{1}{T}}^{x}+\overbrace{\left\{\mathrm{p}K_\mathrm{b}{}'-\frac{\Delta_\mathrm{r}H^\ominus}{RT'(\ln 10)}\right\}}^{\text{intercept}}$$

This expression indicates that a graph of $\mathrm{p}K_\mathrm{b}$ against $1/T$ should be a straight line with a gradient of $\Delta_\mathrm{r}H^\ominus/R\ \ln 10$, where $\Delta_\mathrm{r}H^\ominus$ is the standard reaction enthalpy for the reaction

$$\mathrm{B} + \mathrm{H_2O} \rightleftharpoons \mathrm{BH^+} + \mathrm{OH^-}$$

Figure 8.2 shows a graph of $pK_b$ against $1/T$. Note that the temperature values must be converted from units of degrees celsius to degrees kelvin, using the relationship

$$T/K = \theta/°C + 273.15$$

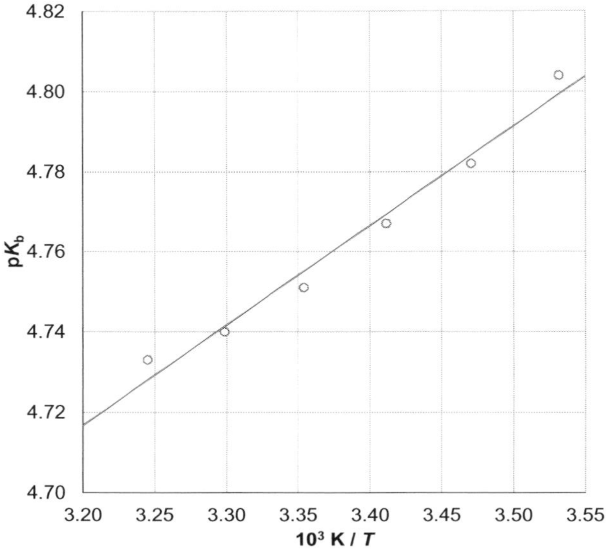


**Figure 8.2**

The slope of the graph is

$$\frac{\Delta_r H^\ominus}{R\ (\ln 10)} = 248.8\ \mathrm{K}$$

so that

$$\Delta_r H^\ominus = (248.8\ \mathrm{K}) \times R \ln 10 = (248.8\ \mathrm{K}) \times (8.3145\ \mathrm{J\ K^{-1} mol^{-1}}) \times \ln 10$$
$$= +4.763 \times 10^3\ \mathrm{J\ mol^{-1}} = \mathbf{+4.763\ kJ\ mol^{-1}}$$

**E8.11** The nicotine protonation reaction is

$$\mathrm{Nic(aq) + H_2O(l) \rightleftharpoons NicH^+(aq) + OH^-(aq)}$$

The corresponding deprotonation reaction of the conjugate acid is

$$\mathrm{NicH^+(aq) + H_2O(l) \rightleftharpoons Nic(aq) + H_3O^+}$$

From eqn 8.8b,

$$pK_a = pK_w - pK_b = 14.00 - 5.98 = \mathbf{8.02}$$

**E8.12** (a) For the deprotonationof benzoic acid,

$$C_6H_5COOH(aq) + H_2O(l) \rightleftharpoons C_6H_5CO_2^-(aq) + H_3O^+(aq)$$

the acidity constant is given, from eqn 8.4, by

$$K_a = \frac{a_{C_6H_5CO_2^-(aq)}a_{H_3O^+(aq)}}{a_{C_6H_5COOH(aq)}a_{H_2O(l)}} \approx \frac{[C_6H_5CO_2^-][H_3O^+]}{[C_6H_5COOH]c^{\ominus}} = 6.5 \times 10^{-4}$$

with the value taken from Table 8.1. If the fraction of acid deprotonated is

$$x = [C_6H_5CO_2^-]/[C_6H_5COOH]_0$$

where $[C_6H_5COOH]_0 = 0.25$ mol dm$^{-3}$ is the initial concentration of the acid, then, according to the stoichiometry of the reaction,

$$[C_6H_5CO_2^-] = [H_3O^+] = x[C_6H_5COOH]_0$$
$$[C_6H_5COOH] = (1-x)[C_6H_5COOH]_0$$

so that,

$$K_a = \frac{x^2[C_6H_5COOH]_0^2}{(1-x)[C_6H_5COOH]_0c^{\ominus}} = \frac{x^2}{1-x}([C_6H_5COOH]_0/c^{\ominus})$$

If we assume that because benzoic acid is a weak acid, so that the degree of deprotonation is sufficiently small that $(1-x) \approx 1$, then

$$x^2 = K_a/([C_6H_5COOH]_0/c^{\ominus})$$
$$x = \{6.5 \times 10^{-4}/0.25\}^{1/2} = \mathbf{0.05} = \mathbf{5\ per\ cent}$$

Alternatively, solving this quadratic equation using the method given in *The chemist's toolkit 7.1*, gives $x = 0.0497$, suggesting that our approximation is justified.

(b) In the same way for the protonation of hydrazine,

$$NH_2NH_2(aq) + H_2O(l) \rightleftharpoons NH_2NH_3^+(aq) + OH^-(aq)$$

$$K_b = \frac{x^2}{1-x}([NH_2NH_2]_0/c^{\ominus}) = 1.7 \times 10^{-6}$$

Assuming that hydrazine is a sufficiently weak base that we may make the same approximation,

$$x^2 = K_b/([NH_2NH_2]_0/c^{\ominus})$$
$$x = (1.7 \times 10^{-6}/0.150)^{1/2} = \mathbf{3.4 \times 10^{-3}} = \mathbf{0.34\ per\ cent}$$

(c) For trimethylamine,

$$(CH_3)_3N(aq) + H_2O(l) \rightleftharpoons (CH_3)_3NH^+(aq) + OH^-(aq)$$

$$K_b = \frac{x^2}{1-x}([(CH_3)_3N]_0/c^{\ominus}) = 6.5 \times 10^{-5}$$

Once again assuming that hydrazine is a sufficiently weak base that we may make the same approximation,

$$x^2 = K_b/([(CH_3)_3N]_0/c^{\ominus})$$
$$x = (6.5 \times 10^{-5}/0.112)^{1/2} = \mathbf{0.024} = \mathbf{2.4\ per\ cent}$$

**E8.13** (a) Lactic acid is a weak acid, with, from Table 8.1, $K_a = 8.6 \times 10^{-4}$. Thus, we may calculate the fraction of acid molecules deprotonated, $x$,

$$CH_3CH(OH)COOH(aq) + H_2O(l) \rightleftharpoons H_3O^+(aq) + CH_3CH(OH)CO_2^-(aq)$$

using the method used in the previous exercise. Thus,

$$K_a = \frac{x^2}{1-x}([CH_3CH(OH)COOH]_0/c^{\ominus})$$

and so, because the degree of deprotonation is sufficiently small that $(1-x) \approx 1$,

$$x^2 = K_a/([CH_3CH(OH)COOH]_0/c^{\ominus})$$
$$x = \{8.6 \times 10^{-4}/0.150\}^{1/2} = 0.076 = 7.6\text{ per cent}$$

It follows that, because $[H_3O^+] = x\,[CH_3CH(OH)COOH]$,

$$\begin{aligned} pH &= -\log a_{H_3O^+(aq)} \approx -\log_{10}([H_3O^+]/c^{\ominus}) \\ &= -\log(x[CH_3CH(OH)COOH]_0/c^{\ominus}) \\ &= -\log(0.076 \times 0.150) = \mathbf{1.94} \end{aligned}$$

and, from eqn 8.8b

$$pOH = pK_w - pH = 14.00 - 1.94 = \mathbf{12.1}$$

(b) In this case, the formal concentration of lactic acid is comparable to the value of the acidity constant, $K_a$. Thus, we cannot use the approximation that $(1-x) \approx 1$ to solve the quadratic equation

$$K_a = \frac{x^2}{1-x}([CH_3CH(OH)COOH]_0/c^{\ominus})$$

Instead, we must rearrange equation so that it is of the form $ax^2 + bx + c = 0$ and solve using the method outlined in The chemist's toolkit 7.1,

$$\overbrace{[CH_3CH(OH)COOH]_0}^{a} x^2 + \overbrace{K_a}^{b} x \overbrace{-K_a}^{c} = 0$$

which has solutions

$$\begin{aligned} x &= \frac{-b \pm \sqrt{b^2 - 4ac}}{2a} = \frac{-K_a \pm \sqrt{K_a^2 - 4 \times [CH_3CH(OH)COOH]_0 \times (-K_a)}}{2 \times [CH_3CH(OH)COOH]_0} \\ &= 0.815 \text{ or } -4.40 \end{aligned}$$

The degree of deprotonation, $0 \le x \le 1$, so that

$$x = 0.82 = 82\text{ per cent}$$

It follows that, because $[H_3O^+] = x\,[CH_3CH(OH)COOH]$,

$$\begin{aligned}\mathrm{pH} &= -\log a_{\mathrm{H_3O^+(aq)}} \approx -\log([\mathrm{H_3O^+}]/c^{\ominus}) \\ &= -\log(x[\mathrm{CH_3CH(OH)COOH}]_0/c^{\ominus}) \\ &= -\log(0.82 \times 2.4 \times 10^4) = \mathbf{3.7}\end{aligned}$$

and, from eqn 8.8b

$$\mathrm{pOH} = \mathrm{p}K_\mathrm{w} - \mathrm{pH} = 14.00 - 3.7 = \mathbf{10.3}$$

(c) For the deprotonation of benzenesulfonic acid,

$$\mathrm{C_6H_5SO_3H(aq) + H_2O(l) \rightleftharpoons H_3O^+(aq) + C_6H_5SO_3^-(aq)}$$

the value of the acidity constant is, from Table 8.1, $K_a = 0.2$. For a solution of initial concentration 0.15 mol dm$^{-3}$, the formal concentration of acid is comparable to the value of the acidity constant, and we must once again solve exactly the quadratic equation

$$K_\mathrm{a} = \frac{x^2}{1-x}([\mathrm{C_6H_5SO_3H}]_0/c^{\ominus})$$

In this case,

$$\begin{aligned}x &= \frac{-b \pm \sqrt{b^2 - 4ac}}{2a} = \frac{-K_\mathrm{a} \pm \sqrt{K_\mathrm{a}^2 - 4 \times [\mathrm{C_6H_5SO_3H}]_0 \times (-K_\mathrm{a})}}{2 \times [\mathrm{C_6H_5SO_3H}]_0} \\ &= 0.58 \text{ or } -1.4\end{aligned}$$

where we have, as before, taken the only valid solution. Thus,

$$\begin{aligned}\mathrm{pH} &= -\log a_{\mathrm{H_3O^+(aq)}} \approx -\log([\mathrm{H_3O^+}]/c^{\ominus}) \\ &= -\log(x[\mathrm{C_6H_5SO_3H}]_0/c^{\ominus}) \\ &= -\log(0.58 \times 0.2) = \mathbf{0.9}\end{aligned}$$

and, from eqn 8.8b

$$\mathrm{pOH} = \mathrm{p}K_\mathrm{w} - \mathrm{pH} = 14.00 - 0.9 = \mathbf{13.1}$$

**E8.14** Rearranging the Henderson–Hasselbalch equation, eqn 8.13,

$$\frac{[\text{acid}]}{[\text{base}]} = 10^{-(\mathrm{pH}-\mathrm{p}K_\mathrm{a})}$$

(a) Thus, for pH = 7,

$$\frac{[\text{acid}]}{[\text{base}]} = 10^{-(7-2.2)} = \mathbf{1.6 \times 10^{-5}}$$

(b) And for pH = 2.2,

$$\frac{[\text{acid}]}{[\text{base}]} = 10^{-(2.2-2.2)} = \mathbf{1}$$

(c) And for pH = 1.5,

$$\frac{[\text{acid}]}{[\text{base}]} = 10^{-(1.5-2.2)} = \mathbf{5.0}$$

**E8.15** (a) Boric acid acts as a monoprotic acid, so we need consider only the deprotonation

$$H_3BO_3(aq) + 2\,H_2O(l) \rightleftharpoons H_3O^+(aq) + B(OH)_4^-(aq)$$

for which $K_a = 7.2 \times 10^{-10}$. Denoting the degree of deprotonation as $x$, then, from the stoichiometry of the reaction,

$$[B(OH)_4^-] = [H_3O^+] = x[H_3BO_3]_0$$
$$[H_3BO_3] = (1-x)[H_3BO_3]_0$$

Assuming that the solution is sufficiently dilute that we may replace activities by concentrations,

$$K_a = \frac{a_{B(OH)_4^-(aq)}a_{H_3O^+(aq)}}{a_{H_3BO_3(aq)}a_{H_2O(l)}} = \frac{[B(OH)_4^-][H_3O^+]}{[H_3BO_3]c^\ominus} = \frac{x^2}{1-x}([H_3BO_3]_0/c^\ominus)$$

Boric acid is a weak acid. The degree of deprotonation is therefore sufficiently small that we may make the approximation $(1-x) \approx 1$. Thus,

$$x = \{K_a/([H_3BO_3]_0/c^\ominus)\}^{1/2}$$

and therefore, from eqn 8.3,

$$\begin{aligned}
\text{pH} &= -\log a_{H_3O^+} \approx -\log([H_3O^+]/c^\ominus)\\
&= -\log(x[H_3BO_3]_0/c^\ominus)\\
&= -\log\left\{\left(\frac{K_a}{[H_3BO_3]_0/c^\ominus}\right)^{1/2} \times ([H_3BO_3]_0/c^\ominus)\right\}\\
&= -\log(K_a[H_3BO_3]_0/c^\ominus)^{1/2} \overset{\log x^y = y\log x}{=} -\tfrac{1}{2}\log(K_a[H_3BO_3]_0/c^\ominus)\\
&= -\tfrac{1}{2}\log[(7.2\times 10^{-10})\times(1.0\times 10^{-4})] = \mathbf{6.6}
\end{aligned}$$

This value is not much different from the value for pure water. Were we to require a more precise value, we should consider also the autoprotolysis of water. The problem would then become more complicated because we could no longer make the simplification that $[B(OH)_4^-] = [H_3O^+]$.

(b) Phosphoric acid, $H_3PO_4$, is a triprotic acid, and all three deprotonation steps

$$H_3PO_4(aq) + H_2O(l) \rightleftharpoons H_3O^+(aq) + H_2PO_4^-(aq)$$
$$H_2PO_4^-(aq) + H_2O(l) \rightleftharpoons H_3O^+(aq) + HPO_4^{2-}(aq)$$
$$HPO_4^{2-}(aq) + H_2O(l) \rightleftharpoons H_3O^+(aq) + PO_4^{3-}(aq)$$

contribute to the acidity in solution. Thus

$$[H_3O^+] = [H_2PO_4^-] + [HPO_4^{2-}] + [PO_4^{2-}]$$

For solutions that are sufficiently dilute that we may replace the activities of the components by concentrations, then the acidity constants for each of the steps are

$$K_{a1} = \frac{a_{H_2PO_4^-(aq)}a_{H_3O^+(aq)}}{a_{H_3PO_4(aq)}a_{H_2O(l)}} \approx \frac{[H_2PO_4^-][H_3O^+]}{[H_3PO_4]c^{\ominus}} = -7.6 \times 10^{-3}$$
$$K_{a2} = \frac{a_{HPO_4^{2-}(aq)}a_{H_3O^+(aq)}}{a_{H_2PO_4^-(aq)}a_{H_2O(l)}} \approx \frac{[HPO_4^{2-}][H_3O^+]}{[H_2PO_4^-]c^{\ominus}} = 6.2 \times 10^{-8}$$
$$K_{a3} = \frac{a_{PO_4^{3-}(aq)}a_{H_3O^+(aq)}}{a_{HPO_4^{2-}(aq)}a_{H_2O(l)}} \approx \frac{[PO_4^{3-}][H_3O^+]}{[HPO_4^{2-}]c^{\ominus}} = 2.1 \times 10^{-13}$$

Thus, substituting in turn

$$[H_2PO_4^-] = K_{a1}[H_3PO_4]c^{\ominus}/[H_3O^+]$$
$$[HPO_4^{2-}] = K_{a2}[H_2PO_4^-]c^{\ominus}/[H_3O^+] = K_{a1}K_{a2}[H_3PO_4]c^{\ominus^2}/[H_3O^+]^2$$
$$[HPO_4^{2-}] = K_{a3}[HPO_4^{2-}]c^{\ominus}/[H_3O^+] = K_{a1}K_{a2}K_{a3}[H_3PO_4]c^{\ominus^3}/[H_3O^+]^3$$

But

$$[H_3PO_4] = [H_3PO_4]_0 - ([H_2PO_4^-] + [HPO_4^{2-}] + [HPO_4^{2-}]) = [H_3PO_4]_0 - [H_3O^+]$$

so that

$$[H_3O^+] = (K_{a1}[H_3PO_4]c^{\ominus}/[H_3O^+]) + \left(K_{a1}K_{a2}[H_3PO_4]c^{\ominus^2}/[H_3O^+]^2\right) + \left(K_{a1}K_{a2}K_{a3}[H_3PO_4]c^{\ominus^3}/[H_3O^+]^3\right)$$

Multiplying throughout by $[H_3O^+]^3$

$$[H_3O^+]^4 = \left(K_{a1}[H_3O^+]^2c^{\ominus} + K_{a1}K_{a2}[H_3O^+]c^{\ominus^2} + K_{a1}K_{a2}K_{a3}c^{\ominus^3}\right)[H_3PO_4]$$
$$= \left(K_{a1}[H_3O^+]^2c^{\ominus} + K_{a1}K_{a2}[H_3O^+]c^{\ominus^2} + K_{a1}K_{a2}K_{a3}c^{\ominus^3}\right) \times ([H_3PO_4]_0 - [H_3O^+])$$

This quartic equation is difficult to solve analytically. However, because $K_{a1} \gg K_{a2} \gg K_{a3}$, we may safely ignore all but the first term, so that

$$[H_3O^+]^4 \approx K_{a1}[H_3O^+]^2([H_3PO_4]_0 - [H_3O^+])c^{\ominus}$$

which simplifies to the quadratic equation

$$[H_3O^+]^2 + K_{a1}[H_3O^+]c^{\ominus} - K_{a1}[H_3PO_4]_0c^{\ominus} \approx 0$$

This equation is of the form $ax^2 + bx + c = 0$ and has solutions

$$[H_3O]^+/c^{\ominus} = \frac{-b \pm \sqrt{b^2 - 4ac}}{2a} = \frac{-K_{a1} \pm \sqrt{K_{a1}^2 - 4 \times (-K_{a1}[H_3PO_4]_0)}}{2}$$
$$= \frac{-7.6 \times 10^{-3} \pm \sqrt{(7.6 \times 10^{-3})^2 + (4 \times 7.6 \times 10^{-3} \times 0.015)}}{2}$$
$$= 7.5 \times 10^{-3}$$

Thus,

$$\text{pH} \approx -\log([H_3O^+]/c^{\ominus}) = -\log(7.5 \times 10^{-3}) = \mathbf{2.1}$$

(c) Sulfurous acid is diprotic and undergoes two deprotonation steps,

$$H_2SO_3(aq) + H_2O(l) \rightleftharpoons H_3O^+(aq) + HSO_3^-(aq)$$
$$HSO_3^-(aq) + H_2O(l) \rightleftharpoons H_3O^+(aq) + SO_3^{2-}(aq)$$

with, if we assume that the solution is sufficiently dilute that we may replace activities by concentrations

$$K_{a1} = \frac{a_{HSO_3^-(aq)}a_{H_3O^+(aq)}}{a_{H_2SO_3(aq)}a_{H_2O(l)}} \approx \frac{[HSO_3^-][H_3O^+]}{[H_2SO_3]c^\ominus}$$

$$K_{a2} = \frac{a_{SO_3^{2-}(aq)}a_{H_3O^+(aq)}}{a_{HSO_3^-(aq)}a_{H_2O(l)}} \approx \frac{[SO_3^{2-}][H_3O^+]}{[HSO_3^-]c^\ominus}$$

Allowing for both deprotonation steps to make a contribution to the concentration of $H_3O^+$ ions,

$$[H_3O^+] = [HSO_3^-] + [SO_3^{2-}]$$

It follows that

$$[HSO_3^-] = \frac{K_{a1}[H_2SO_3]c^\ominus}{[H_3O^+]}$$
$$[SO_3^{2-}] = \frac{K_{a2}[HSO_3^-]c^\ominus}{[H_3O^+]} = \frac{K_{a1}K_{a2}[H_2SO_3]c^{\ominus 2}}{[H_3O^+]^2}$$
$$[H_2SO_3] = [H_2SO_3]_0 - ([HSO_3^-] + [SO_3^{2-}]) = [H_2SO_3]_0 - [H_3O^+]$$

Hence

$$[H_3O^+] = \underbrace{\frac{K_{a1}\overbrace{([H_2SO_3]_0 - [H_3O^+])}^{[H_2SO_3]}c^\ominus}{[H_3O^+]}}_{[HSO_3^-]} + \underbrace{\frac{K_{a1}K_{a2}\overbrace{([H_2SO_3]_0 - [H_3O^+])}^{[H_2SO_3]}c^{\ominus 2}}{[H_3O^+]^2}}_{[SO_3^{2-}]} =$$

In the first deprotonation step, $H_2SO_3$ acts as a relatively strong acid with, from Table 8.2, $pK_{a1} = 1.5 \times 10^{-2}$. In the second step, however, $HSO_3^-$ acts as a much weaker acid, with $pK_{a2} = 1.2 \times 10^{-7}$. Thus, we may safely ignore the second term, which arises from the second deprotonation step. Rearranging

$$[H_3O^+]^2 - K_{a1}[H_3O^+]c^\ominus - K_{a1}[H_2SO_3]_0c^\ominus = 0$$

This equation is of the form $ax^2 + bx + c = 0$ and has solutions

$$[H_3O]^+/c^\ominus = \frac{-b \pm \sqrt{b^2 - 4ac}}{2a} = \frac{-K_{a1} \pm \sqrt{K_{a1}^2 - 4 \times (-K_{a1}[H_2SO_3]_0)}}{2}$$
$$= \frac{-1.5 \times 10^{-2} \pm \sqrt{(1.5 \times 10^{-2})^2 + (4 \times 1.5 \times 10^{-2} \times 0.10)}}{2}$$
$$= 3.2 \times 10^{-2}$$

Thus,

$$\text{pH} \approx -\log([\text{H}_3\text{O}^+]/c^{\ominus}) = -\log(3.2 \times 10^{-2}) = \mathbf{1.5}$$

**E8.16** Oxalic acid, $(COOH)_2$, is diprotic, and undergoes two deprotonation steps in aqueous solution with acidity constants $K_{a1} = 5.9 \times 10^{-2}$ and $K_{a2} = 6.5 \times 10^{-5}$. For the first deprotonation step,

$$(\text{COOH})_2(\text{aq}) + \text{H}_2\text{O(l)} \rightleftharpoons \text{HOOCCO}_2^-(\text{aq}) + \text{H}_3\text{O}^+(\text{aq})$$

Denoting the degree of deprotonation as

$$x = \frac{[\text{HOOCCO}_2^-]}{[\text{HOOCCO}_2^-] + [(\text{COOH})_2]} = \frac{[\text{HOOCCO}_2^-]}{[(\text{COOH})_2]_0}$$

it follows that

$$[(\text{COOH})_2] = (1 - x)[(\text{COOH})_2]_0$$
$$[\text{HOOCCO}_2^-] = x[(\text{COOH})_2]_0$$

In the same way for the second deprotonation step,

$$\text{HOOCCO}_2^-(\text{aq}) + \text{H}_2\text{O(l)} \rightleftharpoons (\text{CO}_2)_2^{2-}(\text{aq}) + \text{H}_3\text{O}^+(\text{aq})$$

and denoting the degree of deprotonation as $y$

$$y = \frac{[(\text{CO}_2)_2^{2-}]}{[\text{HOOCCO}_2^-] + [(\text{CO}_2)_2^{2-}]} = \frac{[(\text{CO}_2)_2^{2-}]}{x[(\text{COOH})_2]_0 + [(\text{CO}_2)_2^{2-}]}$$

Rearranging,

$$[(\text{CO}_2)_2^{2-}] = \frac{xy}{1-y}[(\text{COOH})_2]_0$$

The acidity constant for this second deprotonation is small, suggesting that the degree of deprotonation is sufficiently low that we may make the approximation,

$$x[(\text{COOH})_2]_0 \gg [(\text{CO}_2)_2^{2-}]$$

so that

$$y \approx [(\text{CO}_2)_2^{2-}]/(x[(\text{COOH})_2]_0)$$
$$[(\text{CO}_2)_2^{2-}] \approx xy[(\text{COOH})_2]_0$$

In theory, both deprotonation steps make a contribution to the concentration of $H_3O^+$ ions, so that

$$\begin{aligned}[\text{H}_3\text{O}^+] &= \overbrace{[\text{HOOCCO}_2^-]}^{\text{contribution from first deprotonation}} + \overbrace{[(\text{CO}_2)_2^{2-}]}^{\text{contribution from second deprotonation}} \\ &= x[(\text{COOH})_2]_0 + \frac{xy}{1-y}[(\text{COOH})_2]_0 \\ &= \frac{x(1-y) + xy}{(1-y)}[(\text{COOH})_2]_0\end{aligned}$$

$$= \frac{x}{1-y}[(\text{COOH})_2]_0$$

but, in practice, because $y \ll 1$, we may make the approximation that

$$[\text{H}_3\text{O}^+] = x[(\text{COOH})_2]_0$$

If we assume that the solution is sufficiently dilute that activities may be approximated by concentrations,

$$K_{a1} = \frac{a_{\text{HOOCCO}_2^-(\text{aq})}a_{\text{H}_3\text{O}^+(\text{aq})}}{a_{(\text{COOH})_2(\text{aq})}a_{\text{H}_2\text{O(l)}}}$$

$$\approx \frac{\overbrace{[\text{HOOCCO}_2^-]}^{x[(\text{COOH})_2]_0}\ \overbrace{[\text{H}_3\text{O}^+]}^{x[(\text{COOH})_2]_0}}{\underbrace{[(\text{COOH})_2]}_{(1-x)[(\text{COOH})_2]_0}\ c^{\ominus}} = \frac{x^2}{(1-x)} \times ([(\text{COOH})_2]_0/c^{\ominus})$$

and

$$K_{a2} = \frac{a_{(\text{CO}_2)_2^{2-}}a_{\text{H}_3\text{O}^+(\text{aq})}}{a_{\text{HOOCCO}_2^-(\text{aq})}a_{\text{H}_2\text{O(l)}}}$$

$$\approx \frac{\overbrace{[(\text{CO}_2)_2^{2-}]}^{\{xy\}[(\text{COOH})_2]_0}\ \overbrace{[\text{H}_3\text{O}^+]}^{x[(\text{COOH})_2]_0}}{\underbrace{[\text{HOOCCO}_2^-]}_{x[(\text{COOH})_2]_0}\ c^{\ominus}} = xy \times ([(\text{COOH})_2]_0/c^{\ominus})$$

The first equation may be rearranged to be of the form $ax^2 + bx + c = 0$

$$\overbrace{[\text{H}_2\text{C}_2\text{O}_4]_0}^{a}\, x^2 + \overbrace{K_{a1}}^{b}\, x \overbrace{-K_{a1}}^{c} = 0$$

According to the method outlined in The chemist's toolkit 7.1, this equation has solutions

$$x = \frac{-b \pm \sqrt{b^2 - 4ac}}{2a} = \frac{-K_{a1} \pm \sqrt{K_{a1}^2 - 4 \times [\text{H}_2\text{C}_2\text{O}_4]_0 \times (-K_{a1})}}{2 \times [\text{H}_2\text{C}_2\text{O}_4]_0}$$

$$= 0.46 \text{ or } -0.85$$

Hence

$$[(\text{COOH})_2] = (1-x)[(\text{COOH})_2]_0 = (1-0.46) \times (0.15 \text{ mol dm}^{-3})$$
$$= \mathbf{0.08\ mol\ dm^{-3}}$$
$$[\text{HOOCCO}_2^-] = x[(\text{COOH})_2]_0 = 0.46 \times (0.15 \text{ mol dm}^{-3})$$
$$= \mathbf{0.07\ mol\ dm^{-3}}$$

Rearranging the second equation,

$$y = \frac{K_{a2}}{x([(\text{COOH})_2]_0/c^{\ominus})} = \frac{6.5 \times 10^{-5}}{0.461 \times 0.15} = 9.4 \times 10^{-4}$$

Substituting,

$$[(\text{CO}_2)_2^{2-}] = xy[(\text{COOH})_2]_0$$

$$= \overbrace{0.46}^{x} \times \overbrace{9.4 \times 10^{-4}}^{y} \times (0.15\ \text{mol dm}^{-3}) = \mathbf{6.5 \times 10^{-5}\ mol\ dm^{-3}}$$

and, because the degree of dissociation for the second step is small, so that $1 - y \approx 1$,

$$[\text{H}_3\text{O}^+] = \frac{x}{1-y}[(\text{COOH})_2]_0 \approx x[(\text{COOH})_2]_0 = 0.46 \times (0.15\ \text{mol dm}^{-3})$$
$$= \mathbf{0.07\ mol\ dm^{-3}}$$

It follows, from eqn 8.7 that

$$[\text{OH}^-] = K_\text{w}/[\text{H}_3\text{O}^+] = 10^{-14}/(0.07\ \text{mol dm}^{-3}) = \mathbf{1.4 \times 10^{-13}\ mol\ dm^{-3}}$$

**E8.17** In aqueous solution, hydrogen sulphide may be considered as the diprotic acid, hydrosulfuric acid. The acidity constants for the two deprotonation steps

$$\overbrace{\text{H}_2\text{S(aq)}}^{\text{acid}} + \text{H}_2\text{O(l)} \rightleftharpoons \text{H}_3\text{O}^+\text{(aq)} + \overbrace{\text{HS}^-\text{(aq)}}^{\text{base}}$$
$$\overbrace{\text{HS}^-\text{(aq)}}^{\text{acid}} + \text{H}_2\text{O(l)} \rightleftharpoons \text{H}_3\text{O}^+\text{(aq)} + \overbrace{\text{S}^{2-}\text{(aq)}}^{\text{base}}$$

are, from Table 8.2, $K_{\text{a1}} = 1.3 \times 10^{-7}$ and $K_{\text{a2}} = 7.1 \times 10^{-15}$. Defining the degrees of deprotonation in the first step as

$$x = [\text{HS}^-]/([\text{H}_2\text{S}] + [\text{HS}^-] + [\text{S}^{2-}]) = [\text{HS}^-]/[\text{H}_2\text{S}]_0$$

and

$$y = [\text{S}^{2-}]/([\text{H}_2\text{S}] + [\text{HS}^-] + [\text{S}^{2-}]) = [\text{S}^{2-}]/[\text{H}_2\text{S}]_0$$

it follows that

$$[\text{HS}^-] = x[\text{H}_2\text{S}]_0$$
$$[\text{S}^{2-}] = y[\text{H}_2\text{S}]_0$$

where $[\text{H}_2\text{S}]_0$ is the formal concentration of hydrosulfuric acid, and so

$$[\text{H}_2\text{S}] = [\text{H}_2\text{S}]_0 - ([\text{HS}^-] + [\text{S}^{2-}]) = (1 - x - y)[\text{H}_2\text{S}]_0$$
$$[\text{H}_3\text{O}^+] = [\text{HS}^-] + [\text{S}^{2-}] = (x + y)[\text{H}_2\text{S}]_0$$

Both deprotonation steps make a contribution to the concentration of $\text{H}_3\text{O}^+$ in solution. However, because $K_{\text{a1}}, K_{\text{a2}} \ll 1$, we may assume that $(1 - x - y) \approx 1$ and because $K_{\text{a1}} \gg K_{\text{a2}}$, $(x + y) \approx x$, such that

$$[\text{H}_2\text{S}] \approx [\text{H}_2\text{S}]_0$$
$$[\text{H}_3\text{O}^+] \approx x[\text{H}_2\text{S}]_0$$

Then, if we assume that the solution is sufficiently dilute that we may replace activities by molar concentrations,

$$K_{\text{a1}} = \frac{a_{\text{HS}^-\text{(aq)}}a_{\text{H}_3\text{O}^+\text{(aq)}}}{a_{\text{H}_2\text{S(aq)}}} \approx \frac{[\text{HS}^-][\text{H}_3\text{O}^+]}{[\text{H}_2\text{S}]c^\ominus} = x^2([\text{H}_2\text{S}]_0/\ c^\ominus)$$

so that

$$x = \{K_{a1}/([H_2S]_0/c^{\ominus})\}^{1/2} = (1.3 \times 10^{-7}/0.065) = 1.4 \times 10^{-3}$$

and

$$K_{a2} = \frac{a_{S^{2-}(aq)}a_{H_3O^+(aq)}}{a_{HS^-(aq)}} \approx \frac{[S^{2-}][H_3O^+]}{[HS^-]c^{\ominus}} = \frac{yx}{x} \times ([H_2S]_0/c^{\ominus}) = y([H_2S]_0/c^{\ominus})$$

$$y = K_{a2}/([H_2S]_0/c^{\ominus}) = 7.1 \times 10^{-15}/0.065 = 1.1 \times 10^{-13}$$

Thus,

$$\begin{aligned} [H_2S] \approx [H_2S]_0 &= \mathbf{0.065\ mol\ dm^{-3}} \\ [HS^-] = x[H_2S]_0 &= (1.4 \times 10^{-3}) \times (0.065\ \text{mol dm}^{-3}) \\ &= \mathbf{9.2 \times 10^{-5} mol\ dm^{-3}} \\ [S^{2-}] = y[H_2S]_0 &= (1.1 \times 10^{-13}) \times (0.065\ \text{mol dm}^{-3}) \\ &= \mathbf{7.2 \times 10^{-15} mol\ dm^{-3}} \\ [H_3O^+] \approx x[H_2S]_0 &= (1.4 \times 10^{-3}) \times (0.065\ \text{mol dm}^{-3}) \\ &= \mathbf{9.2 \times 10^{-5} mol\ dm^{-3}} \end{aligned}$$

and so, from eqn 8.9,

$$\begin{aligned} [OH^-] = K_w c^{\ominus 2}/[H_3O^+] &= (10^{-14}/9.2 \times 10^{-5})\ \text{mol dm}^{-3} \\ &= \mathbf{1.1 \times 10^{-10}\ mol\ dm^{-3}} \end{aligned}$$

**E8.18** Glycine, $NH_2CH_2COOH$, is amphiprotic, and may exist in aqueous solution in one of three forms, which we denote as HGly, $Gly^-$, or $H_2Gly^+$, according to the equilibria

$$HGly(aq) + H_2O(l) \rightleftharpoons Gly^-(aq) + H_3O^+(aq) \qquad pK_{a1} = 9.60$$
$$H_2Gly^+(aq) + H_2O(l) \rightleftharpoons HGly(aq) + H_3O^+(aq) \qquad pK_{a2} = 2.35$$

If we assume that the solutions are sufficiently dilute that we may approximate activities by concentrations,

$$K_{a1} = \frac{a_{Gly^-(aq)}a_{H_3O^+(aq)}}{a_{HGly(aq)}a_{H_2O(l)}} = \frac{[Gly^-][H_3O^+]}{[HGly]c^{\ominus}}$$

Thus,

$$[Gly^-]/c^{\ominus} = K_{a1}[HGly]/[H_3O^+]$$

$$K_{a2} = \frac{a_{HGly(aq)}a_{H_3O^+(aq)}}{a_{H_2Gly^+(aq)}a_{H_2O(l)}} = \frac{[HGly][H_3O^+]}{[H_2Gly^+]c^{\ominus}}$$

and

$$[HGly]/c^{\ominus} = K_{a2}[H_2Gly^+]/[H_3O^+]$$

Substituting,

$$[Gly^-]/c^{\ominus} = K_{a1}K_{a2}[H_2Gly^+]/[H_3O^+]^2$$

Hence, the fraction of the various forms are

$$f(\mathrm{Gly^-}) = \frac{[\mathrm{Gly^-}]}{[\mathrm{Gly^-}] + [\mathrm{HGly}] + [\mathrm{H_2Gly^+}]}$$
$$= \frac{K_{a1}K_{a2}[\mathrm{H_2Gly^+}]/[\mathrm{H_3O^+}]^2}{(K_{a1}K_{a2}[\mathrm{H_2Gly^+}]/[\mathrm{H_3O^+}]^2) + (K_{a2}[\mathrm{H_2Gly^+}]/[\mathrm{H_3O^+}]) + [\mathrm{H_2Gly^+}]}$$
$$= \frac{K_{a1}K_{a2}}{K_{a1}K_{a2} + K_{a2}[\mathrm{H_3O^+}] + [\mathrm{H_3O^+}]^2}$$

$$f(\mathrm{HGly}) = \frac{[\mathrm{HGly}]}{[\mathrm{Gly^-}] + [\mathrm{HGly}] + [\mathrm{H_2Gly^+}]}$$
$$= \frac{K_{a2}[\mathrm{H_2Gly^+}]/[\mathrm{H_3O^+}]}{K_{a1}K_{a2}[\mathrm{H_2Gly^+}]/[\mathrm{H_3O^+}]^2 + K_{a2}[\mathrm{H_2Gly^+}]/[\mathrm{H_3O^+}] + [\mathrm{H_2Gly^+}]}$$
$$= \frac{K_{a2}}{K_{a1}K_{a2} + K_{a2}[\mathrm{H_3O^+}] + [\mathrm{H_3O^+}]^2}$$

$$f(\mathrm{H_2Gly^+}) = \frac{[\mathrm{H_2Gly^+}]}{[\mathrm{Gly^-}] + [\mathrm{HGly}] + [\mathrm{H_2Gly^+}]}$$
$$= \frac{[\mathrm{H_2Gly^+}]}{K_{a1}K_{a2}[\mathrm{H_2Gly^+}]/[\mathrm{H_3O^+}]^2 + K_{a2}[\mathrm{H_2Gly^+}]/[\mathrm{H_3O^+}] + [\mathrm{H_2Gly^+}]}$$
$$= \frac{[\mathrm{H_3O^+}]^2}{K_{a1}K_{a2} + K_{a2}[\mathrm{H_3O^+}] + [\mathrm{H_3O^+}]^2}$$

Figure 8.3 shows a plot of these fractions against pH. It can be seen that at low pH, the dominant form is $H_2Gly^+$. At pH = $pK_{a2}$ = 2.35, HGly becomes the most abundant form, until at at pH = $pK_{a1}$ = 9.60, $Gly^-$ dominates.

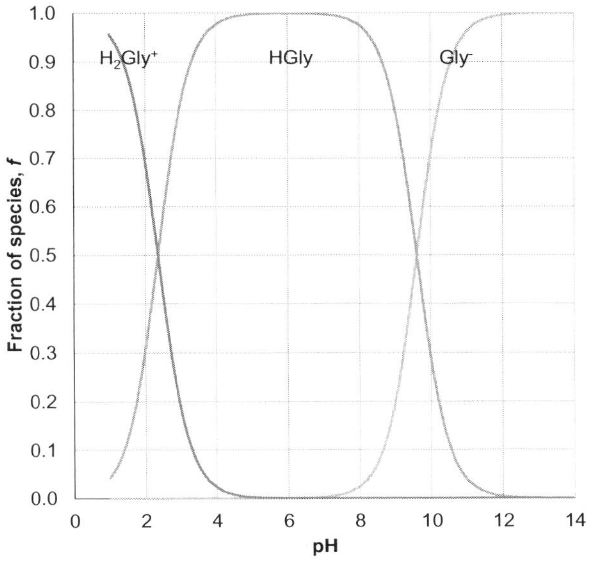


Figure 8.3

We may calculate the molar concentration of a species at a specified pH from these fractions. For example, if pH = 9 and the formal concentration of glycine is 20 mmol $dm^{-3}$, then we find from the plot that $f(HGly) = 0.80$ and $f(Gly^-) = 0.20$ so that

$$[HGly] = (20\ \text{mmol dm}^{-3}) \times (0.80) = \mathbf{16\ mmol\ dm^{-3}}$$

and

$$[Gly^-] = (20\ \text{mmol dm}^{-3}) \times (0.20) = \mathbf{4\ mmol\ dm^{-3}}$$

The fraction, and therefore the concentration, of $H_2Gly^+$ at this pH is negligible.

**E8.19** The pH of a solution of an amphiprotic species is given by eqn 8.12, so that, using the data given in Table 8.2,

$$pH = ½(pK_{a1} + pK_{a2}) = ½(1.81 + 6.92) = \mathbf{4.37}$$

meaning that the solution is acidic.

**E8.20** (a) $NH_4^+$ is the conjugate acid of the weak base $NH_3$. The equilibrium

$$NH_4^+(aq) + H_2O(l) \rightleftharpoons H_3O^+(aq) + NH_3(aq)$$

is established, creating an **acidic** solution.

(b) $CO_3^{2-}$ is the conjugate base of carbonic acid, $H_2CO_3$, and results in a **basic** solution.

$$H_2O(l) + CO_3^{2-}(aq) \rightleftharpoons HCO_3^-(aq) + OH^-(aq)$$

(c) $F^-$ is the conjugate base of hydrofluoric acid, HF, and therefore also results in a **basic** solution

$$H_2O(l) + F^-(aq) \rightleftharpoons HF(aq) + OH^-(aq)$$

(d) $Br^-$ is the conjugate base of hydrobromic acid, HBr. However, hydrobromic acid is strong, and is completely dissociated in aqueous solution.

$$HBr(aq) + H_2O(l) \rightarrow H_3O^+(aq) + Br^-(aq)$$

The $Br^-$ ions do not, therefore change the proportion of $H_3O^+$ and $OH^-$ ions in solution. Thus, a solution of KBr is expected to be **neutral**.

(e) The solution $AlCl_3(aq)$ is **acidic** because $Al^{3+}$ acts as a Lewis acid in water:

$$[Al(H_2O)_6]^{3+}(aq) + H_2O(l) \rightleftharpoons [Al(H_2O)OH]^{2+}(aq) + H_3O^+(aq)$$

(f) Likewise, $Co(NO_3)_2$ is **acidic**:

$$[Co(H_2O)_6]^{2+}(aq) + H_2O(l) \rightleftharpoons [Co(H_2O)OH]^+(aq) + H_3O^+(aq)$$

The examples allow us to predict that an aqueous solution containing a/an:

acid or a conjugate acid of a weak base is **acidic**;
base or a conjugate base of a weak acid is **basic**;
small, highly charged metal cation is **acidic**;
salt of a strong acid and strong base is **neutral**.

**E8.21** We expect a solution of sodium acetate, $NaCH_3CO_2$, to be basic, because the $CH_3CO_2^-$ ion is the conjugate base of acetic acid, $CH_3COOH$

$$H_2O(l) + CH_3CO_2^-(aq) \rightleftharpoons CH_3COOH(aq) + OH^-(aq)$$

If we assume that the solution is sufficiently dilute that we may replace activities by concentrations,

$$K_b = \frac{a_{CH_3COOH(aq)}a_{OH^-(aq)}}{a_{CH_3CO_2^-(aq)}a_{H_2O(l)}} = \frac{[CH_3COOH][OH^-]}{[CH_3CO_2^-]c^{\ominus}}$$

Denoting the fractional change in the molar concentration of $CH_3CO_2^-$ ions as $x$, so that

$$[CH_3COOH] = [OH^-] = x[CH_3CO_2^-]_0$$
$$[CH_3CO_2^-] = (1-x)[CH_3CO_2^-]_0$$

then

$$K_b = \frac{\overbrace{x[CH_3CO_2^-]_0}^{[CH_3COOH]}\overbrace{x[CH_3CO_2^-]_0}^{[OH^-]}}{\underbrace{(1-x)[CH_3CO_2^-]_0}_{[CH_3CO_2^-]}c^{\ominus}} = \frac{x^2}{1-x}([CH_3CO_2^-]_0/c^{\ominus})$$

Acetic acid is a weak acid with, from Table 8.1, $K_b = 5.6 \times 10^{-10}$. We may therefore assume that $(1-x) \approx 1$, so that $K_b \approx x^2([CH_3CO_2^-]/c^{\ominus})$, and hence

$$x = (K_b c^{\ominus}/[CH_3CO_2^-]_0)^{1/2}$$

The pOH of the solution is thus

$$pOH = -\log a_{OH^-} \approx -\log([OH^-]/c^{\ominus})$$
$$= -\log(x[CH_3CO_2^-]_0/c^{\ominus}) = -\log\{(K_b[CH_3CO_2^-]_0/c^{\ominus})^{1/2}\}$$

The initial concentration of acetate ions is

$$[CH_3CO_2^-]_0 = \frac{n}{V} = \frac{\overbrace{m}^{\text{mass}} / \overbrace{M}^{\text{molar mass}}}{\underbrace{V}_{\text{volume}}}$$
$$= \frac{(7.4\ \text{g})}{(82.03\ \text{g mol}^{-1}) \times (250 \times 10^{-3}\ \text{dm}^3)} = 0.36\ \text{mol dm}^{-3}$$

so that

$$pOH = -\log_{10}[(5.6 \times 10^{-10}) \times (0.36)]^{1/2} = \mathbf{4.8}$$

and

$$\mathrm{pH} = \mathrm{p}K_\mathrm{w} - \mathrm{pOH} = 14.0 - 4.8 = \mathbf{9.2}$$

**E8.22** The ammonium ion, $NH_4^+$, is the conjugate acid of ammonia

$$NH_4^+(aq) + H_2O(l) \rightleftharpoons H_3O^+ + NH_3(aq)$$

so we should expect a solution of $NH_4Cl$ to be acidic. For a dilute solution, we may express the acidity constant in terms of concentrations,

$$K_\mathrm{a} = \frac{a_{\mathrm{NH_3(aq)}}a_{\mathrm{H_3O^+}}}{a_{\mathrm{NH_4^+(aq)}}a_{\mathrm{H_2O(l)}}} \approx \frac{[\mathrm{NH_3}][\mathrm{H_3O^+}]}{[\mathrm{NH_4^+}]c^\ominus}$$

and if we denote the degree of dissociation as $x$, so that

$$[\mathrm{NH_3}] = [\mathrm{H_3O^+}] = x[\mathrm{NH_4Cl}]_0$$
$$[\mathrm{NH_4Cl}] = (1-x)[\mathrm{NH_4Cl}]_0$$

then

$$K_\mathrm{a} = \frac{x^2}{1-x}([\mathrm{NH_4Cl}]_0/c^\ominus)$$

Ammonia is a weak base, so we might expect the degree of dissociation to be small. Thus, we may make the approximation $(1-x) \approx 1$, so that $K_\mathrm{a} \approx x([\mathrm{NH_4Cl}/c^\ominus])^{1/2}$, and therefore

$$x = K_\mathrm{a}/([\mathrm{NH_4Cl}]_0/c^\ominus)^{1/2}$$

The formal concentration of $NH_4Cl$ is given by

$$[\mathrm{NH_4Cl}]_0 = \frac{n}{V} = \frac{\overbrace{m}^{\text{mass}} / \overbrace{M}^{\text{molar mass}}}{\underbrace{V}_{\text{volume}}}$$

Thus

$$\begin{aligned}\mathrm{pH} &= -\log a_{\mathrm{H_3O^+}} \approx -\log([\mathrm{H_3O^+}]/c^\ominus)\\ &= -\log(x[\mathrm{NH_4Cl}]_0/c^\ominus) = -\log(K_\mathrm{a}[\mathrm{NH_4Cl}]_0/c^\ominus)^{1/2}\\ &= -\log\left(\frac{K_\mathrm{a}m}{MVc^\ominus}\right)^{1/2}\\ &= -\log\left\{\frac{(5.6\times10^{-10})\times(2.75\ \mathrm{g})}{(53.54\ \mathrm{g\ mol^{-1}})\times(100\times10^{-3}\ \mathrm{dm^3})\times(1\ \mathrm{mol\ dm^{-3}})}\right\}^{1/2}\\ &= \mathbf{4.8}\end{aligned}$$

**E8.23** KBr is the salt of the strong acid HBr. Therefore, none of the $Br^-$ is protonated.

**E8.24** The titration is equivalent to the neutralization reaction

$$2\ HCl(aq) + Ba(OH)_2 \rightleftharpoons 2\ H_2O(l) + BaCl_2(aq)$$

The titration corresponds to the addition of a strong acid to a strong base, and we may therefore ignore the contribution to the concentration of $H_3O^+$ and $OH^-$ ions from autoprotolysis. The $Ba(OH)_2$ solution is initially basic, and we can track the progress of the titration towards the stoichiometric point through the concentration of $OH^-$ ions

$$[OH^-] = \frac{n_{OH^-}}{V} = \frac{2c_{Ba(OH)_2}V_{Ba(OH)_2} - c_{HCl}V_{HCl}}{V_{Ba(OH)_2} + V_{HCl}}$$

After the stoichiometric point, when the HCl is in excess,

$$[H_3O^+] = \frac{n_{H_3O^+}}{V} = \frac{c_{HCl}V_{HCl} - 2c_{Ba(OH)_2}V_{Ba(OH)_2}}{V_{Ba(OH)_2} + V_{HCl}}$$

The pH of the solution then follows because

$$pH = -\log a_{H_3O^+} \approx -\log_{10}([H_3O^+]/c^{\ominus}) = pK_w - \log_{10}([OH^-]/c^{\ominus})$$

Figure 8.4 shows a plot of pH against the volume of HCl added. The initial pH is

$$\begin{aligned} pH &= pK_w - \log([OH^-]_0/c^{\ominus}) = 14.00 - \log\left(2c_{Ba(OH)_2}V_{Ba(OH)_2}/c^{\ominus}\right) \\ &= 14.00 - \log(2 \times 0.15) = \mathbf{13.5} \end{aligned}$$

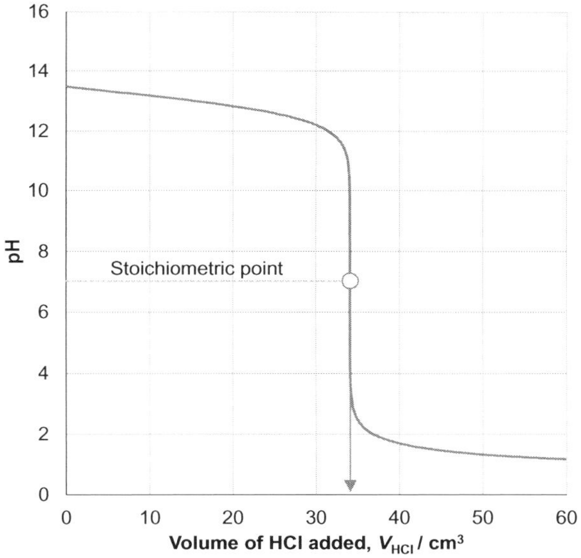


**Figure 8.4**

At the stoichiometric point, the HCl added neutralizes exactly the $Ba(OH)_2$ so that the concentrations of $H_3O^+$ and $OH^-$ are given by the autoprotolysis of water. Thus,

$$c_{HCl}V_{HCl} - 2c_{Ba(OH)_2}V_{Ba(OH)_2} = 0$$

$$\begin{aligned} V_{HCl} &= 2c_{Ba(OH)_2}V_{Ba(OH)_2}/c_{HCl} \\ &= 2 \times (0.15\ \text{mol dm}^{-3}) \times (25 \times 10^{-3}\text{dm}^3)/(0.22\ \text{mol dm}^{-3}) \end{aligned}$$

$$= 34 \times 10^{-3}\,\text{dm}^3 = \mathbf{34\ cm^3}$$

**E8.25** Tyrosine (HTyr) may exist in the protonated form as $H_3Tyr^+$, or deprotonated form as $HTyr^-$ and $Tyr^{2-}$, which are related through the deprotonation reactions:

$$H_3Tyr^+(aq) + H_2O(l) \rightleftharpoons H_3O^+(aq) + H_2Tyr(aq) \qquad pK_{a1} = 2.20$$
$$H_2Tyr(aq) + H_2O(l) \rightleftharpoons H_3O^+(aq) + HTyr^-(aq) \qquad pK_{a2} = 9.11$$
$$HTyr^-(aq) + H_2O(l) \rightleftharpoons H_3O^+(aq) + Tyr^{2-}(aq) \qquad pK_{a3} = 10.07$$

Following the method adopted in Example 8.5, and Exercise 8.18, we assume that the solution is sufficiently dilute that we may replace activities by concentrations and so write

$$K_{a1} = \frac{a_{H_2Tyr(aq)}a_{H_3O^+(aq)}}{a_{H_3Tyr^+(aq)}a_{H_2O(l)}} \approx \frac{[H_2Tyr][H_3O^+]}{[H_3Tyr^+]c^{\ominus}}$$

so that

$$[H_2Tyr] = K_{a1}[H_3Tyr^+]c^{\ominus}/[H_3O^+]$$

In the same way for the other reactions,

$$[HTyr] = K_{a2}[H_2Tyr]c^{\ominus}/[H_3O^+] = K_{a1}K_{a2}[H_3Tyr^+]c^{\ominus 2}/[H_3O^+]^2$$
$$[Tyr^{2-}] = K_{a3}[HTyr^-]c^{\ominus}/[H_3O^+] = K_{a1}K_{a2}K_{a3}[H_3Tyr^+]c^{\ominus 3}/[H_3O^+]^3$$

The fraction of $H_3Tyr^+$ is thus

$$f(H_3Tyr^+) = \frac{[H_3Tyr^+]}{[H_3Tyr^+] + [H_2Tyr] + [HTyr^-] + [Tyr^{2-}]}$$
$$= \frac{[H_3Tyr^+]}{\left\{\begin{array}{c}[H_3Tyr^+] + (K_{a1}[H_3Tyr^+]c^{\ominus}/[H_3O^+]) \\ +(K_{a1}K_{a2}[H_3Tyr^+]c^{\ominus 2}/[H_3O^+]^2) \\ +(K_{a1}K_{a2}K_{a3}[H_3Tyr^+]c^{\ominus 3}/[H_3O^+]^3)\end{array}\right\}}$$
$$= \frac{([H_3O^+]/c^{\ominus})^3}{\left\{\begin{array}{c}([H_3O^+]/c^{\ominus})^3 + K_{a1}([H_3O^+]/c^{\ominus})^2 \\ +K_{a1}K_{a2}([H_3O^+]/c^{\ominus}) + K_{a1}K_{a2}K_{a3}\end{array}\right\}}$$

and similarly for the other species. The molar concentration of each component is then given by the product of the fraction and formal concentration, 30 mmol $dm^{-3}$. These concentrations are plotted against pH in Figure 8.5.

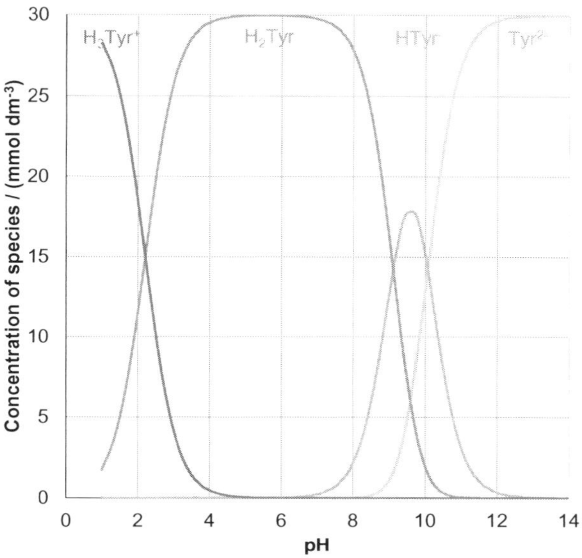


**Figure 8.5**

**E8.26** The pH of a solution of an amphiprotic salt system is given by eqn 8.12

$$\mathrm{pH} = ½(\mathrm{p}K_{\mathrm{a1}} + \mathrm{p}K_{\mathrm{a2}})$$

Sodium hydrogenoxalate, $NaHCOOCO_2^-$, is the salt of oxalic acid, $(COOH)_2$ for which Table 8.2 gives $\mathrm{p}K_{\mathrm{a1}} = 1.23$ and $\mathrm{p}K_{\mathrm{a1}} = 4.19$, and therefore

$$\mathrm{pH} = ½(1.23 + 4.19) = \mathbf{2.71}$$

The expression is valid provided that

$$S/c^{\ominus} \gg K_{\mathrm{a1}} = 10^{-1.23} = 58.8 \times 10^{-3}$$

so that

$$S \gg 58.8 \text{ mmol dm}^{-3}$$

where $S$ is the initial concentration of the salt. The requirement that

$$S/c^{\ominus} \gg K_{\mathrm{w}}/K_{\mathrm{a2}} = 10^{-14}/10^{-4.19} \approx 10^{-9}$$

is then automatically met.

**E8.27** (a) The $NH_4^+$ ions formed by disolving ammonium chloride, $NH_4Cl$, in aqueous solution will result in an acidic solution through the equilibrium

$$NH_4^+(aq) + H_2O(l) \rightleftharpoons H_3O^+(aq) + NH_3(aq)$$

If we assume that the solution is sufficiently dilute that we may express the acidity constant in terms of concentrations rather than activities,

$$K_a = \frac{a_{H_3O^+(aq)}a_{NH_3(aq)}}{a_{NH_4^+(aq)}a_{H_2O(l)}} = \frac{[H_3O^+][NH_3]}{[NH_4^+]c^{\ominus}}$$

then, because $[NH_3] = [H_3O^+]$ and $[NH_4^+] = [NH_4^+]_0 - [H_3O^+]$,

$$K_a = \frac{[H_3O^+]^2}{([NH_4^+]_0 - [H_3O^+])c^{\ominus}}$$

Because $NH_3$ is a weak base, $[NH_4^+]_0 \gg [H_3O^+]$, so we may make the approximation that $[NH_4^+]_0 - [H_3O^+] \approx [NH_4^+]_0$ and therefore

$$K_a \approx \frac{[H_3O^+]^2}{[NH_4^+]_0 c^{\ominus}}$$

so that

$$\begin{aligned} pH &= -\log_{10} a_{H_3O^+} = -\log_{10}[H_3O^+]/c^{\ominus} = -\log_{10}(K_a[NH_4^+]_0/c^{\ominus})^{1/2} \\ &= -\log_{10}(5.6 \times 10^{-10} \times 0.10)^{1/2} = \mathbf{5.1} \end{aligned}$$

(b) A solution of sodium acetate, $NaCH_3CO_2$, is basic, because of the establishment of the equilibrium

$$H_2O(l) + CH_3CO_2^-(aq) \rightleftharpoons CH_3COOH(aq) + OH^-(aq)$$

Following the method and approximations used in part (a),

$$\begin{aligned} K_b &= \frac{a_{CH_3COOH(aq)}a_{OH^-(aq)}}{a_{H_2O(l)}a_{CH_3CO_2^-(aq)}} \\ &\approx \frac{[CH_3COOH][OH^-]}{[CH_3CO_2^-]} \approx \frac{[OH^-]^2}{[CH_3CO_2^-]_0 - [OH^-]} \approx \frac{[OH^-]^2}{[CH_3CO_2^-]_0} \end{aligned}$$

so that

$$\begin{aligned} pH &= pK_w - pOH = pK_w - \log_{10} a_{OH^-} = pK_w - \log_{10}[OH^-]/c^{\ominus} \\ &= pK_w - \log_{10}(K_b[CH_3CO_2^-]_0/c^{\ominus})^{1/2} = 14.00 - \log_{10}(5.6 \times 10^{-10} \times 0.25)^{1/2} \\ &= \mathbf{9.1} \end{aligned}$$

(c) In the same way for a solution of acetic acid,

$$CH_3COOH(aq) + H_2O(l) \rightleftharpoons H_3O^+(aq) + CH_3CO_2^-(aq)$$

$$\begin{aligned} K_a &= \frac{a_{CH_3CO_2^-(aq)}a_{H_3O^+(aq)}}{a_{H_2O(l)}a_{CH_3COOH(aq)}} \\ &\approx \frac{[CH_3CO_2^-][H_3O^+]}{[CH_3COOH]} \approx \frac{[H_3O^+]^2}{[CH_3COOH]_0 - [H_3O^+]} \approx \frac{[H_3O^+]^2}{[CH_3COOH]_0} \end{aligned}$$

so that

$$\begin{aligned} pH &= -\log a_{H_3O^+} = -\log([H_3O^+]/c^{\ominus}) = -\log(K_a[CH_3COOH]_0/c^{\ominus})^{1/2} \\ &= -\log(1.8 \times 10^{-5} \times 0.200)^{1/2} = \mathbf{2.7} \end{aligned}$$

In each case, we can test the validity of our approximations by solving for $[H_3O^+]$ or $[OH^-]$ exactly.

**E8.28** (a) For a solution of acetic acid,

$$CH_3COOH(aq) + H_2O(l) \rightleftharpoons H_3O^+(aq) + CH_3CO_2^-(aq)$$

and if we assume that the solution is sufficiently dilute that we may replace activities by concentrations, and that the degree of deprotonation is small,

$$K_a = \frac{a_{CH_3CO_2^-(aq)}a_{H_3O^+(aq)}}{a_{H_2O(l)}a_{CH_3COOH(aq)}}$$
$$\approx \frac{[CH_3CO_2^-][H_3O^+]}{[CH_3COOH]c^{\ominus}} \approx \frac{[H_3O^+]^2}{([CH_3COOH]_0 - [H_3O^+])} \approx \frac{[H_3O^+]^2}{[CH_3COOH]_0 c^{\ominus}}$$

so that

$$\mathrm{pH} = -\log_{10} a_{H_3O^+} = -\log_{10}[H_3O^+]/c^{\ominus} = -\log_{10}(K_a[CH_3COOH]_0/c^{\ominus})^{1/2}$$
$$= -\log_{10}(1.8\times10^{-5}\times0.10)^{1/2} = \mathbf{2.9}$$

(b) The addition of NaOH neutralises the $H_3O^+$ ions formed by the deprotonation of $CH_3COOH$ until all of the $OH^-$ ions are used up; one $CH_3COOH$ molecule is lost and one $CH_3CO_2^-$ ion is created until the $OH^-$ is completely neutralised. The point of equilibrium between the $CH_3COOH$ and $CH_3CO_2^-$ therefore adjusts as the $OH^-$ ions are added and $H_3O^+$ ions removed. Thus, it is no longer true that $[CH_3CO_2^-] = [H_3O^+]$. The volume of the solution also changes as the NaOH is added.

The amount of $CH_3COOH$ molecules removed is equal to the amount lost through neutralisation of the $H_3O^+$ by the NaOH, and the amount deprotonated in achieving equilibrium

$$\overbrace{n_{CH_3COOH,eq}}^{\substack{\text{amount of}\\ CH_3COOH\text{ at}\\ \text{equilibrium}}} = \overbrace{n_{CH_3COOH,0}}^{\substack{\text{amount of}\\ CH_3COOH\\ \text{initially}}} - \overbrace{n_{NaOH,0}}^{\substack{\text{amount of}\\ \text{NaOH added}}} - \overbrace{n_{H_3O^+,eq}}^{\substack{\text{amount of}\\ H_3O^+\text{ at}\\ \text{equilibrium}}}$$

For each $CH_3COOH$ molecule lost, one $CH_3CO_2^-$ ion is created, so that

$$n_{CH_3CO_2^-} = \overbrace{n_{NaOH,0}}^{\substack{\text{amount of}\\ \text{NaOH added}}} + \overbrace{n_{H_3O^+,eq}}^{\substack{\text{amount of}\\ H_3O^+\text{ at}\\ \text{equilibrium}}}$$

Thus,

$$K_{a1} \approx \frac{[CH_3CO_2^-][H_3O^+]}{[CH_3COOH]/c^{\ominus}} = \frac{\{(n_{NaOH,0} + n_{H_3O^+,eq})/V\}\{n_{H_3O^+,eq}/V\}}{\{(n_{CH_3COOH,0} - n_{NaOH,0} - n_{H_3O^+,eq})/V\}/c^{\ominus}}$$
$$= \frac{(n_{NaOH,0} + n_{H_3O^+,eq})n_{H_3O^+,eq}}{(n_{CH_3COOH,0} - n_{NaOH,0} - n_{H_3O^+,eq})(V_{CH_3COOH,0} + V_{NaOH,0})/c^{\ominus}}$$

It is reasonable, given the concentration and volume of NaOH added, and because acetic acid is a weak acid, to assume that $n_{\mathrm{NaOH,0}} \gg n_{\mathrm{H_3O^+,eq}}$, so that

$$\begin{aligned} K_{\mathrm{a1}} &\approx \frac{n_{\mathrm{NaOH,0}} n_{\mathrm{H_3O^+,eq}}}{(n_{\mathrm{CH_3COOH,0}} - n_{\mathrm{NaOH,0}})(V_{\mathrm{CH_3COOH,0}} + V_{\mathrm{NaOH,0}})/c^{\ominus}} \\ &= \frac{c_{\mathrm{NaOH,0}} V_{\mathrm{NaOH,0}}([\mathrm{H_3O^+}]/c^{\ominus})}{c_{\mathrm{CH_3COOH,0}} V_{\mathrm{CH_3COOH,0}} - c_{\mathrm{NaOH,0}} V_{\mathrm{NaOH,0}}} \end{aligned}$$

Rearranging,

$$\begin{aligned} [\mathrm{H_3O^+}] &= K_{\mathrm{a1}} \times \frac{c_{\mathrm{CH_3COOH,0}} V_{\mathrm{CH_3COOH,0}} - c_{\mathrm{NaOH,0}} V_{\mathrm{NaOH,0}}}{c_{\mathrm{NaOH,0}} V_{\mathrm{NaOH,0}}} c^{\circ} \\ &= 1.8 \times 10^{-5} \\ &\quad \times \frac{(0.10\ \mathrm{mol\ dm^{-3}}) \times (25.0\ \mathrm{cm^3}) - (0.10\ \mathrm{mol\ dm^{-3}}) \times (10.0\ \mathrm{cm^3})}{(0.10\ \mathrm{mol\ dm^{-3}}) \times (10.0\ \mathrm{cm^3})} \\ &= 2.7 \times 10^{-5}\ \mathrm{mol\ dm^{-3}} \end{aligned}$$

which is equivalent to a pH of

$$\mathrm{pH} = -\log a_{\mathrm{H_3O^+}} \approx -\log([\mathrm{H_3O^+}]/c^{\circ}) = -\log(2.7 \times 10^{-5}) = \mathbf{4.6}$$

(c) At the stoichiometric point, the amount of sodium hydroxide must equal the initial amount of acetic acid. Thus, halfway to the stoichiometric point

$$\begin{aligned} n_{\mathrm{NaOH}} &= \tfrac{1}{2} n_{\mathrm{CH_3COOH}} \\ c_{\mathrm{NaOH}} V_{\mathrm{NaOH}} &= \tfrac{1}{2} c_{\mathrm{CH_3COOH,0}} V_{\mathrm{CH_3COOH,0}} \\ V_{\mathrm{NaOH}} &= \tfrac{1}{2} c_{\mathrm{CH_3COOH,0}} V_{\mathrm{CH_3COOH,0}} / c_{\mathrm{NaOH}} \end{aligned}$$

Because, in this exercise, the acetic acid and sodium hydroxide solutions have equal molar concentrations, $V_{\mathrm{NaOH}} = V_{\mathrm{CH_3COOH,0}}$

$$V_{\mathrm{NaOH}} = \tfrac{1}{2} V_{\mathrm{CH_3COOH,0}} = 0.5 \times 25.0\ \mathrm{cm^3} = \mathbf{12.5\ cm^3}$$

(d) At the halfway point, pH = p$K_a$ = **4.74**.

(e) At the stoichiometric point, the amount of sodium hydroxide is equal to the initial amount of acetic acid. Thus, because the concentrations of acid and base are equal, the volume of sodium hydroxide that must be added is **25.0 cm³**.

(f) At the stoichiometric point, the solution is effectively 0.050 mol dm$^{-3}$ sodium ethanoate, $NaCH_3CO_2$. Thus, the pH depends upon the equilibrium

$$\overbrace{\mathrm{H_2O(l)}}^{\text{acid}} + \underbrace{\mathrm{CH_3CO_2(aq)}}_{\text{base}} \rightleftharpoons \underbrace{\mathrm{CH_3COOH(aq)}}_{\text{acid}} + \overbrace{\mathrm{OH(aq)}}^{\text{base}}$$

If we assume that the solution is sufficiently dilute that we may replace activities by concentrations

$$K_b = \frac{a_{CH_3COOH(aq)}a_{OH^-(aq)}}{\underbrace{a_{H_2O(l)}}_{1}\, a_{CH_3CO_2^-(aq)}} \approx \frac{[CH_3COOH][OH^-]}{[CH_3CO_2^-]c^{\ominus}} = \frac{\overbrace{[OH^-]^2}^{[CH_3COOH]=[OH^-]}}{([CH_3CO_2^-]_0 - [CH_3COOH])c^{\ominus}}$$

Sodium ethanoate is a weak base, with $K_b = 5.56 \times 10^{-10}$, so we may assume that

$$[CH_3CO_2^-]_0 - [CH_3COOH] \approx [CH_3CO_2^-]_0 = 0.050 \text{ mol dm}^{-3}$$

Thus, rearranging,

$$[OH^-] = (K_b[CH_3CO_2^-]_0 c^{\ominus})^{1/2}$$

and therefore

$$\begin{aligned}
pH &= pK_w - pOH \\
&= pK_w + \log a_{OH^-(aq)} \approx pK_w + \log([OH^-]/c^{\ominus}) \\
&= pK_w + \log(K_b[CH_3CO_2^-]_0/c^{\ominus})^{1/2} \\
&= 14.00 + ½\log\{(5.56 \times 10^{-10} \times 0.050)\} = \mathbf{8.72}
\end{aligned}$$

**E8.29** At the halfway point in the titration, the concentration of acid and base are equal, so that applying the Henderson–Hasselbalch equation, gives

$$pH = pK_a - \log\frac{[acid]}{[base]} = pK_a$$

Thus, the $pK_a$ of the acid is given by the pH of the solution so that $pK_a = \mathbf{5.16}$ and

$$K_a = 10^{-pK_a} = 10^{-5.16} = \mathbf{6.92 \times 10^{-6}}$$

For the equilibrium

$$HA(aq) + H_2O(l) \rightleftharpoons H_3O^+(aq) + A^-(aq)$$

if we assume that the solution is sufficiently dilute that we may replace the activities of the components by concentrations, and write

$$K_a = \frac{a_{A^-(aq)}a_{H_3O^+(aq)}}{a_{HA(aq)}a_{H_2O(l)}} \approx \frac{([A^-]/c^{\ominus})([H_3O^+]/c^{\ominus})}{([HA]/c^{\ominus})} = \frac{[A^-][H_3O^+]}{[HA]c^{\ominus}}$$

If we ignore the autopyrolysis of water, we may assume that $[A^-] = [H_3O^+]$, and also express the concentration of acid at equilibrium in terms of the initial concentration and the concentration of $H_3O^+$, $[HA] = [HA]_0 - [H_3O^+]$. Furthermore, if we assume that the degree of dissociation is small, we may also make the approximation $[HA]_0 - [H_3O^+] \approx [HA]_0$. Thus,

$$K_a \approx \frac{[H_3O^+]^2}{[HA]_0 c^{\ominus}}$$

and rearranging,

$$[H_3O^+] = \sqrt{K_a[HA]_0 c^{\ominus}}$$
$$= \sqrt{6.92\times10^{-6}\times(0.025\ \text{mol dm}^{-3})\times(1\ \text{mol dm}^{-3})} = 4.16\times10^{-4}$$

so that

$$\text{pH} = -\log a_{H_3O^+} \approx -\log([H_3O^+]/c^{\circ})$$
$$= -\log(4.16\times10^{-4}) = \mathbf{3.38}$$

**E8.30** At the stoichiometric point in a titration, the amount of base added is equal to the amount of acid initially present. For this particular system, the pH of the solution at this point is then determined by the equilibrium

$$H_2O(l) + CH_3CH(OH)CO_2^-(aq) \rightleftharpoons CH_3CH(OH)COOH(aq) + OH^-(aq)$$

For simplicity, we may denote lactic acid, $CH_3CH(OH)COOH$, as HL and lactate ions, $CH_3CH(OH)CO_2^-$, as $L^-$. At this point, the concentration of $OH^-$ ions is equal to the concentration of lactic acid, so that $[OH^-] = [HL]$. The concentration of lactate ions is given by the difference between the formal concentration of acid, $[HL]_0$, and the concentration of acid present as undissociated HL at equilibrium, $[L^-] = [HL]_0 - [HL]$. Thus, if we assume that the solution is sufficiently dilute that we may express the activities of the various components in terms only of concentrations,

$$K_b = \frac{a_{HL}a_{OH^-(aq)}}{a_{L^-(aq)}a_{H_2O(l)}} = \frac{([HL]/c^{\ominus})([OH^-]/c^{\ominus})}{([L^-]/c^{\ominus})} = \frac{[HL]\overbrace{[OH^-]}^{[HL]}}{\underbrace{[L^-]}_{[HL]_0-[HL]}c^{\ominus}} = \frac{[HL]^2}{([HL]_0-[HL])c^{\ominus}}$$

The lactate ion is a weak base with, from Table 8.1, $K_b = 1.2\times10^{-11}$. It is therefore reasonable to assume that the concentration of acid present in the undissociated form, [HL], is small, so that $[HL]_0 - [HL] \approx [HL]_0$. Thus,

$$K_b \approx \frac{[HL]^2}{[HL]_0 c^{\circ}}$$

The formal concentration of lactic acid, $[HL]_0$, depends upon the initial amount of acid and the total volume. The volume of base required to reach the stoichiometric point is

$$V_{base} = V_{acid}\times(c_{acid}/c_{base})$$

where $c_{acid}$ and $c_{base}$ are the molar concentrations of the acid and base solutions, so that

$$[HL]_0 = \frac{n_{HL,0}}{V} = \frac{n_{HL,0}}{V_{acid}+V_{base}} = \frac{c_{acid}V_{acid}}{V_{acid}+V_{acid}(c_{acid}/c_{base})} = \frac{c_{acid}}{1+(c_{acid}/c_{base})}$$

$$[OH^-] = [HL] = (K_b[HL]_0c^{\ominus})^{1/2} = \left(\frac{c_{acid}K_bc^{\ominus}}{1+(c_{acid}/c_{base})}\right)^{1/2}$$
$$= \left(\frac{(0.150\ \text{mol dm}^{-3})\times(1.2\times10^{-11})\times(1\ \text{mol dm}^{-3})}{1+\{(0.150\ \text{mol dm}^{-3})/(0.188\ \text{mol dm}^{-3})\}}\right)^{1/2}$$

$$= 1.00 \times 10^{-6}\ \text{mol dm}^{-3}$$

The pH of the solution is thus

$$\text{pH} = \text{p}K_\text{w} - \text{pOH} = 14.00 + \log_{10} a_{\text{OH}^-} \approx 14.00 + \log_{10}([\text{OH}^-]/c^\circ)$$
$$= 14.00 - \log_{10}(1.00 \times 10^{-6}) = \mathbf{8.00}$$

**E8.31** The pH of the solution is determined by the equilibrium

$$\text{CH}_3\text{CO}_2^-(\text{aq}) + \text{H}_2\text{O(l)} \rightleftharpoons \text{CH}_3\text{COOH(aq)} + \text{OH}^-(\text{aq})$$

with, if we assume that the solution is sufficiently dilute that activities may be replaced by concentrations,

$$K_\text{b} = \frac{a_{\text{CH}_3\text{COOH(aq)}}a_{\text{OH}^-(\text{aq})}}{a_{\text{CH}_3\text{CO}_2^-(\text{aq})}a_{\text{H}_2\text{O(l)}}} \approx \frac{([\text{CH}_3\text{COOH}]/c^\ominus)([\text{OH}^-]/c^\ominus)}{([\text{CH}_3\text{CO}_2^-]/c^\ominus)} = \frac{[\text{CH}_3\text{COOH}][\text{OH}^-]}{[\text{CH}_3\text{CO}_2^-]/c^\ominus}$$

Initially, with no acetic acid added, the concentration of $CH_3COOH$ and $OH^-$ must be equal, $[CH_3COOH] = [OH^-]$, with the concentration of $CH_3CO_2^-$ ions being given by the difference between the formal concentration of the solution and the concentration of the protonated species, $[CH_3CO_2^-] = [CH_3CO_2^-]_0 - [CH_3COOH]$. Furthermore, because acetic acid is a weak acid, we may assume that the degree of protonation is small, so that $[CH_3CO_2^-]_0 >> [CH_3COOH]$ and we may make the approximation

$$K_\text{b} = \frac{[\text{OH}^-]^2}{([\text{CH}_3\text{CO}_2^-]_0 - [\text{CH}_3\text{COOH}])/c^\ominus} \approx \frac{[\text{OH}^-]^2}{[\text{CH}_3\text{CO}_2^-]_0/c^\ominus}$$

Rearranging allows us to calculate the initial pH of the $NaCH_3CO_2$ solution. Taking the value of $K_b$ for acetic acid from Table 8.1,

$$\text{pH} = \text{p}K_\text{w} - \text{pOH} = \text{p}K_\text{w} + \log a_{\text{OH}^-(\text{aq})}$$
$$\approx \text{p}K_\text{w} + \log([\text{OH}^-]/c^\ominus) = \text{p}K_\text{w} + \log(K_\text{b}[\text{CH}_3\text{CO}_2^-]_0/c^\ominus)^{1/2}$$
$$= 14.00 + \log(5.6 \times 10^{-10} \times 0.10) = 8.88$$

The pH of the solution once additional acetic acid has been added may be calculated from the Henderson–Hasselbalch equation, eqn 8.13

$$\text{pH} = \text{p}K_\text{a} - \log\frac{[\text{acid}]}{[\text{base}]} = \text{p}K_\text{a} - \log\frac{[\text{CH}_3\text{COOH}]}{[\text{CH}_3\text{CO}_2^-]}$$

Acetic acid is a weak acid, and we may therefore assume that the degree of deprotonation is small. The concentration of acid may therefore be taken to be the formal concentration of acetic acid added, $[CH_3COOH] \approx [CH_3COOH]_0$, and the concentration of base to be that of the initial $NaCH_3CO_2$ solution. Thus,

$$\mathrm{pH} = \mathrm{p}K_\mathrm{a} - \log \overbrace{\frac{n_{\mathrm{CH_3COOH}}/V}{n_{\mathrm{CH_3CO_2^-}}/V}}^{c=n/V} = \mathrm{p}K_\mathrm{a} - \log \frac{n_{\mathrm{CH_3COOH}}}{n_{\mathrm{CH_3CO_2^-}}}$$
$$= \mathrm{p}K_\mathrm{a} - \log \frac{[\mathrm{CH_3COOH}]_0 V_{\mathrm{CH_3COOH}}}{[\mathrm{CH_3CO_2^-}] V_{\mathrm{CH_3CO_2^-}}}$$

where $V_{\mathrm{CH_3COOH}}$ and $V_{\mathrm{CH_3CO_2^-}}$ are the volumes of the initial solutions and $V$ is the total volume of the resulting mixture. If, for simplicity, we assume that the $NaCH_3CO_2$ and $CH_3COOH$ solutions are of the same molar concentration, then this expression reduces to

$$\mathrm{pH} = \mathrm{p}K_\mathrm{a} - \log_{10}\left(V_{\mathrm{CH_3COOH}}/V_{\mathrm{CH_3CO_2^-}}\right)$$

Figure 8.6 shows a plot of pH against the ratio of the volume of the acetic solution added to the volume of the initial sodium acetate solution.

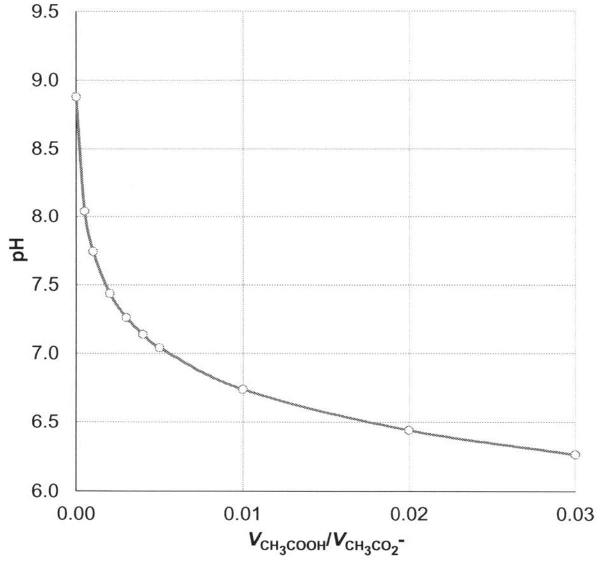


**Figure 8.6**

**E8.32** (a) From the Henderson–Hasselbalch equation, eqn 8.13, if [acid] = [base],

$$\mathrm{pH} = \mathrm{p}K_\mathrm{a} - \log \frac{[\mathrm{acid}]}{[\mathrm{base}]} = \mathrm{p}K_\mathrm{a} - \log(1) = \mathrm{p}K_\mathrm{a}$$

Thus, $\mathrm{p}K_\mathrm{a} = \mathrm{pH} = \mathbf{3.08}$ and

$$K_\mathrm{a} = 10^{-\mathrm{p}K_\mathrm{a}} = 10^{-3.08} = \mathbf{8.32 \times 10^{-4}}$$

(b) In the same way, if [acid] = 2 × [base]

$$\mathrm{pH} = \mathrm{p}K_\mathrm{a} - \log \frac{[\mathrm{acid}]}{[\mathrm{base}]} = \mathrm{p}K_\mathrm{a} - \log \frac{2 \times [\mathrm{base}]}{[\mathrm{base}]}$$

$$= 3.08 - \log_{10}(2) = \mathbf{2.78}$$

**E8.33** From the Henderson–Hasselbalch equation, eqn 8.13, if [acid] = [base],

$$\mathrm{pH} = \mathrm{p}K_\mathrm{a} - \log\frac{[\mathrm{acid}]}{[\mathrm{base}]} = \mathrm{p}K_\mathrm{a} - \log(1) = \mathrm{p}K_\mathrm{a} = 8.3$$

this is the pH at which the buffering action is best, as solution components provide the capacity to neutralize small amounts of either base or acid that may be added without a drastic effect on solution pH.

**E8.34** (a) The concentration of acid and base in the initial solution are equal so that, using the Henderson–Hasselbalch equation, eqn 8.13, and the value for the p$K_\mathrm{a}$ of acetic acid from Table 8.1,

$$\mathrm{pH} = \mathrm{p}K_\mathrm{a} - \log\frac{[\mathrm{CH_3COOH}]}{[\mathrm{CH_3CO_2^-}]} = 4.75 - \log(1) = \mathbf{4.75}$$

(b) The addition of 3.3 mmol of NaOH causes a change in the concentration of acid and base: The amount of $CH_3COOH$ decreases by 3.3 mmol because it is neutralised by the $OH^-$ ions, creating an additional 3.3 mmol of $CH_3CO_2^-$ ions. The concentrations of acid and base therefore become

$$[\mathrm{CH_3COOH}] = \frac{n_{\mathrm{CH_3COOH}}}{V} = \frac{\overbrace{n_{\mathrm{CH_3COOH,0}}}^{\text{initial amount}} - \overbrace{n_{\mathrm{NaOH}}}^{\text{amount lost through neutralisation by NaOH}}}{V}$$
$$= \frac{n_{\mathrm{CH_3COOH,0}}}{V} - \frac{n_{\mathrm{NaOH}}}{V} = [\mathrm{CH_3COOH}]_0 - \frac{n_{\mathrm{NaOH}}}{V}$$

In the same way,

$$[\mathrm{CH_3CO_2^-}] = [\mathrm{CH_3CO_2^-}]_0 + \frac{n_{\mathrm{NaOH}}}{V}$$

Thus,

$$\mathrm{pH} = \mathrm{p}K_\mathrm{a} - \log\frac{[\mathrm{CH_3COOH}]}{[\mathrm{CH_3CO_2^-}]}$$
$$= \mathrm{p}K_\mathrm{a} - \log\left\{\frac{[\mathrm{CH_3COOH}]_0 - (n_{\mathrm{NaOH}}/V)}{[\mathrm{CH_3CO_2^-}]_0 + (n_{\mathrm{NaOH}}/V)}\right\}$$
$$= 4.75 - \log\left[\frac{(0.100\ \mathrm{mol\ dm^{-3}}) - \{(3.3\times10^{-3}\mathrm{mol})/(100\times10^{-3}\ \mathrm{dm^3})\}}{(0.100\ \mathrm{mol\ dm^{-3}}) + \{(3.3\times10^{-3}\mathrm{mol})/(100\times10^{-3}\ \mathrm{dm^3})\}}\right]$$
$$= 4.75 - \log\left(\frac{0.100 - 0.033}{0.100 + 0.033}\right) = \mathbf{5.0}$$

(c) Similarly, the addition of 6.6 mmol of $HNO_3$ will also affect equally the concentration of acid and base in solution. Thus,

$$\begin{aligned}
pH &= pK_a - \log\frac{[CH_3COOH]}{[CH_3CO_2^-]} \\
&= pK_a - \log\left\{\frac{[CH_3COOH]_0 + (n_{HNO_3}/V)}{[CH_3CO_2^-]_0 - (n_{HNO_3}/V)}\right\} \\
&= 4.75 - \log\left[\frac{(0.100\ \text{mol dm}^{-3}) + \{(6.6\times10^{-3}\text{mol})/(100\times10^{-3}\ \text{dm}^3)\}}{(0.100\ \text{mol dm}^{-3}) - \{(6.6\times10^{-3}\text{mol})/(100\times10^{-3}\ \text{dm}^3)\}}\right] \\
&= 4.75 - \log\left(\frac{0.100+0.066}{0.100-0.066}\right) = \mathbf{4.1}
\end{aligned}$$

**E8.35** A buffer solution is most effective when the concentrations of acid and base are equal, which corresponds to half way to the stoichiometric point. Under these conditions, small amounts of either acid or base may be added with only a small effect on the pH of the solution. Thus, the most effective pH region of a buffer is centred at the $pK_a$ of the acid used. Hence:

(a) $pK_a = 3.08$; pH range, **2–4**
(b) $pK_a = 4.19$; pH range, **3–5**
(c) $pK_{a3} = 12.68$; pH range, **11.5–13.5**
(d) $pK_{a2} = 7.21$;pH range, **6–8**
(e) $pK_b = 7.97$, $pK_a = 6.03$; pH range, **5–7**

**E8.36** We should choose a buffer system in which the conjugate acid has a $pK_a$ close to the desired pH. Therefore, suitable systems would be:

(a) $H_3PO_4$ and $NaH_2PO_4$
(b) $NaH_2PO_4$ and $Na_2HPO_4$, or $NaHSO_3$ and $Na_2SO_3$

**E8.37** (a) The dissolution of silver iodide, AgI, corresponds to the equilibrium

$$AgI(s) \rightleftharpoons Ag^+(aq) + I^-(aq)$$

The activity of a pure solid or liquid is 1. Furthermore, because the salt is only sparingly soluble, the resulting solution will be sufficiently dilute that we may replace activies by concentrations. Thus, the solubility product may be written as

$$K_s = \frac{a_{Ag^+(aq)}a_{I^-(aq)}}{\underbrace{a_{AgI(s)}}_{1}} \approx ([Ag^+]/c^{\ominus})([I^-]/c^{\ominus})$$

or if, for simplicity, we neglect the terms in the standard concentration,

$$K_s = [Ag^+][I^-]$$

Denoting the solubility of silver iodide as $s$, then we may write $[Ag^+] = [I^-] = s$, so that

$$K_s = s^2$$

(b) In the same way for $Hg_2S$,

$$Hg_2S(s) + H_2O(l) \rightleftharpoons Hg_2^{2+}(aq) + S^{2-}(aq)$$

$$K_s = [Hg_2^{2+}][S^{2-}] = s^2$$

(c) For the dissolution of $Fe(OH)_3$,

$$Fe(OH)_3(s) \rightleftharpoons Fe^{3+}(aq) + 3\ OH^-(aq)$$

and so, because the concentration of $OH^-$ ions is three times the concentration of $Fe^{3+}$ ions, $[OH^-] = 3\ [Fe^{3+}] = 3\ s$,

$$K_s = [Fe^{3+}][OH^-]^3 = s \times (3s)^3 = 27s^4$$

(d) And for $Ag_2CrO_4$,

$$Ag_2CrO_4(s) + H_2O(l) \rightleftharpoons 2\ Ag^+(aq) + CrO_4^{2-}(aq)$$

Thus, because the concentration of $Ag^+$ ions in solution is twice that of $CrO_4^{2-}$ ions, $[Ag^+] = 2\ [CrO_4^{2-}] = 2\ s$

$$K_s = [Ag^+]^2[CrO_4^-] = (2s)^2 s = 4s^3$$

**E8.38** (a) For the dissolution of $BaSO_4$,

$$BaSO_4(s) + H_2O(l) \rightleftharpoons Ba^{2+}(aq) + SO_4^{2-}(aq)$$

the solubility constant, $K_s$, may be expressed in terms of the solubility, $s$, as

$$K_s = \frac{\overbrace{a_{Ba^{2+}(aq)}}^{[Ba^{2+}]/c^\ominus}\ \overbrace{a_{SO_4^{2-}}}^{[SO_4^{2-}]/c^\ominus}}{\underbrace{a_{BaSO_4(s)}}_{1}} = \overbrace{[Ba^{2+}]}^{s}\ \overbrace{[SO_4^{2-}]}^{s} = s^2$$

with activities of the ions in solution replaced by concentrations because, for a sparingly soluble salt such as $BaSO_4$, the solution is dilute. Thus,

$$s = K_s^{1/2} = (1.1 \times 10^{-10})^{1/2} = \mathbf{1.0 \times 10^{-5}\ mol\ dm^{-3}}$$

(b) In the same way for $Ag_2CO_3$,

$$Ag_2CO_3(s) + H_2O(l) \rightleftharpoons 2\ Ag^+(aq) + CO_3^{2-}(aq)$$

so that, because the concentration of $Ag^+$ ions is twice that of the $CO_3^{2-}$ ions,

$$K_s = \overbrace{[Ag^+]^2}^{(2s)^2}\ \overbrace{[CO_3^{2-}]}^{s} = 4s^2 \times s = 4s^3$$

Thus,

$$s = (K_s/4)^{1/3} = (6.2 \times 10^{-10}/4)^{1/3} = \mathbf{1.2 \times 10^{-4}\ mol\ dm^{-3}}$$

(c) And for $Fe(OH)_3$,

$$Fe(OH)_3(s) \rightleftharpoons Fe^{3+}(aq) + 3\ OH^-(aq)$$

and so, because the concentration of $OH^-$ ions is three times the concentration of $Fe^{3+}$ ions, $[OH^-] = 3\,[Fe^{3+}] = 3\,s$,

$$K_s = \overbrace{[Fe^{3+}]}^{s}\,\overbrace{[OH^-]^3}^{(3s)^3} = s \times 27s^3 = 27s^4$$

Thus,

$$s = (K_s/27)^{1/4} = (2.0 \times 10^{-39}/27)^{1/4} = \mathbf{9.3 \times 10^{-11}\ mol\ dm^{-3}}$$

(d) In the same way for $Hg_2Cl_2$,

$$Hg_2Cl_2(s) \rightleftharpoons Hg_2^{2+}(aq) + 2\ Cl^-(aq)$$

the concentration of $Cl^-$ ions is twice that of the $Hg_2^{2+}$ ions, so that

$$K_s = \overbrace{[Hg_2^{2+}]}^{s}\,\overbrace{[Cl^-]^2}^{(2s)^2} = s \times 4s^2 = 4s^3$$

and

$$s = (K_s/4)^{1/3} = (1.3 \times 10^{-18}/4)^{1/3} = \mathbf{6.9 \times 10^{-7}\ mol\ dm^{-3}}$$

**E8.39** (a) For the dissolution of AgBr,

$$AgBr(s) \rightleftharpoons Ag^+(aq) + Br^-(aq)$$

if we assume that the solution is sufficiently dilute that the activities of the components may be replaced by concentrations, the solubility constant may be written as

$$K_s = \frac{a_{Ag^+(aq)}a_{Br^-(aq)}}{a_{AgBr(s)}} \approx ([Ag^+]/c^{\ominus})([Br^-]/c^{\ominus})$$

The concentration of $Ag^+$ ions is equal to the solubility, $[Ag^+] = s$. The $Br^-$ ions result both from the NaBr solution and from the dissolution of AgBr, $[Br^-] = C + s$. Because the AgBr is only sparingly soluble, $C \gg s$, so that $[Br^-] \approx C$. Thus,

$$K_s \approx sC/c^{\ominus 2}$$

and rearranging,

$$s = \frac{K_s c^{\ominus 2}}{C} = \frac{7.7 \times 10^{-13} \times (1\ \text{mol dm}^{-3})^2}{1.4 \times 10^{-3}\text{mol dm}^{-3}} = \mathbf{5.5 \times 10^{-10} mol\ dm^{-3}}$$

(b) For the dissolution of $MgCO_3$,

$$MgCO_3(s) \rightleftharpoons Mg^{2+}(aq) + CO_3^{2-}(aq)$$

Because the magnitude of the solubility constant is similar to the concentration of the solution containing the common ion, we cannot make the approximation that $[CO_3^{2-}] \approx C$. Instead, we must write

$$K_s = \frac{a_{Mg^{2+}(aq)}a_{CO_3^{2-}(aq)}}{a_{MgCO_3(s)}} \approx (\overbrace{[Mg^{2+}]}^{s}/c^{\ominus})(\overbrace{[CO_3^{2-}]}^{C+s}/c^{\ominus}) = s(C+s)/c^{\ominus 2}$$

Rearranging, we obtain the quadratic equation

$$s^2 + Cs - K_s c^{\ominus 2} = 0$$

which is of the form $ax^2 + bx + c = 0$ and therefore has a solution

$$\begin{aligned} s &= \frac{-b \pm \sqrt{b^2 - 4ac}}{2a} = \frac{-C \pm \sqrt{C^2 - 4 \times 1 \times -K_s c^{\ominus 2}}}{2} \\ &= \frac{-1.1 \times 10^{-5} \pm \sqrt{(1.1 \times 10^{-5})^2 + (4 \times 1.0 \times 10^{-5})}}{2} \text{ mol dm}^{-3} \\ &= \mathbf{3.2 \times 10^{-3}\ mol\ dm^{-3}} \end{aligned}$$

Because the concentration of the solution containing the secondary ion is so weak, it has only a negligible effect on the solubility of the $MgCO_3$. Indeed, we would have obtained the same value had we ignored the effect of the $Na_2CO_3$ solution altogether.

(c) For the dissolution of lead (II) sulfate,

$$PbSO_4(s) \rightleftharpoons Pb^{2+}(aq) + SO_4^{2-}(aq)$$

$$K_s = \frac{a_{Pb^{2+}(aq)}a_{SO_4^{2-}(aq)}}{a_{PbSO_4(s)}} = (\overbrace{[Pb^{2+}]}^{s}/c^{\ominus})(\overbrace{[SO_4^{2-}]}^{C}/c^{\ominus}) \approx \frac{sC}{c^{\ominus 2}}$$

and so, rearranging,

$$s = \frac{K_s c^{\ominus 2}}{C} = \frac{1.6 \times 10^{-8} \times (1 \text{ mol dm}^{-3})^2}{0.10 \text{ mol dm}^{-3}} = \mathbf{1.6 \times 10^{-7}\ mol\ dm^{-3}}$$

(d) In the same way for the dissolution of nickel (II) hydroxide,

$$Ni(OH)_2(s) \rightleftharpoons Ni^{2+}(aq) + 2\,OH^-(aq)$$

Nickel (II) hydroxide is sparingly soluble. We may therefore, once again, safely ignore the the contribution to the $Ni^{2+}$ ion concentration from the dissolution. Thus,

$$K_s = \frac{a_{Ni^{2+}(aq)}a^2_{OH^-(aq)}}{a_{Ni(OH)_2(s)}} = (\overbrace{[Ni^{2+}]}^{C+S\approx C}/c^{\ominus})(\overbrace{[OH^-]}^{2s}/c^{\ominus})^2 \approx \frac{4s^2C}{c^{\ominus 3}}$$

and rearranging,

$$s = \left(\frac{K_s c^{\ominus 3}}{4C}\right)^{1/2} = \left\{\frac{(6.5 \times 10^{-18}) \times (1 \text{ mol dm}^{-3})^3}{4 \times (2.7 \times 10^{-5} \text{ mol dm}^{-3})}\right\}^{1/2} = \mathbf{2.5 \times 10^{-7}\ mol\ dm^{-3}}$$

**E8.40** For the dissolution of mercuric iodide, $Hg_2I_2$,

$$Hg_2I_2(s) \rightleftharpoons Hg_2^{2+}(aq) + 2\,I^-(aq)$$

The salt is sparingly soluble, so we may write the expression for the solubility constant in terms of concentrations rather than activities

$$K_s = \frac{\overbrace{a_{Hg_2^{2+}(aq)}}^{[Hg_2^{2+}]/c^\ominus}\ \overbrace{a^2_{I^-(aq)}}^{([I^-]/c^\ominus)^2}}{\underbrace{a_{Hg_2I_2(s)}}_{1}} \approx (\overbrace{[Hg_2^{2+}]}^{s}/c^\ominus)(\overbrace{[I^-]}^{2s}/c^\ominus)^2 = s \times (2s^2)/c^{\ominus 3} = 4s^3/c^{\ominus 3}$$

But, from eqn 7.8,

$$\begin{aligned}\Delta_s G^\ominus &= -RT\ln K_s = -RT\ln(4s^3/c^{\ominus 3})\\ &= -(8.3145\ \mathrm{J\,K^{-1}mol^{-1}}) \times (298.15\ \mathrm{K}) \times \ln[4\times(1\times10^{-15})^3]\\ &= +253\times10^3\ \mathrm{J\,mol^{-1}} = \mathbf{+253\ kJ\,mol^{-1}}\end{aligned}$$

The standard Gibbs energy of dissolution is large and positive, as we should expect for a sparingly soluble salt.

**E8.41** We may express the Gibbs energy of dissolution of mercury(II) chloride

$$HgCl_2(s) \rightleftharpoons Hg^{2+}(aq) + 2\,Cl^-(aq)$$

in terms of the standard enthalpies of formation of the various components by analogy with eqn 7.12. Thus, using the values for the standard Gibbs energies of formation from the text *Data section*,

$$\begin{aligned}\Delta_s G^\ominus &= \sum \nu\Delta_f G^\ominus(\text{products}) - \sum \nu\Delta_f G^\ominus(\text{reactants})\\ &= \overbrace{\{\Delta_f G^\ominus(Hg^{2+},aq) + 2\,\Delta_f G^\ominus(Cl^-,aq)\}}^{\text{products}} - \overbrace{\{\Delta_f G^\ominus(HgCl_2,s)\}}^{\text{reactants}}\\ &= [\{+164.40\ + 2\times(-131.23)\} - \{-178.6+0\}]\ \mathrm{kJ\,mol^{-1}}\\ &= +\,80.54\ \mathrm{kJ\,mol^{-1}}\end{aligned}$$

But,

$$\begin{aligned}K_s &= \frac{\overbrace{a_{Hg^{2+}(aq)}}^{[Hg^{2+}]/c^\ominus}\ \overbrace{a^2_{Cl^-(aq)}}^{([Cl^-]/c^\ominus)^2}}{\underbrace{a_{HgCl_2(s)}}_{1}} \approx (\overbrace{[Hg^{2+}]}^{s}/c^\ominus)(\overbrace{[Cl^-]}^{2s}/c^\ominus)^2\\ &= s\times(2s^2)/c^{\ominus 3} = 4s^3/c^{\ominus 3}\end{aligned}$$

Thus, rearranging and using eqn 7.8, $\Delta G = -RT\ln K$,

$$\begin{aligned}s &= (K_s/4)^{1/3}c^\ominus = \{e^{-(\Delta_s G^\ominus/RT)}/4\}^{1/3}c^\ominus\\ &= [e^{-\{(80.54\times10^3\,\mathrm{J\,mol^{-1}})/(8.3145\,\mathrm{J\,K^{-1}mol^{-1}})\times(298.15\,\mathrm{K})\}}/4]^{1/3}c^\ominus\\ &= \mathbf{1.25\times10^{-5}\ mol\,dm^{-3}}\end{aligned}$$

**E8.42** (a) Silver chloride, AgCl, is sparingly soluble. We may therefore assume that the resulting solution will be sufficiently dilute that we may write the solubility constant for the dissolution of silver chloride, AgCl,

$$\mathrm{AgCl(s)} \rightleftharpoons \mathrm{Ag^{+}(aq)} + \mathrm{Cl^{-}(aq)}$$

in terms of concentrations

$$K_\mathrm{s} = \frac{\overbrace{a_{\mathrm{Ag^+(aq)}}}^{[\mathrm{Ag^+}]/c^\ominus}\,\overbrace{a_{\mathrm{Cl^-(aq)}}}^{[\mathrm{Cl^-}]/c^\ominus}}{\underbrace{a_{\mathrm{AgCl(s)}}}_{1}} \approx (\overbrace{[\mathrm{Ag^+}]}^{s}/c^\ominus)(\overbrace{[\mathrm{Cl^-}]}^{s}/c^\ominus) = s^2/c^{\ominus 2}$$

We may use the van 't Hoff equation, eqn 7.15, to derive an expression for the ratio of the solubility constants at two different temperatures. Thus,

$$\ln K_\mathrm{s}(T) - \ln K_\mathrm{s}(T') = \frac{\Delta_\mathrm{s}H^\ominus}{R}\left\{\frac{1}{T'} - \frac{1}{T}\right\}$$

But,

$$\ln K_\mathrm{s}(T) - \ln K_\mathrm{s}(T') = \ln \frac{\overbrace{K_\mathrm{s}(T)}^{(s(T)/c^\ominus)^2}}{\underbrace{K_\mathrm{s}(T')}_{(s(T')/c^\ominus)^2}} = \ln \frac{s(T)^2}{s(T')^2} = \ln\left\{\frac{s(T)}{s(T')}\right\}^2 = 2\ln\left\{\frac{s(T)}{s(T')}\right\}$$

Thus, combining the two equations gives us an expression for the ratio of the solubilities at different temperatures.

$$\ln\left\{\frac{s(T)}{s(T')}\right\} = \frac{\Delta_\mathrm{s}H^\ominus}{2R}\left\{\frac{1}{T'} - \frac{1}{T}\right\}$$

If the temperature is raised, so that $T > T'$, then the term in parentheses is positive. Thus, the logarithm of the ratio of the solubilities is positive if the standard enthalpy of dissolution is positive. The solubility therefore increases with temperature if dissolution is an exothermic process and decreases if dissolution is an endothermic process.

(b) For the dissolution of AgCl, we may calculate the standard enthalpy of dissolution from the standrad enthalpies of formation of the various components. Thus, from eqn 3.5,

$$\Delta_\mathrm{s}H^\ominus = \sum \nu\Delta_\mathrm{f}H^\ominus(\text{products}) - \sum \nu\Delta_\mathrm{f}H^\ominus(\text{reactants})$$

$$= \overbrace{\{\Delta_\mathrm{f}H^\ominus(\mathrm{Ag^+,aq}) + \Delta_\mathrm{f}H^\ominus(\mathrm{Cl^-,aq})\}}^{\text{products}} - \overbrace{\{\Delta_\mathrm{f}H^\ominus(\mathrm{AgCl,s})\}}^{\text{reactants}}$$
$$= [\{105.58 + (-167.16)\} - \{-127.07 + 0\}]\ \mathrm{kJ\ mol^{-1}}$$
$$= +65.49\ \mathrm{kJ\ mol^{-1}}$$

Dissolution is therefore endothermic, and we should expect the solubility of silver chloride to **increase** as the temperature is raised.

# Answers to projects

**P8.43** Lysine, HLys, is amphiprotic. In basic solution, it exists in the deprotonated form $Lys^-$; in more acidic solutions, it exists in protonated forms as $H_2Lys^+$ or even as $H_3Lys^{2+}$.

$$HLys(aq) + H_2O(l) \rightleftharpoons H_3O^+(aq) + Lys^-(aq) \qquad pK_{a1} = 10.53$$
$$HLys(aq) + H_2O(l) \rightleftharpoons H_3O^+(aq) + H_2Lys^+(aq) \qquad pK_{a2} = 8.95$$
$$H_2Lys^+(aq) + H_2O(l) \rightleftharpoons H_3O^+(aq) + H_3Lys^{2+}(aq) \qquad pK_{a2} = 2.18$$

We may deduce expressions for the fractional composition of each protonated species by analogy with those for oxalic acid in Example 8.5 and glycine in Exercise 8.18. Thus, it follows that

$$f(Lys^-) = \frac{K_{a1}K_{a2}K_{a3}}{[H_3O^+]^3 + K_{a1}[H_3O^+]^2 + K_{a1}K_{a2}[H_3O^+] + K_{a1}K_{a2}K_{a3}}$$
$$f(HLys) = \frac{K_{a1}K_{a2}[H_3O^+]}{[H_3O^+]^3 + K_{a1}[H_3O^+]^2 + K_{a1}K_{a2}[H_3O^+] + K_{a1}K_{a2}K_{a3}}$$
$$f(H_2Lys^+) = \frac{K_{a1}[H_3O^+]^2}{[H_3O^+]^3 + K_{a1}[H_3O^+]^2 + K_{a1}K_{a2}[H_3O^+] + K_{a1}K_{a2}K_{a3}}$$
$$f(H_3Lys^{2+}) = \frac{[H_3O^+]^3}{[H_3O^+]^3 + K_{a1}[H_3O^+]^2 + K_{a1}K_{a2}[H_3O^+] + K_{a1}K_{a2}K_{a3}}$$

Figure 8.7 shows the resulting speciation diagram, which shows how the fractional composition of each species varies as a function of pH.

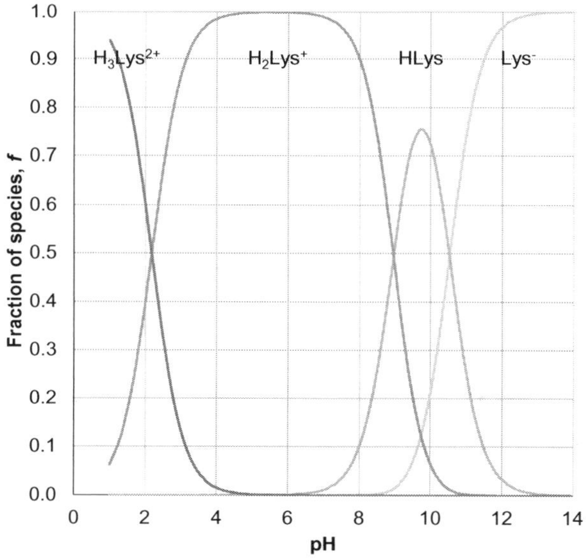


**Figure 8.7**

The diagram shows that, as expected, the concentration of each species reaches a maximum at a pH close to the $pK_a$ of the appropriate acid dissociation step.

**P8.44** Histidine, HHis, is also amphiprotic, and can exist in aqueous solution as $His^-$, HHis, $H_2His^+$ and $H_3His^{2+}$. We should therefore expect its beahviour in solution to be very similar to that of lysine, with the concentration of each species reaching a maximum at a pH close to the $pK_a$ of the appropriate acid dissociation step. The speciation diagram for histidine is shown in Figure 8.8.

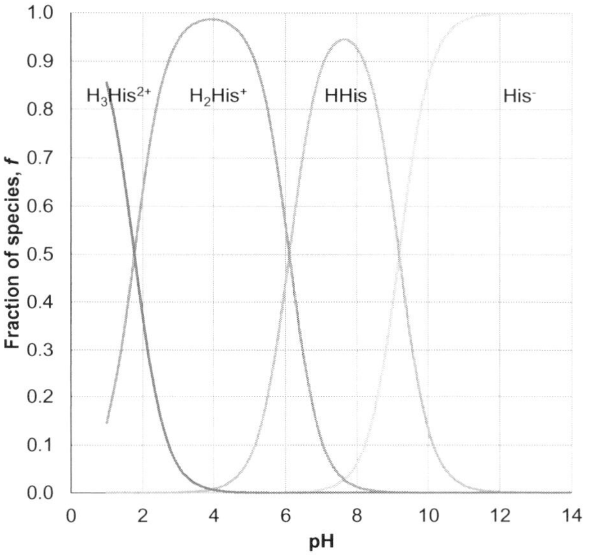


**Figure 8.8**

**P8.45** (a) For the acid dissociation of carbonic acid,

$$H_2CO_3(aq) + H_2O(l) \rightleftharpoons H_3O^+(aq) + HCO^-(aq)$$

if we asume that the solution is sufficiently dilute that we may express the activities of the components in terms only of their concentrations, then we may write the acidity constant as

$$K_a = \frac{\overbrace{a_{H_3O^+(aq)}}^{[H_3O^+]/c^\ominus}\,\overbrace{a_{HCO_3^-(aq)}}^{[HCO_3^-]/c^\ominus}}{\underbrace{a_{H_2CO_3(aq)}}_{[H_2CO_3]/c^\ominus}\,\underbrace{a_{H_2O(l)}}_{1}} \approx \frac{([H_3O^+]/c^\ominus)([HCO_3^-]/c^\ominus)}{([H_2CO_3]/c^\ominus)} = \frac{[H_3O^+][HCO_3^-]}{[H_2CO_3]c^\ominus}$$

At the physiological temperature of 37 °C, $K_a = 7.9 \times 10^{-7}$. Thus, at the normal blood pH of 7.40,

$$\frac{[HCO_3^-]}{[H_2CO_3]} = \frac{K_a c^\ominus}{[H_3O^+]} = \frac{K_a c^\ominus}{10^{-pH}} = \frac{7.9 \times 10^{-7}\ \text{mol dm}^{-3}}{10^{-7.40}} = \mathbf{20.0}$$

The onset of acidosis occurs at pH = 7.35, so that

$$\frac{[HCO_3^-]}{[H_2CO_3]} = \frac{7.9 \times 10^{-7}\ \text{mol dm}^{-3}}{10^{-7.35}\ \text{mol dm}^{-3}} = \mathbf{17.8}$$

and alkalosis at pH = 7.45,

$$\frac{[HCO_3^-]}{[H_2CO_3]} = \frac{7.9 \times 10^{-7}\ \text{mol dm}^{-3}}{10^{-7.45}\text{mol dm}^{-3}} = \mathbf{22.3}$$

(b) The Bohr effect observes that haemoglobin binds $O_2$ more strongly when it is deprotonated at slightly higher blood pH. That is, the Hb saturation $s$, which is proportional to bound $O_2$, increases. The Hill coefficient, $\nu$, is defined by the mathematical model

$$\log\left(\frac{s}{1-s}\right) = \nu \log(p_{O_2}/p^{\ominus}) - \nu \log K$$

At high partial pressures, the last term is not the major influence. Ignoring it, we see that the left side of the equation increases as $s$ increases and, consequently, the Hill coefficient must increase should this occur at constant pressure. We conclude that the Hill coefficient increases with a slight increase in pH.

# Chapter 9

# Chemical equilibria: electrochemistry

## Answers to discussion questions

**D9.1** The **Debye–Hückel theory** of very dilute ionic solutions yields a method for calculating the **mean activity coefficient,** $\gamma_{\pm}$, of an electrolyte. The theory emphasizes the long-range Coulombic (electrostatic) interaction between ions that brings anions and cations into energetically favourable proximity. Averaged over time, **counter ions** (ions of opposite charge) are more likely to be found near any given ion. This time-averaged, spherical haze around the central ion, in which counter ions outnumber ions of the same charge as the central ion, has a net charge equal in magnitude but opposite in sign to that on the central ion, and is called the **ionic atmosphere**. The energy, and therefore the chemical potential, of any given central ion is lowered below its ideal value as a result of its net electrostatic attraction with its ionic atmosphere. The ideal value of both an activity coefficient and a mean activity coefficient is equal to 1 but the attraction of the ionic atmosphere causes $\gamma_{\pm}$ to be less than 1. The Debye–Hückel theory is correct in the limit of infinitely dilute electrolyte molality, but a rule-of-thumb accepts its application when the total ion concentration is less than around $10^{-3}$ mol kg$^{-1}$. When interested in property trends alone, we often accept, within limits, the estimate that activity coefficients are approximately equal to 1 and activities equal concentration.

The Debye–Hückel limiting theory of activity coefficients fails in more concentrated electrolyte solutions because ionic size becomes important and the effective hydration spheres of ions is reduced by competitive attraction by ions for available water molecules. These affect the ionic atmosphere stabilization effect of the Debye–Hückel limiting theory. First, direct association of oppositely charged ions yields ion pairs of zero net charge. The ion pairs have a dipole but a reduced attraction to the ionic atmosphere. Secondly, strong repulsions between either cations or anions diminish the validity of the hazy ionic atmosphere model. The charge imbalance of the ionic atmosphere may decrease or ions may begin to align in very small, localized patterns that resemble an ionic crystal lattice when time-averaged. Consequently, as concentration approaches moderate levels the activity coefficient stops the decline of the Debye–Hückel limiting theory and begins to grow toward a value of 1 as the ionic atmosphere stabilization effect is lost. At higher concentrations the activity coefficient may even become larger than 1.

**D9.2** The migration of aqueous protons is mechanistically very different from the migration of other ions. In a simplified view, a proton on one water molecule migrates to a neighbouring water molecule, a proton on that water molecule then migrates to its neighbour, and so on along a chain of water molecules. The motion of protons is therefore an *effective* motion of a proton, not the actual motion of a single proton. This causes proton migration to be far more rapid than the migration of other ions, which must move as a single, individual unit from one position to another; compare the ionic mobilities of Table 9.2.

According to the detailed **Grotthus mechanism**, there is an effective motion of a proton that involves the rearrangement of bonds in a group of water molecules. However, the actual mechanism is still highly contentious. Attention focuses on the $H_9O_4^+$ unit in which the nearly trigonal planar $H_3O^+$ ion is linked to three strongly solvating $H_2O$ molecules. This cluster of atoms is itself hydrated, but the hydrogen bonds in the secondary sphere are weaker than in the primary sphere. It is envisaged that the rate-determining step is the cleavage of one of the weaker hydrogen bonds of this secondary sphere. After this bond cleavage has taken place, and the released molecule has rotated through a few degrees (a process that takes about 1 ps), there is a rapid adjustment of bond lengths and angles in the remaining cluster, to form an $H_5O_2^+$ cation of structure $H_2O\cdots H^+\cdots OH_2$. Shortly after this reorganization has occurred, a new $H_9O_4^+$ cluster forms as other molecules rotate into a position where they can become members of a secondary hydration sphere, but now the positive charge is located one molecule to the right of its initial location. According to this model, there is no coordinated motion of a proton along a chain of molecules, simply a very rapid hopping between neighbouring sites, with low activation energy. The model is consistent with the observation that the molar conductivity of protons increases as the pressure is raised, for increasing pressure ruptures the hydrogen bonds in water.

**D9.3** A **galvanic cell** uses a spontaneous chemical reaction to generate a potential difference and deliver an electric current to an external device. An **electrolytic cell** uses an external potential difference to drive a chemical reaction in the cell that is by itself non-spontaneous. In their essential features, these two kinds of cells can be considered opposites of each other, in the sense that an electrolytic cell can be thought of as a galvanic cell operating in the reverse direction. For some electrochemical cells, this is easy to accomplish. We say they are rechargeable. The most common example is the lead-acid battery used in automobiles. For many other cells, however, this kind of reversibility cannot be achieved. A **fuel cell**, like the galvanic cell, uses a spontaneous chemical reaction to generate a potential difference and deliver an electric current to an external device. Unlike the galvanic cell, the fuel cell must receive reactants from an external storage tank.

A **salt bridge** connecting two half-cells compartments is usually a U-tube filled with potassium chloride in agar jelly. It provides the mobile electrolyte for completing the circuit of an electrochemical cell. In its absence, the cell cannot generate an electrical current through the single wire that connects the two electrodes and the circuit is said to be open. No electron can leave, or enter, either half-cell, because this act would cause the net electronic charge of the half-cell to be non-zero. The strong electrostatic force prevents this from happening and causes macroscopic objects to normally have a zero net electrical charge. However, a salt bridge provides an anion to the anodic half-cell for every electron that leaves while simultaneously providing a cation to the cathodic half-cell for every electron that enters. This is a closed electrical circuit in which the net charge of each half-cell remains zero but an electric current can be generated. The salt bridge uses KCl specifically because the mobilities of the $K^+$ and $Cl^-$ ions are very similar, which minimizes the **liquid junction potential** across the interface of the two electrolyte compartments.

**D9.4** The **electrochemical series** lists metallic elements and hydrogen in the order of their reducing power as measured by their standard potentials in aqueous solution (Table 9.3). It is used to quickly determine whether one metal can spontaneously displace another from solution at 298 K. A couple with a low standard potential has a thermodynamic tendency to reduce a couple with a high standard potential.

| Couple | $Ag^+/Ag$ | $Cu^{2+}/Cu$ | $H^+/H_2$ | $Zn^{2+}/Zn$ |
|---|---|---|---|---|
| $E^\ominus$ / V at 25 °C | +0.80 | +0.34 | 0, by definition | −0.76 |

For example, zinc is lower than hydrogen in the series, so zinc will spontaneously react with the hydronium cation, $H^+(aq)$, to form the zinc cation and hydrogen gas: $Zn(s) + 2\,H^+(aq) \rightarrow Zn^{2+}(aq) + H_2(g)$. Silver is higher in the series so it will not displace the hydronium ion.

**D9.5** The table of standard potentials provides the starting point for the determination of thermodynamic properties of a redox reaction. To calculate the standard reaction potential we take the difference of the difference of the right (R, cathode) and left (L, anode) standard potential of the half-reactions, eqn 9.18,

$$E^\ominus_{\text{cell}} = E^\ominus_{\text{R}} - E^\ominus_{\text{L}}$$

The standard reaction Gibbs energy and equilibrium constant can be calculated from eqns 9.14 and 9.17

$$\Delta_r G^\ominus = -\nu F E^\ominus_{\text{cell}}$$
$$\ln K = \nu F E^\ominus_{\text{cell}}/RT$$

where $\nu$ is the amount of electrons transferred in the reaction. With $E^\ominus_{\text{cell}}$ measured at temperature $T$ and $E^\ominus_{\text{cell}}$ measured at temperature $T'$ the standard reaction entropy is given by eqn 9.19

$$\Delta_r S^\ominus = \frac{\nu F\left(\mathrm{E}^\ominus_{\text{cell}} - \mathrm{E}^\ominus_{\text{cell}}{}'\right)}{T - T'}$$

Finally, the standard reaction enthalpy is calculated by rearranging eqn 4.16

$$\Delta_r H^{\ominus} = \Delta_r G^{\ominus} + T\Delta_r S^{\ominus}$$

The cell potential $E_{cell}$ is measured with a high impedance voltmeter under zero current conditions. When using a standard hydrogen electrode (SHE) as a reference electrode, $E_{cell}$ is the desired half-reaction potential. However, in practice, the standard hydrogen electrode is awkward to set up, and we often use other reference electrodes. Rarely will all of the components in the cell be in their standard states. We may use, however, the Nernst equation, eqn 9.15, to determine $E^{\ominus}_{cell}$ from the measured value of $E_{cell}$.

$$E_{cell} = E^{\ominus}_{cell} - \frac{RT}{vF}\ln Q$$

It would seem that substitution of $E$ and $Q$ values would allow the computation of the standard redox potential $E^{\ominus}_{cell}$ for the couple. However, a problem arises for aqueous systems because the calculation of $Q$ requires not only knowledge of the concentrations of the species involved in the cell reaction but also of their activity coefficients. These coefficients are not usually available, so the calculation cannot be directly completed. However, at very low concentrations, the Debye–Hückel limiting law for the coefficients holds. The procedure then is to substitute the Debye–Hückel law for the activity coefficients into the specific form of the Nernst equation for the cell under investigation. The standard cell potential, $E^{\ominus}_{cell}$, may then be determined by extrapolating an appropriate graph to the limit of infinite dilution. For example, for the Harned cell,

$$\tfrac{1}{2}H_2(g) + AgCl(s) \rightarrow HCl(aq) + Ag(s)$$

the Nernst equation may be written as

$$E_{cell} = E^{\ominus}_{cell} - \frac{RT}{vF}\ln Q = E^{\ominus}_{cell} - \frac{RT}{vF}\ln \frac{\overbrace{a_{HCl(aq)}}^{\gamma_{\pm}(b_{HCl}/b^{\ominus})}\ \overbrace{a_{Ag(s)}}^{1}}{\underbrace{a^{1/2}_{H_2(g)}}_{(p_{H_2}/p^{\ominus})^{1/2}}\ \underbrace{a_{AgCl(s)}}_{1}}$$

and if we assume that the gaseous hydrogen is in its standard state, $p_{H_2}=p^{\ominus}$, and express the activity of HCl in terms of molality using the Debye–Hückel limiting law,

$$\begin{aligned}
E_{cell} &= E^{\ominus}_{cell} - \frac{RT}{vF}\ln \gamma_{\pm}(b_{HCl}/b^{\ominus}) \\
&= E^{\ominus}_{cell} - \frac{RT}{vF}\overbrace{\ln\gamma_{\pm}}^{-A'|z_+z_-|I^{1/2}} - \frac{RT}{vF}\ln(b_{HCl}/b^{\ominus}) \\
&= E^{\ominus}_{cell} - \frac{RT}{vF}\overbrace{\ln\gamma_{\pm}}^{-A'|z_+z_-|I^{1/2}} - \frac{RT}{vF}\ln(b_{HCl}/b^{\ominus}) \\
&= E^{\ominus}_{cell} + \frac{RT}{vF}A'\overbrace{|z_+z_-|}^{1}\ \overbrace{I^{1/2}}^{b^{1/2}_{HCl}} - \frac{RT}{vF}\ln(b_{HCl}/b^{\ominus}) \\
&= E^{\ominus}_{cell} + \frac{RT}{vF}b^{1/2}_{HCl} - \frac{RT}{vF}\ln(b_{HCl}/b^{\ominus})
\end{aligned}$$

This expression may be rearranged so that it has the form of a straight-line graph, $y = ax + b$

$$\overbrace{E_{\text{cell}} + \frac{RT}{\nu F}\ln(b_{\text{HCl}}/b^{\ominus})}^{y} = \overbrace{\frac{RT}{\nu F}}^{\text{slope},a}\overbrace{b_{\text{HCl}}^{1/2}}^{x} + \overbrace{E^{\ominus}_{\text{cell}}}^{\text{intercept},b}$$

with $E^{\ominus}_{\text{cell}}$ given by the intercept.

## Solutions to exercises

**E9.1** An aqueous solution of KCl and $CuSO_4$ will contain $K^+$(aq), $Cl^-$(aq), $Cu^{2+}$(aq) and $SO_4^{2-}$(aq) ions. From eqn 9.5b,

$$\begin{aligned} I &= ½\sum_i z_i^2(b_i/b^{\ominus}) \\ &= ½\left\{z_{\text{K}^+}^2(b_{\text{K}^+}/b^{\ominus}) + z_{\text{Cl}^-}^2(b_{\text{Cl}^-}/b^{\ominus}) + z_{\text{Cu}^{2+}}^2(b_{\text{Cu}^{2+}}/b^{\ominus}) + z_{\text{SO}_4^{2-}}^2\left(b_{\text{SO}_4^{2-}}/b^{\ominus}\right)\right\} \\ &= ½[\{(+1)^2 \times 0.15\} + \{(-1)^2 \times 0.15\} + \{(+2)^2 \times 0.30\} + \{(-2)^2 \times 0.30\}] \\ &= \mathbf{1.35} \end{aligned}$$

**E9.2** (a) The ionic strength of the combined solution is given by eqn 9.5b,

$$I = ½\sum_i z_i^2(b_i/b^{\ominus})$$

The summation runs over all of the ions in solution. Thus,

$$\begin{aligned} I &= ½\{z_{\text{Ca}^{2+}}^2(b_{\text{Ca}^{2+}}/b^{\ominus}) + z_{\text{K}^+}^2(b_{\text{K}^+}/b^{\ominus}) + z_{\text{NO}_3^-}^2\left(b_{\text{NO}_3^-}/b^{\ominus}\right)\} \\ &= ½\left[\{(+2)^2\left(b_{\text{Ca(NO}_3)_2}/b^{\ominus}\right)\} + \{(+1)^2\left(b_{\text{KNO}_3}/b^{\ominus}\right)\}\right. \\ &\qquad \left.+ \{(-1)^2\left(2b_{\text{Ca(NO}_3)_2} + b_{\text{KNO}_3}\right)/b^{\ominus}\}\right] \\ &= ½\{\left(6b_{\text{Ca(NO}_3)\_2} + 2b_{\text{KNO}_3}\right)/b^{\ominus}\} = \left(3b_{\text{Ca(NO}_3)\_2} + b_{\text{KNO}_3}\right)/b^{\ominus} \end{aligned}$$

Rearranging, the molality of $Ca(NO_3)_2$ is

$$b_{\text{Ca(NO}_3)_2} = {}^1/_3\ \left(Ib^{\ominus} - b_{\text{KNO}_3}\right)$$

But, from the definition of molality, $b_J = n_J/m_{\text{solvent}}$,

$$m_{\text{Ca(NO}_3)_2} = \overbrace{n_{\text{Ca(NO}_3)_2}}^{b_{\text{Ca(NO}_3)_2}m_{\text{solvent}}} M_{\text{Ca(NO}_3)_2} = b_{\text{Ca(NO}_3)_2}m_{\text{solvent}}M_{\text{Ca(NO}_3)_2}$$

If the required ionic strength is $I = 0.250$, and the molality of the $KNO_3$ solution is $b_{\text{KNO}_3} = 0.150$ mol kg$^{-1}$, then,

$$\begin{aligned} m_{\text{Ca(NO}_3)_2} &= \overbrace{{}^1/_3\left(Ib^{\ominus} - b_{\text{KNO}_3}\right)}^{b_{\text{Ca(NO}_3)_2}} m_{\text{solvent}}M_{\text{Ca(NO}_3)_2} \\ &= {}^1/_3\{(0.250 \times 1\ \text{mol kg}^{-1}) - (0.150\ \text{mol kg}^{-1})\} \end{aligned}$$

$$\times (0.500\ \text{kg}) \times (164\ \text{g mol}^{-1})$$
$$= \mathbf{2.73\ g}$$

(b) In the same way for a solution of NaCl and $KNO_3$,

$$\begin{aligned} I &= ½\{z_{Na^+}^2(b_{Na^+}/b^\ominus) + z_{Cl^-}^2(b_{Cl^-}/b^\ominus) + z_{K^+}^2(b_{K^+}/b^\ominus) + z_{NO_3^-}^2(b_{NO_3^-}/b^\ominus)\} \\ &= ½[\{(+1)^2(b_{NaCl}/b^\ominus)\} + \{(-1)^2(b_{NaCl}/b^\ominus)\} + \{(+1)^2(b_{KNO_3}/b^\ominus)\} \\ &\qquad + \{(-1)^2(b_{KNO_3}/b^\ominus)\}] \\ &= ½\{(2b_{NaCl} + 2b_{KNO_3})/b^\ominus\} = (b_{NaCl} + b_{KNO_3})/b^\ominus \end{aligned}$$

so that

$$b_{NaCl} = (Ib^\ominus - b_{KNO_3})$$

and

$$\begin{aligned} m_{NaCl} &= \overbrace{(Ib^\ominus - b_{KNO_3})}^{b_{NaCl}} m_{solvent} M_{NaCl} \\ &= \{(0.250 \times 1\ \text{mol kg}^{-1}) - (0.150\ \text{mol kg}^{-1})\} \\ &\qquad \times (0.500\ \text{kg}) \times (58.4\ \text{g mol}^{-1}) \\ &= \mathbf{2.92\ g} \end{aligned}$$

**E9.3** From eqn 9.3b, the mean activity coefficient for the salt $M_pX_q$ is defined as

$$\gamma_\pm = (\gamma_+^p \gamma_-^q)^{1/s}, \text{ where } s = p + q$$

Thus, for $MgF_2$, with $p = 1$, $q = 2$ so that $s = 3$

$$\boldsymbol{\gamma_\pm = (\gamma_+\gamma_-^2)^{1/3}}$$

**E9.4** The ionic strength of the combined solution is given by eqn 9.5b,

$$I = ½\sum_i z_i^2(b_i/b^\ominus)$$

The summation runs over all of the ions in solution. Thus,

$$\begin{aligned} I &= ½\{z_{Mg^{2+}}^2(b_{Mg^{2+}}/b^\ominus) + z_{F^-}^2(b_{F^-}/b^\ominus) + z_{Na^+}^2(b_{Na^+}/b^\ominus) + z_{Cl^-}^2(b_{NO_3^-}/b^\ominus)\} \\ &= ½[\{(+2)^2(b_{MgF_2}/b^\ominus)\} + \{(-1)^2(2b_{MgF_2}/b^\ominus)\} + \{(+1)^2(b_{NaCl}/b^\ominus)\} \\ &\qquad + \{(-1)^2(b_{NaCl}/b^\ominus)\}] \\ &= (3b_{MgF_2} + b_{NaCl})/b^\ominus \end{aligned}$$

The solution is sufficiently dilute for the Debye-Hückel limiting law to give a reasonable estimate of the mean ionic activity coefficients. Thus, from eqn 9.4,

$$\log \gamma_\pm = -A|z_+z_-|I^{1/2} = -A|z_+z_-|\{(3b_{MgF_2} + b_{NaCl})/b^\ominus\}^{1/2}$$

so that for $MgF_2(aq)$

$$\log \gamma_{\pm,MgF_2} = -0.509 \times |(+2)(-1)| \times \{(3 \times 0.015) + 0.025\}^{1/2} = -0.269$$

Thus, the mean activity coefficient of $MgF_2$ is

$$\gamma_{\pm,MgF_2} = 10^{\log \gamma_{\pm,MgF_2}} = 10^{-0.269} = \mathbf{0.538}$$

with, using the definition of activity, eqn 9.1a, $a_J = \gamma_{\pm,J}(b_J/b^{\ominus})$

$$a_{Mg^{2+}} = \gamma_{\pm,MgF_2}(b_{Mg^{2+}}/b^{\ominus}) = \gamma_{\pm,MgF_2}(b_{MgF_2}/b^{\ominus}) = 0.538 \times 0.015 = \mathbf{0.024}$$
$$a_{Mg^{2+}} = \gamma_{\pm,MgF_2}(b_{F^-}/b^{\ominus}) = \gamma_{\pm,MgF_2}(2b_{MgF_2}/b^{\ominus}) = 0.538 \times 0.030 = \mathbf{0.048}$$

In the same way for NaCl,

$$\log \gamma_{\pm,NaCl} = -0.509 \times |(+1)(-1)| \times \{(3 \times 0.015) + 0.025\}^{1/2} = -0.135$$

$$\gamma_{\pm,MgF_2} = 10^{\log \gamma_{\pm,MgF_2}} = 10^{-0.135} = \mathbf{0.733}$$

$$a_{Na^+} = \gamma_{\pm,Na^+}(b_{Na^+}/b^{\ominus}) = \gamma_{\pm,NaCl}(b_{NaCl}/b^{\ominus}) = 0.733 \times 0.025 = \mathbf{0.018}$$
$$a_{Cl^-} = \gamma_{\pm,Cl^-}(b_{Cl^-}/b^{\ominus}) = \gamma_{\pm,NaCl}(b_{NaCl}/b^{\ominus}) = 0.733 \times 0.025 = \mathbf{0.018}$$

**E9.5** According to the Debye–Hückel extended law, eqn 9.5a, the logarithm of the mean activity coefficient depends upon ionic strength as

$$\log \gamma_{\pm} = -\frac{A|z_+z_-|I^{1/2}}{1 + BI^{1/2}} + CI$$

with $A = 0.509$ and $B$ and $C$ as adjustable parameters. Unfortunately, it is not possible to rearrange this expression easily into the form of a straight-line graph in order to determine the values of $B$ and $C$. If, however, we assume that the value of $C$ is negligible, then we may rearrange the extended law as

$$\overbrace{\frac{1}{\log \gamma_{\pm}}}^{y} = \overbrace{\frac{1}{A|z_+z_-|}}^{\text{slope},a} \times \overbrace{\frac{1}{I^{1/2}}}^{x} + \overbrace{\frac{B}{A|z_+z_-|}}^{\text{gradient},b}$$

For HBr, $z_+ = +1$, and $z_- = -1$, and because

$$I = ½\sum_i z_i^2(b_i/b^{\ominus}) = ½\{z_{H^+}^2(b_{H^+}/b^{\ominus}) + z_{Br^-}^2(b_{Br^-}/b^{\ominus})\}$$
$$= ½\{(+1)^2(b_{HBr}/b^{\ominus}) + (-1)^2(b_{HBr}/b^{\ominus})\}$$
$$= b_{HBr}/b^{\ominus}$$

a plot of $1/(\log\gamma_{\pm})$ against $(b^{\ominus}/b_{HBr})^{1/2}$ should be a straight line with an intercept of $B/A$. Figure 9.1 shows that this indeed the case, justifying our assumption that $C \approx 0$. The intercept of this plot is $B/A = -3.972$, giving

$$B = -3.972 \times -0.509 = \mathbf{2.022}$$

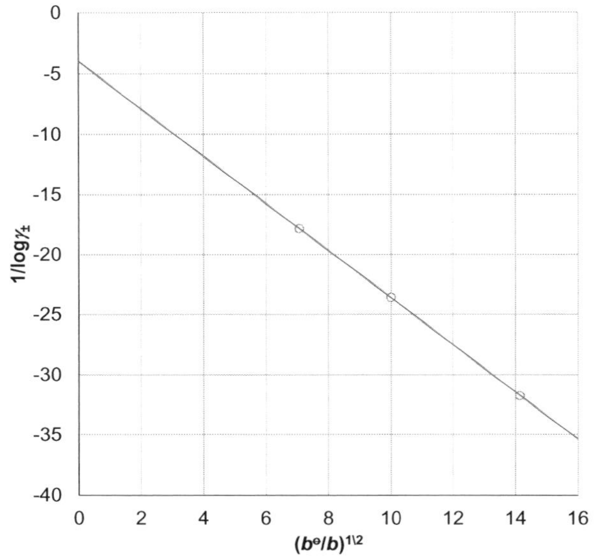


**Figure 9.1**

**E9.6** At low concentration, we may assume that the ions in solution are sufficiently far apart that they migrate independently. Thus, the limiting molar conductivity of a solution may be expressed as the sum of the ionic conductivities of the individual cations and anions, eqn 9.9,

$$\Lambda_m^o = \lambda_+ + \lambda_-$$

Hence,

$$\Lambda_m^o(\text{KCl}) = \lambda_{K^+} + \lambda_{Cl^-} = 14.99\ \text{mS m}^2\text{mol}^{-1}$$
$$\Lambda_m^o(\text{KNO}_3) = \lambda_{K^+} + \lambda_{NO_3^-} = 14.50\ \text{mS m}^2\text{mol}^{-1}$$
$$\Lambda_m^o(\text{AgNO}_3) = \lambda_{Ag^+} + \lambda_{NO_3^-} = 13.34\ \text{mS m}^2\text{mol}^{-1}$$

By combining these equations, we can obtain an expression for the limiting molar conductivity of AgCl,

$$\Lambda_m^o(\text{AgCl}) = \lambda_{Ag^+} + \lambda_{Cl^-}$$

because

$$\begin{aligned}\Lambda_m^o(\text{AgNO}_3) + \Lambda_m^o(\text{KCl}) - \Lambda_m^o(\text{KNO}_3) &= \left(\lambda_{Ag^+} + \lambda_{NO_3^-}\right) + \left(\lambda_{K^+} + \lambda_{Cl^-}\right) - \left(\lambda_{K^+} + \lambda_{NO_3^-}\right) \\ &= \lambda_{Ag^+} + \lambda_{Cl^-} = \Lambda_m^o(\text{AgCl})\end{aligned}$$

Thus,

$$\Lambda_m^o(\text{AgCl}) = (13.34 + 14.99 - 14.50)\ \text{mS m}^2\text{mol}^{-1} = \mathbf{13.83\ mS\ m^2 mol^{-1}}$$

**E9.7** Molar ionic conductivity $\lambda$ is related to mobility $u$ through eqn 9.11b, so that

$$\begin{aligned}\lambda_{\mathrm{Cl^-}} &= |z_{\mathrm{Cl^-}}|u_{\mathrm{Cl^-}}F \\ &= |-1| \times 7.91 \times 10^{-8}\,\mathrm{m^2 s^{-1} V^{-1}} \times (9.6485 \times 10^4\ \mathrm{C\,mol^{-1}}) \\ &= 7.63 \times 10^{-3}\ \overbrace{\mathrm{C\,V^{-1} s^{-1}}}^{1\,\mathrm{C\,V^{-1}s^{-1}}=1\,\mathrm{S}}\ \mathrm{m^2 mol^{-1}} = \mathbf{7.63\ mS\ m^2 mol^{-1}}\end{aligned}$$

**E9.8** A potential difference $\Delta\phi$ applied between the electrodes separated by a distance $l$ creates an electric field

$$\mathcal{E} = \Delta\phi/l$$

The drift velocity $s$ of an ion with mobility $u$ as a result of an electric field is given by eqn 9.10, so that

$$\begin{aligned}s &= u\mathcal{E} = u(\Delta\phi/l) \\ &= (7.92 \times 10^{-8}\ \mathrm{m^2 s^{-1} V^{-1}}) \times \{(35.0\ \mathrm{V})/(8.00 \times 10^{-3}\mathrm{m})\} \\ &= 3.47 \times 10^{-4}\ \mathrm{m\,s^{-1}} = \mathbf{347\ \mu m\ s^{-1}}\end{aligned}$$

**E9.9** (a) We may express the Kohlrausch law, eqn 9.8,

$$\Lambda_\mathrm{m} = \Lambda_\mathrm{m}^\circ - \mathcal{K}c^{1/2}$$

in terms of the resistance of the cell by recognising that the conductivity of the cell, $\kappa$, is related to the resistance, $R$, through the cell constant, $C$,

$$\kappa = C/R$$

Thus,

$$\overbrace{\Lambda_\mathrm{m}}^{\kappa/c} = \overbrace{\kappa}^{C/R}/c = (C/Rc) = \Lambda_\mathrm{m}^\circ - \mathcal{K}c^{1/2}$$

Rearranging yields an expression of the form $y = mx + b$

$$\overbrace{(1/Rc)}^{y} = \overbrace{-(\mathcal{K}/C)}^{\mathrm{slope},m}\,\overbrace{c^{1/2}}^{x} + \overbrace{(\Lambda_\mathrm{m}^\circ/C)}^{\mathrm{intercept},b}$$

We may therefore verify that the system obeys the Kohlrausch law by plotting a graph of $1/Rc$ against $c^{1/2}$ and obtain the limiting molar conductivity $\Lambda_\mathrm{m}^\circ$ from the intercept and the the coefficient $\mathcal{K}$ from the slope. Figure 9.2 shows that, within the limits of experimental uncertainty, the plot is indeed a straight line, and that Kohlrausch's law is obeyed. The intercept of this plot is 0.6086 $\Omega^{-1}$ mol$^{-1}$ dm$^3$ so that the limiting molar conductivity is

$$\begin{aligned}\Lambda_\mathrm{m}^\circ &= \mathrm{intercept} \times C \\ &= (0.6086 \times \overbrace{10^{-3}\ \Omega^{-1}\ \mathrm{mol^{-1}\ m^3}}^{1\ \mathrm{dm^3}=10^{-3}\mathrm{m^3}}) \times (\overbrace{0.2063 \times 10^2\ \mathrm{m^{-1}}}^{1\ \mathrm{cm^{-1}}=10^2\mathrm{m^{-1}}}) \\ &= 12.6 \times \overbrace{10^{-3}\ \Omega^{-1}}^{10^{-3}\ \Omega^{-1}=1\ \mathrm{mS}}\ \mathrm{m^2\ mol^{-1}} = \mathbf{12.6\ mS\ m^2\ mol^{-1}}\end{aligned}$$

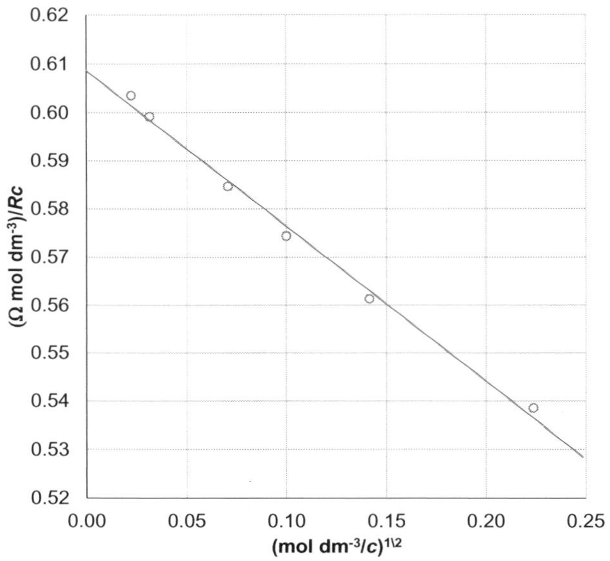


**Figure 9.2**

(b) The slope of the graph is $-0.3226\ \Omega^{-1}\ \text{mol}^{-1/2}\ \text{dm}^{3/2}$, and it follows that

$$\mathcal{K} = -\text{slope} \times C$$

$$= -\{(-0.3226\ \Omega^{-1}\ \text{mol}^{-1/2}) \times \underbrace{(10^{-1}\text{m})}_{1\ \text{dm}=10^{-1}\text{m}}{}^{3/2}\} \times \overbrace{(0.2063 \times 10^{2}\ \text{m}^{-1})}^{1\ \text{cm}^{-1}=10^{2}\text{m}^{-1}}$$

$$= 210\ \Omega^{-1}\text{mol}^{1/2}\text{m}^{1/2} = \mathbf{210\ S\ mol^{1/2}m^{1/2}}$$

**E9.10** We may calculate the concentration of the solution, and thus the solubility of AgCl, from the definition of molar conductivity, eqn 9.9. The limiting molar conductivity of AgCl is given in tables as

$$\Lambda_{\text{m}}^{\text{o}} = 138.3\ \text{S cm}^{2}\ \text{mol}^{-1} = 138.3 \times \overbrace{10^{-4}\ \text{S m}^{2}\text{mol}^{-1}}^{1\ \text{cm}^{2}=(10^{-2}\text{m})^{2}=10^{-4}\text{m}^{2}}$$

Thus,

$$s = c = \kappa/\Lambda_{\text{m}}^{\text{o}}$$

$$= (0.1887 \times 10^{-3}\ \text{S m}^{-1})/(138.3 \times 10^{-4}\ \text{S m}^{2}\ \text{mol}^{-1})$$

$$= \overbrace{1.364 \times 10^{-2}\text{mol m}^{-3}}^{1\ \text{mol m}^{-3}=10^{-3}\text{mol dm}^{-3}} = \mathbf{1.364 \times 10^{-5}\ mol\ dm^{-3}}$$

**E9.11** Formic acid is a weak acid. We may therefore express the acidity constant for the dissociation

$$\text{HCOOH(aq)} + \text{H}_2\text{O(l)} \rightleftharpoons \text{H}_3\text{O}^{+}\text{(aq)} + \text{HCO}_2^{-}\text{(aq)}$$

in terms of concentrations as

$$K_a = \frac{a_{H_3O^+(aq)}a_{HCO_2^-(aq)}}{a_{HCOOH(aq)}\underbrace{a_{H_2O(l)}}_{1}} = \frac{([H_3O^+]/c^\ominus)([HCO_2^-]/c^\ominus)}{([HCOOH]/c^\ominus)} = \frac{[H_3O^+][HCO_2^-]}{[HCOOH]c^\ominus}$$

Denoting, for simplicity, the concentration of $HCO_2^-$ ions as $x$, and assuming that the contribution to the concentration of $H_3O^+$ ions from the autoprotolysis of water is negligible, then

$$[HCOOH] = [HCOOH]_0 - x$$
$$[H_3O^+] = x$$

so that

$$K_a = \frac{\overbrace{x}^{[H_3O^+]} \times \overbrace{x}^{[HCO_2^-]}}{\underbrace{([HCOOH]_0 - x)}_{[HCOOH]} c^\ominus} = \frac{\alpha^2}{1-\alpha}([HCOOH]_0/c^\ominus)$$

where $\alpha$ is the fraction of acid dissociated,

$$\alpha = [HCO_2^-]/[HCOOH]_0 = x/[HCOOH]_0$$

We may express the measured molar conductivity of the solution in terms of the and the fraction of acid dissociated

$$\Lambda_m = \alpha\Lambda_m^o = \alpha(\lambda_{H_3O^+} + \lambda_{HCO_2^-})$$

so that, taking the values for the ionic condictivities from Table 9.1,

$$\alpha = \Lambda_m/(\lambda_{H_3O^+} + \lambda_{HCO_2^-})$$
$$= 3.83\ \text{mS m}^2\text{mol}^{-1}/(34.96\ \text{mS m}^2\text{mol}^{-1} + 5.46\ \text{mS m}^2\text{mol}^{-1})$$

Hence,

$$K_a = \frac{\{\Lambda_m/(\lambda_{H_3O^+} + \lambda_{HCO_2^-})\}^2}{1 - \{\Lambda_m/(\lambda_{H_3O^+} + \lambda_{HCO_2^-})\}}([HCOOH]_0/c^\ominus)$$
$$= \frac{\{3.83/(34.96 + 5.46)\}^2}{1 - \{3.83/(34.96 + 5.46)\}} \times (0.020\ \text{mol dm}^{-3})/(1\ \text{mol dm}^{-3})$$
$$= 1.98 \times 10^{-4}$$

so that

$$pK_a = -\log K_a = -\log_{10}(1.98 \times 10^{-4}) = \mathbf{3.70}$$

**E9.12** Figure 9.3 shows a plot of speed against pH. The pH at which the speed is 0 is indicated by the intercept on the $x$ axis. Thus, the isoelectric point is 4.85.

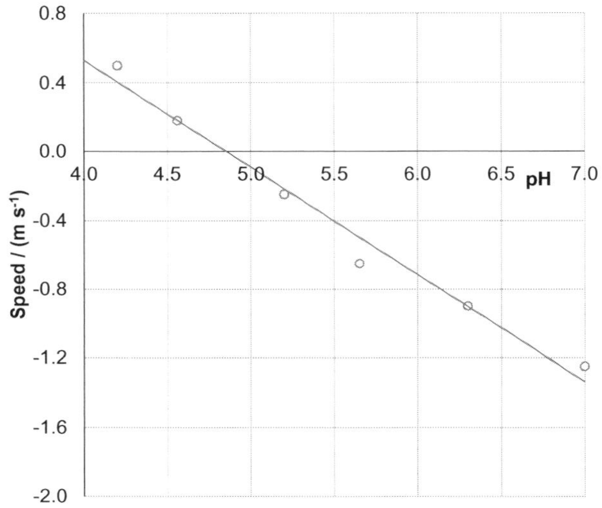


**Figure 9.3**

**E9.13** We must first write a balanced chemical equation for the oxidation of cysteine, $HSCH_2CH(NH_2)COOH$, to cystine, $HOOCCH(NH_2)CH_2SSCH_2CH(NH_2)COOH$. In doing so, we note that two molecules of cystine combine to form every molecule of cysteine, and balance the equation with $O_2$ and $H_2O$, paying careful attention to the stoichiometric coefficients. Thus, the overall cell reaction is

$$4\ \text{cystine(aq)} + O_2 \rightarrow 2\ \text{cysteine(aq)} + 2\ H_2O(l)$$

Subtracting the given half reaction from the overall cell reaction leads to

$$4\ \text{cystine(aq)} - 4\ H^+(aq) - 4\ e^- \rightarrow 2\ \text{cysteine(aq)}$$

which is better written as

$$4\ \text{cystine(aq)} \rightarrow 2\ \text{cysteine(aq)} + 4\ H^+(aq) + 4\ e^-$$

Thus, the oxidation of cystine may be written as the difference between the reactions

$O_2(g) + 4\ H^+(aq) + 4\ e^- \rightarrow 2\ H_2O(l)$ Right-hand
cysteine(aq) + $2\ H^+(aq) + 2\ e^- \rightarrow 2$ cystine(aq) Left-hand

**E9.14** The oxidation of NADH to $NAD^+$ may be written in terms of the half reactions

$O_2(g) + 4\ H^+(aq) + 4\ e^- \rightarrow 2\ H_2O(l)$ Right-hand
$NAD^+(aq) + H^+(aq) + 2\ e^- \rightarrow NADH(aq)$ Left-hand

The $O_2$, $H^+$, $H_2O$ half cell is labelled as the right-hand cell because in the overall reaction, the half-cell reaction proceeds in the forward direction. In contrast, the $NAD^+$, $H^+$, NADH half cell is the left-hand cell, because the half-cell reaction must be reversed in writing the overall reaction. The biological standard potential for the overall reaction is thus

$$E^{\oplus} = E_R^{\oplus} - E_L^{\oplus} = +0.82\text{ V} - (-0.32\text{ V}) = \mathbf{+1.14\ V}$$

If the two half cells are combined together so that the overall cell reaction is written as a four-electron process,

$$2\ \text{NADH(aq)} + 2\ \text{H}^+\text{(aq)} + \text{O}_2\text{(g)} \rightarrow 2\ \text{NAD}^+\text{(aq)} + 2\ \text{H}_2\text{O(l)}$$

then the biological standard reaction Gibbs energy is, from eqn 9.14

$$\begin{aligned}\Delta_r G^{\oplus} &= -\nu F E^{\oplus} = -4 \times (9.6485 \times 10^4\text{ C mol}^{-1}) \times (+1.14\text{ V}) \\ &= -440 \times 10^3\text{ J mol}^{-1} = \mathbf{-440\ kJ\ mol^{-1}}\end{aligned}$$

**E9.15** We may apply the Nernst equation, eqn 9.15, to half cells as well as balanced cell reactions. Thus, for the half-cell reaction

$$2\ \text{H}^+(\text{aq}, c) + 2\ \text{e}^- \rightarrow \text{H}_2(\text{g}, p)$$

$$E = E^{\ominus} - \frac{RT}{\nu F}\ln Q = E^{\ominus} - \frac{RT}{\nu F}\ln\frac{a_{\text{H}_2(\text{g},p)}}{a^2_{\text{H}^+(\text{aq},c)}} = E^{\ominus} - \frac{RT}{\nu F}\ln\frac{p/p^{\ominus}}{(c/c^{\ominus})^2}$$

When the concentration of the solution changes from $c_i$ to $c_f$, the cell potential changes by

$$\begin{aligned}\Delta E &= E_f - E_i \\ &= \left\{E^{\ominus} - \frac{RT}{\nu F}\ln\frac{p_f/p^{\ominus}}{(c_f/c^{\ominus})^2}\right\} - \left\{E^{\ominus} - \frac{RT}{\nu F}\ln\frac{p_i/p^{\ominus}}{(c_i/c^{\ominus})^2}\right\} \\ &= \frac{RT}{\nu F}\ln\left\{\frac{(c_f/c^{\ominus})}{(c_i/c^{\ominus})}\right\}^2 = \frac{2RT}{\nu F}\ln(c_f/c_i) \\ &= \frac{2 \times (8.3145\text{ J K}^{-1}\text{mol}^{-1}) \times (25 + 273.15)\text{K}}{2 \times (9.6485 \times 10^4\text{ C mol}^{-1})} \times \ln\frac{15.0\text{ mmol dm}^{-3}}{5.0\text{ mmol dm}^{-3}} \\ &= +28 \times 10^{-3}\text{ V} = \mathbf{+28\ mV}\end{aligned}$$

**E9.16** We may express the reaction

$$\text{Mn(s)} + \text{Cl}_2\text{(g)} \rightarrow \text{MnCl}_2\text{(aq)}$$

as a combination of the two half-cell reactions

| | | |
|---|---|---|
| $\text{Cl}_2\text{(g)} + 2\ \text{e}^- \rightarrow 2\ \text{Cl}^-\text{(aq)}$ | $E_R^{\ominus} = +1.36\text{ V}$ | Right-hand |
| $\text{Mn}^{2+}\text{(aq)} + 2\ \text{e}^- \rightarrow \text{Mn(s)}$ | $E_L^{\ominus}$ | Left-hand |

with the $Cl_2/Cl^-$ cell as the right-hand half cell because the reaction proceeds in the direction written, and the $Mn^{2+}/Mn$ cell as the left-hand half cell because the direction of this reaction is reversed. The standard cell potential is therefore the difference between the standard potentials of the two half cells. The unknown standard potential of the $Mn^{2+}/Mn$ cell, is thus, from eqn 9.4,

$$E_L^{\ominus} = E_R^{\ominus} - E^{\ominus} = (+1.36\text{ V}) - (+2.54\text{ V}) = \mathbf{-1.18\ V}$$

**E9.17** The overall cell reaction is given by assuming that the right-hand half cell corresponds to a reduction, and the left-hand half cell to an oxidation. In writing the Nernst equations for the cells, we have assumed that the solutions are sufficiently dilute that the activities of species in solution may be replaced by concentrations.

(a)

| | |
|---|---|
| $Ag^+(aq, b_R) + e^- \rightarrow Ag(s)$ | Right-hand |
| $Ag^+(aq, b_L) + e^- \rightarrow Ag(s)$ | Left-hand |
| $Ag^+(aq, b_R) \rightarrow Ag^+(aq, b_L)$ | Overall |

$$E_{cell} = E^{\ominus}_{cell} - \frac{RT}{\nu F}\ln Q = \overbrace{E^{\ominus}_{cell}}^{0} - \frac{RT}{\nu F}\ln\frac{a_{Ag^+(aq,b_L)}}{a_{Ag^+(aq,b_R)}}$$

$$= -\frac{RT}{\nu F}\ln\frac{(b_L/b^{\ominus})}{(b_R/b^{\ominus})} = \boldsymbol{-\frac{RT}{\nu F}\ln(b_L/b_R)}$$

(b)

| | |
|---|---|
| $2\,H^+(aq) + 2\,e^- \rightarrow H_2(g, p_R)$ | Right-hand |
| $2\,H^+(aq) + 2\,e^- \rightarrow H_2(g, p_L)$ | Left-hand |
| $H_2(g, p_L) \rightarrow H_2(g, p_R)$ | Overall |

$$E_{cell} = E^{\ominus}_{cell} - \frac{RT}{\nu F}\ln Q = \overbrace{E^{\ominus}_{cell}}^{0} - \frac{RT}{2F}\ln\frac{a_{H_2(g,p_R)}}{a_{H_2(g,p_L)}}$$

$$= -\frac{RT}{2F}\ln\frac{(p_R/p^{\ominus})}{(p_L/p^{\ominus})} = \boldsymbol{-\frac{RT}{2F}\ln(p_R/p_L)}$$

(c)

| | |
|---|---|
| $MnO_2(s) + 4\,H^+(aq) + 2\,e^- \rightarrow Mn^{2+}(aq) + 2\,H_2O(l)$ | Right-hand |
| $[Fe(CN)_6]^{3-}(aq) + e^- \rightarrow [Fe(CN)_6]^{4-}(aq)$ | Left-hand |
| $MnO_2(s) + 4\,H^+(aq) + 2\,[Fe(CN)_6]^{4-}(aq) \rightarrow$ $Mn^{2+}(aq) + 2\,[Fe(CN)_6]^{3-}(aq) + 2\,H_2O(l)$ | Overall |

$$E_{cell} = E^{\ominus}_{cell} - \frac{RT}{\nu F}\ln Q = E^{\ominus}_{cell} - \frac{RT}{2F}\ln\frac{a_{Mn^{2+}(aq)}\left(a_{[Fe(CN)_6]^{3-}(aq)}\right)^2 \overbrace{a^2_{H_2O(l)}}^{1}}{\underbrace{a_{MnO_2(s)}}_{1}\, a^4_{H^+(aq)}\left(a_{[Fe(CN)_6]^{4-}(aq)}\right)^2}$$

$$\boldsymbol{= E^{\ominus}_{cell} - \frac{RT}{2F}\ln\frac{[Mn^{2+}][[Fe(CN)_6]^{3-}]^2 c^{\ominus}}{[H_3O^+]^4\,[[Fe(CN)_6]^{4-}]^2}}$$

(d)

| | |
|---|---|
| $Br_2(l) + 2\,e^- \rightarrow 2\,Br^-(aq)$ | Right-hand |
| $Cl_2(g) + 2\,e^- \rightarrow 2\,Cl^-(aq)$ | Left-hand |
| $Br_2(l) + 2\,Cl^-(aq) \rightarrow Cl_2(g) + 2\,Br^-(aq)$ | Overall |

$$E_{\text{cell}} = E^{\ominus}_{\text{cell}} - \frac{RT}{\nu F}\ln Q$$

$$= E^{\ominus}_{\text{cell}} - \frac{RT}{2F}\ln\frac{\overbrace{a_{\text{Cl}_2\text{(g)}}}^{p_{\text{Cl}_2}/p^{\ominus}}\, a^2_{\text{Br}^-\text{(aq)}}}{\underbrace{a_{\text{Br}_2\text{(l)}}}_{1}\, a^2_{\text{Cl}^-\text{(aq)}}} = \boldsymbol{E^{\ominus}_{\text{cell}} - \frac{RT}{2F}\ln\frac{(p_{\text{Cl}_2}/p^{\ominus})[\text{Br}^-]^2}{[\text{Cl}^-]^2}}$$

(e)

| | |
|---|---|
| $Sn^{4+}(aq) + 2\ e^- \rightarrow Sn^{2+}(aq)$ | Right-hand |
| $2\ Fe^{3+}(aq) + 2\ e^- \rightarrow 2\ Fe^{2+}(aq)$ | Left-hand |
| $Sn^{4+}(aq) + 2\ Fe^{2+}(aq) \rightarrow Sn^{2+}(aq) + 2\ Fe^{3+}(aq)$ | Overall |

$$E_{\text{cell}} = E^{\ominus}_{\text{cell}} - \frac{RT}{\nu F}\ln Q$$

$$= E^{\ominus}_{\text{cell}} - \frac{RT}{2F}\ln\frac{a_{\text{Sn}^{2+}\text{(aq)}}a^2_{\text{Fe}^{3+}\text{(aq)}}}{a_{\text{Sn}^{4+}\text{(aq)}}a^2_{\text{Fe}^{2+}\text{(aq)}}} = \boldsymbol{E^{\ominus}_{\text{cell}} - \frac{RT}{2F}\ln\frac{[\text{Sn}^{2+}][\text{Fe}^{3+}]^2}{[\text{Sn}^{4+}][\text{Fe}^{2+}]^2}}$$

(f)

| | |
|---|---|
| $MnO_2(s) + 4\ H^+(aq) + 2e^- \rightarrow Mn^{2+}(aq) + 2\ H_2O(l)$ | Right-hand |
| $Fe^{2+}(aq) + 2\ e^- \rightarrow Fe(s)$ | Left-hand |
| $Fe(s) + MnO_2(s) + 4\ H^+(aq) \rightarrow Fe^{2+}(aq) + Mn^{2+}(aq) + 2\ H_2O(l)$ | Overall |

$$E_{\text{cell}} = E^{\ominus}_{\text{cell}} - \frac{RT}{\nu F}\ln Q$$

$$= E^{\ominus}_{\text{cell}} - \frac{RT}{2F}\ln\frac{a_{\text{Fe}^{2+}\text{(aq)}}a_{\text{Mn}^{2+}\text{(aq)}}\,\overbrace{a^2_{\text{H}_2\text{O(l)}}}^{1}}{\underbrace{a_{\text{Fe(s)}}}_{1}\,\underbrace{a_{\text{MnO}_2\text{(s)}}}_{1}\,a^4_{\text{H}^+\text{(aq)}}} = \boldsymbol{E^{\ominus}_{\text{cell}} - \frac{RT}{2F}\ln\frac{[\text{Fe}^{2+}][\text{Mn}^{2+}]c^{\ominus 2}}{[\text{H}_3\text{O}^+]^4}}$$

**E9.18** Using the values for the standard potentials in either Table 9.3 or the *CRC Handbook of Chemistry and Physics*.

(a) The right-hand and left-hand standard half cells are identical, so that the standard cell potential is zero.

$$E^{\ominus} = E^{\ominus}_{\text{R}} - E^{\ominus}_{\text{L}} = \mathbf{0}$$

(b) The right-hand and left-hand standard half cells are identical, so that the standard cell potential is zero.

$$E^{\ominus} = E^{\ominus}_{\text{R}} - E^{\ominus}_{\text{L}} = \mathbf{0}$$

(c) $E^{\ominus} = E^{\ominus}_{\text{R}} - E^{\ominus}_{\text{L}} = (+1.23\ \text{V}) - (+0.36\ \text{V}) = \mathbf{+0.87\ V}$

The standard cell potential is positive, so the reaction is spontaneous in the direction written.

(d) $E^{\ominus} = E^{\ominus}_{\text{R}} - E^{\ominus}_{\text{L}} = (+1.09\ \text{V}) - (+1.36\ \text{V}) = \mathbf{-0.27\ V}$

The standard cell potential is negative, so the reaction is not spontaneous in the direction written.

(e) $E^{\ominus} = E^{\ominus}_{R} - E^{\ominus}_{L} = (+0.15\text{ V}) - (+0.77\text{ V}) = \mathbf{-0.62\text{ V}}$

The standard cell potential is negative, so the reaction is not spontaneous in the direction written.

(f) $E^{\ominus} = E^{\ominus}_{R} - E^{\ominus}_{L} = (+1.23\text{ V}) - (-0.44\text{ V}) = \mathbf{+1.67\text{ V}}$

The standard cell potential is positive, so the reaction is spontaneous in the direction written.

**E9.19** We write the cells using the notation given in Section 9.5. Thus, interfaces between phases are indicated by a vertical bar, |, and interfaces such as a salt bridge, in which junction potentials have been eliminated are indicated by a double vertical bar, ||. For electrodes involving gases, it is necessary that we include a platinum, Pt(s), electrode. Hence, choosing appropriate half cells from the list given in Table 9.3:

(a)

$PbSO_4(s) + 2\,e^- \rightarrow Pb(s) + SO_4^{2-}(aq)$ Right-hand
$Fe^{2+}(aq) + 2\,e^- \rightarrow Fe(s)$ Left-hand

giving a cell

$Fe(s)\,|\,FeSO_4(aq)\,|\,PbSO_4(s)\,|\,Pb(s)$ $\quad \nu = 2$

(b)

$Hg_2Cl_2(s) + 2\,e^- \rightarrow 2\,Hg(l) + 2\,Cl^-(aq)$ Right-hand
$2\,H^+(aq) + 2\,e^- \rightarrow H_2(g)$ Left-hand

giving a cell

$Pt\,|\,H_2(g)\,|\,HCl(aq)\,|Hg_2Cl_2(s)\,|\,Hg(l)$ $\quad \nu = 2$

(c)

$O_2(g) + 4\,H^+(aq) + 4\,e^- \rightarrow 2\,H_2(g)$ Right-hand
$4\,H^+(aq) + 4\,e^- \rightarrow 2\,H_2(g)$ Left-hand

giving a cell

$Pt(s)\,|\,H_2(g)\,|\,H^+(aq), H_2O(l)\,|\,O_2(g)\,|\,Pt(s)$ $\quad \nu = 4$

(d)

$O_2(g) + 2\,H^+(aq) + 2\,e^- \rightarrow H_2O_2(aq)$ Right-hand
$2\,H^+(aq) + 2\,e^- \rightarrow H_2(g)$ Left-hand

giving a cell

$Pt(s) | H_2(g) | H^+(aq), H_2O_2(aq) | O_2(g) | Pt(s)$ $\qquad v = 2$

(e)

$I_2(s) + 2\,e^- \rightarrow 2\,I^-(aq)$ Right-hand
$2\,H^+(aq) + 2\,e^- \rightarrow H_2(g)$ Left-hand

giving a cell

$Pt(s) | H_2(g) | H^+(aq), I^-(aq) | I_2(s) | Pt(s)$

or more simply

$Pt(s) | H_2(g) | HI(aq) | I_2(s) | Pt(s)$ $\qquad v = 2$

(f)

$Cu^{2+}(aq) + e^- \rightarrow Cu(s)$ Right-hand
$Cu^+(aq) + e^- \rightarrow Cu(s)$ Left-hand

giving a cell

$Pt | CuCl_2(aq) || CuCl(aq) | Cu(s)$ $\qquad v = 1$

**E9.20** Using the values for the standard potentials in either Table 9.3 or the *CRC Handbook of Chemistry and Physics*, and applying eqn 9.18,

(a) $E^{\ominus}_{cell} = E^{\ominus}_{R} - E^{\ominus}_{L} = (-0.36\text{ V}) - (-0.44\text{ V}) = \mathbf{+0.08\ V}$

(b) $E^{\ominus}_{cell} = E^{\ominus}_{R} - E^{\ominus}_{L} = (-0.27\text{ V}) - (0\text{ V}) = \mathbf{+1.23\ V}$

(c) $E^{\ominus}_{cell} = E^{\ominus}_{R} - E^{\ominus}_{L} = (-0.36\text{ V}) - (-0.44\text{ V}) = \mathbf{+0.08\ V}$

(d) $E^{\ominus}_{cell} = E^{\ominus}_{R} - E^{\ominus}_{L} = (+0.695\text{ V}) - (0\text{ V}) = \mathbf{+0.695\ V}$

(e) $E^{\ominus}_{cell} = E^{\ominus}_{R} - E^{\ominus}_{L} = (+0.54\text{ V}) - (0\text{ V}) = \mathbf{+0.54\ V}$

(f) $E^{\ominus}_{cell} = E^{\ominus}_{R} - E^{\ominus}_{L} = (-0.52\text{ V}) - (-0.16\text{ V}) = \mathbf{+0.36\ V}$

In all cases, the standard cell potential is positive, so the reaction is spontaneous in the direction written.

**E9.21** (a) For the reaction

$H_2(g) + ½\,O_2 \rightarrow H_2O(l)$

the standard reaction Gibbs energy is $\Delta_r G^{\ominus} = \Delta_f G^{\ominus}(H_2O, l) = -237.13\text{ kJ mol}^{-1}$. The process may be expressed as the combination of two half cells

$½O_2(g) + H_2O(l) + 2\,e^- \rightarrow 2\,OH^-(aq)$
$2\,H_2O(l) + 2\,e^- \rightarrow H_2(g) + 2\,OH^-(aq)$

showing that, as written, the reaction is a two-electron process. Alternatively, we may consider that the oxidation number of the oxygen atom changes from 0, in $O_2$, to –2, in $H_2O$, which corresponds to a two-electron process. Thus, using eqn 9.14,

$$E^{\ominus}_{\text{cell}} = -\frac{\Delta_r G^{\ominus}}{\nu F} = -\frac{(-237.13 \times 10^3 \text{J mol}^{-1})}{2 \times (9.6485 \times 10^4 \text{ C mol}^{-1})} = \mathbf{+1.23\ V}$$

(b) For the combustion of benzene,

$$C_6H_6(l) + {}^{15}/_2\, O_2 \rightarrow 6\, CO_2(g) + 3\, H_2O(l)$$

the standard reaction Gibbs energy may be calculated from the standard Gibbs energies of formation of the various products and reactants, using eqn 7.12

$$\begin{aligned}\Delta_r G^{\ominus} &= \sum_{\text{products}} \nu \Delta_f G^{\ominus}(\text{products}) - \sum \nu \Delta_f G^{\ominus}(\text{reactants}) \\ &= \overbrace{\{6 \times \Delta_f G^{\ominus}(CO_2, g) + 3 \times \Delta_f G^{\ominus}(H_2O, l)\}} \\ &\qquad - \underbrace{\{\Delta_f G^{\ominus}(C_6H_6, l) + 15/2 \times \Delta_f G^{\ominus}(O_2, g)\}}_{\text{reactants}} \\ &= [\{6 \times (-394.36) + 3 \times (-237.13)\} - \{(124.3) + 0\}]\ \text{kJ mol}^{-1} \\ &= -3201.9\ \text{kJ mol}^{-1}\end{aligned}$$

We may deduce the number of electrons transferred by considering the oxidation number of the oxygen atoms. The oxidation number of each oxygen atom changes from 0, in $O_2$, on the left-hand side to –2, in $CO_2$ and $H_2O$, on the right-hand side. There are 15 oxygen atoms in total, meaning that, as written, the oxidation is a $15 \times 2 = 30$ electron process.

Thus,

$$E^{\ominus}_{\text{cell}} = -\frac{\Delta_r G^{\ominus}}{\nu F} = -\frac{(-3201.9 \times 10^3 \text{J mol}^{-1})}{30 \times (9.6485 \times 10^4 \text{ C mol}^{-1})} = \mathbf{+1.11\ V}$$

The net chemical reactions of the hydrogen/oxygen fuel cell and the benzene/oxygen fuel cell are identical to those of complete combustion. Yet, the mechanism by which the reaction occurs in a fuel cell is very different from the mechanism of complete combustion. Collisions occur in a mixture of reactant molecules and their fragments in a combustion reaction. Reactant molecules of a fuel cell, being in separate compartments, do not directly collide but electrons supplied by the reductant flow through an external circuit from the anode to the cathode where they are received by the oxidant. In spite of this remarkable difference, the laws of thermodynamics and electrochemistry emphasize that changes in properties like the Gibbs energy and chemical potential do not depend upon the process path or reaction mechanism.

**E9.22** We may deduce the required half-cell reactions for the two processes by first identifying the number of electrons transferred, and then balancing the equations using $OH^-$, $H^+$ and $H_2O$. The complete combustion of methane in oxygen

$$CH_4(g) + 2\, O_2(g) \rightarrow CO_2(g) + 2\, H_2O(l)$$

is an eight-electron process, because the oxidation number of carbon changes from −4, in $CH_4$, to +4, in $CO_2$. In solution, the equivalent (unbalanced) process would be $CH_4 \rightarrow CO_2 + 8\ e^-$. Balancing first the charges, by including eight $OH^-$ ions, and then the hydrogen and oxygen atoms by including six $H_2O$ molecules, implies that the resulting balanced half-cell reaction must be

$$CO_2(g) + 6\ H_2O(l) + 8\ e^- \rightarrow CH_4(g) + 8\ OH^-(aq)$$

In the same way, the incomplete combustion of methane in oxygen

$$CH_4(g) + {}^3/_2\ O_2(g) \rightarrow CO(g) + 2\ H_2O(l)$$

corresponds to a six-electron process, because the oxidation number of carbon changes from −4, in $CH_4$, to +2, in CO. In solution, the equivalent (unbalanced) process would be $CH_4 \rightarrow CO + 6\ e^-$. Balancing the equation in the same way as before shows that the half-cell reaction is

$$CO(g) + 5\ H_2O(l) + 6\ e^- \rightarrow CH_4(g) + 6\ OH^-(aq)$$

(a) The complete combustion of methane is far more exergonic than incomplete combustion. This leads us to expect that complete oxidation of methane has the strongest tendency to provide electrons. Thus, we may deduce that complete oxidation of methane should occur at the anode. The left-hand electrode is therefore the anode, and the **right-hand** electrode the cathode.

(b) Combining the two half cells gives an overall reaction

$$4\ CO(g) + 2\ H_2O(l) \rightarrow CH_4(g) + 3\ CO_2(g)$$

which corresponds to a 24-electron process. The standard reaction Gibbs energy for the process may be calculated from the standard Gibbs energies of formation for the products and reactants using eqn 7.12,

$$\begin{aligned}\Delta_r G^\ominus &= \sum \nu \Delta_f G^\ominus(\text{products}) - \sum \nu \Delta_f G^\ominus(\text{reactants})\\ &= \overbrace{\{3 \times \Delta_f G^\ominus(CO_2, g) + \Delta_f G^\ominus(CH_4, g)\}}^{\text{products}}\\ &\qquad - \underbrace{\{4 \times \Delta_f G^\ominus(CO, g) + 2 \times \Delta_f G^\ominus(H_2O, l)\}}_{\text{reactants}}\\ &= [\{3 \times (-394.36) + (-50.72)\}\\ &\qquad -\{4 \times (-137.17) + 2 \times (-237.13)\}]\ \text{kJ mol}^{-1}\\ &= -210.86\ \text{kJ mol}^{-1}\end{aligned}$$

Then, from eqn 9.14,

$$E^\ominus_{\text{cell}} = -\frac{\Delta_r G^\ominus}{\nu F} = -\frac{-210.86 \times 10^3\ \text{J mol}^{-1}}{24 \times (9.6485 \times 10^4\ \text{C mol}^{-1})} = \mathbf{+0.09\ V}$$

If all the gases have a partial pressure of 1 bar, then the cell is in its standard state, and $E_{\text{cell}} = E^\ominus$. The negative standard reaction Gibbs energy, and positive standard cell potential, indicate that this fuel cell spontaneously produces methane. However, the small value for the standard cell potential indicates that it is unlikely that such a cell could be used to drive a commercial process.

The simplest methane fuel cell oxidizes methane at the anode and reduces oxygen at the cathode.

$$O_2(g) + 2\,H_2O(l) + 4\,e^- \rightarrow 4\,OH^-(aq) \qquad \text{Cathode}$$
$$CH_4(g) + 8\,OH^-(aq) \rightarrow CO_2(g) + 6\,H_2O(l) + 8\,e^- \qquad \text{Anode}$$

giving a net reaction

$$CH_4(g) + 2\,O_2(g) \rightarrow CO_2(g) + 2\,H_2O(l) \qquad v = 8$$

The standard reaction Gibbs energy for this process is $\Delta_r G^{\ominus} = -817.9$ kJ mol$^{-1}$, so that

$$E^{\ominus}_{\text{cell}} = -\frac{\Delta_r G^{\ominus}}{vF} = -\frac{-817.9 \times 10^3\ \text{J mol}^{-1}}{8 \times (9.6485 \times 10^4\ \text{C mol}^{-1})} = \mathbf{+1.06\ V}$$

This cell consumes methane and produces a potential difference large enough to drive a commercial process.

**E9.23** (a) If we assume that the molar concentration of $AgNO_3$ in the left-hand compartment is less than that in the right-hand compartment, then, by convention, the potential of the cell will be positive. Increasing the molar concentration of the solution in the left-hand compartment will reduce the difference between the two half cells; the measured potential difference will therefore also decrease. When the concentrations in the two compartments are equal, the cell potential will be zero. If, alternatively, we assume that the concentration of the solution in the left-hand cell is greater than that in the right-hand compartment, then the cell potential will be negative. Increasing the concentration of the solution in the left-hand compartment will increase the difference between the two half cells, and the measured potential difference will become more negative. Thus, in both cases, the measured potential difference decreases. This is confirmed by the Nernst equation

$$E_{\text{cell}} = -\frac{RT}{F}\ln(b_L/b_R)$$

If the molar concentration of the solution in the left-hand compartment increases, then the ratio $b_L/b_R$ increases, and the cell potential becomes more negative.

(b) The measured cell potential depends upon the difference between the pressure of $H_2$ in the two compartments. If the pressure is initially lower in the left-hand compartment, then the cell potential will be negative, and will increase if the pressure in the left-hand cell is raised. When the pressures in the two compartments are equal, the cell potential will be zero. If, however, the pressure in the left-hand cell is greater than in the right-hand compartment, the measured cell potential will be positive and will once again increase if the pressure in the left-hand cell is raised further. This is confirmed by the Nernst equation.

$$E_{\text{cell}} = -\frac{RT}{2F}\ln(p_{\text{R}}/p_{\text{L}})$$

If the pressure of $H_2$ in the left-hand compartment increases, then the ratio $p_{\text{R}}/p_{\text{L}}$ decreases, and the cell potential becomes more positive.

(c) The overall cell reaction corresponds to the process

$$MnO_2(s) + 4\,H^+(aq) + 2\,[Fe(CN)_6]^{4-}(aq) \rightarrow Mn^{2+}(aq) + 2\,[Fe(CN)_6]^{3-}(aq) + 2\,H_2O(l)$$

Decreasing the pH of the right-hand compartment will increase the measured cell potential. As the pH decreases, the concentration of $[H_3O^+]$ ions will increase. This term appears in the denominator of the reaction quotient. As a result, the second term on the right-hand side of the Nernst equation increases, so that the measured cell potential must increase.

$$E_{\text{cell}} = E^{\ominus}_{\text{cell}} - \frac{RT}{2F}\ln\frac{[\text{Mn}^{2+}][[\text{Fe(CN)}_6]^{3-}]^2 c^{\ominus 3}}{[\text{H}_3\text{O}^+]^4\,[[\text{Fe(CN)}_6]^{4-}]^2}$$

(d) If the concentration of HCl, and therefore $Cl^-(aq)$ ions is increased, the measured cell potential will also increase. The overall reaction corresponds to the process

$$Br_2(l) + 2\,Cl^-(aq) \rightarrow Cl_2(g) + 2\,Br^-(aq)$$

The concentration of $Cl^-(aq)$ ions appears in the denominminator of the reaction quotient. The second term in the right-hand side of the Nernst equation therefore becomes more positive as $[Cl^-]$ increases.

$$E_{\text{cell}} = E^{\ominus}_{\text{cell}} - \frac{RT}{2F}\ln\frac{(p_{\text{Cl}_2}/p^{\ominus})[\text{Br}^-]^2}{[\text{Cl}^-]^2}$$

The measured cell potential therefore also increases.

(e) If iron(III) chloride is added to the cell, we should expect the cell potential to decrease. As written, the concentration of $Fe^{3+}(aq)$ ions appears in the numerator of the reaction quotient. Increasing the concentration of $Fe^{3+}(aq)$ ions in the cell therefore causes the second term in the right-hand side of the Nernst equation to become more negative.

$$E_{\text{cell}} = E^{\ominus}_{\text{cell}} - \frac{RT}{2F}\ln\frac{[\text{Sn}^{2+}][\text{Fe}^{3+}]^2}{[\text{Sn}^{4+}][\text{Fe}^{2+}]^2}$$

Adding iron(III) chloride must therefore cause the cell potential to decrease.

(f) We should expect the cell potemntial to increase when acid is added. The concentration of $H_3O^+$ ions appears in the denominator of the reaction quotient.

$$E_{cell} = E^{\ominus}_{\text{cell}} - \frac{RT}{2F}\ln\frac{[\text{Fe}^{2+}][\text{Mn}^{2+}]c^{\ominus 2}}{[\text{H}_3\text{O}^+]^4}$$

Thus, as the concentration of acid increases, the second-term in the right-hand side of the Nernst equation must become more negative. The cell potential will therefore decrease.

**E9.24** (a) The addition of $FeSO_4$ will cause the cell potential to dencrease. The Nernst equation for the cell is

$$E_{cell} = E^{\ominus}_{cell} - \frac{RT}{\nu F}\ln Q = E^{\ominus}_{cell} - \frac{RT}{2F}\ln \frac{\overbrace{a_{Fe^{2+}(aq)}}^{[Fe^{2+}]/c^{\ominus}}\overbrace{a_{Pb(s)}}^{1}}{\underbrace{a_{Pb^{2+}(aq)}}_{[Pb^{2+}]/c^{\ominus}}\underbrace{a_{Fe(s)}}_{1}} = E^{\ominus}_{cell} - \frac{RT}{2F}\ln \frac{[Fe^{2+}]}{[Pb^{2+}]}$$

Thus, increasing the concentration of $Fe^{2+}$(aq) ions will cause the value of the reaction quotient to increase and the cell potential to **decrease**.

(b) We should expect the cell potential to decrease with the addition of acid. The Nernst equation for the reaction is

$$E_{cell} = E^{\ominus}_{cell} - \frac{RT}{2F}\ln Q = E^{\ominus}_{cell} - \frac{RT}{2F}\ln \frac{\overbrace{a_{H_3O^+(aq)}}^{[H_3O^+]/c^{\ominus}}{}^{2}\,\overbrace{a_{Hg(l)}}^{1}{}^{2}}{\underbrace{a_{Hg_2Cl_2(s)}}_{1}\underbrace{a_{H_2(g)}}_{p_{H_2}/p^{\ominus}}}$$

$$= E^{\ominus}_{cell} - \frac{RT}{2F}\ln \frac{([H_3O^+]/c^{\ominus})^2}{p_{H_2}/p^{\ominus}}$$

Increasing the concentration of $H_3O^+$(aq) will cause the reaction quotient to increase, and therefore the cell potential to **decrease**.

(c) Increasing the pressure of either gas will cause the cell potential to increase. The Nernst equation for the reaction is

$$E_{cell} = E^{\ominus}_{cell} - \frac{RT}{\nu F}\ln Q = E^{\ominus}_{cell} - \frac{RT}{2F}\ln \frac{\overbrace{a_{H_2O(l)}}^{1}{}^{2}}{\underbrace{a_{H_2(g)}}_{p_{H_2}/p^{\ominus}}{}^{2}\,\underbrace{a_{O_2(g)}}_{p_{O_2}/p^{\ominus}}}$$

$$= E^{\ominus}_{cell} - \frac{RT}{2F}\ln \frac{1}{(p_{H_2}/p^{\ominus})^2(p_{O_2}/p^{\ominus})} = E^{\ominus}_{cell} + \frac{RT}{4F}\ln(p_{H_2}^2 p_{O_2}/p^{\ominus 3})$$

Increasing the pressure of $O_2$ will cause the reaction quotient to decrease, and therefore the cell potential to **increase**.

(d) Increasing the pressure of either gas will cause the cell potential to increase. The Nernst equation for the reaction is

$$E = E^{\ominus}_{cell} - \frac{RT}{\nu F}\ln Q = E^{\ominus}_{cell} - \frac{RT}{2F}\ln \frac{\overbrace{a_{H_2O_2(aq)}}^{[H_2O_2]/c^{\ominus}}}{\underbrace{a_{H_2(g)}}_{p_{H_2}/p^{\ominus}}\underbrace{a_{O_2(g)}}_{p_{O_2}/p^{\ominus}}}$$

$$= E^{\ominus}_{cell} - \frac{RT}{2F}\ln \frac{[H_2O_2]/c^{\ominus}}{(p_{H_2}/p^{\ominus})(p_{O_2}/p^{\ominus})} = E^{\ominus}_{cell} - \frac{RT}{2F}\ln \frac{[H_2O_2]}{p_{H_2}p_{O_2}} \times (p^{\ominus 2}/c^{\ominus})$$

Increasing the pressure of $H_2$ will cause the reaction quotient to decrease, and therefore the cell potential to **increase**.

(e) The addition of acid, either as hydrochloric acid or hydroiodic acid will result in a decrease in the cell potential. We may see from the Nernst equation,

$$E_{\text{cell}} = E^{\ominus}_{\text{cell}} - \frac{RT}{\nu F}\ln Q = E^{\ominus}_{\text{cell}} - \frac{RT}{2F}\ln\frac{\overbrace{a_{\text{H}_3\text{O}^+(\text{aq})}}^{[\text{H}_3\text{O}^+]/c^{\ominus}}{}^{2}\;\overbrace{a_{\text{I}^-(\text{aq})}}^{[\text{I}^-]/c^{\ominus}}{}^{2}}{\underbrace{a_{\text{H}_2(\text{g})}}_{p_{\text{H}_2}/p^{\ominus}}\;\underbrace{a_{\text{I}_2(\text{g})}}_{p_{\text{I}_2}/p^{\ominus}}}$$

$$= E^{\ominus}_{\text{cell}} - \frac{RT}{2F}\ln\frac{([\text{H}_3\text{O}^+]/c^{\ominus})^2([\text{I}^-]/c^{\ominus})^2}{(p_{\text{H}_2}/p^{\ominus})(p_{\text{I}_2}/p^{\ominus})}$$

$$= E^{\ominus}_{\text{cell}} - \frac{RT}{2F}\ln\frac{[\text{H}_3\text{O}^+]^2[\text{I}^-]^2}{p_{\text{H}_2}p_{\text{I}_2}} \times (p^{\ominus 2}/c^{\ominus 4})$$

that an increase in the concentration of $H_3O^+$ ions will result in an increase in the reaction quotient, and thus a decrease in the cell potential. The decrease will be even greater if hydroiodic acid is added, because the cell potential also depends upon the concentration of $I^-$ ions.

(f) The addition of hydrochloric acid should not affect the cell potential. This can be seen immediately from the Nernst equation,

$$E_{\text{cell}} = E^{\ominus}_{\text{cell}} - \frac{RT}{\nu F}\ln Q = E^{\ominus}_{\text{cell}} - \frac{RT}{2F}\ln\frac{\overbrace{a_{\text{Cu}^{2+}(\text{aq})}}^{[\text{Cu}^{2+}]/c^{\ominus}}\;\overbrace{a_{\text{Cu(s)}}}^{1}}{\underbrace{a_{\text{Cu}^+(\text{aq})}}_{[\text{Cu}^+]/c^{\ominus}}{}^{2}}$$

$$= E^{\ominus}_{\text{cell}} - \frac{RT}{2F}\ln\frac{[\text{Cu}^{2+}]/c^{\ominus}}{([\text{Cu}^+]/c^{\ominus})^2} = E^{\ominus}_{\text{cell}} - \frac{RT}{2F}\ln\frac{[\text{Cu}^{2+}]c^{\ominus}}{[\text{Cu}^+]^2}$$

which does not include a term in the concentration of either $H_3O^+$ or $Cl^-$ ions.

**E9.25** (a) The cell, as written, corresponds to the half-cell reactions

| | |
|---|---|
| $2\,Tl^{2+}(aq) + 2\,e^- \rightarrow 2\,Tl(s)$ | Right-hand |
| $Hg^{2+}(aq) + 2\,e^- \rightarrow Hg(l)$ | Left-hand |

and therefore an overall cell reaction

$$2\,Tl^{2+}(aq) + Hg(l) \rightarrow 2\,Tl(s) + Hg^{2+}(aq)$$

The standard cell potential is thus from eqn 9.18, using the values from the Data Section,

$$E^{\ominus}_{\text{cell}} = E^{\ominus}_{\text{R}} - E^{\ominus}_{\text{L}} = (-0.34\text{ V}) - (+0.86\text{ V}) = \mathbf{-1.20\ V}$$

The standard cell potential is negative, meaning that the cell reaction is not spontaneous in the direction written.

(b) The Nernst equation for the cell is, from eqn 9.15,

$$E_{\text{cell}} = E^{\ominus}_{\text{cell}} - \frac{RT}{\nu F}\ln Q = E^{\ominus}_{\text{cell}} - \frac{RT}{2F}\ln\frac{\overbrace{a_{\text{Tl(s)}}}^{1}{}^{2}\,\overbrace{a_{\text{Hg}^{2+}\text{(aq)}}}^{[\text{Hg}^{2+}]/c^{\ominus}}}{\underbrace{a_{\text{Tl}^{2+}\text{(aq)}}}_{[\text{Tl}^{2+}]/c^{\ominus}}{}^{2}\,\underbrace{a_{\text{Hg(l)}}}_{1}}$$

$$= E^{\ominus}_{\text{cell}} - \frac{RT}{2F}\ln\frac{[\text{Hg}^{2+}]/c^{\ominus}}{([\text{Tl}^{2+}]/c^{\ominus})^{2}} = E^{\ominus}_{\text{cell}} - \frac{RT}{2F}\ln\frac{[\text{Hg}^{2+}]c^{\ominus}}{[\text{Tl}^{2+}]^{2}}$$

$$= -1.20\text{ V} - \frac{(8.3145\text{ J K}^{-1}\text{mol}^{-1})\times(298\text{ K})}{2\times(9.6485\times10^{4}\text{ C mol}^{-1})}\ln\left\{\frac{(0.230\text{ mol dm}^{-3})\times(1\text{ mol dm}^{-3})}{(0.720\text{ mol dm}^{-3})^{2}}\right\}$$

$$= \mathbf{-1.19\ V}$$

**E9.26** We must first proceed by writing the overall reaction as the difference between two half cells. The standard cell potential for the reaction may then be calculated, using eqn 9.18,

$$E^{\ominus}_{\text{cell}} = E^{\ominus}_{\text{R}} - E^{\ominus}_{\text{L}}$$

from the half-cell potentials given in Table 9.3 and the Data Section. The standard reaction Gibbs energy then follows from eqn 9.14

$$\Delta_{\text{r}}G^{\ominus} = -\nu F E^{\ominus}_{\text{cell}}$$

(a) The reaction may be written as the difference between the two half cells

| | |
|---|---|
| $2\ H_2O(l) + 2\ e^- \rightarrow H_2(g) + 2\ OH^-(aq)$ | Right-hand |
| $Ca^{2+}(aq) + 2\ e^- \rightarrow Ca(s)$ | Left-hand |

so that

$$E^{\ominus}_{\text{cell}} = E^{\ominus}_{\text{R}} - E^{\ominus}_{\text{L}} = (-0.83\text{ V}) - (-2.87\text{ V}) = +2.04\text{ V}$$

and

$$\Delta_{\text{r}}G^{\ominus} = -\nu F E^{\ominus}_{\text{cell}} = -2\times(9.6485\times10^{4}\text{ C mol}^{-1})\times(+2.04\text{ V})$$
$$= -394\times10^{3}\text{ J mol}^{-1} = \mathbf{-394\ kJ\ mol^{-1}}$$

The standard cell potential is positive, and the standard reaction Gibbs energy is negative, indicating that the reaction is spontaneous in the direction written.

(b) This net reaction is twice the net reaction of part (a). Therefore,

$$\Delta_{\text{r}}G^{\ominus} = 2\times(-394\text{ kJ mol}^{-1}) = \mathbf{-788\ kJ\ mol^{-1}}$$

(c) Hence,

| | |
|---|---|
| $2\ H_2O(l) + 2\ e^- \rightarrow H_2(g) + 2\ OH^-(aq)$ | Right-hand |
| $Fe^{2+}(aq) + 2\ e^- \rightarrow Fe(s)$ | Left-hand |

$$E^{\ominus}_{\text{cell}} = E^{\ominus}_{\text{R}} - E^{\ominus}_{\text{L}} = (-0.83\text{ V}) - (-0.44\text{ V}) = -0.39\text{ V}$$

and

$$\Delta_r G^\ominus = -\nu F E^\ominus_{cell} = -2 \times (9.6485 \times 10^4 \text{ C mol}^{-1}) \times (-0.39 \text{ V})$$
$$= +75 \times 10^3 \text{ J mol}^{-1} = \mathbf{+75 \text{ kJ mol}^{-1}}$$

The standard cell potential is negative, and the standard reaction Gibbs energy is positive, indicating that the reaction is not spontaneous in the direction written.

(d) In the same way,

$S_2O_8^{2-}(aq) + 2\,e^- \rightarrow 2\,SO_4^{2-}(aq)$ Right-hand
$I_2(s) + 2\,e^- \rightarrow 2\,I^-(aq)$ Left-hand

$$E^\ominus_{cell} = E^\ominus_R - E^\ominus_L = (+2.05 \text{ V}) - (-0.54 \text{ V}) = +1.51 \text{ V}$$

and

$$\Delta_r G^\ominus = -\nu F E^\ominus_{cell} = -2 \times (9.6485 \times 10^4 \text{ C mol}^{-1}) \times (+1.51 \text{ V})$$
$$= -291 \times 10^3 \text{ J mol}^{-1} = \mathbf{-291 \text{ kJ mol}^{-1}}$$

The standard cell potential is positive, and the standard reaction Gibbs energy is negative, indicating that the reaction is spontaneous in the direction written.

(e) Although the spectator ions of parts (d) and (e) differ, the equations for the overall reaction and hence the Gibbs energies are identical. Thus

$$\Delta_r G^\ominus = \mathbf{-291 \text{ kJ mol}^{-1}}$$

(f) The reaction may be written as the difference between the half cells

$2\,Na^+(aq) + 2\,e^- \rightarrow 2\,Na(s)$ Right-hand
$Pb^{2+}(aq) + 2\,e^- \rightarrow Pb(s)$ Left-hand

so that

$$E^\ominus_{cell} = E^\ominus_R - E^\ominus_L = (-2.71 \text{ V}) - (-0.13 \text{ V}) = -2.58 \text{ V}$$

and

$$\Delta_r G^\ominus = -\nu F E^\ominus_{cell} = -2 \times (9.6485 \times 10^4 \text{ C mol}^{-1}) \times (-2.58 \text{ V})$$
$$= +498 \times 10^3 \text{ J mol}^{-1} = \mathbf{+498 \text{ kJ mol}^{-1}}$$

The standard cell potential is negative, and the standard reaction Gibbs energy is positive; the reaction is thus spontaneous in the reverse of the direction written.

**E9.27** (a) As written,we may deduce that the reaction

$$2\,NADH(aq) + O_2(g) + 2\,H^+(aq) \rightarrow 2\,NAD^+(aq) + 2\,H_2O(l)$$

is a four-electron process. The oxidation number of each oxygen atom changes from 0 on the left-hand side of the equation, to −2 on the right-hand side; there are two oxygen atoms undergoing this change, so that $\nu = 4$. Hence, applying eqn 9.14

$$\Delta_r G^{\ominus} = -\nu F E^{\ominus}_{\text{cell}} = -4 \times (9.6485 \times 10^4\ \text{C mol}^{-1}) \times (+1.14\ \text{V})$$
$$= -440 \times 10^3\ \text{J mol}^{-1} = \mathbf{-40\ kJ\ mol^{-1}}$$

(b) The reaction

Malate(aq) + $NAD^+$(aq) → oxaloacetate(aq) + NADH + $H^+$(aq)

is a two-electron process. If we consider the structures of the malate and oxaloacetate ion, then we can see that the oxidation number of the starred carbon atom changes from 0 in the malate ion to +2 in the oxaloacetate ion. Thus, $\nu = 2$.

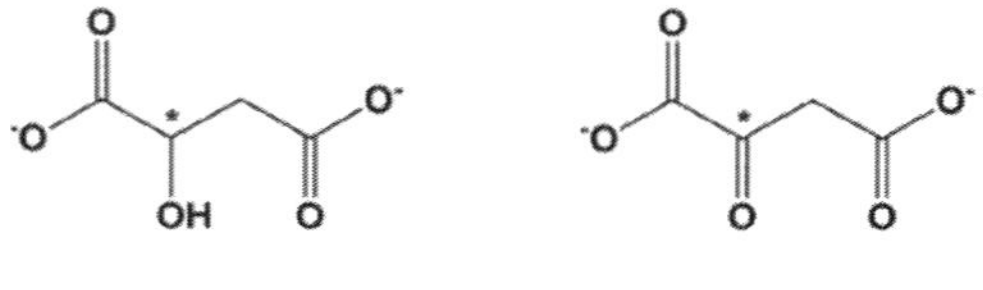


Then, applying eqn 9.14

$$\Delta_r G^{\ominus} = -\nu F E^{\ominus}_{\text{cell}} = -2 \times (9.6485 \times 10^4\ \text{C mol}^{-1}) \times (-0.154\ \text{V})$$
$$= +29.7 \times 10^3\ \text{J mol}^{-1} = \mathbf{+29.7\ kJ\ mol^{-1}}$$

(c) For the reaction

$O_2$(g) + 4 $H^+$(aq) + 4 $e^-$ → 2 $H_2O$(l)

$$\Delta_r G^{\ominus} = -\nu F E^{\ominus}_{\text{cell}} = -4 \times (9.6485 \times 10^4\ \text{C mol}^{-1}) \times (+0.81\ \text{V})$$
$$= -313 \times 10^3\ \text{J mol}^{-1} = \mathbf{-313\ kJ\ mol^{-1}}$$

**E9.28** (a) In the reaction

$K_2CrO_4$(aq) + 2 Ag(s) + 2 $FeCl_3$(aq) → $Ag_2CrO_4$(s) + 2 $FeCl_2$(aq) + 2 KCl(aq)

the iron is reduced from an oxidation state of +3 on the left-hand side to +2 on the right-hand side of the equation. The oxidation number of each iron atom changes by one, but because there are two iron atoms, we conclude that the reaction, as written, is a two-electron process. Thus, rearranging eqn 9.14,

$$E^{\ominus}_{\text{cell}} = -\frac{\Delta_r G^{\ominus}}{\nu F} = \frac{(-62.5 \times 10^3\text{J mol}^{-1})}{-2 \times (9.6485 \times 10^4\ \text{C mol}^{-1})} = \mathbf{+0.324\ V}$$

(b) The reaction may be written as the difference between the two half cells

| | |
|---|---|
| $Fe^{3+}$(aq) + $e^-$ → $Fe^{2+}$(aq) | Right-hand |
| $Ag_2CrO_4$ + 2 $e^-$ → Ag(s) + $CrO_4^{2-}$(aq) | Left-hand |

Thus, from eqn 9.18,

$$E^{\ominus}_{\text{cell}} = E^{\ominus}_{\text{R}} - E^{\ominus}_{\text{L}} = E^{\ominus}(\text{Fe}^{3+}/\text{Fe}^{2+}) - E^{\ominus}(\text{Ag}_2\text{CrO}_4/\text{Ag}, \text{CrO}_4^{2-})$$

so that, taking the value for the standard cell potential of the $Fe^{3+}/Fe^{2+}$ couple from Table 9.3,

$$\begin{aligned} E^\ominus(\mathrm{Ag_2CrO_4/Ag, CrO_4^{2-}}) &= E^\ominus(\mathrm{Fe^{3+}/Fe^{2+}}) - E^\ominus_{\mathrm{cell}} \\ &= (+0.77\ \mathrm{V}) - (+0.324\ \mathrm{V}) = \mathbf{+0.45\ V} \end{aligned}$$

**E9.29** The two half cells

$Ag^+(aq) + e^- \rightarrow Ag(s)$ Right-hand
$AgCl(s) + e^- \rightarrow Ag(s) + Cl^-(aq)$ Left-hand

correspond to the overall one-electron cell reaction

$Ag^+(aq) + Cl^-(aq) \rightarrow AgCl(s)$

The cell potential is, by analogy with eqn 9.18, the difference between the potentials of the two individual half cells under the conditions given. The potentials of the half cells may, in turn be calculated using the Nernst equation, eqn 9.14. Thus, using the values for the standard cell potentials from Table 9.3, and assuming that the solutions are sufficiently dilute that activities may be replaced by molalities,

$$\begin{aligned} E_{\mathrm{cell}} &= E_{\mathrm{R}} - E_{\mathrm{L}} \\ &= \left\{ \overbrace{E^\ominus_{\mathrm{R}}}^{E^\ominus(\mathrm{Ag^+/Ag})} - \frac{RT}{F}\ln\frac{\overbrace{a_{\mathrm{Ag(s)}}}^{1}}{\underbrace{a_{\mathrm{Ag^+(aq)}}}_{b_{\mathrm{AgNO_3}}/b^\ominus}} \right\} - \left\{ \overbrace{E^\ominus_{\mathrm{L}}}^{E^\ominus(\mathrm{AgCl/Ag,Cl^-})} - \frac{RT}{F}\ln\frac{\overbrace{a_{\mathrm{Ag(s)}}}^{1}}{\underbrace{a_{\mathrm{Cl^-(aq)}}}_{b_{\mathrm{AgCl}}/b^\ominus}} \right\} \\ &= \left\{ \overbrace{E^\ominus(\mathrm{Ag^+/Ag})}^{+0.80\ \mathrm{V}} - \overbrace{E^\ominus(\mathrm{AgCl/Ag,Cl^-})}^{+0.22\ \mathrm{V}} \right\} - \frac{RT}{F}\ln\frac{b_{\mathrm{AgCl}}b_{\mathrm{AgNO_3}}}{b^{\ominus 2}} \\ &= \{(+0.80\ \mathrm{V}) - (+0.22\ \mathrm{V})\} \\ &\quad - \frac{(8.3145\ \mathrm{J\ K^{-1}mol^{-1}}) \times (298\ \mathrm{K})}{(9.6485 \times 10^4\ \mathrm{C\ mol^{-1}})}\ln\frac{(0.025\ \mathrm{mol\ kg^{-1}}) \times (0.010\ \mathrm{mol\ kg^{-1}})}{(1\ \mathrm{mol\ kg^{-1}})^2} \\ &= \mathbf{+0.37\ V} \end{aligned}$$

**E9.30** (a) We may combine the equations for the two half cells

$Cu^{2+}(aq) + 2\ e^- \rightarrow Cu(s)$ Right-hand
$Ag^+(aq) + e^- \rightarrow Ag(s)$ Left-hand

to give the overall two-electron reaction for the cell

$2\ Ag(s) + Cu^{2+}(aq) \rightarrow 2\ Ag^+(aq) + Cu(s)$

The potential for the cell may be calculated using eqn 9.18, and the values given in Table 9.3, as

$$\begin{aligned} E^\ominus_{\mathrm{cell}} &= E^\ominus_{\mathrm{R}} - E^\ominus_{\mathrm{L}} = E^\ominus(\mathrm{Cu^{2+}/Cu}) - E^\ominus(\mathrm{Ag^+/Ag}) \\ &= (+0.34\ \mathrm{V}) - (+0.80\ \mathrm{V}) = -0.46\ \mathrm{V} \end{aligned}$$

It then follows, from eqn 9.14, that the standard reaction Gibbs energy for the cell at 25 °C is

$$\begin{aligned}\Delta_r G^\ominus &= -\nu F E^\ominus_{cell} = -2 \times (9.6485 \times 10^4\ \mathrm{C\ mol^{-1}}) \times (-0.46\ \mathrm{V}) \\ &= +88.8 \times 10^3\ \mathrm{J\ mol^{-1}} = \mathbf{+88.8\ kJ\ mol^{-1}}\end{aligned}$$

We may calculate the standard enthalpy for the cell reaction from the values for the standard enthalpies of formation of the products and reactants given in the Data Section. Thus, applying eqn 3.5,

$$\begin{aligned}\Delta_r H^\ominus &= \sum \nu\Delta_f H^\ominus(\text{products}) - \sum \nu\Delta_f H^\ominus(\text{reactants}) \\ &= \overbrace{\{2 \times \Delta_f H^\ominus(\mathrm{Ag^+, aq}) + \Delta_f H^\ominus(\mathrm{Cu, s})\}}^{\text{products}} \\ &\qquad - \underbrace{\{2 \times \Delta_f H^\ominus(\mathrm{Ag, s}) + \Delta_f H^\ominus(\mathrm{Cu^{2+}, aq})\}}_{\text{reactants}} \\ &= [\{2 \times (+105.58) + (0)\} - \{2 \times (0) + -64.77\}]\ \mathrm{kJ\ mol^{-1}} \\ &= \mathbf{+146.39\ kJ\ mol^{-1}}\end{aligned}$$

It follows, from eqn 4.16, that the standard entropy change for the cell reaction is

$$\begin{aligned}\Delta_r S^\ominus &= \frac{\Delta_r G^\ominus - \Delta_r H^\ominus}{T} \\ &= \frac{(88.8 \times 10^3\ \mathrm{J\ mol^{-1}}) - (146.39 \times 10^3\ \mathrm{J\ mol^{-1}})}{(273.15 + 25)\mathrm{K}} = \mathbf{+188\ J\ K^{-1}mol^{-1}}\end{aligned}$$

(b) We may estimate the value of the standard reaction Gibbs energy at any temperature if we assume that the standard enthalpy and entropy of reaction remain constant with temperature. Thus, from eqn 4.16

$$\begin{aligned}\Delta_r G^\ominus(35\ ^\circ\mathrm{C}) &= \Delta_r H^\ominus - T\Delta_r S^\ominus \\ &= (+146.39 \times 10^3\mathrm{J\ mol^{-1}}) - \{(273.15 + 35)\ \mathrm{K} \times (+188\ \mathrm{J\ K^{-1}mol^{-1}})\} \\ &= +88.5 \times 10^3\ \mathrm{J\ mol^{-1}} = \mathbf{+88.5\ kJ\ mol^{-1}}\end{aligned}$$

**E9.31** The two half cells correspond to reactions

$O_2(g) + 4\ H^+(aq) + 4\ e^- \rightarrow 2\ H_2O\ (l)$ — Right-hand

cystine(aq) + 2 $H^+$(aq) + 2 $e^-$ $\rightarrow$ 2 cysteine(aq) — Left-hand

with cell potentials $E^\ominus_R = +1.23$ V and $E^\ominus_L = -0.34$ V. Combining these two half cells leads to the balanced overall reaction,

2 cysteine(aq) + $O_2$ (g) $\rightarrow$ 4 cystine(aq) + 2 $H_2O$(1)

which is a four-electron process. The standard cell potential is thus, from eqn 9.18,

$$E^\ominus_{cell} = E^\ominus_R - E^\ominus_L = (+1.23\ \mathrm{V}) - (-0.34\ \mathrm{V}) = \mathbf{+1.57\ V}$$

We may then calculate the standard reaction Gibbs energy from eqn 9.14

$$\begin{aligned}\Delta_r G^\ominus &= -\nu F E^\ominus_{cell} = -4 \times (9.6485 \times 10^4\ \mathrm{C\ mol^{-1}}) \times (+1.57\ \mathrm{V}) \\ &= -606 \times 10^3\ \mathrm{J\ mol^{-1}} = \mathbf{-606\ kJ\ mol^{-1}}\end{aligned}$$

If we assume that the standard enthalpy and entropy of reaction do not vary with temperature, then we may use eqn 4.16, to determine the standard reaction Gibbs energy at a different temperature.

$$\begin{aligned}\Delta_r G^\ominus(T') &= \Delta_r H^\ominus - T'\Delta_r S^\ominus = \overbrace{(\Delta_r G^\ominus(T) - T\Delta_r S^\ominus)}^{\Delta_r H^\ominus} - T'\Delta_r S^\ominus \\ &= \Delta_r G^\ominus(T) - (T' - T)\Delta_r S^\ominus\end{aligned}$$

We may calculate the standard reaction entropy using eqn 4.13. The entropy of the gaseous $O_2$ is so much greater than that of the solution and liquid-phase components, that the contribution to the entropy change from these components may be ignored. Thus, taking the value for the entropy of $O_2$ from the Data Section,

$$\begin{aligned}\Delta_r S^\ominus &= \sum \nu S^\ominus(\text{products}) - \sum \nu S^\ominus(\text{reactants}) \\ &= \overbrace{\{2\times S^\ominus(\text{cystine, aq}) + 2\times S^\ominus(\text{H}_2\text{O, l})\}}^{\text{products}} \\ &\qquad - \underbrace{\{4\times S^\ominus(\text{cysteine, aq}) + S^\ominus(\text{O}_2\text{, g})\}}_{\text{reactants}} \\ &\approx -S^\ominus(\text{O}_2\text{, g}) = -205\ \text{J K}^{-1}\text{mol}^{-1}\end{aligned}$$

so that

$$\begin{aligned}\Delta_r G^\ominus(308.15\ \text{K}) &= \Delta_r G^\ominus(298.15\ \text{K}) - \Delta_r S^\ominus(308.15\ \text{K} - 298.15\ \text{K}) \\ &= -606\times 10^3\text{J mol}^{-1} - \{(-205\ \text{J K}^{-1}\text{mol}^{-1})\times(10\ \text{K})\} \\ &= -604\times 10^3\text{J mol}^{-1} = \mathbf{-606\ kJ\ mol^{-1}}\end{aligned}$$

**E9.32** We should proceed in each case by first writing the overall cell reaction in terms of two half cells. We may thus calculate the standard cell potential, using eqn 9.18, as the difference between the potentials of the two half cells. Knowing the standard cell potential, we may then determine the equilibrium constant using eqn 9.17

$$\ln K = \nu F E^\ominus_{\text{cell}}/RT = \nu F(E^\ominus_R - E^\ominus_L)/RT$$

(a) $Sn^{4+}(s) + 2e^- \rightleftharpoons Sn^{2+}(aq)$ $\qquad E^\ominus_R = +0.15$ V
$Sn^{2+}(s) + 2e^- \rightleftharpoons Sn(s)$ $\qquad E^\ominus_L = -0.14$ V

$$\ln K = \frac{2\times(9.6485\times 10^4\ \text{C mol}^{-1})\times\{(+0.15\ \text{V}) - (-0.14\ \text{V})\}}{(8.3145\ \text{J K}^{-1}\text{mol}^{-1})\times(298\ \text{K})} = 22.6$$

$$K = \text{e}^{22.6} = \mathbf{6.5\times 10^9}$$

(b) $AgBr(s) + e^- \rightleftharpoons Ag(s) + Br^-(aq)$ $\qquad E^\ominus_R = +0.07$ V
$Sn^{2+}(s) + 2e^- \rightleftharpoons Sn(s)$ $\qquad E^\ominus_L = -0.14$ V

$$\ln K = \frac{2\times(9.6485\times 10^4\ \text{C mol}^{-1})\times\{(+0.07\ \text{V}) - (-0.14\ \text{V})\}}{(8.3145\ \text{J K}^{-1}\text{mol}^{-1})\times(298\ \text{K})} = 16.3$$

$$K = \text{e}^{16.3} = \mathbf{1.2\times 10^7}$$

(c) $Hg^{2+}(aq) + 2e^- \rightleftharpoons Hg(l)$ $E_R^\ominus = +0.86$ V

$Fe^{2+}(s) + 2e^- \rightleftharpoons Fe(s)$ $E_L^\ominus = -0.44$ V

$$\ln K = \frac{2 \times (9.6485 \times 10^4\ \mathrm{C\ mol^{-1}}) \times \{(+0.86\ \mathrm{V}) - (-0.44\ \mathrm{V})\}}{(8.3145\ \mathrm{J\ K^{-1} mol^{-1}}) \times (298\ \mathrm{K})} = 101$$

$$K = \mathrm{e}^{101} = \mathbf{67.3 \times 10^{43}}$$

(d) $Cu^{2+}(s) + 2e^- \rightleftharpoons Cu(s)$ $E_R^\ominus = +0.34$ V

$Cd^{2+}(s) + 2e^- \rightleftharpoons Cd(s)$ $E_L^\ominus = -0.40$ V

$$\ln K = \frac{2 \times (9.6485 \times 10^4\ \mathrm{C\ mol^{-1}}) \times \{(+0.34\ \mathrm{V}) - (-0.40\ \mathrm{V})\}}{(8.3145\ \mathrm{J\ K^{-1} mol^{-1}}) \times (298\ \mathrm{K})} = 57.6$$

$$K = \mathrm{e}^{57.6} = \mathbf{1.0 \times 10^{25}}$$

(e) $Cu^{2+}(s) + 2e^- \rightleftharpoons Cu(s)$ $E_R^\ominus = +0.16$ V

$Cu^{+}(s) + e^- \rightleftharpoons Cu(s)$ $E_L^\ominus = +0.52$ V

$$\ln K = \frac{2 \times (9.6485 \times 10^4\ \mathrm{C\ mol^{-1}}) \times \{(+0.16\ \mathrm{V}) - (-0.14\ \mathrm{V})\}}{(8.3145\ \mathrm{J\ K^{-1} mol^{-1}}) \times (298\ \mathrm{K})} = -14.0$$

$$K = \mathrm{e}^{-14.0} = \mathbf{8.3 \times 10^{-7}}$$

(f) $Au^{+}(s) + e^- \rightleftharpoons Au(s)$ $E_R^\ominus = +1.69$ V

$Cd^{2+}(s) + 2e^- \rightleftharpoons Cd(s)$ $E_L^\ominus = +1.50$ V

$$\ln K = \frac{2 \times (9.6485 \times 10^4\ \mathrm{C\ mol^{-1}}) \times \{(+1.69\ \mathrm{V}) - (1.50\ \mathrm{V})\}}{(8.3145\ \mathrm{J\ K^{-1} mol^{-1}}) \times (298\ \mathrm{K})} = 7.40$$

$$K = \mathrm{e}^{7.40} = \mathbf{1.6 \times 10^{3}}$$

**E9.33** The half-reaction is

$$Cr_2O_7^{2-}(aq) + 14\ H^+(aq) + 6\ e^- \rightarrow 2\ Cr^{3+}(aq) + 7\ H_2O(l)$$

The Nernst equation, eqn 9.18, for the half cell is thus,

$$E = E^\ominus - \frac{RT}{\nu F}\ln Q = E^\ominus - \frac{RT}{6F}\ln\frac{a^2_{\mathrm{Cr^{3+}(aq)}}a^7_{\mathrm{H_2O(l)}}}{a_{\mathrm{Cr_2O_7^{2-}(aq)}}a^{14}_{\mathrm{H_3O^+}}}$$

The activity of water, $a_{H_2O} = 1$, because it is a pure liquid. Furthermore, we may express the activities of the components in aqueous solution in terms of molalities, $a_J = b_J / b^\ominus$ or, if the solution is sufficiently dilute, in terms of concentrations, $a_J \approx c_J / c^\ominus$, using the expressions in Table 6.2, so that

$$E = E^\ominus - \frac{RT}{6F}\ln\frac{\left(b_{\mathrm{Cr^{3+}(aq)}}/b^\ominus\right)^2}{\left(b_{\mathrm{Cr_2O_7^{2-}(aq)}}/b^\ominus\right)\left(b_{\mathrm{H_3O^+}}/b^\ominus\right)^{14}} = E^\ominus - \frac{RT}{6F}\ln\frac{b^2_{\mathrm{Cr^{3+}(aq)}}b^{\ominus 13}}{b_{\mathrm{Cr_2O_7^{2-}(aq)}}b^{14}_{\mathrm{H_3O^+}}}$$

or

$$E = E^{\ominus} - \frac{RT}{6F}\ln\frac{([\mathrm{Cr}^{3+}]/c^{\ominus})^2}{([\mathrm{Cr_2O_7^{2-}}]/c^{\ominus})([\mathrm{H_3O^+}]/c^{\ominus})^{14}} = \boldsymbol{E^{\ominus} - \frac{RT}{6F}\ln\frac{[\mathrm{Cr}^{3+}]^2 c^{\ominus 13}}{[\mathrm{Cr_2O_7^{2-}}][\mathrm{H_3O^+}]^{14}}}$$

**E9.34** The half-cell reaction is

$$\mathrm{MnO_4^-(aq) + 8\,H^+(aq) + 5\,e^- \rightarrow Mn^{2+}(aq) + 4\,H_2O(l)}$$

Writing the Nernst equation, eqn 9.18, and expressing activities in terms of concentrations,

$$\begin{aligned}E &= E^{\ominus} - \frac{RT}{\nu F}\ln Q = E^{\ominus} - \frac{RT}{5F}\ln\frac{a_{\mathrm{Mn^{2+}(aq)}}\overbrace{a_{\mathrm{H_2O(l)}}}^{1}{}^4}{a_{\mathrm{MnO_4^-(aq)}}a_{\mathrm{H_3O^+}}^8}\\
&= E^{\ominus} - \frac{RT}{5F}\ln\frac{([\mathrm{Mn}^{2+}]/c^{\ominus})}{([\mathrm{MnO_4}^-]/c^{\ominus})([\mathrm{H_3O^+}]/c^{\ominus})^8}\\
&= E^{\ominus} + \frac{RT}{5F}\overbrace{\ln([\mathrm{H_3O^+}]/c^{\ominus})^8}^{\ln x^y = y\ln x} - \frac{RT}{5F}\ln\frac{[\mathrm{Mn}^{2+}]}{[\mathrm{MnO_4}^-]}\\
&= \left\{E^{\ominus} + \frac{8RT}{5F}\ln(10^{-\mathrm{pH}})\right\} - \frac{RT}{5F}\ln\frac{[\mathrm{Mn}^{2+}]}{[\mathrm{MnO_4}^-]}\end{aligned}$$

(a) The modified standard potential at pH = 6.00 is thus

$$\begin{aligned}E^{\ominus\prime} &= E^{\ominus} + \frac{8RT}{5F}\ln(10^{-\mathrm{pH}})\\
&= +1.51\ \mathrm{V} + \frac{8\times(8.3145\ \mathrm{J\,K^{-1}mol^{-1}})\times 298\ \mathrm{K}}{5\times(9.6485\times10^4\ \mathrm{C\,mol^{-1}})}\times\ln(10^{-6.00}) = \mathbf{+0.94\ V}\end{aligned}$$

(b) In general,

$$\begin{aligned}E^{\ominus\prime} &= E^{\ominus} + \frac{8RT}{5F}\ln(10^{-\mathrm{pH}})\\
&= +1.51\ \mathrm{V} + \frac{8\times(8.3145\ \mathrm{J\,K^{-1}mol^{-1}})\times 298\ \mathrm{K}}{5\times(9.6485\times10^4\ \mathrm{C\,mol^{-1}})}\times\ln(10^{-\mathrm{pH}})\\
&= \mathbf{\{1.51 + 9.47\times10^{-2}\ln(10^{-pH})\}\ V}\end{aligned}$$

**E9.35** The pyruvic acid, $CH_3COCOOH$, lactic acid, $CH_3CH(OH)COOH$, couple is

$$\mathrm{CH_3COCOOH(aq) + 2\,H^+(aq) + 2\,e^- \rightarrow CH_3CH(OH)COOH} \qquad E^{\oplus} = -0.19\ \mathrm{V}$$

Denoting pyruvic acid as HP and lactic acid as HL, the Nernst equation for the couple is thus

$$\begin{aligned}E &= E^{\ominus} - \frac{RT}{2F}\ln\frac{a_{\mathrm{HL(aq)}}}{a_{\mathrm{HP(aq)}}a_{\mathrm{H_3O^+(aq)}}^2}\\
&= E^{\ominus} - \frac{RT}{2F}\ln\frac{1}{a_{\mathrm{H_3O^+(aq)}}^2} - \frac{RT}{2F}\ln\frac{a_{\mathrm{HL(aq)}}}{a_{\mathrm{HP(aq)}}} = E^{\ominus} + \frac{RT}{2F}\overbrace{\ln a_{\mathrm{H_3O^+(aq)}}^2}^{\ln x^y = y\ln x} - \frac{RT}{2F}\ln\frac{a_{\mathrm{HL(aq)}}}{a_{\mathrm{HP(aq)}}}\end{aligned}$$

$$= E^\ominus + \frac{RT}{F}\ln a_{H_3O^+(aq)} - \frac{RT}{2F}\ln\frac{a_{HL(aq)}}{a_{HP(aq)}}$$

At the biological standard state pH = 7, so that $a_{H_3O^+(aq)} = 10^{-7}$, $a_{HL} = a_{HP} = 1$, and $E = E^\oplus$. Thus, rearranging,

$$\begin{aligned} E^\ominus &= E^\oplus + \frac{RT}{F}\times\ln(10^{-7}) - \frac{RT}{2F}\ln 1 \\ &= -0.19\text{ V} + \frac{(8.3145\text{ J K}^{-1}\text{mol}^{-1})\times(298\text{ K})}{(9.6485\times10^4\text{ C mol}^{-1})}\times\ln 10^{-7} = \mathbf{+0.22\ V} \end{aligned}$$

**E9.36** (a) The half-cell reaction for the reduction of hydrogencarbonate to carbonate ions is

$$HCO_3^-(aq) + e^- \rightarrow CO_3^{2-}(aq) + \tfrac{1}{2} H_2(g)$$

The standard reaction Gibbs energy is thus, from eqn 7.12,

$$\begin{aligned} \Delta_r G^\ominus &= \sum \nu\Delta_f G^\ominus(\text{products}) - \sum \nu\Delta_f G^\ominus(\text{reactants}) \\ &= \overbrace{\{\Delta_f G^\ominus(CO_3^{2-},aq) + \tfrac{1}{2}\Delta_f G^\ominus(H_2,g)\}}^{\text{products}} - \overbrace{\Delta_f G^\ominus(HCO_3^-,aq)}^{\text{reactants}} \\ &= [\{(-527.81) + (\tfrac{1}{2}\times 0)\} - (-586.77)]\text{ kJ mol}^{-1} \\ &= +58.96\text{ kJ mol}^{-1} \end{aligned}$$

As written, the reaction is a one-electron process, so that, using eqn 9.14,

$$\begin{aligned} E^\ominus &= -\Delta_r G^\ominus/\nu F \\ &= -(+58.96\times10^3\text{ J mol}^{-1})/(9.6485\times10^4\text{ C mol}^{-1}) = \mathbf{-0.6111\ V} \end{aligned}$$

(b) We may write the net ionic reaction

$$CO_3^{2-}(aq) + H_2O(l) \rightarrow HCO_3^-(aq) + OH^-(aq)$$

as the difference between the the carbonate/hydrogencarbonate couple and the half-cell reaction

$$H_2O(l) + e^- \rightarrow \tfrac{1}{2} H_2(g) + OH^-(aq) \qquad E^\ominus = -0.83\text{ V}.$$

The carbonate/hydrogencarbonate couple forms the right-hand half cell and the $H_2O/H_2,OH^-$ couple the left-hand half cell. Thus, the cell standard potential is, from eqn 9.18,

$$\begin{aligned} E^\ominus_{cell} &= E^\ominus_R - E^\ominus_L = E^\ominus(CO_3^{2-}/HCO_3^-) - E^\ominus(H_2O/H^+,OH^-) \\ &= (-0.83\text{ V}) - (-0.61\text{ V}) = \mathbf{-0.22\ V} \end{aligned}$$

(c) The Nernst equation for the one-electron cell is thus

$$E_{cell} = E^\ominus_{cell} - \frac{RT}{\underbrace{\nu}_{1} F}\ln\frac{a_{HCO_3^-(aq)}a_{OH^-(aq)}}{a_{CO_3^{2-}(aq)}\underbrace{a_{H_2O(l)}}_{1}} = E^\ominus_{cell} - \frac{RT}{F}\ln\frac{a_{HCO_3^-(aq)}a_{OH^-(aq)}}{a_{CO_3^{2-}(aq)}}$$

(d) At the biological standard state, pH = pOH = 7, so that $a_{OH^-(aq)} = 10^{-pOH} = 10^{-7}$. Furthermore, $a_{CO_3^{2-}(aq)} = a_{HCO_3^-(aq)} = 1$, so that the change in potential is

$$E^{\oplus}{}_{\text{cell}} - E^{\ominus}_{\text{cell}} = -\frac{RT}{F}\ln\frac{\overbrace{a_{\text{HCO}_3^-(\text{aq})}}^{1}\overbrace{a_{\text{OH}^-(\text{aq})}}^{10^{-7}}}{\underbrace{a_{\text{CO}_3^{2-}(\text{aq})}}_{1}} = -\frac{RT}{F}\ln 10^{-7}$$

$$= -\frac{(8.3145\ \text{J K}^{-1}\text{mol}^{-1}) \times (298\ \text{K})}{(9.6485 \times 10^4\ \text{C mol}^{-1})}\ln 10^{-7}$$

$$= \mathbf{+0.41\ V}$$

(e) We may calculate the $pK_b$, for $CO_3^{2-}$ ion from the standard cell potential derived in part (b) using eqn 9.17,

$$\ln K_b = \nu F E^{\ominus}_{\text{cell}}/RT$$

The equivalent $pK_a$ is thus

$$pK_a = pK_w - pK_b = 14.00 - \nu F E^{\ominus}_{\text{cell}}/RT$$

$$= 14.00 - \frac{(9.6485 \times 10^4\ \text{C mol}^{-1}) \times (-0.22\ \text{V})}{(9.6485 \times 10^4\ \text{C mol}^{-1}) \times (298\ \text{K})} = \mathbf{10.33}$$

**E9.37** The production of zinc metal from aqueous zinc sulfate using mercury is equivalent to the reaction

$$Zn^{2+}(aq) + 2\ Hg(l) \rightarrow Zn(s) + Hg_2^{2+}(aq)$$

which may be expressed as the difference between the two half-cell reactions

$Zn^{2+}(aq) + 2\ e^- \rightarrow Zn(s)$ $\quad E^{\ominus}_R = -0.76\ V$

$Hg_2^{2+}(aq) + 2\ e^- \rightarrow 2\ Hg(l)$ $\quad E^{\ominus}_L = +0.79\ V$

Then, from eqn 9.18,

$$E^{\ominus}_{\text{cell}} = E^{\ominus}_R - E^{\ominus}_L = E^{\ominus}(\text{Zn}^{2+}/\text{Zn}) - E^{\ominus}(\text{Hg}_2{}^{2+}/\text{Hg})$$

$$= (-0.76\ \text{V}) - (+0.79\ \text{V}) = -1.55\ \text{V}$$

The standard cell potential is thus negative, implying that the reaction is not spontaneous in the direction written. Thus, **no**, mercury does not displace zinc from solution.

(b) In the same way, the oxidation of water to oxygen using chlorine gas corresponds to the reaction

which may be expressed as the difference between the two half-cell reactions

$Cl_2(g) + 2\ e^- \rightarrow 2\ Cl^-(aq)$ $\quad E^{\ominus}_R = +1.36\ V$

$O_2(g) + 4\ H^+(aq) + 4\ e^- \rightarrow 2\ H_2O(l)$ $\quad E^{\ominus}_L = +1.23\ V$

Then, from eqn 9.18,

$$E^{\ominus}_{\text{cell}} = E^{\ominus}_R - E^{\ominus}_L = E^{\ominus}(\text{Cl}_2/\text{Cl}^-) - E^{\ominus}(\text{O}_2/\text{H}_2\text{O})$$

$$= (+1.36\ \text{V}) - (+1.23\ \text{V}) = +0.13\ \text{V}$$

The standard cell potential is positive, implying that the reaction is indeed spontaneous in the direction written. Thus, **yes**, under standard conditions chlorine gas may be used to oxidise water and generate oxygen gas. Although the process is thermodynamically favourable, the reaction may occur too slowly to be exploited in the generation of oxygen. We could use the Nernst equation, eqn 9.14, to predict whether the reaction is spontaneous under other conditions.

**E9.38** Following the method outlined in Example 9.8, then using eqn 9.19,

$$\begin{aligned}\Delta_r S^\ominus &= \frac{\nu F\{E^\ominus_{cell}(T) - E^\ominus_{cell}(T')\}}{T - T'} \\ &= \frac{4 \times (9.6485 \times 10^4\ \mathrm{C\,mol^{-1}}) \times \{(1.2335\ \mathrm{V}) - (1.2251\ \mathrm{V})\}}{293\ \mathrm{K} - 303\ \mathrm{K}} \\ &= -324\ \mathrm{J\,K^{-1}mol^{-1}}\end{aligned}$$

Taking a mean value of the two values of the standard cell potential to represent the value at a temperature of 298 K, then rearranging eqn 7.12,

$$\begin{aligned}\Delta_r H^\ominus &= \Delta_r G^\ominus + T\Delta_r S^\ominus = -\nu F E^\ominus_{cell}(T) + T\Delta_r S^\ominus \\ &= -\{4 \times (9.6485 \times 10^4\ \mathrm{C\,mol^{-1}}) \times (1.2293\ \mathrm{V})\} \\ &\qquad + \{298\ \mathrm{K} \times (-324\ \mathrm{J\,K^{-1}mol^{-1}})\} \\ &= \mathbf{-571\ kJ\,mol^{-1}}\end{aligned}$$

## Answers to projects

**P9.39** (a) The cell reaction for the Harned cell may be written as a one-electron process as

$$\tfrac{1}{2}\,\mathrm{H_2(g)} + \mathrm{AgCl(s)} \rightarrow \mathrm{HCl(aq)} + \mathrm{Ag(s)}$$

The cell potential is given by the Nernst equation, eqn 9.18. The silver and silver chloride are both pure solids in their standard states, so that $a_{Ag(s)} = a_{AgCl(s)} = 1$. The hydrogen gas is also in its standard state, because it is at a partial pressure of $p = 1$ bar , so that $a_{H_2(g)} = 1$. Thus,

$$\begin{aligned}E_{cell} &= E^\ominus_{cell} - \frac{RT}{\nu F}\ln Q \\ &= E^\ominus_{cell} - \frac{RT}{\underbrace{\nu}_{1} F}\ln\frac{a_{H_3O^+(aq)}a_{Cl^-(aq)}\overbrace{a_{Ag(s)}}^{1}}{\underbrace{a_{H_2(g)}{}^{1/2}}_{1}\underbrace{a_{AgCl(s)}}_{1}} = E^\ominus_{cell} - \frac{RT}{F}\ln a_{H_3O^+(aq)}a_{Cl^-(aq)}\end{aligned}$$

In general, the activity of a solute in solution is given by eqn 9.1a, so that

$$a_{H_3O^+(aq)} = a_{Cl^-(aq)} = \gamma_\pm(b_{HCl}/b^\ominus)$$

and therefore

$$E_{cell} = E^\ominus_{cell} - \frac{RT}{F}\overbrace{\ln\{\gamma_\pm(b_{HCl}/b^\ominus)\}^2}^{\ln x^y = y\ln x} = E^\ominus_{cell} - \frac{2RT}{F}\overbrace{\ln\{\gamma_\pm(b_{HCl}/b^\ominus)\}}^{\ln xy = \ln x + \ln y}$$

$$= E^{\ominus}_{\text{cell}} - \frac{2RT}{F}\ln\gamma_{\pm} - \frac{2RT}{F}\ln(b_{\text{HCl}}/b^{\ominus})$$

From the Debye–Hückel limiting law, eqn 9.4,

$$\begin{aligned}\log\gamma_{\pm} &= -A|z_{+}z_{-}|I^{1/2} = -A|z_{+}z_{-}|\{½(z_{+}^{2}b_{+} + z_{-}^{2}b_{-})/b^{\ominus}\}^{1/2}\\ &= -A\left|\overbrace{z_{\text{H}^+}}^{+1}\overbrace{z_{\text{Cl}^-}}^{-1}\right|\left\{½\left(z_{\text{H}^+}^{2}\overbrace{b_{\text{H}^+}}^{b_{\text{HCl}}} + z_{\text{Cl}^-}^{2}\overbrace{b_{\text{Cl}^-}}^{b_{\text{HCl}}}\right)/b^{\ominus}\right\}^{1/2}\\ &= -A|(+1)\times(-1)|\{½((+1)^{2} + (-1)^{2})b_{\text{HCl}}/b^{\ominus}\}^{1/2}\\ &= -A(b_{\text{HCl}}/b^{\ominus})^{1/2}\end{aligned}$$

Using the rules for the manipulation of logarithms outlined in *The chemist's toolkit 2.2*

$$\ln\gamma_{\pm} = \overbrace{\ln(10)\times\log\gamma_{\pm}}^{\log_a x = (\log_a b)\times(\log_b x)} = \ln(10)\times -A(b_{\text{HCl}}/b^{\ominus})^{1/2}$$

so that

$$\begin{aligned}E_{\text{cell}} &= E^{\ominus}_{\text{cell}} - \frac{2RT}{F}\{-A\ln(10)\,(b_{\text{HCl}}/b^{\ominus})^{1/2}\} - \frac{2RT}{F}\ln(b_{\text{HCl}}/b^{\ominus})\\ &= E^{\ominus}_{\text{cell}} + \frac{2RTA\ln(10)}{F}(b_{\text{HCl}}/b^{\ominus})^{1/2} - \frac{2RT}{F}\ln(b_{\text{HCl}}/b^{\ominus})\end{aligned}$$

Rearranging gives an expression of the form $y = ax + b$,

$$\overbrace{E_{\text{cell}} + \frac{2RT}{F}\ln(b_{\text{HCl}}/b^{\ominus})}^{y} = \overbrace{\frac{2RTA\ln(10)}{F}}^{\text{slope},a}\overbrace{(b_{\text{HCl}}/b^{\ominus})^{1/2}}^{x} + \overbrace{E^{\ominus}_{\text{cell}}}^{\text{intercept},b}$$

(b) Figure 9.4 shows a graph of the form described in part (a).

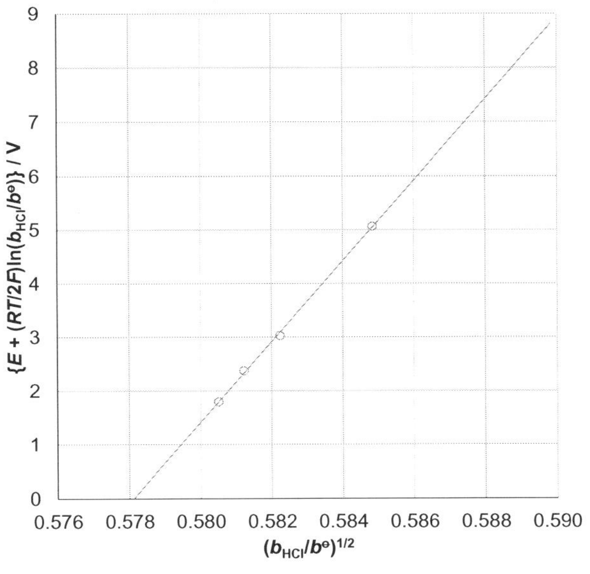


**Figure 9.4**

The graph is indeed a straight line, demonstrating that the system follows the Debye–Hückel limiting law. The standard cell potential is given by the intercept of the graph,

$$E^{\ominus}_{\text{cell}} = \text{intercept} = +0.2234\ \text{V}$$

**P9.40** (a) We may express the one-electron reduction of cytochrome c as the difference between the two half reactions

$$\text{cyt}_{\text{ox}} + \text{e}^- \rightleftharpoons \text{cyt}_{\text{red}} + \text{D}_{\text{ox}} \qquad E^{\ominus}_{\text{R}} = E^{\ominus}_{\text{cyt}}$$

$$\text{D}_{\text{ox}} + \text{e}^- \rightleftharpoons \text{D}_{\text{red}} \qquad E^{\ominus}_{\text{L}} = E^{\ominus}_{\text{D}}$$

so that, from eqn 9.18,

$$E^{\ominus}_{\text{cell}} = E^{\ominus}_{\text{R}} - E^{\ominus}_{\text{L}} = E^{\ominus}_{\text{cyt}} - E^{\ominus}_{\text{D}}$$

For dilute aqueous solutions, we may write the Nernst equation, eqn 9.14, in terms of molar concentrations rather than activities

$$E_{\text{cell}} = \overbrace{E^{\ominus}_{\text{cell}}}^{E^{\ominus}_{\text{cyt}}-E^{\ominus}_{\text{D}}} - \frac{RT}{F}\ln\frac{\overbrace{a_{\text{cyt}_{\text{red}}}}^{[\text{cyt}_{\text{red}}]/c^{\ominus}}\ \overbrace{a_{\text{D}_{\text{ox}}}}^{[\text{D}_{\text{ox}}]/c^{\ominus}}}{\underbrace{a_{\text{cyt}_{\text{ox}}}}_{[\text{cyt}_{\text{ox}}]/c^{\ominus}}\ \underbrace{a_{\text{D}_{\text{red}}}}_{[\text{D}_{\text{red}}]/c^{\ominus}}} = \left(E^{\ominus}_{\text{cyt}} - E^{\ominus}_{\text{D}}\right) - \frac{RT}{F}\ln\frac{[\text{cyt}_{\text{red}}][\text{D}_{\text{ox}}]}{[\text{cyt}_{\text{ox}}][\text{D}_{\text{red}}]}$$

At equilibrium, by definition, the cell potential is zero so that

$$\left(E^{\ominus}_{\text{cyt}} - E^{\ominus}_{\text{D}}\right) - \frac{RT}{F}\ln\frac{[\text{cyt}_{\text{red}}]_{\text{eq}}[\text{D}_{\text{ox}}]_{\text{eq}}}{[\text{cyt}_{\text{ox}}]_{\text{eq}}[\text{D}_{\text{red}}]_{\text{eq}}} = 0$$

We may rearrange this equation into the form of a straight-line graph, $y = mx + b$

$$\overbrace{\ln\frac{[\text{D}_{\text{ox}}]_{\text{eq}}}{[\text{D}_{\text{red}}]_{\text{eq}}}}^{y} = \overbrace{\ln\frac{[\text{cyt}_{\text{red}}]_{\text{eq}}}{[\text{cyt}_{\text{ox}}]_{\text{eq}}}}^{x} + \overbrace{\frac{F}{RT}\left(E^{\ominus}_{\text{cyt}} - E^{\ominus}_{\text{D}}\right)}^{\text{intercept},b}$$

Thus, a plot of $\ln([\text{D}_{\text{ox}}]_{\text{eq}}/[\text{D}_{\text{red}}]_{\text{eq}})$ against $\ln([\text{cyt}_{\text{red}}]_{\text{eq}}/[\text{cyt}_{\text{ox}}]_{\text{eq}})$ should be a straight line with a slope of 1, and an intercept of $\left(E^{\ominus}_{\text{cyt}} - E^{\ominus}_{\text{D}}\right)F/RT$.

(b) A plot of $\ln([\text{D}_{\text{ox}}]_{\text{eq}}/[\text{D}_{\text{red}}]_{\text{eq}})$ against $\ln([\text{cyt}_{\text{red}}]_{\text{eq}}/[\text{cyt}_{\text{ox}}]_{\text{eq}})$ for the data provided is shown in Figure 9.5. The graph is indeed a straight line, with a slope of 1.012, and an intercept of $\left(E^{\ominus}_{\text{cyt}} - E^{\ominus}_{\text{D}}\right)F/RT = -1.2124$ V. Thus, rearranging the expression for the intercept,

$$\begin{aligned} E^{\ominus}_{\text{cyt}} &= E^{\ominus}_{\text{D}} + \{(-1.2124\ \text{V}) \times (RT/F)\} \\ &= (+0.237\ \text{V}) - \frac{(-1.2124\ \text{V}) \times (8.3145\ \text{J K}^{-1}\text{mol}^{-1}) \times (298\ \text{K})}{(9.6485 \times 10^4\ \text{C mol}^{-1})} \\ &= \mathbf{+0.206\ V} \end{aligned}$$

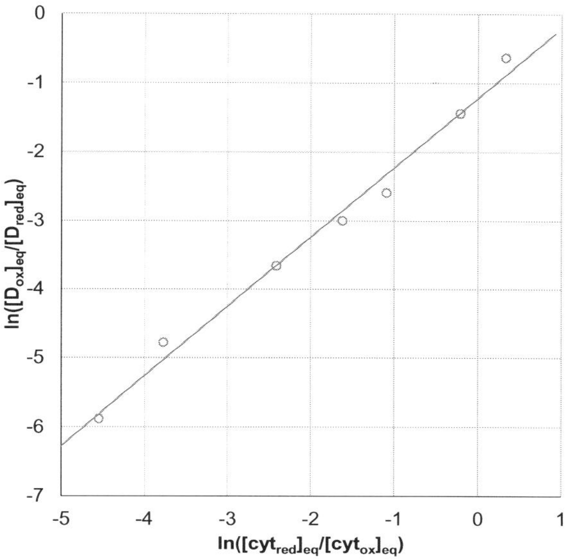


Figure 9.5

## Chapter 10

# Chemical kinetics: the rates of reactions

## Answers to discussion questions

**D10.1** A wide range of **proton-transfer rate constants**, and timescales, are observed in aqueous solution. This is especially illustrated by the reverse transfers in the following reactions at 25 °C:

| | $k_{\text{forward}}$ / mol$^{-1}$ dm$^3$ s$^{-1}$ | $k_{\text{reverse}}$ / mol$^{-1}$ dm$^3$ s$^{-1}$ |
|---|---|---|
| $H_3O^+(aq) + OH^-(aq) \rightleftharpoons 2\ H_2O(l)$ | $1.4 \times 10^{11}$ | $2.5 \times 10^{-5}$ |
| $H_3O^+(aq) + SO_4^{2-}(aq) \rightleftharpoons HSO_4^{2-} + H_2O(l)$ | $1.0 \times 10^{11}$ | $7.0 \times 10^{7}$ |
| $H_3O^+(aq) + NH_3(aq) \rightleftharpoons NH_4^+(aq) + H_2O(l)$ | $4.3 \times 10^{10}$ | $8.4 \times 10^{5}$ |
| $H_3O^+(aq) + C_2H_5O^-(aq) \rightleftharpoons C_2H_5OH(aq) + OH^-(aq)$ | — | $3.0 \times 10^{6}$ |

The time constant $\tau$ provides an indication of the timescale of a second-order reaction. By analogy with eqn 10.18 we take it to be given by $\tau = 1 / (k_r[A])$ where [A] is the molar concentration of reactants. This equation is not strictly correct, because it assumes that these second-order proton-transfer reactions may be treated as pseudo-first-order processes, but it does provide an estimate of the reaction timescale. For the first of the above reactions at pH = pOH = 7

$$\begin{aligned}\tau_{H_3O^+/OH^-} &= 1/(k_{H_3O^+/OH^-}[OH^-]) \\ &= 1/\{(1.4 \times 10^{11}\text{mol}^{-1}\text{dm}^3\text{s}^{-1}) \times (1.0 \times 10^{-7}\text{mol dm}^{-3})\} \\ &= 7.1 \times 10^{-5}\text{s} = 71\ \mu\text{s}\end{aligned}$$

For the reverse of this proton transfer

$$\begin{aligned}\tau_{H_2O/H_2O} &= 1/(k_{H_2O/H_2O}[H_2O]) \\ &= 1/\{(2.5 \times 10^{-5}\text{mol}^{-1}\text{dm}^3\text{s}^{-1}) \times (55.5\text{ mol dm}^{-3})\} = 7.2 \times 10^2\text{ s}\end{aligned}$$

Proton transfer between the hydronium and hydroxide ions is about 10 million times more rapid than transfer between water molecules. It is very interesting to compare these rate constants to the rate constant for a **diffusion-controlled limit** (also called the **encounter-controlled limit**) in which reactants immediately react upon diffusing into proximity. This topic is discussed in the next chapter, where it is shown that in the diffusion-controlled limit the rate constant is inversely proportional to the media viscosity and for aqueous solution at 25 °C it equals $7.4 \times 10^9$ mol$^{-1}$ dm$^3$ s$^{-1}$. The fact that the proton-transfer reactions involving the hydronium ion have larger rate constants than the diffusion limit is evidence that the proton-carrying species does not necessarily need to diffuse into proximity with a Brønsted base; the proton may rapidly migrate in a cooperative process along a network of hydrogen-bonded water molecules according to the **Grotthus mechanism** discussed in Section 9.2.

A one-electron transfer event between complex ions in aqueous solution often takes place by **outer-sphere electron transfer** in which no change occurs in the coordination sphere of the atom undergoing a change of oxidation number (i.e., the redox centre). Transfer rates can be fast for this mechanism and logarithms of rates are often observed to be proportional to differences in standard potentials. Self-exchange rate constants of the type $M(L)_6^{3+} + M(L)_6^{2+} \rightarrow M(L)_6^{2+} + M(L)_6^{3+}$ exhibit outer-sphere electron transfer rates of 4 mol$^{-1}$ dm$^3$ s$^{-1}$ for the $Fe(H_2O)_6^{3+}/Fe(H_2O)_6^{2+}$ couple, 50 mol$^{-1}$ dm$^3$ s$^{-1}$ for the $Ru(H_2O)_6^{3+}/Ru(H_2O)_6^{2+}$ couple, $2.8 \times 10^4$ mol$^{-1}$ dm$^3$ s$^{-1}$ for the $Ru(NH_3)_6^{3+}/Ru(NH_3)_6^{2+}$ couple, and $8 \times 10^{-6}$ mol$^{-1}$ dm$^3$ s$^{-1}$ for the $Co(NH_3)_6^{3+}/Co(NH_3)_6^{2+}$ couple. Only the $Co(NH_3)_6^{3+}/Co(NH_3)_6^{2+}$ couple occurs on a long timescale and this happens because the transfer requires an electron spin flip that is forbidden by the rules of quantum chemistry. Taking the smallest and largest of these rate constants and assuming concentrations of the order of 1 mol dm$^{-3}$, we find a timescale range for electron transfer of about $4 \times 10^{-5}$ s to $1 \times 10^5$ s.

A one-electron transfer event can also occur by **inner-sphere electron transfer** in which a change does occur in the coordination sphere of the complex ion. An example is the reduction

$$[Co(NH_3)_5Cl]^{2+} + Cr(H_2O)_6^{2+} + 6\ H_2O \rightarrow Co(H_2O)_6^{2+} + [Cr(H_2O)_5Cl]^{2+} + 5\ NH_3.$$

for which the second-order rate constant is $k_r = 6 \times 10^5$ mol$^{-1}$ dm$^3$ s$^{-1}$. This electron transfer occurs following the formation of a chloro bridge between Co(III) and Cr(II): $[(NH_3)_5Co{-}Cl{-}Cr(H_2O)_5]^{4+}$.

The **harpoon mechanism** of one-electron transfer is between neutral molecular or atomic entities in which long-range electron transfer is followed by a considerable reduction of the distance between donor and acceptor sites as a result of the electrostatic attraction in the ion pair created. In the gas-phase transfer of an electron from a potassium atom to a bromine molecule, the gaseous $K^+$ and $Br_2^-$ ions are observed to form when their centres are no more than about 580 pm apart. The strong attractive Coulomb force brings the two ions together after which KBr forms with the ejection of a Br atom. We assume that (a) the transfer must occur before the potassium atom (235 pm radius) and bromine molecule (228 pm bond length and radius of about 228 pm) are spaced by 463 pm and (b) the relative approach speed is 437 m s$^{-1}$, which is the average speed of a K atom at 298 K, then the timescale for the transfer must be less than the time needed to close the reactants from 580 pm to 463 pm: (580 – 463) pm / (437 m s$^{-1}$) = 0.3 ps. Relative speed in crossed atom/molecular-beam measurements may be 1/10th this value so an estimated timescale of about 1 ps is reasonable.

There are two important timescales for **collisions in liquids**. The first involves the concept of collisions between a molecule or ion and members of its solvent cage, a situation for which an exact definition of collision may not be possible as the central molecule and its solvent cage are in continuous contact. However, it is reasonable to assume that something like one collision occurs in each vibrational cycle of the central molecule so the timescale for a collision has an order of magnitude similar to the inverse of the molecular vibrational frequency. With typical vibrational frequencies between $1.2 \times 10^{13}$ Hz and $9.0 \times 10^{13}$ Hz, which corresponds to infrared vibrational absorbances in the range 400 cm$^{-1}$ and 3000 cm$^{-1}$, the range of timescales between collisions with the solvent cage is 0.01 ps to 0.1 ps.

The second timescale for collisions in liquids concerns the question of the average time between collisions of solute molecule A with solute molecule B. We see in the next chapter how the rate constant for a diffusion-controlled encounter depends upon solvent viscosity according to $k_{r,d} = 8RT/3\eta = 7.4 \times 10^9$ mol$^{-1}$ dm$^3$ s$^{-1}$ at 25 °C. Assuming solute concentrations of the order of 1 mol dm$^{-3}$, this gives a timescale of about 100 ps as the lower limit estimate for the time between collisions by a solute molecule with other solute molecules; lower concentrations have longer average times between encounter collisions.

**D10.2** The information provided by the determination of a reaction rate under different conditions of pressure, temperature, and the presence of a catalyst makes it possible to quickly predict reactant and product concentrations throughout the reaction progression toward equilibrium. With this knowledge we may be able to optimize the rate by the appropriate choice of conditions. Also, the study of reaction rates is a prerequisite to the understanding of the **mechanism of a reaction**, its analysis into a sequence of elementary steps.

**D10.3** The determination of a rate law is simplified by the **isolation method** in which the concentrations of all the reactants except one are in large excess. Thus, for a general reaction

$$A + B \rightarrow P$$

if B is in large excess, for example, then to a good approximation its concentration is constant throughout the reaction. Although the true rate law might be rate $= v = k_r[A][B]$, we can approximate [B] by $[B]_0$ and write

$$v = k_r[A][B] \approx k_r[A][B]_0 = \overbrace{(k_r[B])}^{k_{\text{eff}}}[A] = k_{\text{eff}}[A]$$

which has the form of a first-order rate law. Because the true rate law has been forced into first-order form by assuming that the concentration of B is constant, it is called a **pseudo-first-order** rate law; the concentration, [A] has been isolated. The dependence of the rate on the concentration of each of the reactants may be found by isolating them in turn (by having all the other substances present in large excess), and so constructing a picture of the overall rate law.

In the **method of initial rates**, which is often used in conjunction with the isolation method, the rate is measured at the beginning of the reaction for several different initial concentrations of reactants. We shall suppose that the rate law for a reaction with A isolated is $v = k_r[A]^a$; then its initial rate, $v_0$, is given by the initial values of the concentration of A, and we write $v_0 = k_r[A]_0^a$. Taking logarithms gives:

$$\log v_0 = \log k_r + a \log[A]_0$$

For a series of initial concentrations, a plot of the logarithms of the initial rates against the logarithms of the initial concentrations of A should be a straight lime with slope $a$.

The method of initial rates might not reveal the full rate law, for the products may participate in the reaction and affect the rate. For example, products participate in the synthesis of HBr, where the full rate law depends on the concentration of HBr. To avoid this difficulty, the rate law should be fitted to the data throughout the reaction. The fitting may be done, in simple cases at least, by using a proposed rate law to predict the concentration of any component at any time, and comparing it with the data.

Because rate laws are differential equations, we must integrate them if we want to find the concentrations as a function of time. Even the most complex rate laws may be integrated numerically. However, in a number of simple cases analytical solutions are easily obtained, and prove to be very useful. A first-order rate law shows linearity when the logarithm of concentration is plotted against time while a second-order rate law exhibits linearity in a plot of inverse concentration against time. The slope of the linear plot equals the second-order rate constant in the latter case and the negative of the first-order rate constant in the former case.

**D10.4** Consider a rate law of the form: rate $= v = k_r [A]^m [B]^n$ where the concentration orders $m$ and $n$ are either zero or a positive integer. If the sum $m + n$ equals zero, the reaction is zeroth-order and the rate is independent of species concentration. If the sum equals 1, the reaction is first order; if the sum equals 2, the reaction is second-order, and so on. In the case for which $m = 1$ and $n \neq 0$, the reaction order will appear to be 1 if the concentration of B is a large excess and [B] remains essentially unchanged during the course of reaction. This is the pseudo-first-order reaction rate for which

$$v = k_r[A][B]^n \approx k_r[A][B]_0^n = \overbrace{(k_r[B]_0^n)}^{k_{\text{eff}}}[A] = k_{\text{eff}}[A]$$

The apparent order of a reaction changes whenever a concentration varies to make one term in the rate law smaller, or larger, relative to another term. For example, we shall see in Chapter 11, that a typical rate law for the action of an enzyme E on a substrate S is

$$v = \frac{k_r[\mathrm{E}][\mathrm{S}]}{[\mathrm{S}] + K_\mathrm{M}}$$

where $K_\mathrm{M}$ is a constant. This rate law does not have a definite order overall. If the substrate concentration is so low that $[\mathrm{S}] \ll K_\mathrm{M}$ the rate becomes

$$v = \frac{k_r[\mathrm{E}][\mathrm{S}]}{K_\mathrm{M}}$$

which is first-order in S, first-order in E, and second-order overall. If the substrate concentration is so large that $[\mathrm{S}] \gg K_\mathrm{M}$, the rate becomes

$$v = k_r[\mathrm{E}]$$

which is zero-order in S, first-order in E, and first-order overall.

**D10.5** The **Arrhenius equation**, which may be expressed as eqn 10.20b, or eqn 10.20c,

$$\ln k_r = \ln A - (E_a/RT)$$
$$k_r = A\mathrm{e}^{-E_a/RT}$$

provides for the variation of the reaction rate constant with temperature, $k_r(T)$. The constants $A$ and $E_a$, which are determined by experiment, are called the **Arrhenius parameters**. More specifically, the parameter $A$ is the **pre-exponential factor** and $E_a$ is the **activation energy**. The pre-exponential factor is proportional to the rate at which reactant molecules collide while the activation energy is the minimum kinetic energy required for a collision to result in a reaction. Determination of the Arrhenius parameters involves preparation of a plot of experimentally determined values of $\ln k_r(T)$ against $1/T$. The Arrhenius equation predicts that the plot will be linear with a slope equal to $-E_a/R$ and an extrapolated intercept equal to $\ln A$. Thus, if the plot is linear, a least-square regression fit of the data plot yields values for the slope and intercept from which the Arrhenius parameters are calculated with the relations $E_a = -(R \times \text{slope})$ and $A = \mathrm{e}^{\text{intercept}}$.

The Arrhenius equation describes the variation of the reaction rate constant with temperature whenever the activation energy is temperature independent. There are instances for which the plot of $k_r(T)$ against $1/T$ is a straight line, implying that the kinetics are more complicated that preicted by simple Arrhenius theory. However, it is still possible to define a general activation energy as

$$E_a = -R\frac{\mathrm{d}}{\mathrm{d}(1/T)}(\ln k_r) = RT^2\frac{\mathrm{d}}{\mathrm{d}T}(\ln k_r)$$

This definition accounts for the temperature dependence of the activation energy. It reduces to the Arrhenius equation (as the slope of a straight line) for a temperature-independent activation energy. However, this definition is more general, because it allows $E_a$ to be obtained from the slope (at the temperature of interest) of a plot of $\ln k_r$ against $1/T$ even if the Arrhenius plot is not a straight line. Non-Arrhenius behaviour is observed in ion–molecule reactions and where quantum-mechanical tunnelling is important.

**D10.6** The **quasi-steady state approximation** for the concentration of chemical species X recognizes a situation for which the net rate of reaction of X is negligibly small; the rate of at which X is formed is balanced by the rate at which it is lost. Thus, the concentration, [X], remains constant and small throughout the reaction, except right at the beginning and right at the end. The approximation is often appied to the concentration of an intermediate in a reaction mechanism that consists of multiple elementary steps. Analysis of the reaction mechanism is simplified by making the approximation and insight as to whether the mechanism is compatible to experimental observations, which are often unable to directly measure [X], becomes feasible. For example, suppose that the rate of X depends upon species A, B, and X in the form $d[X]/dt = f_1(A,B,X) + f_2(A,B,X)$ where $f_1$ and $f_2$ are different functions. The quasi-steady state approximation for X assumes that $d[X]/dt \sim 0$ and the mechanism analysis is simplified with the relation $f_1(A,B,X) = -f_2(A,B,X)$.

**D10.7** The Eyring equation, eqn 10.24,

$$k_r = \kappa \times \frac{kT}{h} \times K^{\ddagger}/c^{\ominus}$$

results from transition-state theory, which is an attempt to account for the rate constants of bimolecular reactions of the form $A + B \rightleftharpoons C^{\ddagger} \rightarrow P$ in terms of the formation of an transition state $C^{\ddagger}$. In the formulation of the theory, it is assumed that the transition state and the reactants are in equilibrium. The concentration of the transition state is calculated in terms of an equilibrium constant, which in turn is calculated from the partition functions of the reactants. It is further supposed that one normal vibrational mode of the transition state, the one corresponding to displacement along the reaction coordinate, has a very low force constant and displacement along this normal mode leads to products, provided that the complex enters a certain configuration of its atoms, which is known as the transition state.

Collision theory provides the computational equations for collision rates between gaseous hard spheres but activation energies, collision cross-sections for non-hard spheres, and steric factors remain as empirical parameters in the computation of a rate constant. Consequently, the empirical parameters are often deduced from measured values of a rate constant under a variety of conditions. The Eyring theory of reaction rates provides a computational framework based upon the fundamental principles of quantum chemistry and statistical thermodynamics so the Eyring theory, when computationally feasible, provides detailed insight into formation of the activated complex and movement of atoms to form products in either the solvated or gaseous state. Calculations of the equilibrium constant $K^{\ddagger}$ and transmission coefficient $\kappa$ are very difficult but, when fundamental insight into a reaction mechanism is the goal, the Eyring theory is superior to collision theory. If the aim is the acquisition of activation energies, collision cross-sections for non-hard spheres, and steric factor knowledge and a detailed computation of atomic movement in the activated complex is not feasible or not desired, collision theory is superior.

## Solutions to exercises

**E10.1** If 39.8 per cent of the light was absorbed, then 60.2 per cent must have been transmitted. Thus, rearranging the equation for the Beer–Lambert law, eqn 10.1,

$$\begin{aligned}[\text{cyt}] &= \frac{A}{\epsilon L} = \frac{\log(I_0/I)}{\epsilon L} = -\frac{\log(I/I_0)}{\epsilon L} \\ &= -\frac{\log_{10}(0.602)}{(291\ \text{dm}^3\ \text{mol}^{-1}\text{cm}^{-1}) \times (6.5 \times 10^{-1}\text{cm})} \\ &= 1.2 \times 10^{-3}\text{mol dm}^{-3} = \mathbf{1.2\ mmol\ dm^{-3}}\end{aligned}$$

**E10.2** For the reaction $2\,A + B \rightarrow 4\,C + 3\,D$, then if the rate of formation of C is $3.2\ \text{mol dm}^{-3}\ \text{s}^{-1}$, the rate of consumption and formation of the other components are

$$\text{Rate of consumption of A} = \frac{\overbrace{|\nu_A|}^{\text{stoichiometric number of B}}}{\underbrace{|\nu_C|}_{\text{stoichiometric number of C}}} \times \text{Rate of formation of C}$$

$$= \frac{2}{4} \times (3.2\ \text{mol dm}^{-3}\text{s}^{-1}) = \mathbf{1.6\ mol\ dm^{-3}s^{-1}}$$

$$\text{Rate of consumption of B} = \frac{\overbrace{|\nu_B|}^{\text{stoichiometric number of B}}}{\underbrace{|\nu_C|}_{\text{stoichiometric number of C}}} \times \text{Rate of formation of C}$$

$$= \frac{1}{4} \times (3.2\ \text{mol dm}^{-3}\text{s}^{-1}) = \mathbf{0.80\ mol\ dm^{-3}s^{-1}}$$

$$\text{Rate to formation of D} = \frac{\overbrace{|\nu_D|}^{\text{stoichiometric number of D}}}{\underbrace{|\nu_C|}_{\text{stoichiometric number of C}}} \times \text{Rate of formation of C}$$

$$= \frac{3}{4} \times (3.2\ \text{mol dm}^{-3}\text{s}^{-1}) = \mathbf{2.4\ mol\ dm^{-3}s^{-1}}$$

The corresponding rates of reaction of A, B and D are thus $-1.6\ \text{mol dm}^{-3}\ \text{s}^{-1}$ (with the negative sign indicating consumption), $+0.80\ \text{mol dm}^{-3}\ \text{s}^{-1}$ and $2.4\ \text{mol dm}^{-3}\ \text{s}^{-1}$ respectively.

**E10.3** The unique rate of reaction may be calculated from the stoichiometric numbers of the various components. These stoichiometric numbers are the same as the stoichiometric numbers, $\nu_J$, but written as positive for products and negative for reactants. Thus, using eqn 10.3,

$$\begin{aligned}v &= \frac{1}{\nu_J} \times \frac{\Delta[J]}{\Delta t} = \frac{1}{\nu_A} \times \frac{\Delta[A]}{\Delta t} = \frac{1}{-2} \times \frac{\Delta[A]}{\Delta t} = \frac{1}{-2} \times (-1.6\ \text{mol dm}^{-3}\text{s}^{-1}) \\ &= \frac{1}{\nu_B} \times \frac{\Delta[B]}{\Delta t} = \frac{1}{-1} \times \frac{\Delta[B]}{\Delta t} = -\frac{1}{1} \times (-0.80\ \text{mol dm}^{-3}\text{s}^{-1})\end{aligned}$$

$$= \frac{1}{\nu_C} \times \frac{\Delta[C]}{\Delta t} = \frac{1}{+4} \times \frac{\Delta[C]}{\Delta t} = \frac{1}{4} \times (+3.2 \text{ mol dm}^{-3}\text{s}^{-1})$$
$$= \frac{1}{\nu_D} \times \frac{\Delta[D]}{\Delta t} = \frac{1}{+3} \times \frac{\Delta[D]}{\text{\DElta } t} = \frac{1}{3} \times (2.4 \text{ mol dm}^{-3}\text{s}^{-1})$$
$$= \mathbf{0.80 \text{ mol dm}^{-3}\text{s}^{-1}}$$

**E10.4** For a rate law $v = k_r[A][B][C]$, then because the rate of reaction, $v$, is measured in units of mol dm$^{-3}$ s$^{-1}$, and the conecntrations in units of mol dm$^{-3}$, in order that the equation is dimensionally consistent, so that the units are the same on both sides of the equation, the rate constant $k_r$ must be expressed in units of mol$^{-2}$ dm$^{+6}$ s$^{-1}$

$$\overbrace{v}^{\text{mol dm}^{-3}\text{s}^{-1}} = k_r \overbrace{[A]}^{\text{mol dm}^{-3}} \overbrace{[B]}^{\text{mol dm}^{-3}} \overbrace{[C]}^{\text{mol dm}^{-3}}$$
$$\underbrace{\text{mol dm}^{-3}\text{s}^{-1}}_{v} = \underbrace{\mathbf{mol^{-2}dm^{6}\ s^{-1}}}_{k_r} \times \underbrace{\text{mol}^3\text{dm}^{-9}}_{[A][B][C]}$$

**E10.5** For the rate law

$$v = \frac{k_{r1}[A][B]}{1 + k_{r2}[B]}$$

the units of the two rate constants must be such that that equation is dimensionally consistent. Thus, the term $k_{r2}[B]$ must be dimensionless in order that it may be added to the pure number 1. Thus, the rate constant $k_{r2}$ must have units of **mol$^{-1}$ dm$^3$** so that the units cancel with those of the concentration [B]. If the denominator is dimensionless, the units of the numerator must be equivalent to those of the rate, in order that the units on the right-hand side of the equation match those on the left-hand side. Thus, $k_{r1}$ must have units of **mol$^{-1}$ dm$^3$ s$^{-1}$**. We may confirm this by writing

$$v = \frac{k_{r1}[A][B]}{1 + k_{r2}[B]}$$
$$\text{mol dm}^{-3}\text{s}^{-1} = \frac{\overbrace{(\mathbf{mol^{-1}dm^3s^{-1}})}^{k_{r1}} \times (\text{mol dm}^{-3}) \times (\text{mol dm}^{-3})}{1 + \{\underbrace{(\mathbf{mol^{-1}dm^3})}_{k_{r2}} \times (\text{mol dm}^{-3})\}}$$

**E10.6** We may use dimensional analysis to derive the units for the rate constants in the rate law

$$v = \frac{k_{r1}p_B p_A^{3/2}}{p_A + k_{r2}p_B}$$

The dimensions, and thus the units, of the two terms in the denominator must be the same in order that they may be added together.

$$\overbrace{\text{kPa}}^{p_A} = \overbrace{\text{kPa}}^{k_{r2}p_B}$$

Thus, $k_{r2}$ must be **dimensionless** so that both terms have units of pressure.

$$\overbrace{\text{kPa}}^{k_{r2}p_B} = \overbrace{\underbrace{1}_{\substack{\textbf{dimensionless,}\\ \textbf{no units}}}}^{k_{r2}} \times \overbrace{\text{kPa}}^{p_B}$$

Furthermore, the units of the left and right-hand sides of the equation must be the same. Thus, if rate is measured in units of kPa $s^{-1}$, and the denominator has units of kPa, then the numerator, $k_{r1}p_Bp_A^{3/2}$ must have units of $kPa^2\ s^{-1}$.

$$\overbrace{\text{kPa s}^{-1}}^{v} = \overbrace{\text{kPa}^2\ \text{s}^{-1}}^{k_{r1}p_Bp_A^{3/2}} \ / \ \overbrace{\text{kPa}}^{p_A+k_{r2}p_B}$$

For this to be the case, the rate constant $k_{r1}$ must have units of $\mathbf{kPa^{-1/2}\ s^{-1}}$, so that

$$\overbrace{\text{kPa}^2\text{s}^{-1}}^{k_{r1}p_Bp_A^{3/2}} = \overbrace{\mathbf{kPa^{-1/2}s^{-1}}}^{k_{r1}} \times \overbrace{\text{kPa}^{5/2}}^{p_Bp_A^{3/2}}$$

**E10.7** The rate constant is expressed in terms of a concentration of molecule per cubic centrimetre. To convert to units of mole per cubic decimetre we must multiply by Avogadro's number. The value expressed per mole is thus much greater than the value per molecule. A volume of 1 $cm^3$ is equivalent to $10^{-3}$ $dm^3$, so to convert from units of $cm^3$ to $dm^3$ we must also multiply by $10^{-3}$ $dm^3$ / $cm^3$.

$$\begin{aligned} k_r &= (6.2\times10^{-14}\ \text{cm}^3\ \text{molecule}^{-1}\ \text{s}^{-1}) \\ &\qquad \times \underbrace{(6.022\times10^{23}\text{molecule mol}^{-1})}_{\text{conversion from molecule}^{-1}\text{to mol}^{-1}} \times \underbrace{(10^{-3}\ \text{dm}^3/\text{cm}^3)}_{\text{conversion from cm}^3\text{to dm}^3} \\ &= \mathbf{3.7\times10^7 dm^3\ mol^{-1}s^{-1}} \end{aligned}$$

Including the units explicitly allows us to confirm that we have performed the conversion correctly.

**E10.8** The rate law

$$v = \frac{k_{r1}[A][B]}{k_{r2} + k_{r3}[B]^{1/2}}$$

does not have a definite order overall; the order varies according to the conditions. For example, if $k_{r2} \gg k_{r3}[B]^{1/2}$, then $k_{r2} + k_{r3}[B]^{1/2} \approx k_{r3}[B]^{1/2}$ and the rate law becomes

$$v \approx \frac{k_{r1}[A][B]}{k_{r3}[B]^{1/2}} = (k_{r1}/k_{r3})[A][B]^{1/2}$$

and the reaction has an order of 1 with respect to A and ½ with respect to B. Similarly, if $k_{r2} \ll k_{r3}[B]^{1/2}$, then $k_{r2} + k_{r3}[B]^{1/2} \approx k_{r2}$ and

$$v \approx \frac{k_{r1}[A][B]}{k_{r2}} = (k_{r1}/k_{r2})[A][B]$$

and the reaction is first order with respect to both A and B and second order overall.

**E10.9** We may write the rate for the reaction as

$$v = k_{r,eff}[C_6H_{12}O_6]^a$$

where $a$ is the order of the reaction with respect to glucose, $C_6H_{12}O_6$. Following the method of initial rates, and taking logarithms, yields an expression with the form of the equation for a straight-line graph

$$\overbrace{\log v_0}^{y} = \overbrace{\log k_{r,eff}}^{\text{intercept}} + \overbrace{a}^{\text{slope}} \overbrace{\log[C_6H_{12}O_6]_0}^{x}$$

Thus, a graph of the logarithm of the initial rate, $v_0$, against the logarithm of initial glucose concentration $[C_6H_{12}O_6]_0$ should be a straight line with a slope equal to the order of the reaction with respect to glucose. Figure 10.1 shows that this is indeed the case. The slope of the graph is 0.999, implying that the reaction is first order with respect to glucose. The intecept of the graph is 0.697. Thus,

$$k_{r,eff}/(\text{mol}^{-1}\,\text{dm}^3\text{s}^{-1}) = 10^{\text{intercept}} = 10^{0.697} = 4.977$$

so that $\boldsymbol{k_{r,eff}} = \mathbf{4.977\ mol^{-1}\ dm^3\ s^{-1}}$.

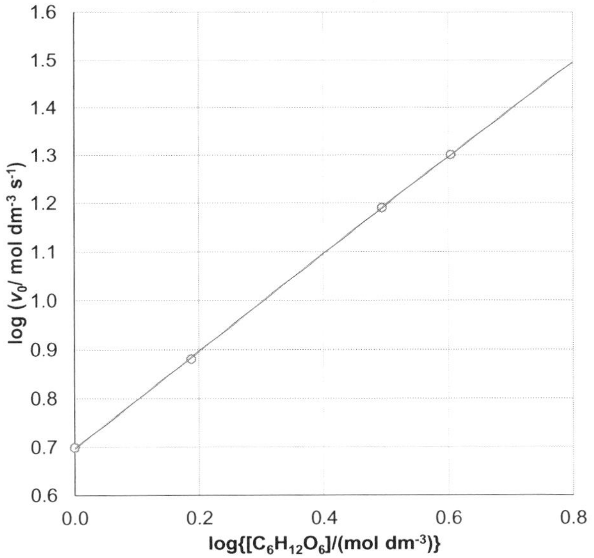


Figure 10.1

**E10.10** We may write the rate law for the reaction as

$$v = k_r[Y]^a[\text{complex}]^b$$

where $a$ is the order of the reaction with respect to Y and $b$ is the order of the reaction with respect to the complex. Thus, if we consider the initial rate and take logarithms, we obtain an expression with the form of the equation of a straight-line graph

$$\overbrace{\log v_0}^{y} = \overbrace{\{\log k_r + a\log[\mathrm{Y}]_0\}}^{\text{intercept}} + \overbrace{b}^{\text{slope}} \overbrace{\log[\text{complex}]_0}^{x}$$

Hence, a graph of the logarithm of initial reaction rate against initial concentration of glucose for a particular concentration of Y should be a straight line, with a slope equal to the order of the reaction. Figure 10.2 shows a plot of the data for both concentrations of Y. The slopes of the two lines are 1.014 and 0.984, indicating that, within experimental error, the reaction is first order with respect to the complex.

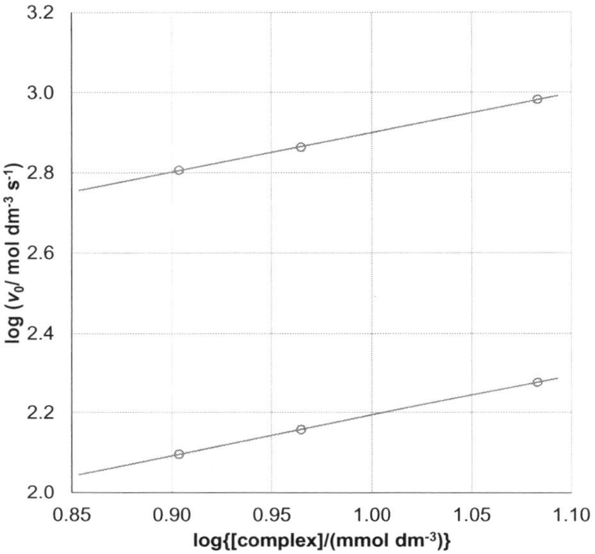


**Figure 10.2**

In theory, we could perform a similar analysis to determine the order of the reaction with respect to Y, plotting the logarithm of the initial reaction rate against the initial concentration of Y for each concentration of the complex. However, the lines on the plot would be defined by only two points. Instead, we proceed by using the values for the intercepts in Figure 10.2. These values allow us to determine both the rate constant and the order of the reaction with respect to Y, because

$$\text{intercept} = \log k_r + a\log[\mathrm{Y}]_0$$

For [Y] = 2.7 mmol dm$^{-3}$, the intercept of the graph is 1.181 and for [Y] = 6.1 mmol dm$^{-3}$, the intercept is 1.916. Solving the following equations simultaneously

$$1.181 = \log\{k_r/(\text{mol}^{-1}\text{dm}^3\text{s}^{-1})\} + a\log(2.7\ \text{mmol dm}^{-3})$$
$$1.916 = \log\{k_r/(\text{mol}^{-1}\text{dm}^3\text{s}^{-1})\} + a\log(6.1\ \text{mmol dm}^{-3})$$

leads to $a = 2.1$, implying that the reaction is **second order**, and $k_r$ =**1.9 mol$^{-1}$ dm$^3$ s$^{-1}$**.

**E10.11** Rearranging the first-order integrated rate law for the consumption of a reactant, eqn 10.14a,

$$\begin{aligned} k_r &= -\{\ln([C_2H_5OH]/[C_2H_5OH]_0)\}/t \\ &= -\{\ln(56.0\ \text{mmol dm}^{-3})/(220\ \text{mmol dm}^{-3})\}/(1.22\times10^4\ \text{s}) \\ &= \mathbf{1.12\times10^{-4}s^{-1}} \end{aligned}$$

**E10.12** We may rearrange the integrated rate law for a second-order reaction, eqn 10.16a,

$$\begin{aligned} k_r &= -\{(1/[A]_0)-(1/[A])\}/t \\ &= -\left(\frac{1}{220\ \text{mmol dm}^{-3}}-\frac{1}{56.0\ \text{mmol dm}^{-3}}\right)/(1.22\times10^4\text{s}) \\ &= 1.09\times10^{-6}\text{mmol}^{-1}\ \text{dm}^3\text{s}^{-1} = \mathbf{1.09\times10^{-3}\ mol^{-1}\ dm^3s^{-1}} \end{aligned}$$

**E10.13** The value of the rate constant depends upon the order of the reaction with respect to carbon dioxide. If the reaction is first order, then applying eqn 10.14a,

$$\begin{aligned} k_r &= -\{\ln([CO_2]/[CO_2]_0)\}/t \\ &= -\{\ln(56.0\ \text{mmol dm}^{-3})/(220\ \text{mmol dm}^{-3})\}/(1.22\times10^4\ \text{s}) \\ &= \mathbf{1.12\times10^{-4}s^{-1}} \end{aligned}$$

If, however, the reaction is second order, then we must use eqn 10.16a,

$$\begin{aligned} k_r &= -\{(1/[CO_2]_0)-(1/[CO_2])\}/t \\ &= -\left(\frac{1}{220\ \text{mmol dm}^{-3}}-\frac{1}{56.0\ \text{mmol dm}^{-3}}\right)/(1.22\times10^4\text{s}) \\ &= 1.09\times10^{-6}\text{mmol}^{-1}\ \text{dm}^3\text{s}^{-1} = \mathbf{1.09\times10^{-3}\ mol^{-1}\ dm^3s^{-1}} \end{aligned}$$

In the same way, we may calculate the rate constant for other possible orders of reaction using the appropriate integrated rate equation.

**E10.14** See Exercise 10.13.

**E10.15** See Exercise 10.13.

**E10.16** If a reaction is zeroth-order reaction with respect to a particular reactant, then the rate is independent of the concentration of that reactant. If other components are in excess so that their concentrations remain effectively constant and the reactant is isolated, the rate is also constant, so that $v = k_{r,\text{eff}}$.

(a) Thus, because the rate constant is equal to the rate

$$\begin{aligned} k_{r,\text{eff}} = v = -\frac{\Delta p_{NH_3}}{\Delta t} &= -\frac{\overbrace{p_{NH_3}(t)}^{\substack{\text{partial}\\\text{pressure}\\\text{at time }t}}-\overbrace{p_{NH_3}(0)}^{\substack{\text{partial}\\\text{presure}\\\text{at time 0}}}}{t} \\ &= -\frac{(10-21)\ \text{kPa}}{770\ \text{s}} = 0.014\ \text{kPa s}^{-1} = \mathbf{14\ Pa\ s^{-1}} \end{aligned}$$

(b) Rearranging,

$$t = -\frac{p_{NH_3}(t) - p_{NH_3}(0)}{k_{r,eff}} = -\frac{(0-21)\ \text{kPa}}{0.014\ \text{kPa s}^{-1}} = \mathbf{1.5 \times 10^3 s}$$

**E10.17** (a) We may see by inspection that doubling the initial concentration of ICl from 1.5 mmol dm$^{-3}$ in Experiment 1, to 3.0 mmol dm$^{-3}$ in Experiment 2, with the concentration of $H_2$ constant, results in a doubling of the initial rate. The rate must therefore be proportional to the concentration of ICl, $v \propto$ [ICl], implying that the reaction is first order with respect to this component. In the same way, we see that tripling the initial concentration of $H_2$ from 1.5 mmol dm$^{-3}$ in Experiment 2, to 4.5 mmol dm$^{-3}$ in Experiment 3, with the concentration of ICl constant, results in a tripling of the initial rate. Thus, the rate must also be proportional to the concentration of $H_2$, $v \propto [H_2]$, meaning that the reaction is first order with respect to this component too. We may therefore write the rate law as

$$v = k_r[\text{ICl}][\text{H}_2]$$

(b) In theory, we could calculate the rate constant as an average of the result from each of the experiments.

$$k_r = v_0/([\text{ICl}]_0[\text{H}_2]_0)$$

A more elegant approach that should be used whenever we have several sets of data, is to plot a graph of the initial rate against the product of the initial concentrations. The rate constant is then given by the slope of the graph.

$$\overbrace{v_0}^{y} = \overbrace{k_r}^{\text{slope}} \times \overbrace{([\text{ICl}]_0[\text{H}_2]_0)}^{x}$$

Figure 10.3 shows such a graph for the data provided. The slope of the graph is $\boldsymbol{k_r = 0.162\ \text{mol}^{-1}\ \text{dm}^3\ \text{s}^{-1}}$.

(c) Hence, for Experiment 4,

$$\begin{aligned}\overbrace{v_0}^{y} &= \overbrace{k_r}^{\text{slope}}\ [\text{ICl}]_0[\text{H}_2]_0 \\ &= (0.162\ \text{mol}^{-1}\text{dm}^3\text{s}^{-1}) \times (4.7 \times 10^{-3}\text{mol dm}^{-3})(\times\ 2.7 \times 10^{-3}\text{mol dm}^{-3}) \\ &= \mathbf{20.6 \times 10^{-7}mol\ dm^{-3}s^{-1}}\end{aligned}$$

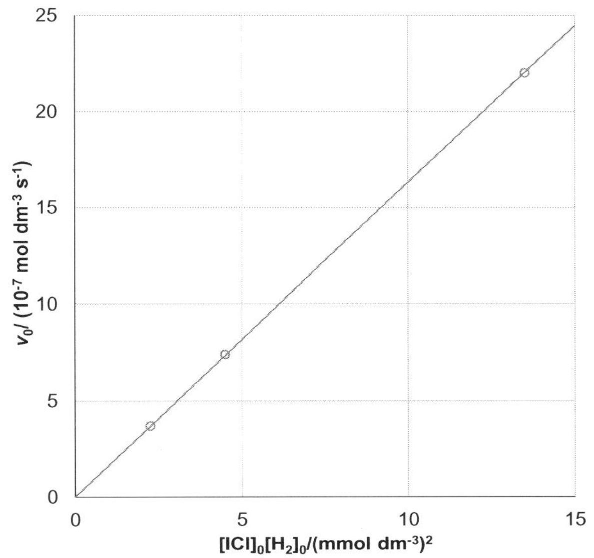


Figure 10.3

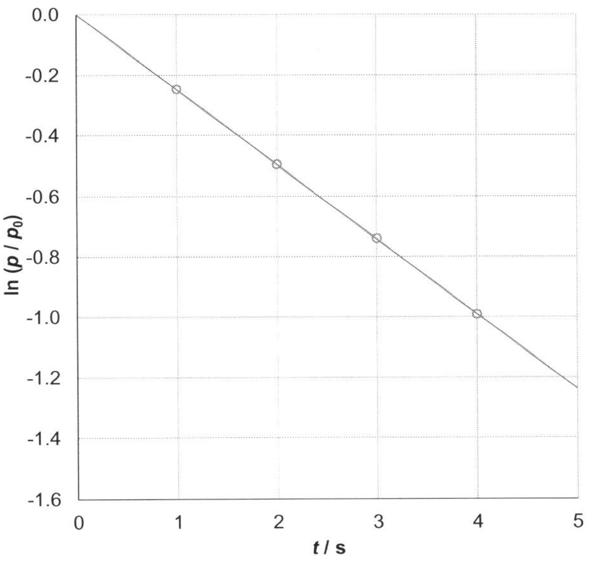


Figure 10.4

**E10.18** We may express an integrated rate law in terms of pressure as well as concentration. Thus, eqn 10.14a becomes

$$\overbrace{\ln(p/p_0)}^{y} = \overbrace{-k_r}^{\text{slope}}\overbrace{t}^{x}$$

This expression has the same form as the equation for a straight-line graph.

Figure 10.4 shows a plot of the logarithm of the ratio of the pressure relative to the initial pressure against time. The graph is indeed a straight line, confirming that the reaction is first order with respect to mercury dimethyl. The slope of this graph is $-0.248\ \text{s}^{-1}$, so that the rate constant for the reaction is $\mathbf{0.248\ s^{-1}}$.

**E10.19** (a) For the reaction

$$2\text{HI(g)} \rightleftharpoons \text{H}_2\text{(g)} + \text{I}_2\text{(g)}$$

we may write the differential rate law as

$$v = -\frac{\text{d[HI]}}{\text{d}t} = k_\text{r}[\text{HI}]^a$$

where $a$ is the order of the reaction and the negative sign indicates that the concentration of HI decreases with time.

If the reaction is first order with respect to hydrogen iodide then we may integrate to derive an equation similar to eqn 10.14,

$$\overbrace{\ln([\text{HI}]/[\text{HI}]_0)}^{y} = \overbrace{-k_\text{r}}^{\text{slope}}\overbrace{t}^{x}$$

and a graph of ln $[\text{HI}]/[\text{HI}]_0$ against time should be a straight line with a slope of magnitude equal to the rate constant for the reaction. Figure 10.5 shows such a plot for the data provided. The graph is a smooth curve, and not a straight line, indicating that the reaction is not first order with respect to HI.

If, instead, the reaction is second order with respect to hydrogen iodide then, we may obtain an expression similar to eqn 10.16a,

$$\overbrace{(1/[\text{HI}])}^{y} = \overbrace{(1/[\text{HI}]_0)}^{\text{intercept}} + \overbrace{k_\text{r}}^{\text{slope}}\ \overbrace{t}^{x}$$

and a graph of 1/[HI] against time should be a straight line with a slope equal to the rate constant. Figure 10.6 shows that this indeed the case. The plot is a straight line, indicating that the second-order rate law is obeyed.

(b) The slope of the graph shown in Figure 10.5, and thus the value of the second-order rate constant is $\mathbf{7.80 \times 10^{-3}\ dm^3\ mol^{-1}\ s^{-1}}$. We should note that had we chosen to define the rate law in terms of the unique rate, so that

$$v' = \frac{1}{\underbrace{\nu_\text{HI}}_{\substack{\text{stoichiometric}\\\text{number of HI}}}}\frac{\text{d[HI]}}{\text{d}t} = -\frac{1}{2}\frac{\text{d[HI]}}{\text{d}t} = -k_\text{r}'[\text{HI}]^2$$

then the rate constant would be half this value.

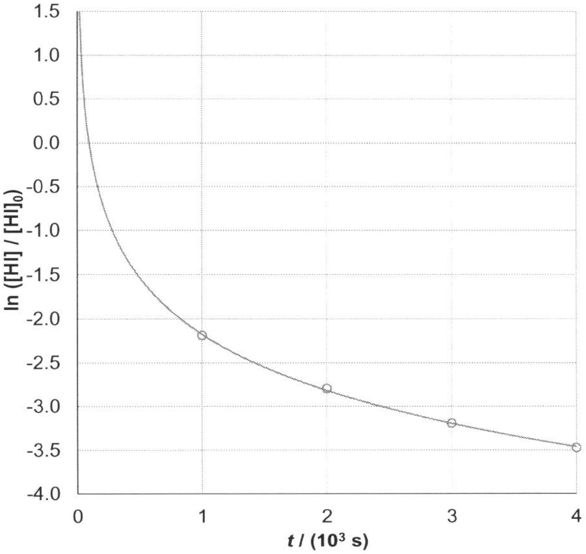


Figure 10.5

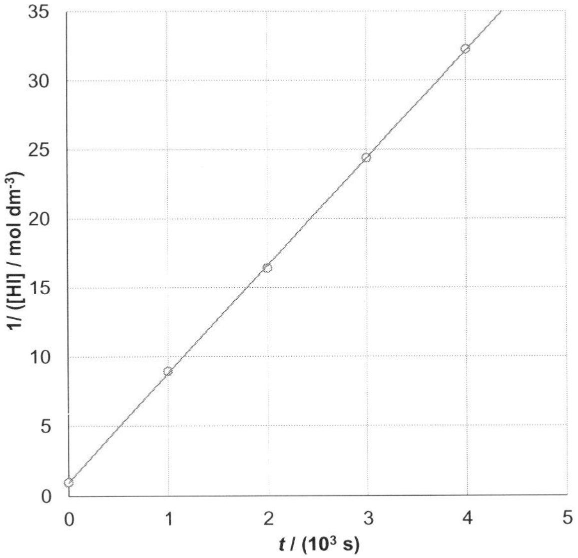


Figure 10.6

**E10.20** We adopt the same method as for the previous exercise. Figure 10.7 shows a plot of the logarithm of the concentration of HI against time. The graph is a smotth curve, confirming that the reaction is not first order under these conditions. Figure 10.8 shows a plot of the reciprocal of the concentration of HI against time. This graph is indeed a straight line, showing that the reaction is **second order** with respect to HI. The slope of this plot, which is equal to the value of the rate constant, is **1.32 $mol^{-1}$ $dm^3$ $s^{-1}$**.

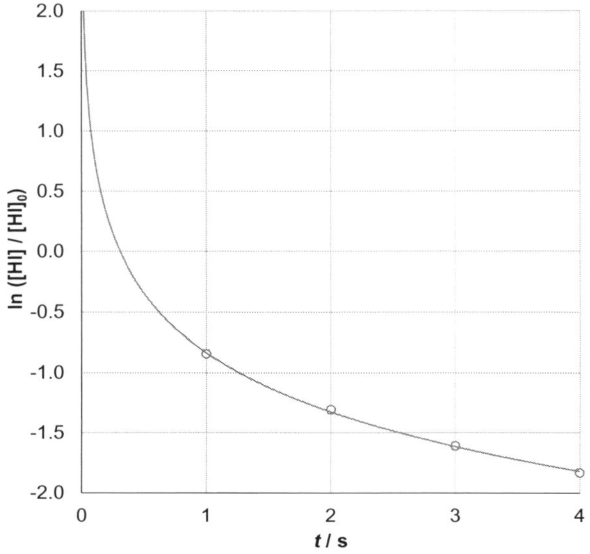


Figure 10.7

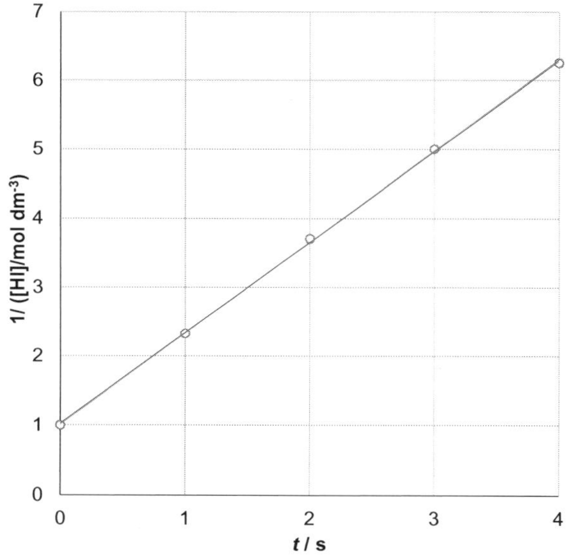


Figure 10.8

**E10.21** For the conditions given, the concentration of carbon monoxide is much greater than the concentration of myoglobin. Thus, we may assume that because the carbon monoxide is in excess, its concentration remains effectively constant, so that the myoglobin is isolated. Hence, we may write the rate law as a pseudo-first-order process, with the rate depending only upon the concentration of myoglobin

$$v = k_r[\mathrm{CO}][\mathrm{Mb}] \approx \overbrace{k_r[\mathrm{CO}]_0}^{k_{r,\mathrm{eff}}}[\mathrm{Mb}] = k_{r,\mathrm{eff}}[\mathrm{Mb}]$$

and with the pseudo-first-order rate constant

$$\begin{aligned} k_{r,\mathrm{eff}} &= k_r[\mathrm{CO}]_0 \\ &= (5.8 \times 10^5\,\mathrm{dm^3\,mol^{-1}\,s^{-1}}) \times (400 \times 10^{-3}\,\mathrm{mol\,dm^{-3}}) = 2.3 \times 10^5\,\mathrm{s^{-1}} \end{aligned}$$

The concentration of myoglobin is then given by eqn 10.14b,

$$[\mathrm{Mb}] = [\mathrm{Mb}]_0 e^{-k_{r,\mathrm{eff}}\,t}$$

The variation of the concentration of myoglobin with time is shown in Figure 10.9.

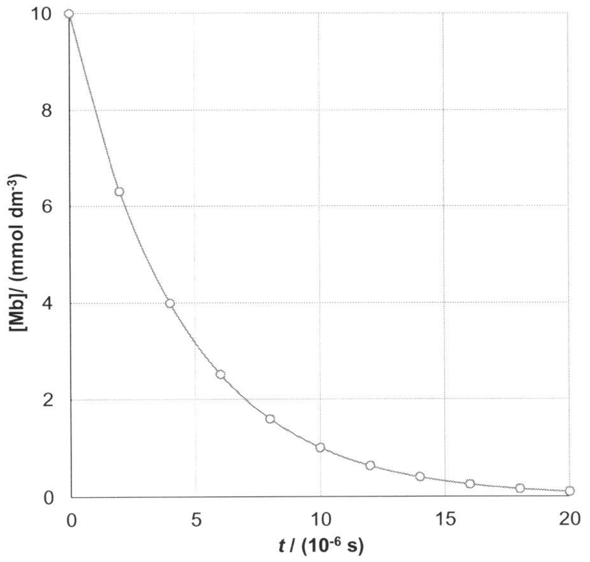


**Figure 10.9**

**E10.22** The stoichiometry of the reaction

$$3\,\mathrm{A} \rightarrow \mathrm{B}$$

is such that one molecule of B is formed for every three molecules of A that are lost. Thus,

$$[\mathrm{B}] = [\mathrm{B}]_0 + \{\overbrace{([\mathrm{A}]_0 - [\mathrm{A}])}^{\text{loss of A}}/3\}$$

Hence, if

$$[\mathrm{A}]=\frac{[\mathrm{A}]_0}{1+k_\mathrm{r}t[\mathrm{A}]_0}$$

then, rearranging,

$$\begin{aligned}[\mathrm{A}]-[\mathrm{A}]_0&=\overbrace{\frac{[\mathrm{A}]_0}{1+k_\mathrm{r}t[\mathrm{A}]_0}}^{[\mathrm{A}]}-[A]_0\\&=\frac{[\mathrm{A}]_0-\{[\mathrm{A}]_0(1+k_\mathrm{r}t[\mathrm{A}]_0)\}}{1+k_\mathrm{r}t[\mathrm{A}]_0}\\&=\frac{[\mathrm{A}]_0-[\mathrm{A}]_0-k_\mathrm{r}t[\mathrm{A}]_0^2}{1+k_\mathrm{r}t[\mathrm{A}]_0}\\&=-\frac{k_\mathrm{r}t[\mathrm{A}]_0^2}{1+k_\mathrm{r}t[\mathrm{A}]_0}\end{aligned}$$

Hence,

$$\boldsymbol{[\mathrm{B}]=[\mathrm{B}]_0-\frac{k_\mathrm{r}t[\mathrm{A}]_0^2}{3(1+k_\mathrm{r}t[\mathrm{A}]_0)}}$$

**E10.23** We may express the rate law for the reaction $2\mathrm{A}\rightarrow\mathrm{B}$ in terms of the concentration of the reactant A as

$$v=\frac{\mathrm{d}[\mathrm{A}]}{\mathrm{d}t}=-k_\mathrm{r}[\mathrm{A}]^a$$

where $a$ is the order of the reaction with respect to A. For every molecule of B that is produced, two molecules of A are consumed. The concentration of A may therefore be expressed in terms of the concentration of the product B, $[\mathrm{A}]=[\mathrm{A}]_0-2[\mathrm{B}]$. It follows that the initial concentration of A is twice the ultimate concentration of B, so that

$$[\mathrm{A}]=[\mathrm{A}]_0-2[\mathrm{B}]=2[\mathrm{B}]_\infty-2[\mathrm{B}]=2([\mathrm{B}]_\infty-[\mathrm{B}])$$

If the reaction is first order with respect to A,

$$\ln([\mathrm{A}]/[\mathrm{A}]_0)=-k_\mathrm{r}t$$

Expressing the concentration of A in terms of the concentration of B,

$$\ln\frac{[\mathrm{A}]}{[\mathrm{A}]_0}=\ln\frac{[\mathrm{A}]_0-2[\mathrm{B}]}{[\mathrm{A}]_0}=\ln\frac{2[\mathrm{B}]_\infty-2[\mathrm{B}]}{2[\mathrm{B}]_\infty}=\ln\frac{[\mathrm{B}]_\infty-[\mathrm{B}]}{[\mathrm{B}]_\infty}=-k_\mathrm{r}t$$

This integrated rate law may be rearranged into the same form as the equation of a straight-line graph

$$\overbrace{\ln([\mathrm{B}]_\infty-[\mathrm{B}])}^{y}=\overbrace{\ln[\mathrm{B}]_\infty}^{\text{intercept}}+\overbrace{-k_\mathrm{r}}^{\text{slope}}\,\overbrace{t}^{x}$$

If the reaction is indeed first order with respect to A, then a graph of ln([B]$_\infty$ − [B]) against $t$ should be a straight line with a slope of $-k_r$. Figure 10.10 shows that this is not the case, indicating that the reaction is not first order with respect to A.

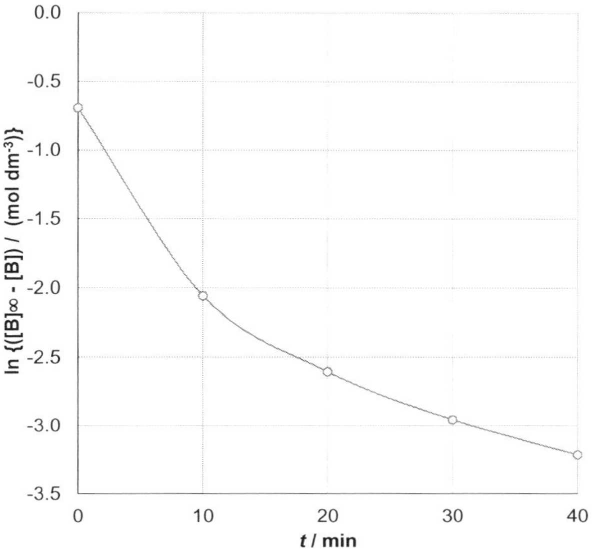


**Figure 10.10**

If, instead, the reaction is second order with respect to A, then, from eqn 10.16a,

$$\frac{1}{\underbrace{[\mathrm{A}]_0}_{2[\mathrm{B}]_\infty}} - \frac{1}{\underbrace{[\mathrm{A}]}_{2([\mathrm{B}]_\infty - [\mathrm{B}])}} = -k_r t$$

Substituting for [A] and $[\mathrm{A}]_0$, we obtain an expression with the same form as the equation for a straight-line graph

$$\overbrace{\frac{1}{([\mathrm{B}]_\infty - [\mathrm{B}])}}^{y} = \overbrace{\frac{1}{[\mathrm{B}]_\infty}}^{\text{intercept}} + \overbrace{(2k_r)}^{\text{slope}}\overbrace{t}^{x}$$

Figure 10.11 shows a graph of 1/([B]$_\infty$ − [B]) against $t$. This graph is indeed a straight line, confirming that the reaction is second order with respect to A. The slope of the graph is 0.574 $\mathrm{mol^{-1}\,dm^3\,min^{-1}}$, which is equivalent to a rate constant of

$$k_r = \text{slope}/2 = (0.574\ \mathrm{mol^{-1}dm^3min^{-1}})/2 = \mathbf{0.287\ mol^{-1}dm^3min^{-1}}$$

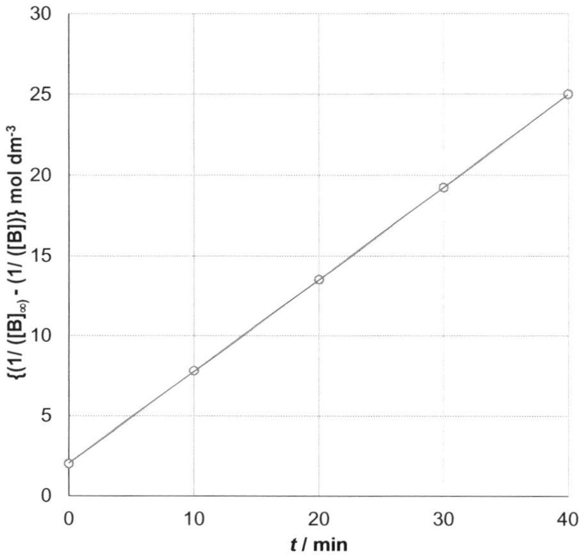


**Figure 10.11**

**E10.24** For the reaction in Example 10.3,

$$CH_3N_2CH_3(g) \rightarrow CH_3CH_3(g) + N_2(g)$$

we may denote the partial pressures of azomethane, $CH_3N_2CH_3$, as $p_A$, ethane, $C_2H_6$, as $p_E$ and nitrogen as $p_N$. The reaction is first order with respect to azomethane, so that the partial pressure of the reactant decreases exponentially

$$p_A = p_{A,0}e^{-k_r t}$$

In the same way, the partial pressures of the products increase exponentially

$$p_E = p_N = p_{A,0} - p_{A,0}e^{-k_r t} = p_{A,0}(1 - e^{-k_r t})$$

The total pressure is thus

$$p = p_A + p_E + p_N = p_{A,0}e^{-k_r t} + 2p_{A,0}(1 - e^{-k_r t}) = p_{A,0}(2 - e^{-k_r t})$$

A plot of the total pressure is presented in Figure 10.12.

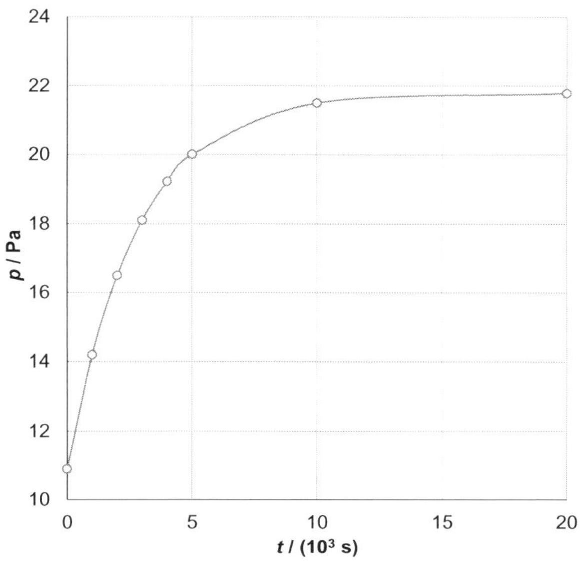


**Figure 10.12**

**E10.25** A decrease in concentration to 1/64 of the initial value is equivalent to halving the concentration six times because $(1/2)^6\,[\mathrm{A}]_0 = 1/64\,[\mathrm{A}]_0$. Thus, the time taken to achieve this decrease must be six half lives, or

$$t_{1/64} = 6 \times t_{1/2} = 6 \times (221\ \mathrm{s}) = \mathbf{1326\ s}$$

**E10.26** The radioactive decay is first order, so that

$$\ln([^{14}\mathrm{C}]/[^{14}\mathrm{C}]_0) = -k_\mathrm{r}t$$

The rate constant of the reaction is related to the half life through eqn 10.17. Thus, rearranging,

$$t = -\frac{\ln([^{14}\mathrm{C}]/[^{14}\mathrm{C}]_0)}{k_\mathrm{r}} = -\frac{\ln([^{14}\mathrm{C}]/[^{14}\mathrm{C}]_0)}{(\ln 2)/t_{1/2}} = \frac{\ln(0.69)}{\ln(2)\,/(1\ \mathrm{a})} = \mathbf{3100\ a}$$

**E10.27** Radioactive decay follows first-order kinetics. We may express the rate constant in terms of the half life using eqn 10.17, $k_\mathrm{r} = (\ln 2)/t_{1/2}$, so that, from eqn 10.14a,

$$[^{90}\mathrm{Sr}] = [^{90}\mathrm{Sr}]_0\mathrm{e}^{-k_\mathrm{r}t} = [^{90}\mathrm{Sr}]_0\mathrm{e}^{-\ln(2)(t/t_{1/2})}$$

Thus, after 19 years,

$$[^{90}\mathrm{Sr}] = 1.00\ \mu\mathrm{g} \times \mathrm{e}^{-\ln(2)\times(19\,/28.1)} = \mathbf{0.63\ \mu g}$$

and after 75 years,

$$[^{90}\mathrm{Sr}] = 1.00\ \mu\mathrm{g} \times \mathrm{e}^{-\ln(2)\times(75\,/28.1)} = \mathbf{0.16\ \mu g}$$

**E10.28** The reaction

$$CH_3COOC_2H_5(aq) + OH^-(aq) \rightarrow CH_3CO_2^-(aq) + CH_3CH_2OH(aq)$$

is of the form A + B → P, where A is ethyl acetate, $CH_3COOC_2H_5$, B is $OH^-$ and P is either of the products, acetate ion, $CH_3CO_2^-$ or ethanol, $CH_3CH_2OH$. Thus, using the integrated rate equation given in Table 6.4, the concentration of ethyl actetate after time $t$ is

$$[A] = [A]_0 - [P] = [A]_0 - \frac{[A]_0[B]_0(1 - e^{-([B]_0-[A]_0)k_r t})}{[A]_0 - [B]_0 e^{-([B]_0-[A]_0)k_r t}}$$
$$= [A]_0 - \frac{[B]_0\{1 - e^{-([B]_0-[A]_0)k_r t}\}}{1 - ([B]_0/[A]_0)e^{-([B]_0-[A]_0)k_r t}}$$

Hence, after 15 s, the concentration of ethyl acetate is

$$\left(0.150 - \frac{0.055 \times (1 - e^{-\{(0.150-0.055)\times 0.11\times 15\}})}{1 - [(0.055/0.150) \times e^{-\{(0.150-0.055)\times 0.11\times 15\}}]}\right) \text{mol dm}^{-3}$$
$$= \mathbf{0.138\ mol\ dm^{-3}}$$

and after 15 min = (15 × 60) = 900 s,

$$\left(0.150 - \frac{0.055 \times (1 - e^{-\{(0.150-0.055)\times 0.11\times 900\}})}{1 - [(0.055/0.150) \times e^{-\{(0.150-0.055)\times 0.11\times 900\}}]}\right) \text{mol dm}^{-3}$$
$$= \mathbf{0.095\ mol\ dm^{-3}}$$

**E10.29** Writing the second-order rate law for the reaction 2A → P as

$$v = k_r[A]^2$$

then, rearranging eqn 10.16a, the time taken for the concentration of A to fall from 0.460 mol $dm^{-3}$ to 0.046 mol $dm^{-3}$ is

$$t = \frac{1}{k_r}\left(\frac{1}{[A]} - \frac{1}{[A]_0}\right)$$
$$= \frac{1}{1.44\text{dm}^3\text{mol}^{-1}\text{s}^{-1}} \times \left(\frac{1}{0.460 \text{ mol dm}^{-3}} - \frac{1}{0.046 \text{ mol dm}^{-3}}\right)$$
$$= \mathbf{13.6\ s}$$

**E10.30** For a first-order reaction, the half life is related to the rate constant through eqn 10.17, so that

$$t_{1/2} = (\ln 2)/k_r = (\ln 2)/(3.38 \times 10^{-5}\text{s}^{-1}) = 20.5 \times 10^3 \text{ s} = \mathbf{5.69\ h}$$

Then, using the integrated rate law, eqn 10.14b, after 5 s

$$p_{N_2O_5} = p_{N_2O_5,0}e^{-k_r t} = (78.4 \text{ kPa}) \times e^{-(3.38\times 10^{-5}\text{s}^{-1})\times(5\text{ s})} = \mathbf{78.4\ kPa}$$

The reaction is sufficiently slow that the partial pressure of $N_2O_5$ is, effectively, unchanged. After 5 min, however, the partial pressure has decreased slightly

$$p_{N_2O_5} = p_{N_2O_5,0}e^{-k_r t} = (78.4\ \text{kPa}) \times e^{-(3.38\times10^{-5}\text{s}^{-1})\times(5\times60\ \text{s})} = \mathbf{77.6\ kPa}$$

**E10.31** Combining eqn 10.17 and 10.18,

$$\tau = 1/k_r = 1/\{(\ln 2)/t_{1/2}\} = t_{1/2}/(\ln 2) = (439\ \text{s})/(\ln 2) = \mathbf{633\ s}$$

**E10.32** The half life of a reaction is related to the rate constant through eqn 10.17. Thus, substituting the Arrhenius expression for the rate constant, eqn 10.20

$$t_{1/2} = (\ln 2)/k_r = (\ln 2)/\overbrace{(A\,e^{-E_a/RT})}^{k_r}$$

(a) Hence, at 20 °C,

$$t_{1/2} = \frac{\ln 2}{(10^{15.6}\ \text{s}^{-1}) \times e^{-\{(261\times10^3\text{J mol}^{-1})/(8.3145\ \text{J K}^{-1}\text{mol}^{-1})\times(29+273.15)\text{K}\}}}$$
$$= \mathbf{1.86 \times 10^{23}a}$$

The combination of high activation energy and low temperature causes an essentially infinite time for appreciable reaction.

(b) At 500 °C, however,

$$t_{1/2} = \frac{\ln 2}{(10^{15.6}\ \text{s}^{-1}) \times e^{-\{(261\times10^3\text{J mol}^{-1})/(8.3145\ \text{J K}^{-1}\text{mol}^{-1})\times(500+273.15)\text{K}\}}}$$
$$= \mathbf{27.1\ s}$$

**E10.33** Rearranging the Arrhenius equation, eqn 10.21

$$E_a = \frac{R\ln(k_{r,2}/k_{r,1})}{(1/T_1) - (1/T_2)}$$
$$= (8.3145\ \text{J K}^{-1}\text{mol}^{-1}) \times \frac{\ln\{(2.78\times10^{-4}\ \text{dm}^3\text{mol}^{-1}\text{s}^{-1})/(3.38\times10^{-3}\ \text{dm}^3\text{mol}^{-1}\text{s}^{-1})\}}{\{1/(273.15+37)\text{K}\} - \{1/(273.15+19)\text{K}\}}$$
$$= 104\times10^3\text{J mol}^{-1} = \mathbf{104\ kJ\ mol^{-1}}$$

We may calculate the value of the Arrhenius pre-exponential factor by rearranging eqn 10.20, and substituting the parameters for either temperature

$$A = k_{r,1}e^{+(E_a/RT_1)}$$
$$= (3.38\times10^{-3}\ \text{dm}^3\text{mol}^{-1}\text{s}^{-1}) \times e^{(104\times10^3\text{J mol}^{-1})/\{(8.3145\ \text{J K}^{-1}\text{mol}^{-1})\times(273.15+19)\text{K}\}}$$
$$= \mathbf{1.12\times10^{15}dm^3mol^{-1}s^{-1}}$$

**E10.34** We may rearrange the Arrhenius equation, eqn 10.21,

$$\frac{1}{T_2} = -\frac{R\ln(k_{r,2}/k_{r,1})}{E_a} + \frac{1}{T_1}$$

$$= -\left\{\frac{(8.3145\ \mathrm{J\,K^{-1}mol^{-1}}) \times \ln(1.10)}{99.1 \times 10^3\ \mathrm{J\,mol^{-1}}}\right\} + \left\{\frac{1}{(25+273.15)\ \mathrm{K}}\right\}$$
$$= \mathbf{298.86\ K}$$

Thus, the temperature need only be increased by 0.71 K to achieve a 10 per cent rate increase. This demonstrates that the rate is very sensitive to temperature when the activation energy is large.

**E10.35** The kinetics of a reaction respond most strongly to changes in temperature if the activation energy is large. We may prove this by considering the Arrhenius equation, written in the form of eqn 10.21,

$$\ln\left(\frac{k_{r,2}}{k_{r,1}}\right) = \frac{E_a}{R}\left\{\frac{1}{T_1} - \frac{1}{T_2}\right\}$$

For a particular pair of temperatures, the logarithm of the ratio of the rate constants is directly proportional to the activation energy. Thus, the variation of reaction rate with temperature will be greater for the reaction with an activation energy of **52 kJ mol$^{-1}$**.

**E10.36** Rearranging the Arrhenius equation, eqn 10.21

$$E_a = \frac{R\ln(k_{r,2}/k_{r,1})}{(1/T_1)-(1/T_2)} = \frac{(8.3145\ \mathrm{J\,K^{-1}mol^{-1}}) \times \ln(1.41)}{\{1/(273.15+27)\mathrm{K}\} - \{1/(273.15+20)\mathrm{K}\}}$$
$$= 35.9 \times 10^3\ \mathrm{J\,mol^{-1}} = \mathbf{35.9\ kJ\ mol^{-1}}$$

**E10.37** The Arrhenius plot of $\ln k_r$ against $1/T$ is shown in Figure 10.13.

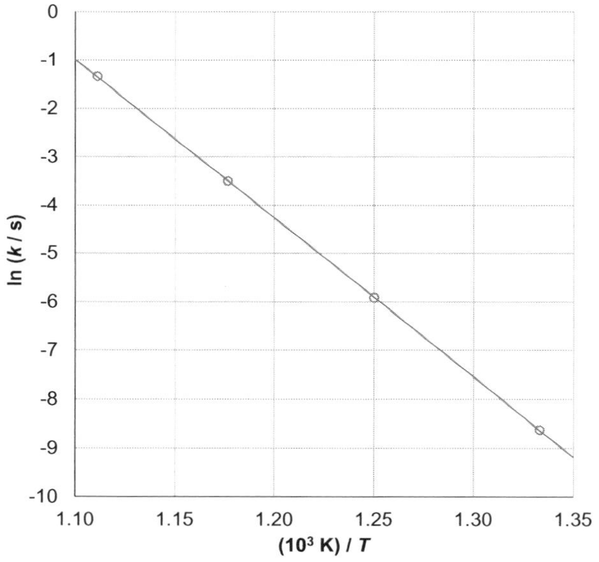


**Figure 10.13**

The slope of the plot is $-32.74 \times 10^3$ K, so that

$$E_a = -\text{slope} \times R = -(-32.7 \times 10^3\ \text{K}) \times (8.3145\ \text{J K}^{-1}\text{mol}^{-1})$$
$$= 272 \times 10^3\ \text{J mol}^{-1} = \mathbf{272\ kJ\ mol^{-1}}$$

**E10.38** Rearranging the Arrhenius equation, eqn 10.21

$$E_a = \frac{R\ln(k_{r,2}/k_{r,1})}{(1/T_1)-(1/T_2)}$$
$$= \frac{(8.3145\ \text{J K}^{-1}\text{mol}^{-1}) \times \ln(40)}{\{1/(273.15+25)\text{K}\} - \{1/(273.15+4)\text{K}\}}$$
$$= 121 \times 10^3\text{J mol}^{-1} = \mathbf{121\ kJ\ mol^{-1}}$$

**E10.39** Rearranging the Arrhenius equation, eqn 10.21

$$E_a = \frac{R\ln(k_{r,2}/k_{r,1})}{(1/T_1)-(1/T_2)}$$
$$= \frac{(8.3145\ \text{J K}^{-1}\text{mol}^{-1}) \times \ln(1/1.23)}{\{1/(273.15+27)\text{K}\} - \{1/(273.15+20)\text{K}\}}$$
$$= -21.6 \times 10^3\text{J mol}^{-1} = \mathbf{-21.6\ kJ\ mol^{-1}}$$

Our simple theory of the temperature dependence of reaction rates assumes that the activation energy must be positive. The negative value implies that, in this instance, this theory is not valid.

**E10.40** We know from eqn 10.17 that the rate constant is inversely proportional to the half life. Thus, we may write

$$E_a = \frac{R\ln(k_{r,2}/k_{r,1})}{(1/T_1)-(1/T_2)} = \frac{R\ln(t_{1/2}(T_2)/t_{1/2}(T_1))}{(1/T_1)-(1/T_2)}$$
$$= \frac{(8.3145\ \text{J K}^{-1}\text{mol}^{-1}) \times \ln(2)}{\{1/(273.15+10)\text{K}\} - \{1/(273.15+20)\text{K}\}}$$
$$= 47.8 \times 10^3\text{J mol}^{-1} = \mathbf{47.8\ kJ\ mol^{-1}}$$

**E10.41** The proportion of molecules colliding with sufficient energy to react is, from eqn 10.22,

$$f = e^{-E_a/RT}$$

so that

$$f(20\ °\text{C}) = e^{-(111\times10^3\ \text{J mol}^{-1})/\{(8.3145\ \text{J K}^{-1}\text{mol}^{-1})\times(273.15+20)\text{K}\}} = \mathbf{1.6 \times 10^{-20}}$$
$$f(200\ °\text{C}) = e^{-(111\times10^3\ \text{J mol}^{-1})/\{(8.3145\ \text{J K}^{-1}\text{mol}^{-1})\times(273.15+200)\text{K}\}} = \mathbf{5.5 \times 10^{-13}}$$

We use eqn 10.23 to predict the value of the pre-exponential factor, including a factor of Avogadro's number to ensure that the value is given as a molar quantity.

$$A = \sigma(8kT/\pi\mu)^{1/2} \times N_A$$

The value for the collision cross section may be taken to be $\sigma = 0.5\ \text{nm}^2$, which is typical for a triatomic molecule. We may calculate the effective mass exactly, but given the other approximations, it is reasonable to take the value as $\mu = 10^{-26}$ kg. Hence,

$$A = 0.5 \times (10^{-9}\ \text{m})^2 \times \left\{\frac{8 \times (1.38 \times 10^{-23}\ \text{J K}^{-1}) \times (500\ \text{K})}{\pi \times (10^{-26}\ \text{kg})}\right\}^{1/2} \times 6.022 \times 10^{23}\text{mol}^{-1}$$

$$= 4 \times 10^{8}\ \text{mol}^{-1}\text{m}^3\text{s}^{-1} = \mathbf{4 \times 10^{11} mol^{-1}\ dm^3\ s^{-1}}$$

The estimated value of the pre-exponential factor is much larger than the experimental value of $2 \times 10^9\ \text{dm}^3\ \text{mol}^{-1}\text{s}^{-1}$. A possible explanation of the discrepancy is that a steric factor $P \approx 5 \times 10^{-3}$ must be included in the pre-exponential factor to account for the probability that the $NO_2$ molecules collide in the specific orientation required for reaction.

**E10.42** Applying eqn 10.23, and estimating the collision cross section to have a value of $\sigma = 0.5\ \text{nm}^2$ and the effective mass $\mu = 10^{-26}$ kg,

$$A = \sigma(8kT/\pi\mu)^{1/2} \times N_A$$

$$= 0.5 \times (10^{-9}\ \text{m})^2 \times \left\{\frac{8 \times (1.38 \times 10^{-23}\ \text{J K}^{-1}) \times (298\ \text{K})}{\pi \times (10^{-26}\ \text{kg})}\right\}^{1/2} \times 6.022 \times 10^{23}\text{mol}^{-1}$$

$$= 3 \times 10^{8}\ \text{mol}^{-1}\text{m}^3\text{s}^{-1} = \mathbf{3 \times 10^{11} mol^{-1}\ dm^3\ s^{-1}}$$

We might expect the measured value to be lower than that calculated because we have not taken into account that many collisions do not occur with the $CH_3$ radicals in the correct orientation. We usually make allowance for this discrepancy by including a steric factor, *P*.

**E10.43** If reaction occurs when the separation between reactants is less than $d = 500$ pm, then, by analogy with collision theory, if we assume a circular collision cross section,

$$\sigma = \pi d^2 = \pi \times (500 \times 10^{-12}\ \text{m})^2 = 0.8 \times 10^{-18}\text{m}^2 = \mathbf{0.8\ nm^2}$$

**E10.44** We may use the Eyring equation, eqn 10.26

$$k_r = \kappa(kT/h)e^{-\Delta G^{\ddagger}/RT}$$

then, rearranging,

$$\Delta G^{\ddagger} = -RT\ln(k_r h/\kappa kT)$$

so that, if we assume that the transmission coefficient $\kappa$ has a value of one,

$$\Delta G^{\ddagger}(60\ ^\circ\text{C}) = -\{(8.3145\ \text{J K}^{-1}\text{mol}^{-1}) \times (273.15 + 60)\text{K}\} \times \ln\left\{\frac{(1.2 \times 10^{-7}\text{s}^{-1}) \times (6.626 \times 10^{-34}\text{J s})}{1 \times (1.38 \times 10^{-23}\ \text{J K}^{-1}) \times (273.15 + 60)\text{K}}\right\}$$

$$= 126 \times 10^3\ \text{J mol}^{-1} = \mathbf{126\ kJ\ mol^{-1}}$$

We obtain the same value at 70 °C, demonstrating that the activation Gibbs energy is constant over this narrow temperature range.

**E10.45** Rearranging eqn 10.26

$$k_r = \left(\frac{kT}{h}e^{\Delta S^{\ddagger}/R}\right)e^{-\Delta H^{\ddagger}/RT}$$

and taking logarithms, allows us to obtain a linear expression in the activation entropy and enthalpy

$$-RT\ln(k_r h/kT) = \Delta H^{\ddagger} - T\Delta S^{\ddagger}$$

Substitution of the rate constant and temperatures leads to two equations that we may solve simultaneously, one at 60 °C, which is equivalent to 333.15 K,

$$-(8.3145\ \text{J K}^{-1}\text{mol}^{-1}) \times (333.15\ \text{K}) \times \ln\left\{\frac{(1.2\times10^{-7}\ \text{s}^{-1})\times(6.626\times10^{-34}\text{J s})}{(1.38\times10^{-23}\ \text{J K}^{-1})\times(333.15\ \text{K})}\right\}$$
$$= -12.60\times10^{5}\ \text{J mol}^{-1} = \Delta H^{\ddagger} - (333.15\ \text{K})\Delta S^{\ddagger}$$

and the other at 70 °C, or 343.15 K,

$$-(8.3145\ \text{J K}^{-1}\text{mol}^{-1}) \times (343.15\ \text{K}) \times \ln\left\{\frac{(4.6\times10^{-7}\ \text{s}^{-1})\times(6.626\times10^{-34}\text{J s})}{(1.38\times10^{-23}\ \text{J K}^{-1})\times(343.15\ \text{K})}\right\}$$
$$= -12.61\times10^{5}\ \text{J mol}^{-1} = \Delta H^{\ddagger} - (343.15\ \text{K})\Delta S^{\ddagger}$$

Solving simultaneously gives the activation entropy as **3.4 J K$^{-1}$ mol$^{-1}$**.

# Answers to projects

**P10.46** (a) For a third-order differential rate law,

$$v = -\frac{d[A]}{dt} = k_r[A]^3$$

we may integrate,

$$-\int_{[A]_0}^{[A]}\frac{d[A]}{[A]^3} = \int_0^t k_r dt$$
$$[½[A]^{-2}]_{[A]_0}^{[A]} = [kt]_0^t$$
$$\frac{1}{[A]^2} - \frac{1}{[A]_0^{\ 2}} = 2kt$$

This expression has the same form as the equation for a straight-line graph, $y = b + ax$

$$\overbrace{\frac{1}{[A]^2}}^{y} = \overbrace{\frac{1}{[A]_0^{\,2}}}^{\text{intercept}} + \overbrace{2k}^{\text{slope}} \times \overbrace{t}^{x}$$

Thus, if the reaction is third-order in A, a plot of $1/[A]^2$ against $t$ should be a straight line with a gradient of $2k$.

(b) For a rate law

$$v = -\frac{d[A]}{dt} = -\frac{d[B]}{dt} = k_r[A][B]$$

if we introduce a variable $x$ as a measurement of the progress of the reaction, so that $[A] = [A]_0 - x$ and $[B] = [B]_0 - x$, then the rate is defined by

$$v = -\frac{dx}{dt} = k_r([A]_0 - x)([B]_0 - x)$$

If the initial concentrations of A and B are not equal, then rearranging and using the standard integral given,

$$-\int_0^x \frac{dx}{([A]_0 - x)([B]_0 - x)} = \int_0^t k_r dt$$

$$\frac{1}{[A]_0 - [B]_0}\left[\ln\left(\frac{1}{[A]_0 - x}\right) - \ln\left(\frac{1}{[B]_0 - x}\right)\right]_0^x = [k_r t]_0^t$$

$$\frac{1}{[A]_0 - [B]_0}\left[\ln \frac{\overbrace{[B]_0 - x}^{[B]}}{\underbrace{[A]_0 - x}_{[A]}}\right]_0^x = [k_r t]_0^t$$

$$\frac{1}{[A]_0 - [B]_0}\left[\ln\left(\frac{[B]}{[A]}\right)\right]_{[A]_0,[B]_0}^{[A],[B]} = [k_r t]_0^t$$

$$\frac{1}{[A]_0 - [B]_0}\left\{\ln\left(\frac{[B]}{[A]}\right) - \ln\left(\frac{[B]_0}{[A]_0}\right)\right\} = k_r t$$

$$\boldsymbol{\frac{1}{[A]_0 - [B]_0}\ln\left(\frac{[B]/[B]_0}{[A]/[A]_0}\right) = k_r t}$$

If, however, the initial concentrations of A and B are equal, then $[A] = [B]$, we may write the rate law as

$$v = -\frac{d[A]}{dt} = -\frac{d[B]}{dt} = k_r[A][B] = k_r[A]^2$$

so that the integrated form is

$$-\int_0^{[A]} \frac{d[A]}{[A]^2} = \int_0^t k_r dt$$

$$\left[\frac{1}{[A]}\right]_{[A]_0}^{[A]} = [k_r t]_0^t$$

$$\frac{1}{[A]} - \frac{1}{[A]_0} = k_r t$$

**P10.47** (a) The variation of the rate constant and the equilibrium constant for the reaction

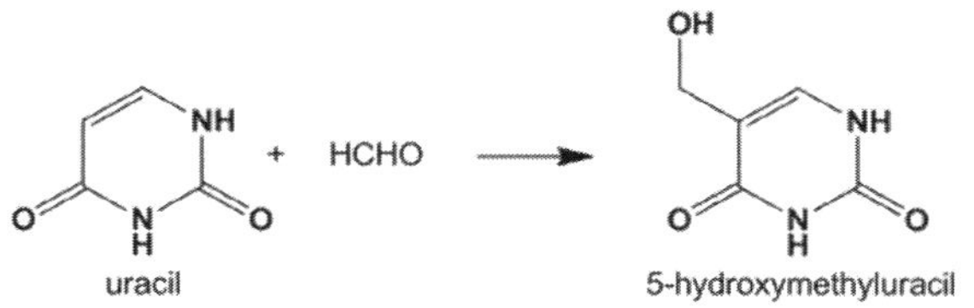


are shown in Figures 10.14 and 10.15 respectively. In drawing these plots, we have been careful to remember that the expressions are functions of the temperature, measured in kelvin. It can be seen that the rate constant increases, as expected, with temperature. The equilibrium constant, however, decreases with temperaure, implying that the reaction is exothermic. Thus, from a kinetic point of view the reaction becomes more favourable at higher temperatures; from a thermodynamic point of view it becomes less favourable.

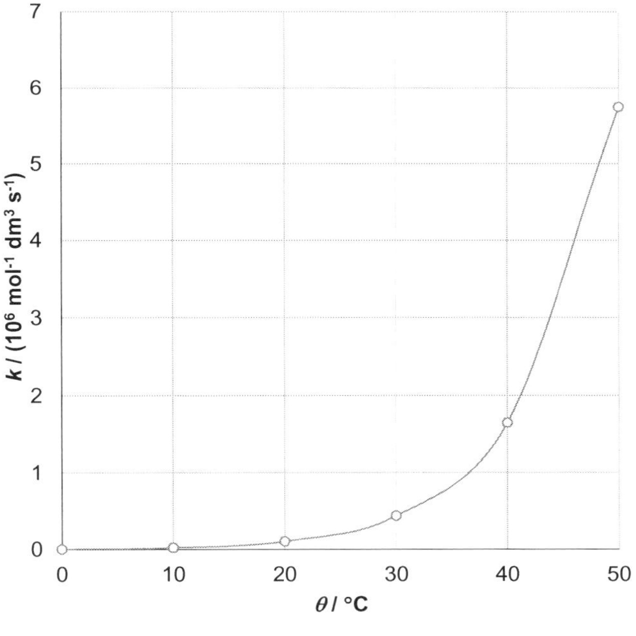


**Figure 10.14**

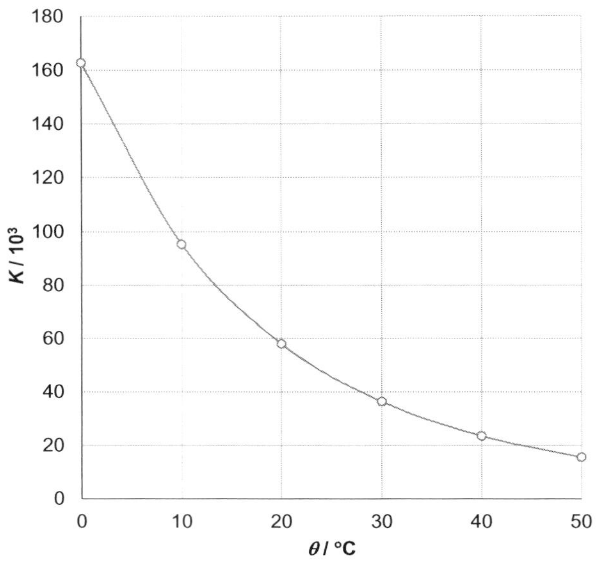


**Figure 10.15**

(b) The activation energy is defined through eqn 10.20a as the slope of a plot of ln $k_r$ against 1 / $T$. We may write the expression given for the variation of the rate constant with temperature

$$\log(k_r/\text{mol}^{-1}\text{dm}^3\text{s}^{-1}) = 11.75 - 5488(T/K)$$

in terms of the natural logarithm using the relationship, that if $\log x = y$, then $\ln x = (\ln 10) \times y$. Thus,

$$\ln(k_r/\text{mol}^{-1}\text{dm}^3\text{s}^{-1}) = \ln 10 \times \overbrace{\{11.75 - 5488(T/K)\}}^{\log k_r}$$
$$= \overbrace{\{\ln 10 \times 11.75\}}^{\ln A} - \overbrace{\{\ln 10 \times 5488(T/K)\}}^{E_a/RT}$$

The expression has the same form as eqn 10.20b, $\ln k_r = \ln A - E_a / RT$, so that

$$E_a = (\ln 10 \times 5488) \times R = (\ln 10 \times 5488) \times (8.3145\ \text{J K}^{-1}\text{mol}^{-1})$$
$$= 105.1 \times 10^3\ \text{J mol}^{-1} = \mathbf{105.1\ kJ\ mol^{-1}}$$

The standard reaction Gibbs energy follows in the same way using eqn 7.8

$$\Delta_r G^{\ominus} = -RT \ln K = -RT\,\overbrace{\{(\ln 10) \times \log K\}}^{\ln K}$$
$$= -RT \ln 10 \times \{-1.36 + 1794/(T/\text{K})\}$$
$$= (1.36 \times \ln 10)\, RT - \{(1794\ \text{K}) \times (\ln 10) \times R\}$$

so that at 25 °C = 298.15 K,

$$\Delta_r G^{\ominus} = \{1.36 \times \ln 10 \times (8.3145\ \text{J K}^{-1}\text{mol}^{-1}) \times (298.15\ \text{K})\}$$

$$-\{(1794\ \text{K}) \times \ln 10 \times (8.3145\ \text{J K}^{-1}\text{mol}^{-1})\}$$
$$= 26.6 \times 10^3\ \text{J mol}^{-1} = \mathbf{+26.6\ kJ\ mol^{-1}}$$

We may obtain an average value for standard reaction enthalpy using the van't Hoff equation, eqn 7.15, and calculating the value for the equilibrium constant at a temperature below and above 25 °C. It is, however, more elegant to use calculus. Combining eqns 7.8 and 4.16,

$$\ln K = -\frac{\Delta_r G^\ominus}{RT} = -\frac{\Delta_r H^\ominus}{RT} + \frac{\Delta_r S^\ominus}{R}$$

Thus, differentiating $\ln K$ with respect to $(1 / T)$,

$$\frac{\mathrm{d}\ln K}{\mathrm{d}(1/T)} = \frac{\mathrm{d}}{\mathrm{d}(1/T)}\left\{-\frac{\Delta_r H^\ominus}{RT} + \frac{\Delta_r S^\ominus}{R}\right\} = -\frac{\Delta_r H^\ominus}{R}$$

Hence,

$$\begin{aligned}
\Delta_r H^\ominus &= -R\frac{\mathrm{d}\ln K}{\mathrm{d}(1/T)} \\
&= -R\frac{\mathrm{d}}{\mathrm{d}(1/T)}\overbrace{\{(\ln 10) \times \log K\}}^{\ln K} \\
&= -R\ln 10\frac{\mathrm{d}}{\mathrm{d}(1/T)}\overbrace{\{-1.36 + 1794/(T/\text{K})\}}^{\log K} \\
&= -R\ln 10\frac{\mathrm{d}}{\mathrm{d}(1/T)}\{-1.36 + (1794\ \text{K})(1/T)\} \\
&= -R\ln 10 \times (1794\ \text{K}) = -(8.3145\ \text{J K}^{-1}\text{mol}^{-1}) \times (\ln 10) \times (1794\ \text{K})
\end{aligned}$$

Thus,

$$\Delta_r H^\ominus = -34.4 \times 10^3 \text{J mol}^{-1} = \mathbf{-34.4\ kJ\ mol^{-1}}$$

(c) The equations for the rate constant $k_r$ and the equilibrium constant $K$ were obtained under conditions corresponding to the biological standard state of pH = 7. The values are thus more appropriate than if calculated for the conventional chemical standard state of pH = 1. Prebiotic conditions are more likely to be near pH = 7 than pH = 1 so we expect the part (a) plot of $K$ against $T$ to be relevant to the prebiotic environment. The plot shows that the reaction will be thermodynamically favorable because the equilibrium constant is always greate than 1. Because, from eqn 7.6, $\Delta_r G = \Delta_r G^\ominus + RT \ln Q$, and because we might expect $Q < 1$ in a prebiotic environment, $\Delta_r G < \Delta_r G^\ominus$. But, as shown in the calculation above, $\Delta_r G^\ominus$ is rather large and negative, so we expect it will still be large and negative under the prebiotic conditions; hence the reaction will be spontaneous for these conditions. We also expect that $\Delta_r G \approx \Delta_r G^\ominus$ under prebiotic conditions because enthalpy changes largely reflect bond breakage and bond formation energies, and so are relatively unaffected by the pH of the solution.

# Chapter 11

# Chemical kinetics: accounting for the rate laws

## Answers to discussion questions

**D11.1** Figure 11.1 shows how the concentration of the reactant and product varies for first and second-order reversible steps with an assumed equilibrium constant equal to 2 for a reaction such as

$$2\,A \rightleftharpoons 2\,B$$

It can be seen that, as expected, the initial rate of change of the concentrations is greater for the second-order reaction than for first order, although qualitatively, the graphs are similar.

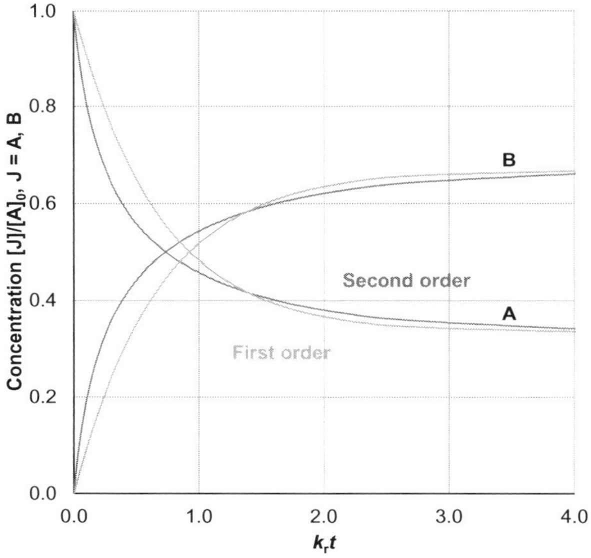


**Figure 11.1**

**D11.2** The rate-determining step is not just the slowest step: it must be slow *and* be a crucial gateway for the formation of products. If a faster reaction can also lead to products, then the slowest step is irrelevant because the slow reaction can then be side-stepped. The rate-determining step is like a slow ferry crossing between two fast highways: the overall rate at which traffic can reach its destination is determined by the rate at which it can make the ferry crossing.

If the first step in a mechanism is the slowest step with the highest activation energy, then it is rate-determining, and the overall reaction rate is equal to the rate of the first step because all subsequent steps are so fast that once the first intermediate is formed it results immediately in the formation of products. Once over the initial barrier, the intermediates cascade into products. However, a rate-determining step may also stem from the low concentration of a crucial reactant or catalyst and need not correspond to the step with highest activation barrier. A rate-determining step arising from the low activity of a crucial enzyme can sometimes be identified by determining whether or not the reactants and products for that step are in equilibrium: if the reaction is not at equilibrium it suggests that the step may be slow enough to be rate-determining.

**D11.3** The steady-state approximation is the assumption that the concentrations of all intermediates remain constant and small throughout the reaction (except right at the beginning and right at the end). The mathematical form of the approximation for intermediate I is

$$\text{Rate of formation of I} = 0$$

or using calculus

$$\frac{d[I]}{dt} = 0$$

A pre-equilibrium approximation is similar in that it is a good approximation when the rate of formation of the intermediate from the reactants and the rate of its reversible decay back to the reactants are both very fast in comparison to the rate of formation of the product from the intermediate. This results in the intermediate being in approximate equilibrium with the reactants over relatively long time periods. Hence the concentration of the intermediate remains approximately constant over the time period that the equilibrium can be considered to be maintained. The rate constants and concentrations may therefore be related to each other through a constant (the pre-equilibrium constant).

To illustrate the two approximations, consider the symbolic generalization of the gas-phase mechanism for the oxidation of the nitric oxide that is discussed in Section 11.5. The generalization is

$$A + A \rightleftharpoons I$$
$$I + B \rightarrow P$$

Application of the steady-state approximation to intermediate I gives

$$\text{Net rate of formation of I} = \frac{d[I]}{dt} = \overbrace{k_a[A]^2}^{\text{formation of I}} - \overbrace{(k_a'[I] + k_b[I][B])}^{\text{loss of I}}$$

Rearranging, we may obtain an expression for the concentration of I

$$[\mathrm{I}] = \frac{k_\mathrm{a}[\mathrm{A}]^2}{k_\mathrm{a}' - k_\mathrm{b}[\mathrm{B}]}$$

It follows that the rate of formation of product is

$$\text{Rate of formation of P} = \frac{\mathrm{d}[\mathrm{P}]}{\mathrm{d}t} = k_\mathrm{b}[\mathrm{B}][\mathrm{I}] = k_\mathrm{b}[\mathrm{B}]\overbrace{\left\{\frac{k_\mathrm{a}[\mathrm{A}]^2}{k_\mathrm{a}' - k_\mathrm{b}[\mathrm{B}]}\right\}}^{[\mathrm{I}]} = \frac{k_\mathrm{a}k_\mathrm{b}[\mathrm{A}]^2[\mathrm{B}]}{k_\mathrm{a}' - k_\mathrm{b}[\mathrm{B}]}$$

In contrast, the pre-equilibrium approximation assumes the equilibrium condition that formation rate of I equals the rate at which I decomposes to reactants. Thus,

$$k_\mathrm{a}[\mathrm{A}]^2 = k_\mathrm{a}'[\mathrm{I}]$$

so that, if we assume that the equilibrium constant may be expressed using concentrations rather than activities, and the terms in the standard concentration are implied,

$$K = \frac{[\mathrm{I}]}{[\mathrm{A}]^2} = \frac{k_\mathrm{a}}{k_\mathrm{a}'}$$

Thus,

$$[\mathrm{I}] = K[\mathrm{A}]^2$$

It follows that the rate of formation of product is

$$\text{Rate of formation of P} = \frac{\mathrm{d}[\mathrm{P}]}{\mathrm{d}t} = k_\mathrm{b}[\mathrm{B}][\mathrm{I}] = k_\mathrm{b}[\mathrm{B}]\overbrace{K[\mathrm{A}]^2}^{[\mathrm{I}]} = k_\mathrm{b}K[\mathrm{A}]^2[\mathrm{B}]$$

By comparing the rate of formation of P in the steady-state approximation with the rate in the pre-equilibrium approximation, we see that in general they give very different predictions about the concentration dependence of the rate of product formation. They do, however, agree in a special case. When the rate at which I decomposes to reactants is much faster than the rate at which it forms product, $k_\mathrm{a}' \gg k_\mathrm{b}[\mathrm{B}]$ and the second term in the denominator of the steady-state approximation is negligibly small. In this case, the steady-state approximation simplifies to the form provided by the pre-equilibrium approximation. Thus, we see that the steady-state approximation describes a greater range of concentrations and rates than that provided by the pre-equilibrium approximation.

**D11.4** Simple diagrams of Gibbs energy against reaction coordinate such as those shown in Figure 11.2, are useful for distinguishing between kinetic and thermodynamic control of a reaction.

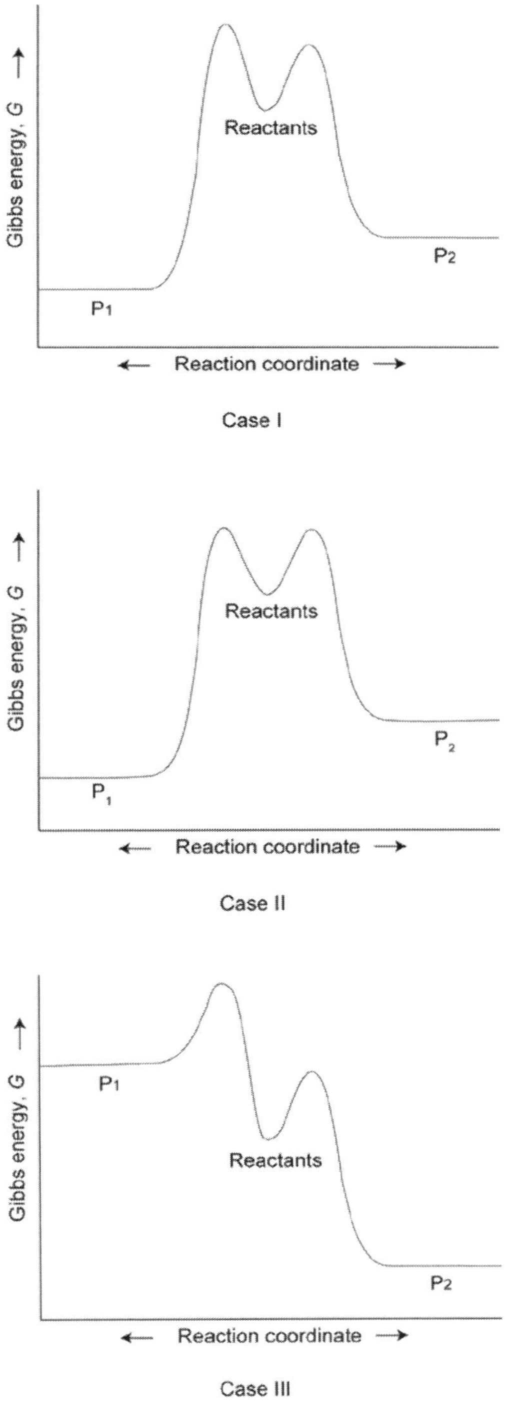
Gibbs energy, G
Reactants
P2
P1
Reaction coordinate
Case I
Gibbs energy, G
Reactants
P2
P1
Reaction coordinate
Case II
Gibbs energy, G
P1
Reactants
P2
Reaction coordinate
Case III

Figure 11.2

For the simple parallel reactions $R \rightarrow P_1$ and $R \rightarrow P_2$, shown in Figure 11.2 as Cases I and II, the product $P_1$ is thermodynamically favoured because the Gibbs energy decreases to a greater extent for its formation. However, the rate at which each product appears does not depend upon thermodynamic favorability. Rate constants depend upon activation energy. In Case I the activation energy for the formation of $P_1$ is much larger than that for formation of $P_2$. At low and moderate temperature the large activation energy may not be readily available and $P_1$ either cannot form or forms at a slow rate. The much smaller activation energy for $P_2$ formation is available and, consequently, $P_2$ is produced even though it is not the thermodynamically favoured product. This is kinetic control. In this case, $[P_2] / [P_1] = k_{r2}/k_{r1} > 1$.

The activation energies for the parallel reactions are equal in Case II and, consequently, the two products appear at identical rates. If the reactions are irreversible, $[P_2] / [P_1] = k_{r2}/k_{r1} = 1$ at all times. The results are very different for reversible reactions. The activation energy for $P_1 \rightarrow R$ is much larger than that for $P_2 \rightarrow R$ and $P_1$ accumulates as the more rapid $P_2 \rightarrow R \rightarrow P_1$ occurs. Eventually the ratio $[P_2] / [P_1]$ approaches the equilibrium value for which

$$\frac{[P_2]}{[P_1]} = e^{-(\Delta G_2 - \Delta G_1)/RT} < 1$$

This is thermodynamic control.

Case III above represents an interesting consecutive reaction series $R \rightarrow P_1 \rightarrow P_2$. The first step has relatively low activation energy and $P_1$ rapidly appears. However, the relatively large activation energy for the second step is not available at low and moderate temperatures. By using low or moderate temperatures and short reaction times it is possible to produce more of the thermodynamically less favorable $P_1$. This is kinetic control. High temperatures and long reaction times will yield the thermodynamically favoured $P_2$.

The ratio of reaction products is determined by relative reaction rates in kinetic controlled reactions. Favorable conditions include short reaction times, lower temperatures, and irreversible reactions. Thermodynamic control is favoured by long reaction times, higher temperatures, and reversible reactions. The ratio of products depends on the relative stability of products for thermodynamically controlled reactions.

**D11.5** The issue of how some gas-phase reactions show first-order kinetics is discussed as an aspect of the **Lindemann mechanism** of unimolecular reactions in Section 11.9. The reactant molecule acquires the activation energy for reaction in a bimolecular collision. The energized, activated molecule may deactivate by loss of energy in subsequent collisions or it may shake itself apart in a unimolecular elementary step to form product. When the unimolecular step is rate-determining, the overall reaction will have first-order kinetics. Many unimolecular decomposition reactions and isomerization reactions have been observed.

**D11.6** The **Michaelis–Menten mechanism** of enzyme activity models the enzyme with one active site that, weakly and reversibly, binds a substrate in homogeneous solution. It is a three-step mechanism. The first and second steps are the reversible formation of the enzyme–substrate complex (ES). The third step is the decay of the complex into the product. The steady-state approximation is applied to the concentration of the intermediate (ES) and its use simplifies the derivation of the final rate expression. However, the justification for the use of the approximation with this mechanism is suspect, in that both rate constants for the reversible step may not be as large, in comparison to the rate constant for the decay to products, as they need to be for the approximation to be valid. The mechanism clearly indicates that the simplest form of the rate law, $v = v_{max} = k_b[E]_0$, occurs when $[S]_0 \gg K_M$ and the general form of the rate law does seem to match the principal experimental features of enzyme catalyzed reactions. It provides a mechanistic understanding of both the turnover number and catalytic efficiency. The model may be expanded to include multisubstrate reactions and it must be modified to accommodate the effects of competitive and noncompetitive inhibition.

## Solutions to exercises

**E11.1** The attachment of the substrate to the active site of the enzyme may be written as

$$E + S \rightleftharpoons ES$$

with rate constants for the forward and backward reactions of $k_r$ and $k_r'$ respectively. The equilibrium constant for the reaction may then be expressed as

$$K = \frac{a_{ES}}{a_E a_S} \approx \frac{([ES]/c^{\ominus})}{([E]/c^{\ominus})([S]/c^{\ominus})} = \frac{[ES]c^{\ominus}}{[E][S]}$$

where we have assumed that the activities may be expressed in terms of concentrations. In order that equilibrium is maintained, the rates of the forward and backward reactions must be equal,

$$k_r[E][S] = k_r'[ES]$$

so that

$$K = \frac{[ES]}{[E][S]} = \frac{k_r}{k_r'}c^{\ominus}$$

Rearranging, the rate constant for the loss of the unreacted substrate from the active site is

$$k_r' = k_r c^{\ominus}/K$$
$$= (1.5 \times 10^8\ \mathrm{dm^3 mol^{-1} s^{-1}}) \times (1\ \mathrm{mol\ dm^{-3}})/200 = \mathbf{7.5 \times 10^5\ s^{-1}}$$

Note the importance of including the terms in the standard concentration. These are often omitted for clarity, but their inclusion is essential for the expressions to be dimensionally correct. The forward reaction is a second-order process with a rate constant with units of

$dm^3\ mol^{-1}\ s^{-1}$. In contrast, the backward reaction is a first-order process with a rate constant with units of $s^{-1}$.

**E11.2** For the reaction

$$NH_3(aq) + H_2O(l) \rightleftharpoons NH_4^+(aq) + OH^-(aq)$$

it is reasonable to assume that both the forward and backward reactions are second-order processes. However, we may treat the forward reaction as a pseudo first-order process, because the water is in such excess that its concentration is effectively constant

$$\text{Rate of forward reaction} = k_r[NH_3][H_2O] \approx k_{r,eff}[NH_3]$$

Thus, the rate of ammonia formation, $d[NH_3]/dt$, is

$$\text{Rate} = \frac{d[NH_3]}{dt} = \overbrace{-k_{r,eff}[NH_3]}^{\text{forward reaction}} + \overbrace{k_r'[NH_4^+][OH^-]}^{\text{backward reaction}}$$

If we neglect the autoprotolysis of water, then we may assume that $[OH^-] = [NH_4^+]$, so that

$$\text{Rate} = \frac{d[NH_3]}{dt} = -k_{r,eff}[NH_3] + k_r'[NH_4^+]^2$$

We may express the concentrations of $NH_3$ and $NH_4^+$ after the temperature jump in terms of the concentrations at equilibrium

$$[NH_3] = [NH_3]_{eq} + x$$
$$[NH_4^+] = [NH_4^+]_{eq} - x$$

and so may write

$$\begin{aligned}\text{Rate} = \frac{d[NH_3]}{dt} &= -k_{r,eff}\left([NH_3]_{eq} + x\right) + k_r'\left([NH_4^+]_{eq} - x\right)^2 \\ &= -k_{r,eff}[NH_3]_{eq} + k_r'[NH_4^+]_{eq}^2 - k_{r,eff}x - 2k_r'x[NH_4^+]_{eq} + 2k_r'x^2\end{aligned}$$

If $x$ is a small fraction of $c^\ominus$, the $x^2$ term is negligibly small and can be neglected. The first two terms cancel as they represent the fact that the forward and reverse rates are equal at equilibrium. Thus,

$$\text{Rate} = \frac{d[NH_3]}{dt} = -k_{r,eff}x - 2k_r'x[NH_4^+]_{eq} = -\overbrace{\left(k_{r,eff} + 2k_r'[NH_4^+]_{eq}\right)}^{1/\tau}x = -\frac{1}{\tau}x$$

where $\tau$ is the relaxation time.

Writing the basicity constant in terms of concentrations,

$$\begin{aligned}K_b &= \frac{a_{NH_4^+(aq)}a_{OH^-(aq)}}{a_{NH_3(aq)}a_{H_2O(l)}} \\ &\approx \frac{\left([NH_4^+]_{eq}/c^\ominus\right)\left([OH^-]_{eq}/c^\ominus\right)}{\left([NH_3]_{eq}/c^\ominus\right)} = \frac{[NH_4^+]_{eq}[OH^-]_{eq}}{[NH_3]_{eq}c^\ominus} = \frac{[NH_4^+]_{eq}^2}{[NH_3]_{eq}c^\ominus}\end{aligned}$$

so that

$$[NH_4^+]_{eq} = \left(K_b[NH_3]_{eq}c^\ominus\right)^{1/2}$$

The condition that the rates of the forward and backward reactions are equal,

$$-k_{r,eff}[NH_3]_{eq} + k_r'[NH_4^+]^2_{eq}$$

also allows us to express the rate constant for the backward reaction in terms of known quantities

$$k_r' = k_{r,eff}[NH_3]_{eq}/[NH_4^+]^2_{eq} = k_{r,eff}[NH_3]_{eq}/\left(K_b[NH_3]_{eq}c^\ominus\right) = k_{r,eff}/(K_b c^\ominus)$$

Substitution into the expression for the relaxation time $\tau$ gives

$$\tau^{-1} = k_{r,eff} + 2\overbrace{\{k_{r,eff}/(K_b c^\ominus)\}}^{k_r'}\overbrace{\left(K_b[NH_3]_{eq}c^\ominus\right)^{1/2}}^{[NH_4^+]_{eq}} = k_{r,eff} + 2k_{r,eff}\left(\frac{[NH_3]_{eq}}{K_b c^\ominus}\right)^{1/2}$$

Rearranging,

$$\begin{aligned} k_{r,eff} &= \frac{\tau^{-1}}{1 + 2\{[NH_3]_{eq}/(K_b c^\ominus)\}} \\ &= \frac{(7.61\times10^{-9}\text{s}^{-1})}{1 + 2[(0.15\text{ mol dm}^{-3})/\{(1.78\times10^{-5})\times(1\text{ mol dm}^{-3})\}]^{1/2}} \\ &= \mathbf{7.12\times10^5 s^{-1}} \end{aligned}$$

and so

$$\begin{aligned} k_r' &= k_{r,eff}/(K_b c^\ominus) \\ &= \frac{(7.12\times10^5\text{s}^{-1})}{(1.78\times10^{-5}\text{ mol dm}^{-3})\times(1\text{ mol dm}^{-3})} = \mathbf{4.00\times10^{10} mol^{-1}\,dm^3 s^{-1}} \end{aligned}$$

**E11.3** For consecutive reactions such as this, the time to reach the maximum concentration is given by eqn 11.6. We may use eqn 10.17 to express the rate constant in terms of the half lives, so that

$$\begin{aligned} t &= \frac{1}{k_b - k_a}\ln(k_a/k_b) = \frac{1}{(\ln 2/\tau_b) - (\ln 2/\tau_a)}\ln\{(\ln 2/\tau_b)/(\ln 2/\tau_a)\} \\ &= \frac{\tau_a\tau_b}{\tau_a - \tau_b}\frac{\ln(\tau_a/\tau_b)}{\ln 2} = \left\{\frac{(22.5\text{ d})\times(33.0\text{ d})}{(22.5\text{ d}) - (33.0\text{ d})}\right\}\frac{\ln\{(22.5\text{ d})/(33.0\text{ d})\}}{\ln 2} \\ &= \mathbf{39.1\ d} \end{aligned}$$

**E11.4** We may assume that, because the first reaction is fast, a pre-equilibrium is established. The rates of the forward and backward reactions are equal, so that

$$k_a[A_2] = k_a'[A]^2$$

If we express the equilibrium constant in terms of concentrations rather than activities

$$K=\frac{[\mathrm{A}]^2}{[\mathrm{A_2}]c^{\ominus}}=\frac{k_{\mathrm{a}}}{k'_{\mathrm{a}}c^{\ominus}}$$

then the concentration of the intermediate A is

$$[\mathrm{A}]=\left(\frac{k_{\mathrm{a}}[\mathrm{A_2}]}{k'_{\mathrm{a}}}\right)^{1/2}$$

The rate of formation of products is given by the rate of the second reaction

$$\begin{aligned}\text{Rate of formation of P} &= k_{\mathrm{b}}[\mathrm{A}][\mathrm{B}]\\ &= k_{\mathrm{b}}\left(\frac{k_{\mathrm{a}}[\mathrm{A_2}]}{k'_{\mathrm{a}}}\right)^{1/2}[\mathrm{B}]=\{\boldsymbol{k_{\mathrm{b}}(k_{\mathrm{a}}/k'_{\mathrm{a}})^{1/2}}\}[\mathbf{A_2}]^{1/2}[\mathbf{B}]\end{aligned}$$

**E11.5** The series of reactions shown represent the Lindemann mechanism for unimolecular reactions. Assuming that the concentration of the activated intermediate, A*, is constant, then we may apply the steady state approximation

$$\text{Rate of change of A}^* = \frac{\mathrm{d}[\mathrm{A}^*]}{\mathrm{d}t}=\overbrace{k_{\mathrm{a}}[\mathrm{A}][\mathrm{M}]}^{\text{Rate of formation}}-\overbrace{\{k'_{\mathrm{a}}[\mathrm{A}^*][\mathrm{M}]+k_{\mathrm{b}}[\mathrm{A}^*]\}}^{\text{Rate of loss}}=0$$

Rearranging, we find that the concentration of A* is given by

$$[\mathrm{A}^*]=\frac{k_{\mathrm{a}}[\mathrm{A}][\mathrm{M}]}{k'_{\mathrm{a}}[\mathrm{M}]+k_{\mathrm{b}}}$$

The rate of production of products is therefore

$$\begin{aligned}\text{Rate of formation of P} &= \frac{\mathrm{d}[\mathrm{P}]}{\mathrm{d}t}=k_{\mathrm{b}}[\mathrm{A}^*]\\ &= k_{\mathrm{b}}\frac{k_{\mathrm{a}}[\mathrm{A}][\mathrm{M}]}{k'_{\mathrm{a}}[\mathrm{M}]+k_{\mathrm{b}}}=\frac{k_{\mathrm{a}}k_{\mathrm{b}}[\mathrm{M}]}{k'_{\mathrm{a}}[\mathrm{M}]+k_{\mathrm{b}}}[\mathrm{A}]=k_{\mathrm{eff}}[\mathrm{A}]\end{aligned}$$

We may investigate the validity of the mechanism by exploring how the effective rate constant, $k_{\mathrm{eff}}$,

$$k_{\mathrm{eff}}=\frac{k_{\mathrm{a}}k_{\mathrm{b}}[\mathrm{M}]}{k'_{\mathrm{a}}[\mathrm{M}]+k_{\mathrm{b}}}$$

varies with the concentration of the inert gas M. We may rearrange this expression so that it has the same form as the equation for a straight-line graph,

$$\overbrace{\frac{1}{k_{\mathrm{eff}}}}^{y}=\frac{k'_{\mathrm{a}}[\mathrm{M}]+k_{\mathrm{b}}}{k_{\mathrm{a}}k_{\mathrm{b}}[\mathrm{M}]}=\overbrace{\frac{1}{k_{\mathrm{a}}}}^{\text{slope}}\times\overbrace{\frac{1}{[\mathrm{M}]}}^{x}+\overbrace{\frac{k'_{\mathrm{a}}}{k_{\mathrm{a}}k_{\mathrm{b}}}}^{\text{intercept}}$$

By doing so, we see that if the Lindemann mechanism is valid, a graph of $k_{\mathrm{eff}}^{-1}$ against $[\mathrm{M}]^{-1}$ should be a straight line. In the limit of very high concentrations of inert gas, the effective rate constant becomes independent of concentration,

$$\frac{1}{k_{\text{eff}}} = \frac{k_{\text{a}}'}{k_{\text{a}}k_{\text{b}}}$$

so that the rate law becomes

$$\text{Rate of formation of P} = \frac{\text{d[P]}}{\text{d}t} = \frac{k_{\text{a}}k_{\text{b}}}{k_{\text{a}}'}[\text{A}]$$

indicating a reaction that is first-order with respect to A. At very low concentrations of inert gas, $k_{\text{a}}'[\text{M}] \ll k_{\text{b}}$, and the rate law becomes

$$\text{Rate of formation of P} = \frac{\text{d[P]}}{\text{d}t} = \frac{k_{\text{a}}k_{\text{b}}[\text{M}]}{\underbrace{k_{\text{a}}'[\text{M}] + k_{\text{b}}}_{\approx k_{\text{b}}}}[\text{A}] = \frac{k_{\text{a}}k_{\text{b}}[\text{M}]}{k_{\text{b}}}[\text{A}] = k_{\text{a}}[\text{A}][\text{M}]$$

so that the reaction is first order with respect to A, first order with respect to M and therefore second order overall.

**E11.6** Modifying the rate law derived in the previous exercise, then if both A and M may participate in the activation of A,

$$\begin{aligned}\text{Rate of formation of P} = \frac{\text{d[P]}}{\text{d}t} &= k_{\text{b}}[\text{A}^*] \\ &= k_{\text{b}}\frac{k_{\text{a}}[\text{A}]([\text{A}] + [\text{M}])}{k_{\text{a}}'([\text{A}] + [\text{M}]) + k_{\text{b}}} = \frac{k_{\text{a}}k_{\text{b}}([\text{A}] + [\text{M}])[\text{A}]}{k_{\text{a}}'([\text{A}] + [\text{M}]) + k_{\text{b}}}\end{aligned}$$

If the concentration of A is such that $[\text{A}] \gg [\text{M}]$, so that $[\text{A}]+[\text{M}] \approx [\text{A}]$, then the rate law may be simplified to

$$\text{Rate of formation of P} = \frac{\text{d[P]}}{\text{d}t} = \frac{k_{\text{a}}k_{\text{b}}[\text{A}]^2}{k_{\text{a}}'[\text{A}] + k_{\text{b}}}$$

The validity of the mechanism may be tested by considering the apparent order of reaction in the limit of high and low concentrations of A. At high concentrations, $k_{\text{a}}'[\text{A}] \gg k_{\text{b}}$ and so $k_{\text{a}}'[\text{A}] + k_{\text{b}} \approx k_{\text{a}}'[\text{A}]$

$$\text{Rate of formation of P} = \frac{\text{d[P]}}{\text{d}t} = \frac{k_{\text{a}}k_{\text{b}}[\text{A}]^2}{k_{\text{a}}'[\text{A}]} = \frac{k_{\text{a}}k_{\text{b}}}{k_{\text{a}}'}[\text{A}]$$

and the reaction appears to be first order in A. Similarly, at very low concentrations, $k_{\text{a}}'[\text{A}] \ll k_{\text{b}}$ and so $k_{\text{a}}'[\text{A}] + k_{\text{b}} \approx k_{\text{b}}$,

$$\text{Rate of formation of P} = \frac{\text{d[P]}}{\text{d}t} = \frac{k_{\text{a}}k_{\text{b}}}{k_{\text{b}}}[\text{A}]^2 = k_{\text{a}}[\text{A}]^2$$

**E11.7** (a) The overall reaction may be determined by summing the equations for the two elementary steps of the mechanism:

$$3\ \text{ClO}^-(\text{aq}) \rightarrow \text{ClO}_3^-(\text{aq}) + 2\ \text{Cl}^-(\text{aq})$$

(b) The rate of the first step is proportional to the square of the hypochlorite concentration

$$\text{Rate} \propto [\text{ClO}^-]^2$$

and that of the second step is proportional to the hypochlorite concentration

$$\text{Rate} \propto [\text{ClO}^-]$$

The observations therefore imply that the **first step** is slow and therefore rate determining.

**E11.8** The second step is slow in comparison to the first and therefore rate determining. Thus,

$$\text{Rate} = k_2[\text{CH}_2\text{ClCH}_2\text{O}^-]$$

However, the concentration of $CH_2ClCH_2O^-$ is determined by the pre-equilibrium created in the first step, so that

$$[\text{CH}_2\text{ClCH}_2\text{O}^-] = K[\text{CH}_2\text{ClCH}_2\text{OH}][\text{OH}^-]$$

and therefore

$$\text{Rate} = k_2K[\text{CH}_2\text{ClCH}_2\text{OH}][\text{OH}^-]$$

**E11.9** For the reaction mechanism

| | |
|---|---|
| $O_3 \rightarrow O_2 + O$ | Rate constant $k_1$ |
| $O + O_2 \rightarrow O_3$ | $k_1'$ |
| $O + O_3 \rightarrow O_2 + O_2$ | $k_2$ |

According to the steady-state approximation, the concentration of an intermediate such as the O atoms may be considered constant, so that

$$\frac{\text{d[O]}}{\text{d}t} = \overbrace{k_1[\text{O}_3]}^{\text{formation of O}} - \overbrace{(k_1'[\text{O}][\text{O}_2] + k_2[\text{O}][\text{O}_3])}^{\text{loss of O}} = 0$$

Rearranging this equation gives us an expression for the concentration of oxygen atoms

$$[\text{O}] = \frac{k_1[\text{O}_3]}{k_1'[\text{O}_2] + k_2[\text{O}_3]}$$

The rate of change of $O_3$ is

$$\text{Rate of change of O}_3 = \frac{\text{d[O}_3]}{\text{d}t} = -k_1[\text{O}_3] + k_{-1}[\text{O}_2][\text{O}] - k_2[\text{O}][\text{O}_3]$$

We know, however, from our application of the steady-state approximation to the concentration of O atoms that

$$k_1[\text{O}_3] - k_{-1}[\text{O}_2][\text{O}] = k_2[\text{O}][\text{O}_3]$$

and therefore, substituting,

$$\text{Rate of change of O}_3 = \frac{\text{d[O}_3]}{\text{d}t} = \overbrace{-k_1[\text{O}_3] + k_{-1}[\text{O}_2][\text{O}]}^{-k_2[\text{O}][\text{O}_3]} - k_2[\text{O}][\text{O}_3]$$

$$= -2k_2[\mathrm{O}][\mathrm{O_3}]$$

$$= k_2\overbrace{\left(\frac{k_1[\mathrm{O_3}]}{k_1'[\mathrm{O_2}]+k_2[\mathrm{O_3}]}\right)}^{[\mathrm{O}]}[\mathrm{O_3}]$$

$$= \frac{k_1k_2}{k_1'[\mathrm{O_2}]+k_2[\mathrm{O_3}]}[\mathrm{O_3}]^2$$

If the second step is slow, then $k_1'[\mathrm{O_2}] \gg k_2[\mathrm{O_3}]$ and $k_1'[\mathrm{O_2}] + k_2[\mathrm{O_3}] \approx k_1'[\mathrm{O_2}]$. This approximation allows us to simplify the rate equation,

$$\text{Rate of change of } \mathrm{O_3} = \frac{\mathrm{d}[\mathrm{O_3}]}{\mathrm{d}t} = \frac{2k_1k_2}{k_1'[\mathrm{O_2}]}[\mathrm{O_3}]^2$$

indicating that the order of reaction with respect to $O_3$ is 2, but −1 with respect to $O_2$.

**E11.10** Denoting the rate constants for the individual steps of the mechanism as

| | |
|---|---|
| A + B → unstable helix | $k_1$ |
| unstable helix → A + B | $k_{-1}$ |
| unstable helix → stable double helix | $k_2$ |

then the rate of reaction is given by the rate law for the rate-determining step and hence the concentration of the unstable helix.

If the concentration of the unstable helix is determined by the pre-equilibrium steps, so that, because the rates of the forward and backward reactions are equal,

$$k_1[\mathrm{A}][\mathrm{B}] = k_{-1}[\text{unstable helix}]$$

and the equilibrium constant is given by

$$K = \frac{[\text{unstable helix}]c^{\ominus}}{[\mathrm{A}][\mathrm{B}]} = k_1/k_{-1}$$

then,

$$\text{Rate} = k_2[\text{unstable helix}] = k_2(K[\mathrm{A}][\mathrm{B}]/c^{\ominus}) = \frac{k_1k_2}{k_{-1}}[\mathrm{A}][\mathrm{B}]$$

Alternatively, if we apply the steady-state approximation and consider that the concentration of the unstable helix is constant,

$$\frac{\mathrm{d}[\text{unstable helix}]}{\mathrm{d}t} = k_1[\mathrm{A}][\mathrm{B}] - (k_{-1}[\text{unstable helix}] + k_2[\text{unstable helix}]) = 0$$

so that

$$[\text{unstable helix}] = \frac{k_1[\mathrm{A}][\mathrm{B}]}{k_{-1}+k_2}$$

then

$$\text{Rate} = k_2[\text{unstable helix}] = k_2\frac{k_1[\text{A}][\text{B}]}{k_{-1}+k_2} = \frac{k_1k_2}{k_{-1}+k_2}[\text{A}][\text{B}]$$

Both methods predict that the reaction will be first order in both A and B. The application of the steady-state approximation, however, recognises that the reaction of the unstable helix to form a stable double helix may occur at a sufficiently fast rate to affect the apparent rate constant. If $k_1 \gg k_2$, then the two results are equivalent.

**E11.11** For the parallel reactions

$$\text{R} \rightarrow \text{P}_1 \qquad \text{Rate constant } k_1$$
$$\text{R} \rightarrow \text{P}_2 \qquad k_2$$

we may write Arrhenius equations that show how the rate constants vary with temperature for the two reactions

$$k_1 = A_1\text{e}^{-E_{\text{a},1}/RT}$$
$$k_2 = A_2\text{e}^{-E_{\text{a},2}/RT}$$

The concentration of the products is directly proportional to the rate of the reaction so that the ratio

$$\frac{[\text{P}_1]}{[\text{P}_2]} = \frac{k_1[\text{R}]}{k_{-1}[\text{R}]} = \frac{A_1\text{e}^{-E_{\text{a},1}/RT}}{A_2\text{e}^{-E_{\text{a},2}/RT}} = (A_1/A_2)\text{e}^{-(E_{\text{a},1}-E_{\text{a},2})/RT}$$

Thus, if the activation energy for the reaction leading to Product 1 is greater than that leading to Product 2, so that the exponent of the function is negative, an increase in temperature will result in an **increase** in the proportion of Product 1 relative to Product 2.

**E11.12** In the discussion of the Lindemann mechanism in the text, the rate laws are formulated in terms of the concentration of either the reactive species or the inert buffer gas. However, for perfect gases, concentration is proportional to pressure, $[\text{J}] = n_\text{J}/V = p_\text{J}/RT$. We may therefore express the effective rate constant in terms of pressure as

$$k_{\text{eff}} = \frac{k_\text{a}k_\text{b}p}{k_\text{a}'p + k_\text{b}}$$

Rearranging this expression,

$$\frac{1}{k_{\text{eff}}} = \frac{k_\text{a}'p + k_\text{b}}{k_\text{a}k_\text{b}p} = \frac{k_\text{a}'p}{k_\text{a}k_\text{b}p} + \frac{k_\text{b}}{k_\text{a}k_\text{b}p} = \frac{k_\text{a}'p}{k_\text{a}k_\text{b}p} + \frac{1}{k_\text{a}p} = \frac{k_\text{a}'}{k_\text{a}k_\text{b}} + \frac{1}{k_\text{a}p}$$

Given values for the rate constant at two pressures, we may set up two simultaneous equations

$$\frac{1}{2.5\times10^{-4}\,\text{s}^{-1}} = \frac{k_\text{a}'}{k_\text{a}k_\text{b}} + \frac{1}{k_\text{a}\times(1.30\times10^{3}\,\text{Pa})}$$

$$\frac{1}{2.10\times10^{-5}\,\mathrm{s}^{-1}}=\frac{k_a'}{k_ak_b}+\frac{1}{k_a\times(12\ \mathrm{Pa})}$$

Subtracting the second equation from the first, we find that

$$\frac{1}{2.5\times10^{-4}\,\mathrm{s}^{-1}}-\frac{1}{2.10\times10^{-5}\,\mathrm{s}^{-1}}=\frac{1}{k_a}\left\{\frac{1}{1.30\times10^{3}\ \mathrm{Pa}}-\frac{1}{12\ \mathrm{Pa}}\right\}$$

Rearranging gives

$$k_a=\mathbf{1.89\times10^{-6}\ Pa^{-1}s^{-1}}$$

**E11.13** The diffusion-controlled rate constant is given by eqn 11.23,

$$k_{r,d}=\frac{8RT}{3\eta}$$

(a) Thus, for a species in water, at 298 K,

$$k_{r,d}=\frac{8\times(8.3145\ \mathrm{J\,K^{-1}mol^{-1}})\times(298\ \mathrm{K})}{3\times(1.00\times10^{-3}\ \mathrm{kg\,m^{-1}s^{-1}})}=\mathbf{6.61\times10^{6}\ m^{3}mol^{-1}s^{-1}}$$

(b) and in pentane,

$$k_{r,d}=\frac{8\times(8.3145\ \mathrm{J\,K^{-1}mol^{-1}})\times(298\ \mathrm{K})}{3\times(2.2\times10^{-4}\ \mathrm{kg\,m^{-1}s^{-1}})}=\mathbf{3.0\times10^{7}\ m^{3}mol^{-1}s^{-1}}$$

**E11.14** (a) The flux of molecules down a concentration gradient is given by Fick's first law, eqn 11.18c,

$$J=-D\frac{d\mathcal{N}}{dx}=-D\frac{d(cN_A)}{dx}=-DN_A\frac{dc}{dx}$$

$$=-(5.22\times10^{-10}\ \mathrm{m^2s^{-1}})\times(6.022\times10^{23}\mathrm{mol^{-1}})\times\overbrace{(0.10\ \mathrm{mol\,dm^{-3}m^{-1}})}^{\text{molar concentration gradient }dc/dx}$$

$$=\mathbf{-5.2\times10^{-8}\ mol\ m^{-2}s^{-1}}$$

The negative sign indicates that the flow of molecules is in the opposite direction to the concentration gradient, with molecules moving from regions of high concentration to low concentration.

(b) The amount of molecules passing through an area $A$ in a time interval $\delta t$ is therefore given by

$$n=|J|A\delta t=|-5.2\times10^{-8}\ \mathrm{mol\,m^{-2}s^{-1}}|\times\overbrace{(5.0\times10^{-6}\ \mathrm{m^2})}^{1\ \mathrm{mm^2}=10^{-6}\mathrm{m^2}}\times\overbrace{(60\ \mathrm{s})}^{1\ \mathrm{min}=60\ \mathrm{s}}$$

$$=\mathbf{1.6\times10^{-11}mol}$$

**E11.15** Diffusing molecules undergo what is known as a random walk, a series of steps in random directions and (in general) through random distances. Although a molecule undergoing a random walk may take many steps in a given time, it has only a small probability of being found far from its starting point because some of the steps lead it away from the starting point but others lead it back. We may show that the time taken for a molecule to travel a given distance, $d$, is

$$t = \frac{d^2}{2D}$$

so that

(a) for a distance of 1 mm,

$$t = \frac{(10 \times 10^{-3}\ \mathrm{m})^2}{2 \times (5.22 \times 10^{-10}\ \mathrm{m^2s^{-1}})} = 9.6 \times 10^4\ \mathrm{s} = \mathbf{27\ h}$$

(b) and for a distance of 1 mm,

$$t = \frac{(10 \times 10^{-2}\ \mathrm{m})^2}{2 \times (5.22 \times 10^{-10}\ \mathrm{m^2s^{-1}})} = 9.6 \times 10^6\ \mathrm{s} = \mathbf{2.7 \times 10^3\ h}$$

(c) and for a distance of 1 mm,

$$t = \frac{(10\ \mathrm{m})^2}{2 \times (5.22 \times 10^{-10}\ \mathrm{m^2s^{-1}})} = 9.6 \times 10^{10}\ \mathrm{s} = \mathbf{3.0 \times 10^3\ a}$$

These times are so long that in practice, stirring and convective motion are much more important than diffusion in causing mixing on a macroscopic scale.

**E11.16** For a molecule undergoing a random walk, taking steps of length $\lambda$ in a time $\tau$, the diffusion coefficient is given by

$$D = \frac{\lambda^2}{2\tau}$$

(a) Thus, if the molecule takes a step of length 150 pm in 1.8 ps,

$$D = \frac{(150 \times 10^{-12}\ \mathrm{m})^2}{2 \times (1.8 \times 10^{-12}\ \mathrm{s})} = \mathbf{6.3 \times 10^{-9}\ m^2s^{-1}}$$

(b) and if the molecule takes a step of 75 pm in 1.8 ps,

$$D = \frac{(75 \times 10^{-12}\ \mathrm{m})^2}{2 \times (1.8 \times 10^{-12}\ \mathrm{s})} = \mathbf{1.6 \times 10^{-9}\ m^2s^{-1}}$$

**E11.17** Diffusion is only important in the absence of macroscopic fluid flow. Mass transport through convection or turbulence is usually much faster than diffusion. The time taken for a molecule to travel a given distance, $d$, is

$$t = \frac{d^2}{2D}$$

We may estimate the value of the diffusion coefficient using the Einstein relation, eqn 11.21, so that

$$t = \frac{d^2}{2\underbrace{\{kT/(6\pi\eta a)\}}_{D}} = \frac{3\pi\eta a d^2}{kT}$$

The viscosity of water at at 25 °C is $\eta$ =8.9 × 10$^{-4}$ kg m$^{-1}$ s$^{-1}$, and taking the radius of a water molecule to be $a$ = 100 pm,

$$t = \frac{3\pi \times (8.9 \times 10^{-4}\ \mathrm{kg\,m^{-1}s^{-1}}) \times (100 \times 10^{-12}\mathrm{m}) \times (100\ \mathrm{m})^2}{(1.38 \times 10^{-23}\ \mathrm{J\,K^{-1}}) \times (273.15 + 25)\ \mathrm{K}}$$
$$= 2 \times 10^{12}\mathrm{s} = \mathbf{6 \times 10^4\ a}$$

An extraordinarily large time is required for a molecule to move across a lake by diffusion alone. A pollutant with a radius of 100 pm (the radius of a water molecule) requires about 60 millennia to travel across of 100 m lake at a mean surface temperature of 25 °C.

**E11.18** Let $N$ be the number of one-dimensional steps of length $\lambda$ that a molecule takes in time $t$ and let $\tau$ be the time each step takes so that $t = \tau N$. Thus,

$$D = \frac{\lambda^2}{2\tau} = \frac{\lambda^2}{2(t/N)} = \frac{N\lambda^2}{2t}$$

Hence, the distance travelled in time $t$ is

$$d = (2Dt)^{1/2} = [2\{(N\lambda^2)/2t\}t]^{1/2} = N^{1/2}\lambda$$

Thus, for a molecules to be found a distance equivalent to 1000 steps away from its origin, $d$ = 1000 $\lambda$, and so

$$1000\,\lambda = N^{1/2}\lambda$$

Rearranging, the number of steps is

$$N = 1000^2 = \mathbf{1 \times 10^6}$$

**E11.19** The temperature dependence of viscosity is given by eqn 11.22

$$\eta(T) = \eta_0 \mathrm{e}^{-E_\mathrm{a}/RT}$$

Hence, considering the viscosity at two temperatures,

$$\frac{\eta(T_1)}{\eta(T_2)} = \frac{\eta_0 \mathrm{e}^{-E_\mathrm{a}/RT_1}}{\eta_0 \mathrm{e}^{-E_\mathrm{a}/RT_2}} = \mathrm{e}^{-E_\mathrm{a}(T_1^{-1} - T_2^{-1})/R}$$

Rearranging, for temperatures of 20 °C = 293 K and 30 °C = 303 K,

$$E_\mathrm{a} = -R\ln\{\eta(T_1)/\eta(T_2)\}/(T_1^{-1} - T_2^{-1})$$
$$= \frac{(8.3145\ \mathrm{J\,K^{-1}mol^{-1}}) \times \ln\{(1.0019\ \mathrm{mN\,s\,m^{-2}})/(0.7982\ \mathrm{mN\,s\,m^{-2}})\}}{\{(293\ \mathrm{K})^{-1} - (303\ \mathrm{K})^{-1}\}}$$
$$= 17 \times 10^3\ \mathrm{J\,mol^{-1}} = \mathbf{17\ kJ\ mol^{-1}}$$

**E11.20** Writing the Arrhenius equation for the catalysed and uncatalysed reactions,

$$k_{\text{cat}} = A_{\text{cat}}\text{e}^{-E_{\text{a,cat}}/RT}$$
$$k_{\text{uncat}} = A_{\text{uncat}}\text{e}^{-E_{\text{a,uncat}}/RT}$$

then, the ratio of the rate constants is

$$\frac{k_{\text{cat}}}{k_{\text{uncat}}} = \frac{A_{\text{cat}}}{A_{\text{uncat}}}\text{e}^{-(E_{\text{a,cat}}-E_{\text{a,uncat}})/RT}$$

If we assume that the values for the pre-exponential parameters are equal, $A_{\text{cat}} = A_{\text{uncat}}$ and use the Gibbs energy of activation as an approximation to the activation energy,

$$\frac{k_{\text{cat}}}{k_{\text{uncat}}} \approx \text{e}^{-(\Delta^{\ddagger}G_{\text{cat}}-\Delta^{\ddagger}G_{\text{uncat}})/RT}$$
$$= \text{e}^{-\{(15\times10^3\ \text{J mol}^{-1})-(150\times10^3\ \text{J mol}^{-1})\}/\{(8.3145\ \text{J K}^{-1}\text{mol}^{-1})\times(273.15+37)\text{K}\}}$$
$$= \mathbf{5.6 \times 10^{22}}$$

In practice, although the value for the ratio of the rate constants is close to the true value, the assumptions made are not usually valid. The catalyzed and uncatalyzed reactions follow different mechanisms, and the pre-exponential factors are unlikely to be equal. Furthermore, the Gibbs energy of activation includes not only terms in the activation energy, but also a contribution from the entropy of activation. This too would be expected to be different for the two reactions.

A more sophisticated method is to use transition-state theory, which takes account both of the differences in the pre-exponential factor and the activation energy.

**E11.21** If the reaction

$$2\ H_2O_2(aq) \rightarrow 2\ H_2O(l) + O_2(g)$$

proceeds by the two-step catalytic mechanism,

$H_2O_2 + Br^- \rightarrow H_2O + BrO^-$ $\quad k_1$, slow

$BrO^- + H_2O_2 \rightarrow H_2O + O_2 + Br^-$ $\quad k_2$, fast

then the first step may be considered as rate determining because it is slow in comparison with the second step. Thus, the rate law may be approximated as

$$\text{Rate} = k_1[H_2O_2][Br^-]$$

suggesting that the reaction is first order in $H_2O_2$ and first order in $Br^-$.

**E11.22** Denoting the rate constants for the steps of the mechanism as

$HA + H^+ \rightarrow HAH^+$ $\quad k_1$, fast

$HAH^+ \rightarrow HA + H^+$ $\quad k_{-1}$, fast

$HAH^+ + B \rightarrow BH^+ + HA$ $\quad k_2$, slow

the rate of production of the product is

$$\text{Rate} = \frac{d[BH^+]}{dt} = k_2[HAH^+][B]$$

The first two steps form a rapid equilibrium, with

$$k_1[HA][H^+] = k_{-1}[HAH^+]$$

Thus, rearranging for the concentration of the intermediate [$HAH^+$], and subsituting,

$$\text{Rate} = \frac{d[BH^+]}{dt} = k_2\overbrace{\{(k_1/k_{-1})[HA][H^+]\}}^{[HAH^+]}[B] = (k_1k_2/k_{-1})[HA][H^+][B]$$

If the source of $H^+$ is the weak acid HA, the conecntration of $H^+$ is given by another equilibrium,

$$HA + H_2O \rightleftharpoons H_3O^+ + A^-$$

with, if the solution is sufficiently dilute that activities may be replaced by concentrations,

$$K_a \approx \frac{[H^+][A^-]}{[HA]c^\ominus} \approx \frac{[H^+]^2}{[HA]c^\ominus}$$

so that

$$[H^+] = (K_a[HA]c^\ominus)^{1/2}$$

and therefore

$$\text{Rate} = \frac{d[BH^+]}{dt} = (k_1k_2/k_{-1})[HA]\overbrace{(K_a[HA]c^\ominus)^{1/2}}^{[H^+]}[B] = \frac{k_1k_2K_a}{k_{-1}}[HA]^{3/2}[B]$$

Thus, under these conditions, the rate is indeed independent of the concentration of $H^+$.

**E11.23** Denoting the rate constants for each step as

$$AH + B \rightarrow BH^+ + A^- \qquad k_1$$
$$A^- + BH^+ \rightarrow AH + B \qquad k_{-1}$$
$$A^- + AH \rightarrow \text{product} \qquad k_2$$

then the rate of reaction may be defined as

$$\text{Rate of production of product} = \frac{d[\text{product}]}{dt} = k_2[A^-][AH]$$

assuming that the concentration of the intermediate, $A^-$ is constant,

$$\frac{d[A^-]}{dt} = \overbrace{k_1[AH][B]}^{\text{rate of formation of } A^-} - \overbrace{(k_{-1}[A^-][BH^+] + k_2[A^-][AH])}^{\text{rate of loss of } A^-} = 0$$

Rearranging to obtain an expression for the concentration of $A^-$ and substituting into the rate law,

$$\text{Rate of production of product} = \frac{d[\text{product}]}{dt}$$
$$= k_2 \overbrace{\left(\frac{k_1[\text{AH}][\text{B}]}{k_{-1}[\text{BH}^+] + k_2[\text{AH}]}\right)}^{[\text{A}^-]} [\text{AH}]$$
$$= \boldsymbol{\frac{k_1 k_2 [\text{AH}]^2[\text{B}]}{k_{-1}[\text{BH}^+] + k_2[\text{AH}]}}$$

**E11.24** For the mechanism

| | |
|---|---|
| $E + S \rightarrow ES$ | $k_a$ |
| $ES \rightarrow E + S$ | $k_a'$ |
| $ES \rightarrow P + E$ | $k_b$ |

then assuming a rapid equilibrium between the first two steps, so that

$$k_a[\text{E}][\text{S}] = k_a'[\text{ES}]$$

Expressing the concentration of the enzyme in terms of the initial concentration and the concentration of the enzyme–substrate complex, $[\text{E}] = [\text{E}]_0 - [\text{ES}]$, and rearranging, we may obtain an expression for the concentration of the intermediate ES

$$k_a \overbrace{([\text{E}]_0 - [\text{ES}])}^{[\text{E}]} [\text{S}] = k_a'[\text{ES}]$$
$$k_a[\text{E}]_0[\text{S}] - k_a[\text{ES}][\text{S}] = k_a'[\text{ES}]$$

so that

$$[\text{ES}] = \frac{k_a[\text{E}]_0[\text{S}]}{k_a[\text{S}] + k_a'}$$

The rate of reaction is thus

$$\text{Rate of production of P} = \frac{d[\text{P}]}{dt} = k_b[\text{ES}] = k_b \overbrace{\frac{k_a[\text{E}]_0[\text{S}]}{k_a[\text{S}] + k_a'}}^{[\text{ES}]} = \frac{k_a k_b}{k_a[\text{S}] + k_a'}[\text{E}]_0[\text{S}]$$

The equivalent expression obtained using the steady-state approximation is

$$\text{Rate of production of P} = \frac{d[\text{P}]}{dt} = \frac{k_a k_b}{k_a[\text{S}] + k_a' + k_b}[\text{E}]_0[\text{S}]$$

The two expressions become equivalent when

$$k_a[\text{S}] + k_a' \gg k_b$$

so that

$$k_a[\text{S}] + k_a' + k_b \approx k_a[\text{S}] + k_a'$$

which would be true if the rate of reaction to give products is slow in comparison with the other two steps. This is consistent with the assumption made that the reactions involved in the pre-equilibrium are rapid.

**E11.25** According to Michaelis–Menten kinetics, the rate of reaction is given by eqn 11.28

$$v = \frac{[\mathrm{S}]}{[\mathrm{S}] + K_\mathrm{M}} v_\mathrm{max}$$

Rearranging,

$$v_\mathrm{max} = \frac{[\mathrm{S}] + K_\mathrm{M}}{[\mathrm{S}]} v = \{1 + (K_\mathrm{M}/[\mathrm{S}])\}v$$

$$= \left[1 + \frac{(0.045\ \mathrm{mol\ dm^{-3}})}{(0.110\ \mathrm{mol\ dm^{-3}})}\right] 1.15\ \mathrm{mmol\ dm^{-3}} = \mathbf{1.62\ mmol\ dm^{-3}}$$

**E11.26** The turnover frequency, or catalytic constant, $k_\mathrm{cat}$, is defined by eqn 11.30, and for reactions that follow Michaelis–Menten kinetics, $k_\mathrm{cat} = k_\mathrm{b}$. Thus, using eqn 11.31

$$k_\mathrm{cat} = \frac{v_\mathrm{max}}{[\mathrm{E}]_0} = \frac{4.25 \times 10^{-4}\ \mathrm{mol\ dm^{-3}s^{-1}}}{3.60 \times 10^{-9}\ \mathrm{mol\ dm^{-3}}} = \mathbf{1.18 \times 10^5\ s^{-1}}$$

The catalytic efficiency is defined by eqn 11.32 so that

$$\eta = \frac{k_\mathrm{cat}}{K_\mathrm{M}} = \frac{1.18 \times 10^5\ \mathrm{s^{-1}}}{0.015\ \mathrm{mol\ dm^{-3}}} = \mathbf{7.9 \times 10^6\ mol^{-1}dm^3s^{-1}}$$

This enzyme is not catalytically perfect as the catalytic efficiency is much less than the diffusion-controlled rate constant calculated using eqn 11.23, $k_\mathrm{r,d} = 7.4 \times 10^9\ \mathrm{dm^3\ mol^{-1}\ s^{-1}}$.

**E11.27** We may fit the data to the Lineweaver–Burk equation, eqn 11.29b,

$$\frac{1}{v} = \frac{1}{v_\mathrm{max}} + \left(\frac{K_\mathrm{M}}{v_\mathrm{max}}\right)\frac{1}{[\mathrm{S}]}$$

Figure 11.3 shows a plot of $1/v$ against $1/[\mathrm{S}]$. The intercept is $1/v_\mathrm{max} = 0.433\ \mathrm{dm^3\ s\ \mu mol^{-1}}$ so that

$$v_\mathrm{max} = \mathbf{2.31\ \mu mol\ dm^{-3}\ s^{-1}}$$

The slope is $K_\mathrm{M}/v_\mathrm{max} = 0.480$ s. Therefore,

$$K_\mathrm{M} = (0.480\ \mathrm{s}) \times (2.31\ \mathrm{\mu mol\ dm^{-3}\ s^{-1}}) = \mathbf{1.11\ \mu mol\ dm^{-3}}$$

The maximum turnover number $k_\mathrm{cat}$ is

$$k_\mathrm{cat} = \frac{v_\mathrm{max}}{[\mathrm{E}]_0} = \frac{2.31\ \mathrm{\mu mol\ dm^{-3}\ s^{-1}}}{0.020\ \mathrm{\mu mol\ dm^{-3}}} = \mathbf{1.2 \times 10^2\ s^{-1}}$$

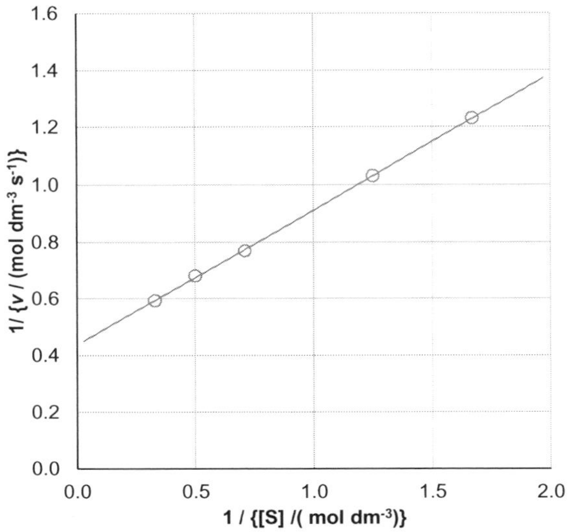


**Figure 11.3**

**E11.28** The Lineweaver–Burk equation, eqn 11.29b,

$$\frac{1}{v} = \frac{1}{v_{\max}} + \left(\frac{K_M}{v_{\max}}\right)\frac{1}{[S]}$$

may be rearranged into different expressions that also have the form of the equation for a straight-line graph. For example, multiplying by ($v \times v_{max}$) leads to

$$v_{\max} = v + K_M\left(\frac{v}{[S]}\right)$$

which may be rearranged to give the Eadie–Hofstee relation

$$\overbrace{\frac{v}{[S]}}^{y} = \overbrace{\left(-\frac{1}{K_M}\right)}^{\text{slope}}\overbrace{v}^{x} + \overbrace{\left(\frac{v_{\max}}{K_M}\right)}^{\text{intercept}}$$

The Michaelis constant is therefore given by the slope of an Eadie–Hofstee plot,

$$K_M = -1/\text{slope}$$

and the maximum velocity by the ratio of the intercept and slope,

$$v_{\max} = -\text{intercept}/\text{slope}$$

Figure 11.4 shows an Eadie–Hofstee plot of the data given in Exercise 11.27. The slope of the plot is –0.906 $\mu mol^{-1}$ $dm^3$, so that

$$K_M = -1/(-0.906\ \mu\text{mol}^{-1}\text{dm}^3) = \mathbf{1.10\ \mu mol\ dm^{-3}}$$

The intercept is 2.09 $s^{-1}$, so that

$$v_{max} = -(2.09\ s^{-1})/(-0.906\ \mu mol^{-1} dm^3) = \mathbf{2.31\ \mu mol\ dm^{-3} s^{-1}}$$

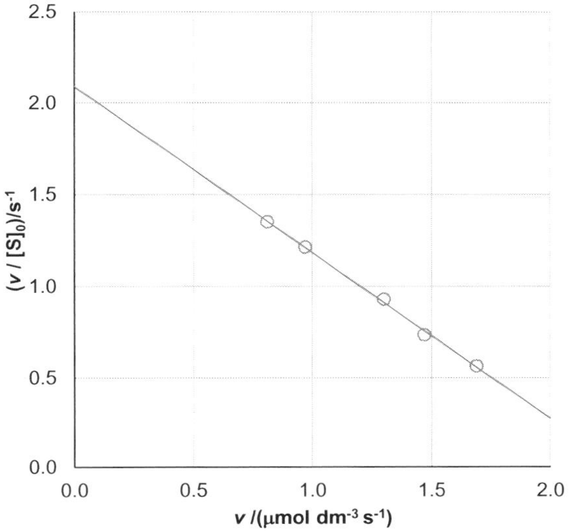


**Figure 11.4**

Multiplication of the Lineweaver–Burk expression by [S] gives the Hane's relation

$$\overbrace{\frac{[S]}{v}}^{y} = \overbrace{\left(\frac{1}{v_{max}}\right)}^{\text{slope}} \overbrace{[S]}^{x} + \overbrace{\left(\frac{K_M}{v_{max}}\right)}^{\text{intercept}}$$

The maximum velocity is given by the slope,

$$v_{max} = 1/\text{slope}$$

and the Michaelis constant by the ratio of the intercept to the slope

$$K_M = \text{intercept}/\text{slope}$$

Figure 11.5 shows a Hane's plot for the data given in Exercise 11.27. The slope of the graph is 0.434 $\mu mol^{-1}\ dm^3$ s so that

$$v_{max} = 1/(0.434\ \mu mol^{-1}\ dm^3 s) = \mathbf{2.31\ \mu mol\ dm^{-3} s^{-1}}$$

and the intercept is 0.479 s, so that

$$K_M = (0.479\ s)/(0.434\ \mu mol^{-1}\ dm^3 s) = \mathbf{1.10\ \mu mol\ dm^{-3}}$$

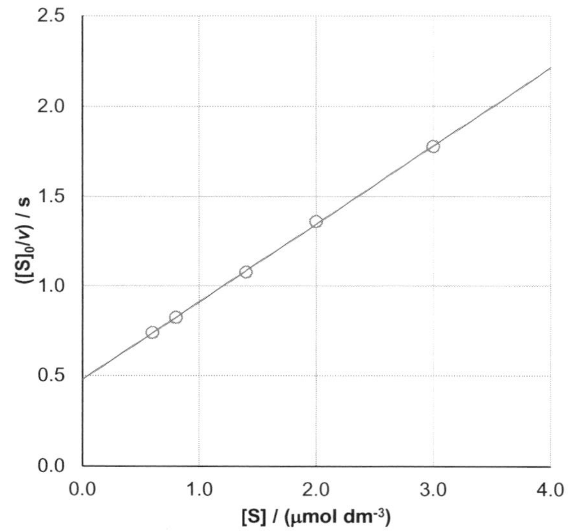


**Figure 11.5**

**E11.29** The first reaction results in the formation of two radicals, and is thus an initiation step. The second and third steps do not result in a change in the net number of radicals and are therefore propogation steps. The fourth step results in a loss of radicals and is a termination step.

We may define the rate of reaction in terms of the rate of production of the product P,

$$\text{Rate} = \frac{\mathrm{d[P]}}{\mathrm{d}t} = k_4[\mathrm{A}][\mathrm{B}]$$

However, applying the steady-state approximation and assuming that the concentrations of the intermediates A· and B· are constant

$$\frac{\mathrm{d[A]}}{\mathrm{d}t} = k_1[\mathrm{AH}] - k_2[\mathrm{A}] + k_3[\mathrm{AH}][\mathrm{B}] - k_4[\mathrm{A}][\mathrm{B}] = 0$$

$$\frac{\mathrm{d[B]}}{\mathrm{d}t} = k_2[\mathrm{A}] - k_3[\mathrm{AH}][\mathrm{B}] - k_4[\mathrm{A}][\mathrm{B}] = 0$$

Addition of the two expressions gives

$$k_1[\mathrm{AH}] - 2k_4[\mathrm{A}][\mathrm{B}] = 0$$

so that, rearranging,

$$\text{Rate} = k_4[\mathrm{A}][\mathrm{B}] = \tfrac{1}{2}k_1[\mathrm{AH}]$$

The reaction is therefore first order with respect to AH.

**E11.30** The rate of decomposition of $R_2$ is

$$\text{Rate} = k_1[R_2] - k_2[R][R_2]$$

If R and R' are radical intermediates and not stable species, it is reasonable to apply the steady-state approximation. Thus,

$$\frac{d[R]}{dt} = 2k_1[R_2] - k_2[R][R_2] + k_3[R'] - 2k_4[R]^2 = 0$$
$$\frac{d[R']}{dt} = k_2[R][R_2] - k_3[R'] = 0$$

Rearranging this second equation gives an expression for the concentration of R'

$$[R'] = (k_2/k_3)[R][R_2]$$

Substituting into the first equation gives

$$2k_1[R_2] - k_2[R][R_2] + k_3\overbrace{\{(k_2/k_3)[R][R_2]\}}^{[R']} - 2k_4[R]^2 = 0$$

Rearranging gives an expression for the concentration of R

$$k_4[R]^2 = k_1[R_2]$$
$$[R] = \{(k_1/k_4)[R_2]\}^{1/2}$$

Substituting into the original rate law,

$$\text{Rate} = k_1[R_2] - \overbrace{[k_2\{(k_1/k_4)[R_2]\}^{1/2}]}^{[R]}[R_2] = \overbrace{\{k_1 - (k_1/k_4)^{1/2}k_2[R_2]^{1/2}\}}^{k_{\text{eff}}}[R_2]$$

The effective rate constant, $k_{\text{eff}}$, therefore depens upon the concentration of $R_2$. It is thus not possible to define the order of the reaction with respect to $R_2$.

**E11.31** (a) Using the mechanism given in *Derivation 11.7*, then the rate of formation of H is

$$\frac{d[H]}{dt} = k_b[Br][H_2] - k_c[H][Br_2] - k_d[H][HBr] = 0$$

and the rate of formation of Br is

$$\frac{d[Br]}{dt} = 2k_a[Br_2] - k_b[Br][H_2] + k_c[H][Br_2] + k_d[H][HBr] - 2k_e[Br]^2 = 0$$

Adding these two expressions together gives

$$2k_a[Br_2] - 2k_e[Br]^2 = 0$$

and hence, by rearranging, an expression for the concentration of [Br]

$$[Br] = \{(\boldsymbol{k_a/k_e})[\mathbf{Br_2}]\}^{1/2}$$

Rearranging the expression for the net rate of formation of H, and subsituting for [Br]

$$[\mathrm{H}] = \frac{k_\mathrm{b}[\mathrm{Br}][\mathrm{H_2}]}{k_\mathrm{c}[\mathrm{Br_2}] + k_\mathrm{d}[\mathrm{HBr}]}$$

$$= \frac{k_\mathrm{b}\overbrace{\{(k_\mathrm{a}/k_\mathrm{e})[\mathrm{Br_2}]\}^{1/2}}^{[\mathrm{Br}]}[\mathrm{H_2}]}{k_\mathrm{c}[\mathrm{Br_2}] + k_\mathrm{d}[\mathrm{HBr}]} = \boldsymbol{\frac{k_\mathrm{b}(k_\mathrm{a}/k_\mathrm{e})^{1/2}[\mathrm{H_2}][\mathrm{Br_2}]^{1/2}}{k_\mathrm{c}[\mathrm{Br_2}] + k_\mathrm{d}[\mathrm{HBr}]}}$$

(b) The rate of formation of HBr is, from *Derivation 11.7*,

$$\frac{\mathrm{d}[\mathrm{HBr}]}{\mathrm{d}t} = \frac{2k_\mathrm{b}(k_\mathrm{a}/k_\mathrm{e})^{1/2}[\mathrm{H_2}][\mathrm{Br_2}]^{3/2}}{[\mathrm{Br_2}] + (k_\mathrm{d}/k_\mathrm{c})[\mathrm{HBr}]}$$

If the concentration of HBr is very low, then $[\mathrm{Br_2}] \gg (k_\mathrm{d}/k_\mathrm{c})[\mathrm{HBr}]$ and $[\mathrm{Br_2}] + (k_\mathrm{d}/k_\mathrm{c})[\mathrm{HBr}] \approx [\mathrm{Br_2}]$, so that

$$\frac{\mathrm{d}[\mathrm{HBr}]}{\mathrm{d}t} = \frac{2k_\mathrm{b}(k_\mathrm{a}/k_\mathrm{e})^{1/2}[\mathrm{H_2}][\mathrm{Br_2}]^{3/2}}{[\mathrm{Br_2}] + (k_\mathrm{d}/k_\mathrm{c})[\mathrm{HBr}]} \approx \frac{2k_\mathrm{b}(k_\mathrm{a}/k_\mathrm{e})^{1/2}[\mathrm{H_2}][\mathrm{Br_2}]^{3/2}}{[\mathrm{Br_2}]}$$
$$= \boldsymbol{2k_\mathrm{b}(k_\mathrm{a}/k_\mathrm{e})^{1/2}[\mathrm{H_2}][\mathrm{Br_2}]^{1/2}}$$

If, however, the concentration of HBr is very high, then $[\mathrm{Br_2}] \ll (k_\mathrm{d}/k_\mathrm{c})[\mathrm{HBr}]$ and $[\mathrm{Br_2}] + (k_\mathrm{d}/k_\mathrm{c})[\mathrm{HBr}] \approx (k_\mathrm{d}/k_\mathrm{c})[\mathrm{HBr}]$, so that

$$\frac{\mathrm{d}[\mathrm{HBr}]}{\mathrm{d}t} = \frac{2k_\mathrm{b}(k_\mathrm{a}/k_\mathrm{e})^{1/2}[\mathrm{H_2}][\mathrm{Br_2}]^{3/2}}{[\mathrm{Br_2}] + (k_\mathrm{d}/k_\mathrm{c})[\mathrm{HBr}]} \approx \boldsymbol{\frac{2k_\mathrm{b}(k_\mathrm{a}/k_\mathrm{e})^{1/2}[\mathrm{H_2}][\mathrm{Br_2}]^{3/2}}{(k_\mathrm{d}/k_\mathrm{c})[\mathrm{HBr}]}}$$

## Answers to projects

**P11.32** (a) Enzyme-catalyzed reactions that require minutes or hours may be followed with standard spectroscopic methods including uv-visible, infrared, fluorescence, and NMR techniques. It may even be possible to determine the progression of substrate consumption, or product formation, with a chemical titration or radioactivity assay. Electrical conductivity may be used when ions are reaction participants; pH measurements are used to follow the reaction rate when an acid or base is a participant. An inhibitor that binds very strongly to the active site may be used to quench the reaction at any time, thereby, making it possible to separate substrate and product with a chromatographic method; after which spectroscopic techniques, and the application of Beer–Lambert law, may prove useful in the case for which substrate and product have overlapping spectra.

A stopped-flow technique provides for the rapid mixing that is necessary to follow reactions that require milliseconds or minutes. Standard spectroscopic, conductivity, or pH measurements are used to follow the reaction rate.

Very fast reactions may be followed by disturbing an equilibrium system with the excitation energy of flash photolysis or by a very sudden temperature jump initiated with a large current burst through the reaction solution. A pulsed laser beam is subsequently used to generate absorption, emission, or fluorescence spectra and the evolution of such spectra yields reaction rates.

(b) The initial rate of an enzyme-catalyzed reaction is acquired by extrapolation of the time evolution of observed rates to the initial mixing time. When repeated over a range of initial substrate concentrations, it is possible to prepare a double reciprocal, Lineweaver–Burk plot of $1/v_0$ against $1/[S]_0$. It is the intercept and slope of this plot that provides the values of the maximum reaction rate and the Michaelis constant. The manner in which an enzyme inhibitor alters the slope and intercept provides both evidence for the type of inhibition (competitive, uncompetitive, or non-competitive) and values of inhibitor binding constants.

(c) The molecular shape of a strongly enzyme-binding, competitive inhibitor gives clues about the intermediate enzyme-substrate activated complex because, like the inhibitor, the activated ES complex must bind strongly to the active site in order to initiate reaction. Clues include charge distribution, hydrogen bonding, and hydrophobic interactions. The idea of a transition-state intermediate involves a slight modification of the Michaelis–Menten mechanism:

$$E + S \rightleftharpoons ES \rightleftharpoons ES^* \rightarrow EP \rightleftharpoons E + P$$

The activated transition-state enzyme-substrate complex, ES*, is a very short lived intermediate because it has the activation energy necessary to react. It has been shown that the enzyme has a higher affinity for the transition-state intermediate than for the substrate and will bind the intermediate more strongly. Good inhibitors are generally transition-state analogues.

**P11.33** The net rate of change of A is given by considering the rate at which A is lost through the forward reaction, and the rate at which A is formed by the backward reaction. Thus,

$$\frac{d[A]}{dt} = \overbrace{-k_r[A]}^{\substack{\text{loss}\\ \text{of A}}} + \overbrace{k_r'[B]}^{\substack{\text{formation}\\ \text{of A}}} = -k_r[A] + k_r'\overbrace{([A]_0 - [A])}^{[B]} = -(k_r + k_r')[A] + k_r'[A]_0$$

where it has been assumed that no B is present initially, so that $[B] = [A]_0 - [A]$. The concentration of [A] is, however, given in eqn 11.2. Thus, differentiating,

$$\frac{d[A]}{dt} = \frac{d}{dt}[A] = \frac{d}{dt}\left[\frac{\{k_r' + k_r e^{-(k_r+k_r')t}\}[A]_0}{k_r + k_r'}\right] = \frac{k_r[A]_0}{k_r + k_r'}\overbrace{\frac{d}{dt}\{e^{-(k_r+k_r')t}\}}^{\frac{d}{dx}e^{ax}=ae^{ax}}$$

$$= \frac{k_r[A]_0}{k_r + k_r'} \times -(k_r + k_r')e^{-(k_r+k_r')t} = -k_r[A]_0 e^{-(k_r+k_r')t}$$

But, if

$$[A] = \frac{\{k_r' + k_r e^{-(k_r+k_r')t}\}[A]_0}{k_r + k_r'}$$

then, rearranging,

$$k_r[A]_0 e^{-(k_r+k_r')t} = (k_r + k_r')[A] - k_r'[A]_0$$

so that we may express this result as

$$\frac{d[A]}{dt} = -(k_r + k_r')[A] + k_r'[A]_0$$

This is identical to the result obtained by considering the net rate of change of the concentration of A through the forward and backward reactions. The expression given for the concentration of A in eqn 11.2a must therefore be a valid solution. We may use the same approach to demonstrate that the expression for [B] given in eqn 11.2b is also a valid solution.

(b) If, however, we do not assume that there is no B present initially, it follows that because $[A] + [B] = [A]_0 + [B]_0$ at all times, and so $[B] = [A]_0 + [B]_0 - [A]$ and therefore

$$\frac{d[A]}{dt} = \overbrace{-k_r[A]}^{\text{loss of A}} + \overbrace{k_r'[B]}^{\text{formation of A}}$$

$$= -k_r[A] + k_r'\overbrace{([A]_0 + [B]_0 - [A])}^{[B]} = -(k_r + k_r')[A] + k_r'([A]_0 + [B]_0)$$

Hence, rearranging,

$$\frac{d[A]}{(k_r + k_r')[A] - k_r'([A]_0 + [B]_0)} = -dt$$

We may obtain an expression for [A] by integrating. The integration is simplified by writing $a = k_r + k_r'$ and $b = k_r'([A]_0 + [B]_0)$, so that it becomes

$$\int_{[A]_0}^{[A]} \frac{d[A]}{a[A] - b} = -\int_0^t dt$$

$$\left[\frac{1}{a}\ln(a[A] - b)\right]_{[A]_0}^{[A]} = -[t]_0^t$$

because

$$\int \frac{dx}{ax - b} = \frac{1}{a}\ln(ax - b) + c$$

Substituting the expressions for $a$ and $b$, and including the limits,

$$\frac{1}{(k_r + k_r')}[\ln\{(k_r + k_r')[A] - k_r'([A]_0 + [B]_0)\} - \ln\{(k_r + k_r')[A]_0 - k_r'([A]_0 + [B]_0)\}] = -t$$

$$\frac{1}{(k_r + k_r')}[\ln\{(k_r + k_r')[A] - k_r'([A]_0 + [B]_0)\} - \ln\{k_r[A]_0 - k_r'[B]_0\}] = -t$$

$$\frac{1}{(k_r + k_r')}\left[\ln\frac{(k_r + k_r')[A] - k_r'([A]_0 + [B]_0)}{k_r[A]_0 - k_r'[B]_0}\right] = -t$$

We may rearrange this equation to obtain an expression for the concentration of [A],

$$\left[\ln\frac{(k_r + k_r')[A] - k_r'([A]_0 + [B]_0)}{k_r[A]_0 - k_r'[B]_0}\right] = -(k_r + k_r')t$$

$$\frac{(k_r + k_r')[A] - k_r'([A]_0 + [B]_0)}{k_r[A]_0 - k_r'[B]_0} = e^{-(k_r+k_r')t}$$

$$(k_r + k_r')[A] - k_r'([A]_0 + [B]_0) = (k_r[A]_0 - k_r'[B]_0)e^{-(k_r+k_r')t}$$

Hence, rearranging,

$$[A] = \frac{k_r'([A]_0 + [B]_0) + (k_r[A]_0 - k_r'[B]_0)e^{-(k_r+k_r')t}}{(k_r + k_r')}$$

A quick check shows that when $t = 0$, $[A] = [A]_0$, as expected. Setting $[B]_0 = 0$, then the solution becomes

$$[A] = \frac{k_r'[A]_0 + k_r[A]_0 e^{-(k_r+k_r')t}}{(k_r + k_r')}$$

which is the same as eqn 11.2a. It follows that

$$\begin{aligned}
[B] &= [A]_0 + [B]_0 - [A] \\
&= ([A]_0 + [B]_0) - \frac{k_r'([A]_0 + [B]_0) + (k_r[A]_0 - k_r'[B]_0)e^{-(k_r+k_r')t}}{(k_r + k_r')} \\
&= \frac{\{(k_r + k_r')([A]_0 + [B]_0)\} - \{k_r'([A]_0 + [B]_0) + (k_r[A]_0 - k_r'[B]_0)e^{-(k_r+k_r')t}\}}{(k_r + k_r')} \\
&= \frac{k_r([A]_0 + [B]_0) + (k_r[A]_0 - k_r'[B]_0)e^{-(k_r+k_r')t}}{(k_r + k_r')}
\end{aligned}$$

Once again, this expression is consistent with eqn 11.2b when $[B]_0 = 0$ and also shows the correct behaviour when $t = 0$.

**P11.34** The rate of change of the concentration of A is given by differentiating eqn 11.5a,

$$\frac{d[A]}{dt} = \frac{d}{dt}([A]_0 e^{-k_a t}) = -k_a \overbrace{[A]_0 e^{-k_a t}}^{[A]} = -k_a[A]$$

This is consistent with the expression derived by considering the loss of A through the first step of the reaction mechanism

$$\text{Rate of change of A} = \frac{d[A]}{dt} = -k_a[A]$$

In the same way, the rate of change of the concentration of the intermediate I may be derived by differentiating eqn 11.5b,

$$\frac{d[I]}{dt} = \frac{d}{dt}\left[\frac{k_a}{k_b - k_a}(e^{-k_a t} - e^{-k_b t})[A]_0\right] = \frac{k_a}{k_b - k_a}\overbrace{(-k_a e^{-k_a t} + k_b e^{-k_b t})}^{\frac{d}{dx}e^{ax} = ae^{ax}}[A]_0$$

The rate of change of the concentration of I may also be derived by considering the rate at which I is formed in the first reaction and lost in the second,

$$\text{Rate of change of I} = \frac{d[I]}{dt} = \overbrace{k_a[A]}^{\text{Formation of I}} - \overbrace{k_b[I]}^{\text{Loss of I}}$$

$$= k_a \overbrace{[A]_0 e^{-k_a t}}^{[A]} - k_b \overbrace{\left[\frac{k_a}{k_b - k_a}(e^{-k_a t} - e^{-k_b t})[A]_0\right]}^{[B]}$$

$$= k_a[A]_0 e^{-k_a t} - \left[\frac{k_a}{k_b - k_a}(k_b e^{-k_a t} - k_b e^{-k_b t})[A]_0\right]$$

$$= \frac{(k_b - k_a)k_a[A]_0 e^{-k_a t} - k_a(k_b e^{-k_a t} - k_b e^{-k_b t})[A]_0}{k_b - k_a}$$

Expanding out the brackets and collecting together the terms,

$$\frac{d[I]}{dt} = \frac{(k_a k_b - k_a^2 - k_a k_b)[A]_0 e^{-k_a t} + k_a k_b [A]_0 e^{-k_b t}}{k_b - k_a}$$

$$= \frac{k_a}{k_b - k_a}(-k_a e^{-k_a t} + k_b e^{-k_b t})[A]_0$$

which is identical to the expression obtained by direct differentiation.

Direct differentiation of the expression for the concentration of P, eqn 11.5c, gives

$$\frac{d[P]}{dt} = \frac{d}{dt}\left\{1 + \frac{k_a e^{-k_b t} - k_b e^{-k_a t}}{k_b - k_a}\right\}$$

$$= \frac{-k_a k_b e^{-k_b t} + k_a k_b e^{-k_a t}}{k_b - k_a} = \frac{k_a k_b}{k_b - k_a}(e^{-k_a t} - e^{-k_b t})[A]_0$$

The product P is formed only in the final step, so that we may also write

$$\text{Rate of change of P} = \frac{d[P]}{dt} = k_b[I]$$

$$= k_b \overbrace{\left[\frac{k_a}{k_b - k_a}(e^{-k_a t} - e^{-k_b t})[A]_0\right]}^{[I]}$$

$$= \frac{k_a k_b}{k_b - k_a}(e^{-k_a t} - e^{-k_b t})[A]_0$$

This is identical to the expression obtained by direct differentiation. Thus, the three expressions for the concentrations of the reactant, intermediate and product are all valid solutions.

**P11.35** (a) For the mechanism

*hhhh…* $\rightleftharpoons$ *hchh….*

*hchh…* $\rightleftharpoons$ *cccc…*

the rate equations are

$$\frac{d[hhhh\ldots]}{dt} = -k_a[hhhh\ldots] + k'_a[hchh\ldots]$$
$$\frac{d[hchh\ldots]}{dt} = k_a[hhhh\ldots] - k'_a[hchh\ldots] - k_b[hchh\ldots] + k'_b[cccc\ldots]$$
$$\frac{d[cccc\ldots]}{dt} = k_b[hchh\ldots] - k'_b[cccc\ldots]$$

(b) Applying the steady-state approximation to the intermediate in the above mechanism,

$$\frac{d[hchh\ldots]}{dt} = k_a[hhhh\ldots] - k'_a[hchh\ldots] - k_b[hchh\ldots] + k'_b[cccc\ldots] = 0$$

so that

$$[hchh\ldots] = \frac{k_a[hhhh\ldots] + k'_b[cccc\ldots]}{k'_a + k_b}$$

Therefore, from the first rate equation,

$$\begin{aligned}\frac{d[hhhh\ldots]}{dt} &= -k_a[hhhh\ldots] + k'_a\overbrace{\left(\frac{k_a[hhhh\ldots] + k'_b[cccc\ldots]}{k'_a + k_b}\right)}^{[hchh\ldots]} \\ &= \frac{k_a k_b}{k'_a + k_b}[hhhh\ldots] + \frac{k_a{}' k_b{}'}{k'_a + k_b}[cccc\ldots] \\ &= -k_{r,\mathrm{eff}}[hhhh\ldots] + k'_{r,\mathrm{eff}}[cccc\ldots]\end{aligned}$$

which is equivalent to the rate law for the simple mechanism

$hhhh \rightleftharpoons$ cccc

with rate constants for the forward and backward reactions of $k_{r,\mathrm{eff}}$ and $k'_{r,\mathrm{eff}}$.

(c) It is difficult to make conclusive inferences about intermediates from kinetic data alone. For example, if rate measurements show formation of coils from helices with a single rate constant, they tell us nearly nothing about the mechanism. The rate law

$$\frac{d[cccc\ldots]}{dt} = k_r[hhhh\ldots]$$

is consistent with a single-step mechanism, with a two-step mechanism with a rate-determining second step, and with a two-step mechanism with a steady-state intermediate. Even if kinetic monitoring of the product shows production with two rate constants, the rate constants could belong to competing paths or to steps of a single reaction path. The best evidence for an intermediate's participation in a reaction is detection of the intermediate, or at least detection of structural features that can belong to a proposed intermediate but not to a reactant or product.

# Chapter 12

# Quantum theory

## Answers to discussion questions

**D12.1** At the end of the nineteenth century and the beginning of the twentieth, there were many experimental results on the properties of matter and radiation that could not be explained on the basis of established physical principles and theories. Here we list only some of the most significant.

(1) The photoelectric effect revealed that electromagnetic radiation, classically considered to be a wave, also exhibits the particle-like behaviour of photons. Each photon is a discrete unit, or quantum, of energy that is absorbed during collisions with electrons. Photons are never partially absorbed. They either completely give up their energy or they are not absorbed. The energy of a photon can be calculated if either the radiation frequency or wavelength is known: $\boldsymbol{E_{\text{photon}} = h\nu = hc/\lambda}$.

(2) Absorption and emission spectra indicated that atoms and molecules can only absorb or emit discrete packets of energy (i.e., photons). This means that an atom or molecule has specific, allowed energy levels and we say that their energies are quantized. During a spectroscopic transition the atom or molecule gains or loses the energy $\Delta E$ by either absorption of a photon or emission of a photon, respectively. Thus, spectral lines must satisfy the **Bohr frequency condition:** $\boldsymbol{\Delta E = h\nu}$.

(3) Neutron and electron diffraction studies indicated that these particles also possess wave-like properties of constructive and destructive interference. The joint particle and wave character of matter and radiation is called **wave-particle duality**. The **de Broglie relation**, $\lambda_{\text{de Broglie}} = h/p$, connects the wave character of a particle ($\lambda_{\text{de Broglie}}$) with its particulate momentum ($p$).

(4) The energy density distribution of blackbody radiation as a function of wavelength.

(5) The heat capacities of monatomic solids such as copper metal.

**D12.2** The wave-particle duality of quantum theory requires a particle wavefunction that does not experience destructive interference upon reflection by a barrier or in motion around a closed loop. These are **boundary conditions** of the wavefunction and they are the cause of energy quantization. The criteria of particle existence and the restrictions of boundary conditions result in quantum conditions that must be satisfied for a wavefunction to be acceptable. The conditions on the wavefunction, $\psi$, are:

(1) $\psi$ must be single valued at each point.

(2) The probability of finding a particle in a very small subatomic region, $\psi^2\delta V$, cannot exceed 1.

(3) $\psi$ is continuous everywhere.

(4) $\psi$ has a continuous slope everywhere.

When applied to a particle of mass $m$ confined to move in a one-dimensional box of length $L$, these requirements restrict the de Broglie wavelength to $\lambda = 2L/n$, where the **quantum number** $n$ is a non-zero, positive integer. Then using the relation $E = E_k = p^2/2m$ and the de Broglie relation $\lambda = h/p$, the energy is quantized at $E_n = n^2h^2/8mL^2$. This derivation applies specifically to the particle in a box but the derivation is similar for the particle on a ring; see Section 12.8(a) of the text.

**D12.3** The lowest energy level possible for a confined quantum mechanical system is the **zero-point energy**, and zero-point energy is not necessarily zero energy. This lowest, irremovable energy is consistent with the uncertainty principle, eqn 12.7, $\Delta x\Delta p_x \geq \frac{1}{2}\hbar$. In this relation the uncertainty in position and the uncertainty of the momentum are along the same line of motion and the uncertainties are defined with the relations $(\Delta x)^2 = (x^2)_{mean} - (x)_{mean}^2$ and $(\Delta p_x)^2 = (p_x^2)_{mean} - (p_x)_{mean}^2$. Should a hypothetical quantum state exhibit both $(p_x^2)_{mean} = 0$ and $(p_x)_{mean}^2 = 0$, so that the momentum uncertainty is zero, a finite value of $\Delta x$ gives $\Delta x\Delta p_x = 0$ and quantum theory indicates that, because the uncertainty principle is violated, the state is invalid and will not be observed in nature. However, should $\Delta x$ be infinitely large the uncertainty principle may be satisfied even though there is no uncertainty in the momentum.

The zero-point energy of the particle in a box is the energy of the $n = 1$ quantum state of eqn 12.9: $E_1 = h^2/8mL^2$. For an electron in a 1 nm box, the zero-point energy is calculated to be $6.0 \times 10^{-20}$ J and 36 kJ mol$^{-1}$, an energy that remains even after cooling to the absolute zero of temperature. This is consistent with the uncertainty principle as quantum theory does not assign a precise location to the particle, it is in the box but the uncertainty of knowing its position equals the length $L$ of the box. Thus, a hypothetical zero-point energy of zero implies zero kinetic energy so that both $(p_x^2)_{mean} = 0$ and $(p_x)_{mean}^2 = 0$. Consequently, there is zero uncertainty in knowledge of the momentum giving $\Delta x\Delta p_x = L \times 0 = 0$ in violation to the uncertainty principle and quantum theory declares that the particle in a box cannot have zero energy.

The zero-point energy of the harmonic oscillator is the energy of the $v = 0$ quantum state of eqn 12.25: $E_0 = \frac{1}{2}h\nu$ where $v$ (italic vee) is the quantum number and $\nu$ (italic Greek nu) is the frequency of the oscillator. A typical chemical bond has a vibrational frequency of $3.0 \times 10^{13}$ Hz (corresponding to a wavenumber of 1000 cm$^{-1}$) so the zero-point energy of molecular vibration is typically about $1 \times 10^{-20}$ J. In this case, a hypothetical zero-point energy of zero implies precise knowledge of the oscillator position; it is at the bottom of the harmonic potential where the potential is zero and the displacement is exactly zero.

Zero energy implies zero uncertainty in knowledge of position. It also implies a precise momentum equal to zero giving $\Delta x \Delta p_x = 0 \times 0 = 0$ in violation to the uncertainty principle. Consequently, quantum theory declares that the harmonic oscillator cannot have zero energy.

The energy levels for a particle confined on a ring of constant potential are given by eqn 12.20

$$E_m = m_l^2 \hbar^2/2I,$$

where $m_l = 0, \pm 1, \pm 2, \ldots$, so that the zero-point energy equals zero because it is the state for which $m_l = 0$. This does not violate the uncertainty principle. To see this, we recognize that the complementary variables of this two-dimensional quantum system are the position angle $\phi$ and the angular momentum $J_z$ and we write the uncertainty principle as $\Delta\phi\Delta J_z \geq \tfrac{1}{2}\hbar$. As the classical particle travels through one cycle of rotation, the angle sweeps from zero through $2\pi$ radians. The second cycle takes the particle through $4\pi$ radian, the third cycle through $6\pi$ radians, etc. In quantum theory, however, we cannot precisely know either the angle within the first cycle or the cycle of rotation. The angular uncertainty is not $2\pi$. It is infinitely large. Thus, even though $J_z$ is precisely known as zero at the zero-point, the uncertainty principle is not violated.

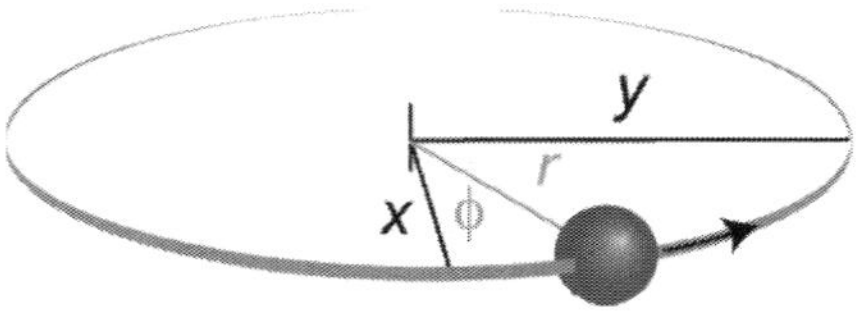


**Figure 12.1**

**D12.4** With the scientifically observed failures of classical physics it became apparent during the first-quarter of the twentieth century that the Newtonian concept of a deterministic particle path over which the precise position and momentum could be specified at each instant is wrong at the atomic/molecular level. The Schrödinger equation, discovered in 1926, resolved the theoretical difficulties of the particulate-wave duality of nature at the microscopic scale by providing a quantum method for calculating atomic and molecular energy levels along with other observable properties. The method involved the calculation and use of the wavefunction $\psi$, a property that is often imaginary and, consequently, non-observable, and an intellectual question arose 'Is the wavefunction an artifact that provides a method for calculating observables or is there a useful physical interpretation for it?' Max Born suggested the interpretation that came to be accepted, and found to be very useful, by the scientific community. It is: The probability of finding a particle in a small region of space of volume $\delta V$ is proportional to $|\psi|^2\,\delta V$, where $\psi$ is the value of the wavefunction in the region. (The modulus square of the wavefunction, $|\psi|^2 = \psi^* \times \psi$, is always real.) This is the probabilistic **Born interpretation** of the wavefunction and $|\psi|^2$ is called the **probability density** as its SI unit is $m^{-3}$ for one particle quantum systems in three dimensions (like the probability density for an electron in a hydrogen atom). In addition to being an integral part of the quantum methodology, the probability density and Born interpretation are regularly used to provide a rationale for quick understanding of molecular bond angles, bond lengths, bonding types, sites of electrophilic and nucleophilic attack, and more.

The analogy between the Born interpretation of the probability density and the square of the amplitude of an electromagnetic wave is very supportive of the Born interpretation. In classical electromagnetic theory the square of the amplitude is the radiation intensity and therefore proportional to the number of photons present.

**D12.5** The uncertainty principle, eqn 12.7, $\Delta x \Delta p_x \geq \frac{1}{2}\hbar$ implies that complementary variables like $x$ and $p_x$ cannot be simultaneously measured with exact precision. An attempt to increase the measurement precision in one variable (i.e., lower the measurement uncertainty) results in a simultaneous decrease of the precise knowledge of the other variable (i.e, an increase in uncertainty). This is a natural consequence of the wave nature of matter and cannot be circumvented by the invention of perfect measurement tools.

**D12.6** The physical origin of tunnelling is related to the probability density of the particle, which according to the Born interpretation is the square of the wavefunction that represents the particle. This interpretation requires that the wavefunction of the system be everywhere continuous, even at barriers. Therefore, if the wavefunction is non-zero on one side of a barrier it must be non-zero on the other side of the barrier and this implies that the particle has tunnelled through the barrier. The transmission probability depends upon the mass of the particle (specifically $m^{1/2}$): the greater the mass the smaller the probability of tunnelling. Electrons and protons have small masses, molecular groups large masses; therefore, tunnelling effects are more observable in process involving electrons and protons. An electron tunnels more readily than a proton and a proton tunnels more readily than a deuteron.

The very rapid equilibration of proton-transfer reactions is a manifestation of the ability of protons to tunnel through barriers and transfer quickly from an acid to a base. Tunnelling of protons between acidic and basic groups is also an important feature of the mechanism of some enzyme-catalysed reactions. Electron tunnelling is one of the factors that determine the rates of electron transfer reactions at electrodes and in biological systems.

## Solutions to exercises

**E12.1** Combining eqns 12.1 and 0.19,

$$\Delta E = \frac{hc}{\lambda} = \frac{(6.626 \times 10^{-34}\,\text{J s}) \times (2.998 \times 10^{8}\,\text{m s}^{-1})}{(652 \times 10^{-9}\text{m})} = \mathbf{3.05 \times 10^{-19}\,J}$$

**E12.2** Combining the Bohr frequency relation, eqn 12.1, with the definition of wavenumber, eqn 0.20,

$$\tilde{\nu} = 1/\lambda = \Delta E/hc = \frac{(10.20\ \text{eV}) \times \overbrace{(1.602 \times 10^{-19}\ \text{J eV}^{-1})}^{1\ \text{eV}=1.602\times10^{-19}\ \text{J}}}{(6.626 \times 10^{-34}\text{J s}) \times (2.998 \times 10^{8}\ \text{m s}^{-1})}$$
$$= \underbrace{8.226 \times 10^{6}\ \text{m}^{-1}}_{1\ \text{m}^{-1}=10^{-2}\ \text{cm}^{-1}} = \mathbf{8.226 \times 10^{4}\ cm^{-1}}$$

**E12.3** Applying eqn 12.1, and noting that the frequency of an oscillation is the reciprocal of the time period for an oscillation, $\nu = 1/\tau$,

(a) $\Delta E = h\nu = (6.626 \times 10^{-34}\text{J s}) \times (1.0 \times 10^{15}\ \text{s}^{-1}) = \mathbf{6.6 \times 10^{-19}\ J}$

which is equivalent to a molar energy of

$$\Delta E_{\text{m}} = N_{\text{A}}\Delta E = (6.022 \times 10^{23}\text{mol}^{-1}) \times (6.6 \times 10^{-19}\ \text{J})$$
$$= 4.0 \times 10^{5}\ \text{J mol}^{-1} = \mathbf{4.0 \times 10^{2}\ kJ\ mol^{-1}}$$

(b) $\Delta E = h/\tau = (6.626 \times 10^{-34}\text{J s})/(20 \times 10^{-15}\ \text{s}) = \mathbf{3.3 \times 10^{-20}\ J}$

$$\Delta E_{\text{m}} = (6.022 \times 10^{23}\text{mol}^{-1}) \times (3.3 \times 10^{-20}\ \text{J})$$
$$= 20 \times 10^{3}\ \text{J mol}^{-1} = \mathbf{20\ kJ\ mol^{-1}}$$

(c) $\Delta E = h/\tau = (6.626 \times 10^{-34}\text{J s})/(0.50\ \text{s}) = \mathbf{1.3 \times 10^{-33}\ J}$

$$\Delta E_{\text{m}} = (6.022 \times 10^{23}\text{mol}^{-1}) \times (1.3 \times 10^{-33}\ \text{J})$$
$$= 1.8 \times 10^{-10}\ \text{J mol}^{-1} = \mathbf{1.8 \times 10^{-13}\ kJ\ mol^{-1}}$$

**E12.4** An electron is ejected if the energy of the photon exceeds the work function of the metal,

$$h\nu = hc/\lambda > \Phi$$

This is not the case for a photon of wavelength 750 nm, because the energy of the photon is equivalent to

$$E = hc/\lambda = \frac{(6.626 \times 10^{-34}\text{J s}) \times (2.998 \times 10^{8}\ \text{m s}^{-1})}{(750 \times 10^{-9}\ \text{m})} = 2.65 \times 10^{-19}\ \text{J}$$

and the work function of the metal is equivalent to an energy of

$$\Phi = (2.14\ \text{eV}) \times (1.602 \times 10^{-19}\ \text{J eV}^{-1}) = 3.43 \times 10^{-19}\ \text{J}$$

However, the radiation of wavelength 250 nm is sufficiently energetic to ionise the metal. Applying eqn 12.3, the kinetic energy of the ejected electron is given by the difference between the energy of the photons and the work function of the metal. The kinetic energy of the electron ejected is $E_{\text{k}} = \tfrac{1}{2}m_{\text{e}}v^{2}$, eqn 0.12a, so that, rearranging

$$v = (2E_{\text{k}}/m_{\text{e}})^{1/2} = \{2(h\nu - \Phi)/m_{\text{e}}\}^{1/2} = \{2(hc/\lambda - \Phi)/m_{\text{e}}\}^{1/2}$$
$$= \left(\frac{2[\{(6.626 \times 10^{-34}\text{J s}) \times (2.998 \times 10^{8}\ \text{m s}^{-1})/(250 \times 10^{-9}\text{m})\} - (3.43 \times 10^{-19}\ \text{J})]}{(9.109 \times 10^{-31}\ \text{kg})}\right)^{1/2}$$
$$= \mathbf{9.96 \times 10^{5}\ m\ s^{-1}}$$

**E12.5** The kinetic energy of the ejected electron is given by eqn 12.3,

$$E_k = hc/\lambda - \Phi$$

This expression has the form of a straight-line graph, so that a plot of $E_k$ against the reciprocal of wavelength should have an intercept equal in magnitude to the work function of the metal. Figure 12.2 shows that, for the data given, such a plot is indeed a straight line, with an intercept of −2.52 eV. Thus, the work function of the metal is **2.52 eV**.

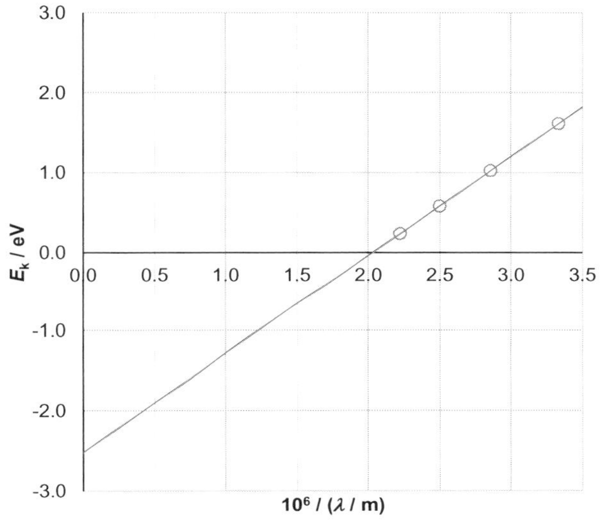


Figure 12.2

**E12.6** Applying the de Broglie relation, eqn 12.4,

$$\lambda = h/p = h/m_e v$$

Rearranging,

$$v = \frac{h}{m_e\lambda} = \frac{6.626 \times 10^{-34}\,\text{J s}}{(9.109 \times 10^{-31}\,\text{kg}) \times (550 \times 10^{-12}\,\text{m})} = \mathbf{1.3 \times 10^6\ m\ s^{-1}}$$

**E12.7** Using the de Broglie relation, eqn 12.4,

$$\lambda = h/p = h/(mv)$$

(a)

$$\lambda = (6.626 \times 10^{-34}\,\text{J s})/\{(1.0 \times 10^{-3}\,\text{kg}) \times (1.0\ \text{m s}^{-1})\} = \mathbf{6.6 \times 10^{-31}\ m}$$

(b)

$$\lambda = (6.626 \times 10^{-34}\,\text{J s})/\{(1.0 \times 10^{-3}\,\text{kg}) \times (1.00 \times 10^8\,\text{m s}^{-1})\}$$

$$= \mathbf{6.6 \times 10^{-39}\ m}$$

(c)

$$\lambda = (6.626 \times 10^{-34}\text{J s})/\{(4.00m_\text{u}) \times (10^3\ \text{m s}^{-1})\}$$
$$= (6.626 \times 10^{-34}\text{J s})/\{4.00 \times (1.661 \times 10^{-27}\ \text{kg}) \times (10^3\ \text{m s}^{-1})\}$$
$$= 9.97 \times 10^{-11}\ \text{m} = \mathbf{99.7\ pm}$$

**E12.8** The kinetic energy of a body is $E_\text{k} = \frac{1}{2}mv^2$, and the momentum, $p = mv$. Thus, combining these two equations,

$$p = mv = (2mE_\text{k})^{1/2}$$

Hence, the de Broglie wavelength of an electron accelerated through a potential difference $\Delta\phi$ is, from eqn 12.4,

$$\lambda = \frac{h}{p} = \frac{h}{(2m_\text{e}E_\text{k})^{1/2}} = \frac{h}{(2m_\text{e}e\Delta\phi)^{1/2}}$$

so that,

(a)

$$\lambda = \frac{(6.626 \times 10^{-34}\text{J s})}{\{2 \times (9.109 \times 10^{-31}\ \text{kg}) \times (1.602 \times 10^{-19}\ \text{C}) \times (1.00\ \text{V})\}^{1/2}}$$
$$= 1.23 \times 10^{-12}\ \text{m} = \mathbf{1.23\ nm}$$

(b)

$$\lambda = \frac{(6.626 \times 10^{-34}\text{J s})}{\{2 \times (9.109 \times 10^{-31}\ \text{kg}) \times (1.602 \times 10^{-19}\ \text{C}) \times (1.00 \times 10^3\ \text{V})\}^{1/2}}$$
$$= 39.6 \times 10^{-12}\ \text{m} = \mathbf{39.6\ pm}$$

(c)

$$\lambda = \frac{(6.626 \times 10^{-34}\text{J s})}{\{2 \times (9.109 \times 10^{-31}\ \text{kg}) \times (1.602 \times 10^{-19}\ \text{C}) \times (1.00 \times 10^5\ \text{V})\}^{1/2}}$$
$$= 3.88 \times 10^{-12}\ \text{m} = \mathbf{3.88\ pm}$$

**E12.9** Assuming a mass of 70 kg, then from eqn 12.4, the de Broglie wavelength of a human is

$$\lambda = \frac{h}{p} = \frac{h}{mv} = \frac{(6.626 \times 10^{-34}\text{J s})}{(70\ \text{kg}) \times (8 \times 10^3\ \text{m h}^{-1})/\ (3600\ \text{s h}^{-1})} = \mathbf{4 \times 10^{-36}m}$$

The de Broglie wavelength increases as the speed of an object decreases, becoming infinite when the object is at rest.

**E12.10** Applying the de Broglie relation, eqn 12.4,

(a) $p = h/\lambda = (6.626 \times 10^{-34}\text{J s})/(600 \times 10^{-9}\ \text{m}) = \mathbf{1.10 \times 10^{-27}\ kg\ m\ s^{-1}}$

(b) $p = h/\lambda = (6.626 \times 10^{-34}\text{J s})/(70 \times 10^{-12}\ \text{m}) = \mathbf{9.5 \times 10^{-24}\ kg\ m\ s^{-1}}$

(c) $$p = h/\lambda = (6.626 \times 10^{-34}\,\text{J s})/(200\ \text{m}) = \mathbf{3.31 \times 10^{-36}\ kg\ m\ s^{-1}}$$

**E12.11** Linear momentum is the product of mass and velocity, $p = mv$. Thus, expressing the momentum of the photon using the de Broglie relation, eqn 12.4,

$$v = \frac{p}{m} = \frac{h/\lambda}{m} = \frac{h}{\lambda m} = \frac{(6.626 \times 10^{-34}\,\text{J s})}{(300 \times 10^{-9}\ \text{m}) \times (1.0 \times 10^{-3}\ \text{kg})} = \mathbf{2.2 \times 10^{-24}\ m\ s^{-1}}$$

**E12.12** (a) Force is defined through Newton's second law of motion, eqn 0.7, as the product of the mass, $m$, and acceleration, $a$, of a body. We may, however, also define force as the rate of change of momentum, $p$, if the mass remains constant, because

$$F = ma = m\frac{\mathrm{d}v}{\mathrm{d}t} = \frac{\mathrm{d}(mv)}{\mathrm{d}t} = \frac{\mathrm{d}p}{\mathrm{d}t}$$

The momentum of each photon may be calculated using the de Broglie relation, eqn 12.4, $p = h / \lambda$. Thus, if we assume that the laser emits, and the sail absorbs, $N_A$ photons per second, then the rate of change of momentum, and thus the force is

$$F = \frac{\mathrm{d}p}{\mathrm{d}t} = \frac{N_A p}{\delta t} = \frac{N_A (h/\lambda)}{\delta t} = \frac{N_A h}{\lambda \delta t}$$
$$= \frac{(6.022 \times 10^{23}\,\text{mol}^{-1}) \times (6.626 \times 10^{-34}\,\text{J s})}{(650 \times 10^{-9}\ \text{m}) \times (1\ \text{s})} = \mathbf{6.1 \times 10^{-4}\ N}$$

(b) Pressure is defined through eqn 0.8 as the ratio of force to area, so that

$$F/A = (6.1 \times 10^{-4}\ \text{N})/\overbrace{(1.0 \times 10^{6}\ \text{m}^2)}^{1\ \text{km}^2 = 10^6\ \text{m}^2} = 6.1 \times 10^{-10}\ \text{N m}^{-2} = \mathbf{6.1 \times 10^{-10}\ Pa}$$

(c) If speed = (force / mass) × time, then rearranging, the time to accelerate to a speed $v$ of 1.0 m s$^{-1}$ is

$$t = (mv)/F = (1.0\ \text{kg}) \times (1.0\ \text{m s}^{-1})/(6.1 \times 10^{-4}\ \text{N}) = \mathbf{1600\ s}$$

**E12.13** According to the Born interpretation, the probability of finding a particle described by the wavefunction $\psi$ in an infinitesimally small region of one-dimensional space $\delta x$, is $\psi^2\delta x$. The value of the normalisation constant, $N$, is such that the total probability is one. In general, the wavefunction is a function of $x$ and we must integrate to find the value of the normalisation constant

$$\int_{-\infty}^{+\infty} \psi^2(x)\,\mathrm{d}x = 1$$

However, in this example, the value of the wavefunction is constant, so that the wavefunction may be written as $\psi = NA$. Furthermore, we know that the particle is confined to the region between $x = 0$ and $x = L$, we may change the limits of the integration.

$$\int_{-\infty}^{+\infty} \psi^2(x)\,\mathrm{d}x = \int_{-\infty}^{+\infty} (NA)^2\,\mathrm{d}x = (NA)^2 \int_0^L \mathrm{d}x = N^2A^2L = 1$$

Rearranging, the constant of integration has a value

$$N = \pm 1/(A^2L)^{1/2}$$

so that the normalised wavefunction is

$$\psi = NA = \pm(\mathbf{1/L^{1/2}})$$

**E12.14** A plot of the wavefunction is shown in Figure 12.3. According to the Born interpretation, the probability of finding the particle in a small region of space at $x$ is proportional to the square of the wavefunction. Thus, the maximum probability corresponds to the maximum in the curve at $x = 0$. At this point, the probability of finding the particle in the small volume $\delta x$ is

$$P_{\max} = \psi^2(x)\delta x = \{Ne^{-ax^2}\}^2\delta x = \{Ne^{-a(0)^2}\}^2 = N^2\delta x$$

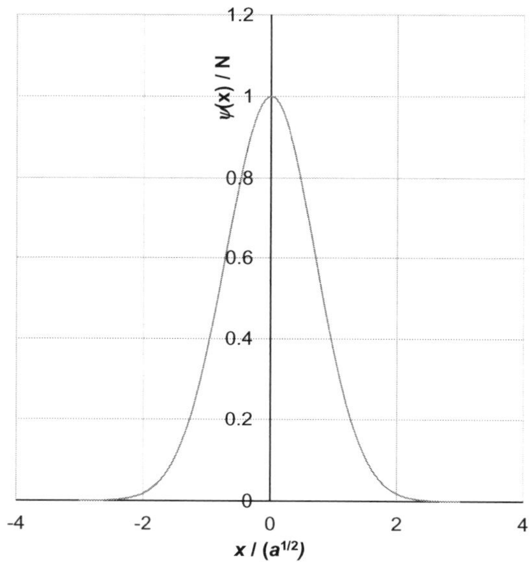


**Figure 12.3**

The point at which the probability is 50 per cent of this value is given by the solution to the equation

$$\psi^2(x)\delta x = P_{\max}/2$$

Thus,

$$\begin{aligned} (Ne^{-ax^2})^2 &= N^2/2 \\ (-ax^2)^2 &= \ln(½) \\ x^2 &= (1/a)\ln(\sqrt{2}) \\ x &= \pm 0.5887/a^{1/2} \end{aligned}$$

**E12.15** The uncertainty in the momentum and position are related through the uncertainty principle, eqn 12.7. Thus,

$$\delta x \geq \frac{\hbar/2}{\delta p} = \frac{h/4\pi}{\delta(m_\mathrm{p}v)} = \frac{h}{4\pi m_\mathrm{p}\delta v} = \frac{h}{4\pi m_\mathrm{p}v \times \underbrace{(\delta v/v)}_{\substack{\text{relative}\\ \text{uncertainty}\\ \text{in speed}}}}$$

$$\geq \frac{(6.626 \times 10^{-34}\,\mathrm{J\,s})}{4\pi \times (1.673 \times 10^{-27}\,\mathrm{kg}) \times (350 \times 10^{3}\,\mathrm{m\,s^{-1}}) \times (0.010 \times 10^{-2})}$$

$$\geq 9.00 \times 10^{-10}\,\mathrm{m} = \mathbf{0.900\,nm}$$

**E12.16** Applying the position–momentum uncertainty relation, eqn 12.7,

$$\delta p \delta x \geq \hbar/2$$

then

$$\delta v = \delta p/m \geq \overbrace{(\hbar/2\delta x)}^{\delta p} m = \frac{h}{4\pi m \delta x}$$

$$\geq \frac{6.626 \times 10^{-34}\,\mathrm{J\,s}}{4\pi \times (500 \times 10^{-3}\,\mathrm{kg}) \times (5.0 \times 10^{-6}\,\mathrm{m})} = \mathbf{2.1 \times 10^{-29}\,m\,s^{-1}}$$

**E12.17** If the speed is known to be between 350.000001 m s$^{-1}$ and 350.000000 m s$^{-1}$ then the uncertainty in the speed is $\delta x = 10^{-6}$ m. Hence, from the position–momentum uncertainty relation, eqn 12.7,

$$\delta x \geq \frac{\hbar}{2\delta p} = \frac{h/2\pi}{2\delta(mv)} = \frac{h}{4\pi m \delta v}$$

$$\geq \frac{6.626 \times 10^{-34}\,\mathrm{J\,s}}{4\pi \times (5.0 \times 10^{-3}\,\mathrm{kg}) \times (10^{-6}\,\mathrm{m\,s^{-1}})} = \mathbf{1.1 \times 10^{-26} m}$$

**E12.18** The uncertainty in the position of the electron is $\delta x = 100\,\mathrm{pm} = 100 \times 10^{-12}$ m. Thus, the uncertainty in the speed is given by rearranging the position–momentum uncertainty relation, eqn 12.7,

$$\delta v = \delta p/m \geq \overbrace{(\hbar/2\delta x)}^{\delta p} m_\mathrm{e} = \frac{h}{4\pi m_\mathrm{e} \delta x}$$

$$\geq \frac{6.626 \times 10^{-34}\,\mathrm{J\,s}}{4\pi \times (9.109 \times 10^{-31}\,\mathrm{kg}) \times (100 \times 10^{-12}\,\mathrm{m})} = \mathbf{5.8 \times 10^{5}\,m\,s^{-1}}$$

**E12.19** From eqn 12.5, the Schrödinger equation takes the form

$$-\frac{\hbar^2}{2m}\frac{\mathrm{d}^2\psi}{\mathrm{d}x^2} + V(x)\psi = E\psi$$

Substituting the function for the potential energy,

$$-\frac{\hbar^2}{2m}\frac{\mathrm{d}^2\psi}{\mathrm{d}x^2} + ax^4\psi = E\psi$$

**E12.20** According to the Born interpretation, the probability of finding the electron within a small region of one-dimensional space, $\delta x$, is $P(x) = \psi^2(x)\,\delta x$. Thus,

$$P(x) = \psi^2(x)\delta x = \{(2/L)^{1/2}\sin(2\pi x/L)\}^2\delta x = (2/L)\sin^2(2\pi x/L)\,\delta x$$

(a) Hence, for the region from $x = 0.1$ and 0.2 nm, so that $\delta x = 0.1$ nm, and assuming that the value of the wavefunction is constant and given by the value at the centre of the region, $x = 0.15$ nm

$$P(x) = (2/L)\sin^2(2\pi x/L)\,\delta x$$
$$= \frac{2}{(10\text{ nm})}\sin^2\left\{\frac{2\pi \times \overbrace{(0.15\text{ nm})}^{x}}{(10\text{ nm})}\right\} \times (0.1\text{ nm}) = \mathbf{1.8 \times 10^{-4}}$$

(b) In the same way for the region from $x = 4.9$ and 5.2 nm

$$P(x) = (2/L)\sin^2(2\pi x/L)\,\delta x$$
$$= \frac{2}{(10\text{ nm})}\sin^2\left\{\frac{2\pi \times \overbrace{(5.05\text{ nm})}^{x}}{(10\text{ nm})}\right\} \times (0.3\text{ nm}) = \mathbf{5.9 \times 10^{-5}}$$

**E12.21** The allowed energy levels for a particle in a square potential well are given by eqn 12.9

$$E_n = \frac{n^2h^2}{8mL^2}, \qquad n = 1, 2, 3, \ldots$$

The energy given up when the atom falls from the level with $n = 2$ to $n = 1$ is given by the difference in the energy of the two levels,

$$\Delta E = E_2 - E_1 = (2^2 - 1^2)\frac{h^2}{8mL^2} = \frac{3h^2}{8mL^2}$$
$$= \frac{3 \times (6.626 \times 10^{-34}\text{ J s})^2}{8 \times (1.673 \times 10^{-27}\text{ kg}) \times (1.0 \times 10^{-9}\text{ m})^2} = \mathbf{9.84 \times 10^{-23}\ J}$$

**E12.22** The energy levels of the two-dimensional box specified are, from eqn 12.14b,

$$E_{n_X,n_Y} = \left\{\frac{n_X^2}{L_X^2} + \frac{n_Y^2}{L_Y^2}\right\}\frac{h^2}{8m} = \left\{\frac{n_X^2}{L^2} + \frac{n_Y^2}{(2L)^2}\right\}\frac{h^2}{8m} = \left\{\frac{n_X^2}{L^2} + \frac{n_Y^2}{4L^2}\right\}\frac{h^2}{8m} = \left\{\frac{4n_X^2 + n_Y^2}{4L^2}\right\}\frac{h^2}{8m}$$
$$= (4n_X^2 + n_Y^2)\frac{h^2}{24mL^2}$$

Degenerate states are those that have the same energy. Thus, for this system, it can be seen that the degenerate states are those whose quantum numbers ($n_X$, $n_Y$) and ($n_X'$, $n_Y'$) that satisfy the relationship

$$(4n_X^2 + n_Y^2) = (4n_X'^2 + n_Y'^2)$$

Calculating the energies systematically for pairs of quantum numbers shows that the lowest states that satisfy this relationship are those with quantum numbers (1,4) and (2,2), which have an energy of $5h^2 / 6mL^2$. The next set of degenerate states are those with (1,6) and (3,2) that have an energy of $5h^2 / 3mL^2$.

**E12.23** The normalised wavefunction for a one-dimensional particle in a box is, from eqn 12.8,

$$\psi_n = N\sin(n\pi x/L)$$

with, according to the Born interpretation, the probability of finding the particle within a small region $\delta x$,

$$P(x) = \psi^2(x)\delta x$$

For $n = 1$, the maximum probability occurs at a position $x = L/2$, so that

$$\begin{aligned} P_{\max} &= \{N\sin(n\pi x/L)\}^2\delta x = N^2\sin^2\left(\overset{1}{\widehat{n}}\pi\,\overset{L/2}{\widehat{x}}\,/L\right)\delta x = N^2\sin^2\{\pi(L/2)/L\}\,\delta x \\ &= N^2\sin^2(\pi/2)\,\delta x = N^2\,\delta x \end{aligned}$$

Thus, the position at which the probability is 50 per cent of the maximum is given by the solution to the equation

$$N^2\sin^2(\pi x/L)\,\delta x = P_{\max}/2 = N^2\delta x/2$$

which may be reduced to

$$\sin(\pi x/L) = \pm 1/2^{1/2}$$

so that

$$\pi x/L = \pi/4 \text{ or } 3\pi/4$$

Hence

$$x = L/4 \text{ or } 3L/4$$

**E12.24** (a) The energy levels of a one-dimensional particle in a box are given by eqn 12.9

$$E_n = \frac{n^2h^2}{8mL^2}, \qquad n = 1, 2, 3, \ldots$$

The spacing between the two levels with $n = 4$ and $n = 5$,

$$\begin{aligned} \Delta E = E_5 - E_4 &= (5^2 - 4^2)\frac{h^2}{8m_eL^2} = \frac{9h^2}{8m_eL^2} \\ &= \frac{9\times(6.626\times10^{-34}\,\mathrm{J\,s})^2}{8\times(9.109\times10^{-31}\,\mathrm{kg})\times(5.0\times10^{-9}\,\mathrm{m})^2} = \mathbf{2.2\times10^{-20}\,J} \end{aligned}$$

(b) According to the Bohr frequency condition, the wavelength of the radiation emitted when an electron undergoes a transition between these two levels is thus

$$\begin{aligned} \lambda = hc/\Delta E &= (6.626\times10^{-34}\,\mathrm{J\,s})\times(2.998\times10^{8}\,\mathrm{m\,s^{-1}})/(2.2\times10^{-20}\,\mathrm{J}) \\ &= 9.2\times10^{-6}\,\mathrm{m} = \mathbf{9.2\ \mu m} \end{aligned}$$

**E12.25** We may treat a conjugated polyene as a one-dimensional particle in a box, with energy levels given by eqn 12.9

$$E_n = \frac{n^2h^2}{8mL^2}, \qquad n = 1, 2, 3, \ldots$$

The spacing between the two levels with $n = 11$ and $n = 12$ is therefore

$$\Delta E = E_{12} - E_{11} = (12^2 - 11^2)\frac{h^2}{8m_eL^2} = \frac{23h^2}{8m_eL^2}$$

The length of the box depends upon the number and length of C–C bonds. Carotene is a chain of 22 carbon atoms; therefore, there are 21 alternating single and double bonds, so that $L = 22 \times 140$ pm.

This energy is equivalent to radiation of wavelength

$$\lambda = hc/\Delta E = hc/\{(23h^2)/(8m_eL^2)\} = \frac{8m_ecL^2}{23h}$$
$$= \frac{8 \times (9.109 \times 10^{-31}\ \text{kg}) \times (2.998 \times 10^{8}\ \text{m s}^{-1}) \times (21 \times 140 \times 10^{-12}\ \text{m})^2}{23 \times (6.626 \times 10^{-34}\text{J s})}$$
$$= 1.2 \times 10^{-6}\ m = \mathbf{1.2\ \mu m}$$

The observed wavelength for this transition is 0.45 μm, so our crude model is of the right order of magnitude.

**E12.26** The potential barrier and wavefunction are shown in Figure 12.4. The form of the wavefunction described assumes that the energy of the particle is less than the height of the barrier.

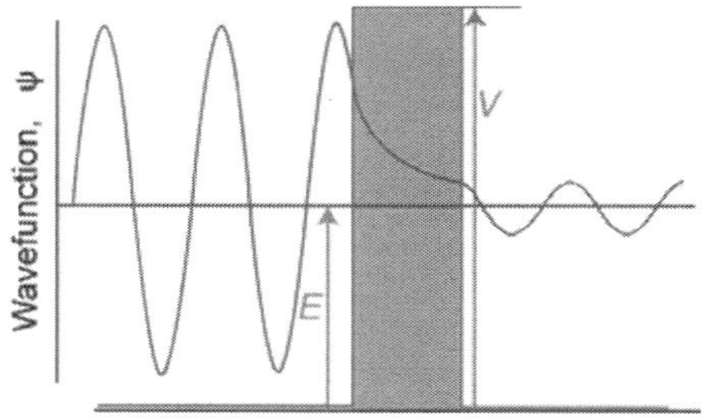


**Figure 12.4**

**E12.27** The probability that the electron will tunnel through the potential-energy barrier is given by the transmission probability, eqn 12.12.

(a) Thus, for an electron with energy $E = V / 10$,

$$\kappa = \frac{\{2m_e(V - E)\}^{1/2}}{\hbar}$$
$$= \frac{[2m_e\{V - (V/10)\}]^{1/2}}{\hbar} = \frac{(18m_eV)^{1/2}}{\hbar} = \frac{\{18m_e(\hbar^2/2m_eL^2)\}^{1/2}}{\hbar} = 3/L$$

$$\epsilon = E/V = (V/10)/V = 0.1$$

and hence the transmission probability is

$$\begin{aligned} T &= 16\epsilon(1-\epsilon)e^{-2\kappa L} \\ &= 16 \times 0.1 \times (1-0.1) \times e^{-2\times(3/L)\times L} = 1.44e^{-6} = \mathbf{3.6 \times 10^{-3}} \end{aligned}$$

(b) In the same way for an electron with energy $E = V/100$,

$$\begin{aligned} \kappa &= \frac{\{2m_e(V-E)\}^{1/2}}{\hbar} \\ &= \frac{[2m_e\{V-(V/100)\}]^{1/2}}{\hbar} = \frac{(198m_eV)^{1/2}}{\hbar} = \frac{\{198m_e(\hbar^2/2m_eL^2)\}^{1/2}}{\hbar} \\ &= 198^{1/2}/L \end{aligned}$$

$$\epsilon = E/V = (V/100)/V = 0.01$$

and hence the transmission probability is

$$\begin{aligned} T &= 16\epsilon(1-\epsilon)e^{-2\kappa L} \\ &= 16 \times 0.01 \times (1-0.01) \times e^{-2\times(198^{1/2}/L)\times L} = 0.158e^{-28.1} = \mathbf{9.4 \times 10^{-14}} \end{aligned}$$

**E12.28** (a) Treating the HI molecule as a H atom rotating at a distance $r = 161$ pm about a stationary I atom, the moment of inertia of the molecule is

$$I = m_H r^2 = (1.673 \times 10^{-27}\ \text{kg}) \times (161 \times 10^{-12}\text{m})^2 = \mathbf{4.34 \times 10^{-47}\ kg\ m^2}$$

(b) The energy levels of a particle rotating in two dimensions are given by eqn 12.20

$$E_l = m_l^2\hbar^2/2I, \qquad \text{with } m_l = 0, \pm 1, \pm 2, \ldots$$

The separation between the levels increases with quantum number $m_l$. Thus, the transition corresponding to the lowest energy, and therefore greatest wavelength is that from $m_l = 0$ to $m_l = 1$

$$\Delta E = E_1 - E_0 = (1^2 - 0^2)\hbar^2/2I = \hbar^2/2I$$

This separation corresponds to a wavelength

$$\begin{aligned} \lambda &= \frac{hc}{\Delta E} = \frac{hc}{\hbar^2/2I} = \frac{8\pi^2 Ic}{h} \\ &= \frac{8\pi^2 \times (4.34 \times 10^{-47}\ \text{kg m}^2) \times (2.998 \times 10^8\ \text{m s}^{-1})}{6.626 \times 10^{-34}\text{J s}} \\ &= 1.55 \times 10^{-3}\ \text{m} = \mathbf{1.55\ mm} \end{aligned}$$

This wavelength is in the microwave region of the electromagnetic spectrum

**E12.29** The angular speed, $\omega$, in radians per second is related to the angular momentum, $J_z$, and moment of inertia, $I$, through a rearrangement of eqn 0.6,

$$\omega = J_z/I$$

There are $2\pi$ radians per revolution, so that the number of revolutions per second around the axis that bisects the HOH angles is $\omega/2\pi$. Thus, if the minimum, non-zero value of $J_z$ equals $\hbar$, the corresponding number of revolutions per second is given by

$$\frac{\omega}{2\pi} = \frac{(J_z/I)}{2\pi} = \frac{J_z}{2\pi I} = \frac{\hbar}{2\pi I} = \frac{h}{4\pi^2 I}$$
$$= \frac{6.626 \times 10^{-34}\text{J s}}{4\pi^2 \times (1.91 \times 10^{-47}\text{kg m}^2)} = \mathbf{8.79 \times 10^{11} s^{-1}}$$

**E12.30** The rotational energy levels of a particle rotating in two dimensions with angular momentum $J_z$ are given by eqn 12.18

$$E = \frac{J_z^2}{2I}$$

The lowest energy level has angular momentum $J_z = 0$, and the first excited energy level $J_z = \hbar$. Thus, the energy needed to excite the molecule between these states is therefore

$$\Delta E = E_1 - E_0 = (\hbar^2 - 0)/2I = \frac{\hbar^2}{2I} = \frac{h^2}{8\pi^2 I}$$
$$= \frac{(6.626 \times 10^{-34}\text{J s})^2}{8\pi^2 \times (1.91 \times 10^{-47}\text{kg m}^2)} = \mathbf{2.91 \times 10^{-22}\ J}$$

**E12.31** The energy levels of a body, such as a $CH_4$ molecule, rotating in three dimensions are given by eqn 12.22. The lowest level, with quantum number $l = 0$ corresponds to the state for which there is no rotational energy. The energy of the first excited state, for which $l = 1$, is thus

$$E = l(l+1)\frac{\hbar^2}{2I} = 1(1+1)\frac{\hbar^2}{2\{(8/3)m_H R^2\}} = \frac{3h^2}{32\pi^2 m_H R^2}$$
$$= \frac{3 \times (6.626 \times 10^{-34}\text{J s})^2}{32\pi^2 \times (1.673 \times 10^{-27}\text{ kg}) \times (109 \times 10^{-12}\text{m})^2} = \mathbf{2.10 \times 10^{-22}\ J}$$

The degeneracy of this first excited energy level is $l\,(l + 1) = 3$.

**E12.32** Classically, the frequency of oscillation of a system is related to the force constant $k$ and mass $m$ through eqn 12.25,

$$\nu = \frac{1}{2\pi}\left(\frac{k_f}{m}\right)^{1/2}$$

The frequency of oscillation is simply the reciprocal of the time period, $\tau$, so that, rearranging,

$$k_f = m(2\pi\nu)^2 = 4\pi^2 m/\tau^2 = 4\pi^2 \times (1 \times 10^{-3}\text{ kg})/(1\text{ s})^2$$
$$= 0.04\text{ kg s}^{-2} = \mathbf{0.04\ N\ m^{-1}}$$

**E12.33** (a) The vibrational frequency of the bond is given by eqn 12.25

$$\nu = \frac{1}{2\pi}\left(\frac{k_f}{m_H}\right)^{1/2} = \frac{1}{2\pi}\left(\frac{314\ \text{N m}^{-1}}{1.673\times 10^{-27}\ \text{kg}}\right)^{1/2} = \mathbf{6.90\times 10^{13}\ s^{-1}}$$

(b) The energy required to excite a vibrational transition from a state with vibrational quantum number $v$ to a state with $v+1$, is, from eqn 12.25,

$$\Delta E = E_{v+1} - E_v = [\{(v+1)+½\} - \{v+½\}]h\nu = h\nu$$

We know, however, from eqn 0.21b that radiation of wavelength $\lambda$ has energy

$$\Delta E = hc/\lambda$$

Equating these two expressions and rearranging,

$$\lambda = c/\nu = (2.998\times 10^8\ \text{m s}^{-1})/(6.90\times 10^{13}\ \text{s}^{-1}) = 4.34\times 10^{-6}\ \text{m} = \mathbf{4.34\ \mu m}$$

**E12.34** The vibrational frequency of a harmonic oscillator is inversely proportional to the square root of the mass of the oscillator,

$$\nu \propto m^{-1/2}$$

Thus, if hydrogen is replaced by deuterium then because the mass of the oscillator doubles, the frequency will be reduced by a factor of $2^{-1/2} = 0.707$. Hence, for DI, the vibrational frequency is, taking the value for HI from the previous exercise,

$$\nu_{HD} = 6.90\times 10^{13}\ \text{s}^{-1}/2^{1/2} = \mathbf{4.87\times 10^{13}\ s^{-1}}$$

## Answers to projects

**P12.35** (a) According to the Born interpretation, the probability of finding the particle within a small region $\delta x$ is

$$P(x) = \psi^2(x)\delta x$$

If we wish to calculate the probability over a wider region, and allow for the variation of the wavefunction with position, then we must integrate,

$$P(x) = \int_{x_1}^{x_2} \psi^2(x)\mathrm{d}x$$

Thus, for the wavefunction given,

$$P(x) = \int_{x_1}^{x_2} (2/L)\sin^2(2\pi x/L)\mathrm{d}x = (2/L)\int_{x_1}^{x_2} (\sin ax)^2\,\mathrm{d}x \quad \text{with } a = 2\pi/L$$

We may evaluate this expression using the standard integral

$$\int (\sin ax)^2\,\mathrm{d}x = ½x - \frac{\sin 2ax}{4a} + c = ½x - \frac{\sin(4\pi x/L)}{(8\pi/L)} + c$$

(a) Thus, for the region $x = 0.1$ to $x = 0.2$ nm, with $L = 10$ nm,

$$P(x) = (2/L)\left[½x - \frac{\sin(4\pi x/L)}{(8\pi/L)}\right]_{0.1\text{ nm}}^{0.2\text{ nm}} = \mathbf{1.84\times10^{-4}}$$

The equivalent value calculated in Exercise 12.20 by assuming that the value of the wavefunction is constant throughout the region was $1.77\times10^{-4}$. The percentage error in adopting this approximation is thus

$$\frac{1.84\times10^{-4} - 1.77\times10^{-4}}{1.84\times10^{-4}}\times 100 = 12.9 \text{ per cent}$$

In the same way, for the region $x = 4.9$ to $x = 5.2$ nm, with $L = 10$ nm,

$$P(x) = (2/L)\left[½x - \frac{\sin(4\pi x/L)}{(8\pi/L)}\right]_{4.9\text{ nm}}^{5.2\text{ nm}} = \mathbf{2.36\times10^{-4}}$$

so that the percentage error is

$$\frac{2.36\times10^{-4} - 5.92\times10^{-5}}{2.36\times10^{-4}}\times 100 = 74.9 \text{ per cent}$$

The error introduced by assuming that the value of the wavefunction is constant over the region of interest, as expected, becomes much greater as the width of the region increases.

(b) The probability of finding the particle in the left-hand third, that is, between limits of $x = 0$ and $x = L / 3$, is thus

$$P(x) = (2/L)\left[½x - \frac{\sin(4\pi x/L)}{(8\pi/L)}\right]_0^{L/3}$$
$$= (2/L)\left[\left\{(L/6) - \frac{\sin(4\pi/3)}{8\pi/L}\right\} - \left\{(0) - \frac{\sin(0)}{4\pi/L}\right\}\right] = \mathbf{0.196}$$

In the same way for the middle third of the box,

$$P(x) = (2/L)\left[½x - \frac{\sin(4\pi x/L)}{(8\pi/L)}\right]_{L/3}^{2L/3}$$
$$= (2/L)\left[\left\{(L/3) - \frac{\sin(8\pi/3)}{8\pi/L}\right\} - \left\{(L/6) - \frac{\sin(4\pi/3)}{8\pi/L}\right\}\right] = \mathbf{0.609}$$

and for the right-hand third,

$$P(x) = (2/L)\left[½x - \frac{\sin(4\pi x/L)}{(8\pi/L)}\right]_{2L/3}^{L}$$

$$= (2/L)\left[\left\{(L/2) - \frac{\sin(4\pi)}{8\pi/L}\right\} - \left\{(L/3) - \frac{\sin(8\pi/3)}{8\pi/L}\right\}\right] = \mathbf{0.196}$$

The probabilities of the particle being found in the left-hand and right-hand thirds of the box are identical, which is to be expected, given the symmetry of the potential function and therefore the wavefunction. A quick check shows that the probabilities do indeed sum to 1.

**P12.36** Writing the normalised wavefunction as $\psi(x)=N\,\mathrm{e}^{-ax^2/2}$, then, for the wavefunction to be normalised,

$$P(x) = \int_{-\infty}^{\infty} \psi^2(x)\,\mathrm{d}x = 1$$
$$= \int_{-\infty}^{\infty} \left(N\,\mathrm{e}^{-ax^2/2}\right)^2 \mathrm{d}x = N^2 \int_{-\infty}^{\infty} \mathrm{e}^{-ax^2}\,\mathrm{d}x$$

Using the standard integral,

$$P(x) = N^2(\pi/a)^{1/2} = 1$$

Rearranging,

$$N = (a/\pi)^{1/4}$$

so that the normalised wavefunction is

$$\boldsymbol{\psi(x) = (a/\pi)^{1/4}\mathrm{e}^{-ax^2/2}}$$

The most probable displacement corresponds to the maximum of the function $\psi^2(x)$ for which

$$\frac{\mathrm{d}P(x)}{\mathrm{d}x} = 0$$

Hence, differentiating

$$\frac{\mathrm{d}}{\mathrm{d}x}\left(N\,\mathrm{e}^{-ax^2/2}\right)^2 = N^2\frac{\mathrm{d}}{\mathrm{d}x}\mathrm{e}^{-ax^2} = -2N^2ax\mathrm{e}^{-ax^2} = 0$$

Solving for $x$, gives solutions of $x = \pm\infty$, which correspond to the minima at infinite displacement and $\boldsymbol{x = 0}$, which corresponds to the maximum.

(b) In the same way for the first excited state with a wavefunction of $\psi(x)=Nx\,\mathrm{e}^{-ax^2/2}$, the normalisation constant is given by the integral

$$P(x) = \int_{-\infty}^{\infty} \psi^2(x)\,\mathrm{d}x = 1$$
$$= \int_{-\infty}^{\infty} \left(N\,x\mathrm{e}^{-ax^2/2}\right)^2 \mathrm{d}x = N^2 \int_{-\infty}^{\infty} x^2\mathrm{e}^{-ax^2}\,\mathrm{d}x$$

Using the standard integral,

$$\int_{-\infty}^{\infty} x^2 e^{-ax^2}\,dx = 2\left(\frac{\pi}{a^3}\right)^{1/2}$$

with $n = 2$, then

$$P(x) = \tfrac{1}{2}N^2(a^3/\pi)^{1/2} = 1$$

Rearranging,

$$N = (4a^3/\pi)^{1/4}$$

so that the normalised wavefunction is

$$\boldsymbol{\psi(x) = (4a^3/\pi)^{1/4} x e^{-ax^2/2}}$$

Differentiating to find the maxima

$$\begin{aligned}\frac{d}{dx}\left(N\,xe^{-ax^2/2}\right)^2 &= N^2\frac{d}{dx}x^2e^{-ax^2} = N^2\left\{x^2\frac{d}{dx}e^{-ax^2} + e^{-ax^2}\frac{d}{dx}x^2\right\}\\ &= N^2\left\{-2ax^3e^{-ax^2} + 2xe^{-ax^2}\right\} = 2N^2xe^{-ax^2}(1-ax^2)\\ &= 0\end{aligned}$$

This, equation is satisfied by any of the following conditions

$$\begin{aligned} x &= 0\\ e^{-ax^2} &= 0\\ (1-ax^2) &= 0\end{aligned}$$

We may demonstrate that the solution $x = 0$ corresponds to a minimum either by sketching the curve or by differentiating again and showing that $d^2\psi/dx^2 > 0$. The exponential factor implies $x = \pm\infty$, which once again correspond to the minima at infinite displacement. The remaining factor, corresponds to $(1 - ax^2) = 0$, and represents the two maxima in the probability. Rearranging gives the most probable displacement for this state as $\boldsymbol{x = \pm 1/a^{1/2}}$.

**P12.37** (a) Modifying the expression for the vibrational frequency of a harmonic oscillator, eqn 12.25, so that it is applicable for a diatomic molecule such as CO,

$$\nu = \frac{1}{2\pi}\left(\frac{k_f}{m}\right)^{1/2} = \frac{1}{2\pi}\left(\frac{k_f}{\mu}\right)^{1/2}$$

For $^{12}C^{16}O$, the effective mass is

$$\mu_{^{12}C^{16}O} = \frac{m_C m_O}{m_C + m_O} = \frac{12.00u \times 16.00u}{12.00u + 16.00u} = (48/7)u$$

Thus,

$$\nu = \frac{1}{2\pi}\left\{\frac{\overbrace{1860\ \mathrm{N\ m^{-1}}}^{k_\mathrm{f}}}{\underbrace{(48/7)\times(1.673\times10^{-27}\ \mathrm{kg})}_{\mu}}\right\}^{1/2} = \mathbf{6.432\times10^{13}\ s^{-1}}$$

(b) The equivalent wavenumber is thus

$$\begin{aligned}\tilde{\nu} &= c/\nu = (2.998\times10^{8}\ \mathrm{m\ s^{-1}})/(6.432\times10^{13}\ \mathrm{s^{-1}})\\ &= \overbrace{2.146\times10^{5}\mathrm{m^{-1}}}^{1\ \mathrm{m^{-1}}=10^{-2}\ \mathrm{cm^{-1}}} = \mathbf{2146\ cm^{-1}}\end{aligned}$$

(c) The vibrational frequency is inversely proportional to the square root of the effective mass. For $^{13}C^{16}O$ ,

$$\mu_{^{13}\mathrm{C}^{16}\mathrm{O}} = \frac{m_\mathrm{C}m_\mathrm{O}}{m_\mathrm{C}+m_\mathrm{O}} = \frac{13.00u\times16.00u}{13.00u+16.00u} = (208/29)u$$

Thus, the vibrational wavenumber of $^{13}C^{16}O$ is

$$\tilde{\nu}_{^{13}\mathrm{C}^{16}\mathrm{O}} = \left(\frac{\mu_{^{12}\mathrm{C}^{16}\mathrm{O}}}{\mu_{^{13}\mathrm{C}^{16}\mathrm{O}}}\right)^{1/2}\times\tilde{\nu}_{^{12}\mathrm{C}^{16}\mathrm{O}} = \left\{\frac{(48/7)u}{(208/29)u}\right\}^{1/2}\times2146\ \mathrm{cm^{-1}} = \mathbf{2098\ cm^{-1}}$$

In the same way for $^{12}C^{18}O$,

$$\tilde{\nu}_{^{12}\mathrm{C}^{18}\mathrm{O}} = \left(\frac{\mu_{^{12}\mathrm{C}^{16}\mathrm{O}}}{\mu_{^{12}\mathrm{C}^{18}\mathrm{O}}}\right)^{1/2}\times\tilde{\nu}_{^{12}\mathrm{C}^{16}\mathrm{O}} = \left\{\frac{(48/7)u}{(36/5)u}\right\}^{1/2}\times2146\ \mathrm{cm^{-1}} = \mathbf{2094\ cm^{-1}}$$

and

$$\tilde{\nu}_{^{13}\mathrm{C}^{18}\mathrm{O}} = \left(\frac{\mu_{^{12}\mathrm{C}^{16}\mathrm{O}}}{\mu_{^{13}\mathrm{C}^{18}\mathrm{O}}}\right)^{1/2}\times\tilde{\nu}_{^{12}\mathrm{C}^{16}\mathrm{O}} = \left\{\frac{(48/7)u}{(234/31)u}\right\}^{1/2}\times2146\ \mathrm{cm^{-1}} = \mathbf{2045\ cm^{-1}}$$

# Chapter 13

# Quantum chemistry: atomic structure

## Answers to discussion questions

**D13.1** The **principal quantum number *n*** determines the energy of the atomic orbitals in a hydrogenic shell through eqn 13.4a. The shells K, L, M, and N correspond to the principal quantum numbers $n = 1, 2, 3$, and 4. Successive shells are further away from the nucleus on average and successively higher in energy. The permitted orbital energies approach zero as $n$ becomes very large because this is defined to be the minimum energy at which the electron and nucleus are infinitely separated.

The **orbital angular momentum quantum number *l***, also called the azimuthal quantum number, determines the magnitude of the orbital angular momentum of a hydrogenic atomic orbital through the formula $\{l(l+1)\}^{1/2}\hbar$. The permitted values of $l$ are 0, 1, 2, 3,..., $n-1$ for the $n^{\text{th}}$ shell and these correspond to the s, p, d, f,... subshells. The degeneracy of a subshell is $2l+1$ because this is the number of orbitals in each subshell. Thus, the s, p, d, and f subshells consist of 1, 3, 5, and 7 orbitals, respectively. In many-electron atoms a maximum of two electrons can be in an orbital; this is the **Pauli exclusion principle**.

The **magnetic quantum number $m_l$** determines the z-component of the angular momentum of a hydrogenic orbital through the formula $m_l\hbar$. The permitted values for subshell $l$ are $l, l-1, l-2, \ldots, -l$, which accounts for the orbital degeneracy of the subshell.

The **spin quantum number *s*** determines the magnitude of the electron spin angular momentum through the formula $\{s(s+1)\}^{1/2}\hbar$. For hydrogenic atomic orbitals, $s$ can only be ½.

The **spin quantum number $m_s$** determines the z-component of the spin angular momentum through the formula $m_s\hbar$. $m_s$ can only be $\pm\frac{1}{2}$. $m_s = +\frac{1}{2}$ corresponds to the $\alpha$ or ↑ spin; $m_s = -\frac{1}{2}$ corresponds to the $\beta$ or ↓ spin.

**D13.2** (a) A **boundary surface** for a hydrogenic orbital is drawn to contain most (say 90 per cent) of the probability density of an electron in that orbital. Its shape varies from orbital to orbital because the electron density distribution is different for different orbitals.

Example boundary surfaces are shown in Figures 13.7 (s orbital), 13.10 (p orbitals), and 13.11 (d orbitals) of the text.

(b) The **radial distribution function** gives the probability that the electron will be found anywhere within a shell of radius $r$ around the nucleus (see Figure 13.8 of the text). It gives a better picture of where the electron is likely to be found with respect to the nucleus than the probability density, which is the square of the wavefunction. The radial distribution function is given by eqn 13.7

$$P(r) = r^2 R_{n,l}(r)^2$$

where $R_{n,l}(r)$ is the radial wavefunction.

The usefulness of the radial distribution function is illustrated in text Figure 13.16 of the text, which shows the relative penetration of the inner core by subshell orbitals of the M shell ($n = 3$). The order of penetration is 3s > 3p > 3d and, consequently, electrons in these subshells have the same order of relative effective nuclear charge attracting them to the nucleus. High effective nuclear charge means lower orbital energy, so the order of subshell energy is 3s < 3p < 3d, a fact that is very important when use the building-up principle to determine the ground electron configuration of many-electron atoms.

**D13.3** In the crudest form of the **orbital approximation**, the many-electron wavefunction for an atom is represented as a simple product of one-electron wavefunctions (see eqn 13.8), each of which has the form of a hydrogenic atomic orbital. This is said to be the independent-electron model. For example, the orbital approximation for the lithium atom ground state wavefunction is the product of the orbitals for each of the three lithium electrons

$$\psi_{\text{Li}} = \psi_{1s}(1)\alpha(1) \times \psi_{1s}(1)\beta(2) \times \psi_{2s}(3)\alpha(3)$$

This is synonymous with the ground-state electronic configuration given by the building-up principle. For the lithium atom it is $1s^2 2s$. The simplest form of this approximation neglects electron repulsions in many-electron atoms so it does not give a very good estimate of the atomic energy. It does, however, provide concepts for the quick analysis of a great many atomic and molecular problems in chemistry and biochemistry.

At a somewhat more sophisticated level, the many-electron wavefunctions are written as linear combinations of such simple product functions that explicitly satisfy the Pauli exclusion principle. Relatively good one-electron functions are generated by the Hartree–Fock self-consistent field method described in Section 13.14 in which an electron moves in the average electron repulsion potential field of all other electrons. We can, in principle, obtain exact energies and wavefunctions with such numerical methods; however, there are significant numerical challenges.

**D13.4** The relationship between the location of a many-electron atom in the periodic table and its electron configuration is fundamentally useful, and even a guiding principle, within the sciences. It provides quick information about valence electrons and bonding characteristics of the elements.

**D13.5** The self-consistent field technique offers a method for the calculation of the energies of many-electron atoms. The orbitals of the atom are initially assumed to be hydrogenic. We then solve the Schrödinger equation for each electron in turn, taking into account the interaction between the particular electron and the nucleus, and the repulsion with the other electrons. The resulting wavefunction for each electron is a better approximation to the true wavefunction than the original hydrogenic orbitals because it takes into account, at least in part, interelectron repulsion. These revised wavefunctions may then be used as the starting point for another cycle of calculations. With each iteration, the orbitals become more accurate. The process stops when the solutions to the Schrödinger equation for all electrons do not change from cycle to cycle. The result is then described as self consistent.

**D13.6** The first ionization energies, shown in Figure 13.22 of the text, increase markedly from Li to Be, decrease slightly from Be to B, again increase markedly from B to N, again decrease slightly from N to O, and finally increase markedly from O to Ne. The general trend is an overall increase of $I_1$ with atomic number across the period. That is to be expected because the principal quantum number (electron shell) of the outer electron remains the same, while its attraction to the nucleus increases. The slight decrease from Be to B is a reflection of the outer electron being in a higher energy subshell (larger $l$ value) in B than in Be. The slight decrease from N to O is due to the half-filled subshell effect; half-filled sub-shells have increased stability. O has one electron outside of the half-filled p subshell and that electron must pair with another resulting in strong electron–electron repulsions between them. Period 3 elements mirror this pattern in going from left to right across the periodic row for the same reasons.

**D13.7** Every electron has a magnetic moment and magnetic field due to its spin angular momentum. An electron in a p, d or f orbital also has a magnetic moment and magnetic field due to its orbital angular momentum (electrons in an s orbital have no orbital angular momentum because $l = 0$). The total spin and oribital angular momentum of an atom are described by the quantum numbers $S$ and $L$ respectively. The relative orientations of the spin and orbital angular momentum have different energies. If the vectors representing the magnetic fields are aligned parallel, the effects of the spin and orbital angular momentum reinforce one another. If, however, the vectors are aligned antiparallel, the fields (partially) counteract one another. This effect is illustrated in Figure 13.24 of the text. Quantum mechanically, only certain relative orientations of the spin and orbital angular momenta are allowed. These correspond to the total orbital angular momentum quantum number $J$,

$$J = L + S, L + S - 1, \ldots |L - S|$$

The different values of $J$ correspond to different spin–orbit levels with different energies and we may use Hund's rules to predict which of the levels is lowest in energy.

This interaction, called **spin-orbit coupling**, therefore separates the energies of states that have different orientations of orbital angular momentum and spin angular momentum giving rise to multiple spectral lines where only one would be expected in the absence of the coupling. An example is provided by the two intense yellow emission lines of sodium. An electric discharge or the high temperatures of a flame can excite the sodium atom to either a $^2P_{1/2}$ level, in which the spin and orbital angular momentum are aligned antiparallel, or a $^2P_{3/2}$ level in which the spin and orbital angular momentum are aligned parallel. Spin–orbit coupling results in a difference in energy for these two levels equivalent to 17 $cm^{-1}$. The ground level of sodium is not, however, subject to spin–orbit coupling because an electron in an s orbital does not possess any orbital angular momentum. Spontaneous emission of radiation from these excited levels therefore corresponds to two spectral lines with wavelengths of 589.76 nm and 589.16 nm.

**D13.8** (a) The selection rules for hydrogenic atoms are:

$$\Delta n = \pm 1, \pm 2, \ldots$$
$$\Delta l = \pm 1$$
$$\Delta m_l = 0, \pm 1$$

In a spectroscopic transition, the atom emits or absorbs a photon. Photons have a spin angular momentum of 1. Therefore, because of the transition, the angular momentum of the electromagnetic field has changed by $\pm\hbar$. The principle of the conservation of angular momentum then requires that the angular momentum of the atom has undergone an equal and opposite change in angular momentum. Hence, the selection rule is $\Delta l = \pm 1$. The principle quantum number $n$ can change by any amount since $n$ does not directly relate to angular momentum. The selection rule on $\Delta m_l$ is harder to account for on basis of these simple considerations alone. One has to evaluate the transition dipole moment between the wavefunctions representing the initial and final states involved in the transition.

(b) The selection rules for relatively light many-electron atoms are:

$$\Delta S = 0$$
$$\Delta L = 0, \pm 1$$
$$\Delta l = \pm 1$$
$$\Delta J = 0, \pm 1 \text{ but } J = 0 \leftrightarrow J = 0 \text{ is forbidden}$$

A change in the total spin angular momentum is forbidden in an electronic transition. This important selection rule applies to both atoms and molecules. Additional rules arise from the conservation of total angular momentum. As discussed in part (a) the orbital angular momentum of an individual electron must change. This may, or may not, affect the total orbital angular momentum.

## Solutions to exercises

**E13.1** The wavenumber of lines in the emission spectrum of atomic hydrogen are given by the Rydberg formula, eqn 13.1, with $n_1 = 2$ for a transition in the Balmer series. Wavenumber is the reciprocal of wavelength so that

$$\lambda = 1/\tilde{\nu} = 1/\left\{R_H\left(\frac{1}{n_1^2} - \frac{1}{n_2^2}\right)\right\} = 1/\left\{109677\ \text{cm}^{-1}\left(\frac{1}{2^2} - \frac{1}{6^2}\right)\right\}$$
$$= 4.10296 \times 10^{-5}\text{cm} = \mathbf{410.296\ nm}$$

**E13.2** Frequency and wavenumber are related through eqn 0.20, $\tilde{\nu} = 1/\lambda = \nu/c$. The Rydberg formula, 13.1, may therefore be written in terms of frequency as

$$\nu = \tilde{\nu}c = R_H c\left(\frac{1}{n_1^2} - \frac{1}{n_2^2}\right)$$

Lines in the Paschen series correspond to lower state quantum numbers with $n_1 = 3$, so that, rearranging,

$$n_2 = \{(1/n_1^2) - (\nu/R_H c)\}^{-1/2}$$
$$= \left\{\frac{1}{3^2} - \frac{(2.7415 \times 10^{14}\text{s}^{-1})}{\underbrace{(109677 \times 10^2\ \text{m}^{-1})}_{1\ \text{cm}^{-1} = 10^2\text{m}^{-1}} \times (2.998 \times 10^8\ \text{m s}^{-1})}\right\}^{-1/2} = \mathbf{6}$$

**E13.3** (a) Lines in atomic spectra result from transitions between different energy levels

$$\Delta E = \frac{hc}{\lambda} = E_1 - E_2$$

The energies of the levels may be expressed using eqn 0.21b as wavenumbers, or terms, so that

$$\Delta E = \frac{hc}{\lambda} = hc\tilde{\nu}_1 - hc\tilde{\nu}_2 = hc(\tilde{\nu}_1 - \tilde{\nu}_2)$$

Thus, rearranging,

$$\tilde{\nu}_2 = \tilde{\nu}_1 - (1/\lambda) = 27414 \times 10^2\ \text{m}^{-1} - \{1/(486.1 \times 10^{-9}\text{m})\}$$
$$= 6.842 \times 10^5\ \text{m}^{-1} = \mathbf{6842\ cm^{-1}}$$

(b) From eqn 0.21b, this term corresponds to an energy

$$E = hc\tilde{\nu} = (6.626 \times 10^{-34}\text{J s}) \times (2.998 \times 10^8\ \text{m s}^{-1}) \times (6.842 \times 10^5\ \text{m}^{-1})$$
$$= \mathbf{1.359 \times 10^{-19}\ J}$$

**E13.4** The Rydberg constant is, from eqn 13.4b

$$R_N = \frac{\mu_N e^4}{8\epsilon_0^2 h^3 c}$$

where the reduced mass is defined as

$$\mu_N = \frac{m_N m_e}{m_N + m_e}$$

Thus,

$$\frac{R_D}{R_H} = \frac{\mu_D}{\mu_H} = \left(\frac{m_D m_e}{m_D + m_e}\right) / \left(\frac{m_H m_e}{m_H + m_e}\right) = \frac{m_D(m_H + m_e)}{m_H(m_D + m_e)} = \frac{(m_p + m_n)(m_p + m_e)}{m_p(m_p + m_n + m_e)}$$

Substituting the masses of a proton, neutron and electron gives

$$R_D/R_H = 1.000272$$

Applying the Rydberg formula, eqn 13.1, the difference in wavenumber for the 3p → 1s transition in deuterium and hydrogen is

$$\begin{aligned}\tilde{\nu}_D - \tilde{\nu}_H &= \left\{R_D\left(\frac{1}{n_1^2} - \frac{1}{n_2^2}\right)\right\} - \left\{R_H\left(\frac{1}{n_1^2} - \frac{1}{n_2^2}\right)\right\} \\ &= R_H\left(\frac{1}{n_1^2} - \frac{1}{n_2^2}\right)(R_D/R_H - 1) \\ &= (109677\ \mathrm{cm^{-1}}) \times \left(\frac{1}{1^2} - \frac{1}{3^2}\right) \times (2.72 \times 10^{-4}) = \mathbf{27\ cm^{-1}}\end{aligned}$$

**E13.5** The energy of a level in a hydrogenic atom is proportional to the square of the nuclear charge

$$E_n \propto Z^2$$

For $He^+$, $Z = 2$, and for H, $Z = 1$, so that ignoring differences in nuclear mass, $R_{He} = 4\,R_H$. Thus, applying the Rydberg formula, eqn 13.1,

$$\nu_N = R_N c\left(\frac{1}{n_1^2} - \frac{1}{n_2^2}\right)$$

and equating the frequencies in hydrogen and helium,

$$\begin{aligned}\nu_{He} &= \nu_H \\ R_{He}c\left(\frac{1}{n_{1,H}^2} - \frac{1}{n_{2,H}^2}\right) &= R_H c\left(\frac{1}{n_{1,He}^2} - \frac{1}{n_{2,He}^2}\right) \\ 4R_H c\left(\frac{1}{n_{1,H}^2} - \frac{1}{n_{2,H}^2}\right) &= R_H c\left(\frac{1}{n_{1,He}^2} - \frac{1}{n_{2,He}^2}\right) \\ \left(\frac{1}{n_{1,He}^2} - \frac{1}{n_{2,He}^2}\right) &= 3/16\end{aligned}$$

Trying different combinations of quantum numbers allows us to find that this equation is satisfied for $\boldsymbol{n_1 = 2}$ and $\boldsymbol{n_2 = 4}$.

**E13.6** The stellar surface temperature of a red star is in the range 3000 K–4000 K. The star surface does not have the energetic particles and photons that are required for either the collisional or radiative excitation of a neutral hydrogen atom. In the absence of excitation, the atoms neither affect the absorption nor the emission lines of these stars. In contrast, a star with a surface temperature of 8000 K–10000 K has a temperature low enough to avoid complete hydrogen ionization but high enough for the radiation environment to cause electronic transitions of atomic hydrogen. Hydrogen spectral lines are intense for these stars.

Blue stars have surface temperatures of 15000 K–20000 K. Both the collision energies and the radiation energy environment of the hydrogen atoms are great enough to ionize a significant fraction of the hydrogen atoms and lacking an electron, the remaining proton cannot affect absorption and emission lines. Atomic hydrogen spectral lines are less intense for these stars.

When a star has a surface temperature above 25000 K, the collision energies and radiation environment are high enough to ionize almost all hydrogen atoms. The percentage of unionized hydrogen atoms is so small that their effects cannot be seen in the spectrum of the star.

**E13.7** The wavenumbers of the transitions are given by the Rydberg formula, eqn 13.1,

$$\nu_{\mathrm{N}} = R_{\mathrm{N}} c \left(\frac{1}{n_1^2} - \frac{1}{n_2^2}\right)$$

The Rydberg constant is, from eqn 13.4b

$$R_{\mathrm{N}} = \frac{\mu_{\mathrm{N}} e^4}{8\epsilon_0^2 h^3 c}$$

and the reduced mass is defined as

$$\mu_{\mathrm{N}} = \frac{m_{\mathrm{N}} m_{\mathrm{e}}}{m_{\mathrm{N}} + m_{\mathrm{e}}} = \left\{\left(\frac{1}{m_{\mathrm{e}}}\right) + \left(\frac{1}{m_{\mathrm{N}}}\right)\right\}^{-1}$$

Thus, the reduced masses of $^3\mathrm{He}^+$ and $^4\mathrm{He}^+$ are

$$\mu_{^3\mathrm{He}^+} = \left\{\left(\frac{1}{m_{\mathrm{e}}}\right) + \left(\frac{1}{m_{\mathrm{n}} + 2m_{\mathrm{p}}}\right)\right\}^{-1} = 9.10773 \times 10^{-31}\ \mathrm{kg}$$

$$\mu_{^4\mathrm{He}^+} = \left\{\left(\frac{1}{m_{\mathrm{e}}}\right) + \left(\frac{1}{2m_{\mathrm{n}} + 2m_{\mathrm{p}}}\right)\right\}^{-1} = 9.10814 \times 10^{-31}\ \mathrm{kg}$$

Hence,

$$R_{^3\mathrm{He}^+} = \frac{(9.10773 \times 10^{-31}\ \mathrm{kg}) \times (1.60218 \times 10^{-19}\ \mathrm{C})^4}{8 \times (8.85419 \times 10^{-12}\mathrm{J}^{-1}\mathrm{C}^2\mathrm{m}^{-1})^2 \times (6.62607 \times 10^{-34}\mathrm{J\ s})^3 \times (2.99792 \times 10^8\ \mathrm{m\ s}^{-1})}$$

$$= 1.09718 \times 10^7 = \mathbf{109718\ cm^{-1}}$$

and in the same way,

$$R_{\,^4\mathrm{He}^+} = \mathbf{109723\ cm^{-1}}$$

The wavenumbers of the $n = 3 \rightarrow 2$ transitions are therefore given by

$$\tilde{\nu}_{\,^3\mathrm{He}^+} = R_{\,^4\mathrm{He}^+}\left(\frac{1}{n_1^2} - \frac{1}{n_2^2}\right) = 109718\ \mathrm{cm}^{-1} \times \left(\frac{1}{2^2} - \frac{1}{3^2}\right) = \mathbf{42668\ cm^{-1}}$$

$$\tilde{\nu}_{\,^4\mathrm{He}^+} = R_{\,^4\mathrm{He}^+}\left(\frac{1}{n_1^2} - \frac{1}{n_2^2}\right) = 109723\ \mathrm{cm}^{-1} \times \left(\frac{1}{2^2} - \frac{1}{3^2}\right) = \mathbf{42670\ cm^{-1}}$$

and the $n = 2 \rightarrow 1$ transitions are therefore given by

$$\tilde{\nu}_{\,^3\mathrm{He}^+} = R_{\,^4\mathrm{He}^+}\left(\frac{1}{n_1^2} - \frac{1}{n_2^2}\right) = 109718\ \mathrm{cm}^{-1} \times \left(\frac{1}{1^2} - \frac{1}{2^2}\right) = \mathbf{54859\ cm^{-1}}$$

$$\tilde{\nu}_{\,^4\mathrm{He}^+} = R_{\,^4\mathrm{He}^+}\left(\frac{1}{n_1^2} - \frac{1}{n_2^2}\right) = 109723\ \mathrm{cm}^{-1} \times \left(\frac{1}{1^2} - \frac{1}{2^2}\right) = \mathbf{54862\ cm^{-1}}$$

The resolution of astronomical instruments is easily sufficient to distinguish between transitions separated by a few reciprocal centimetres.

**E13.8** The energy levels of hydrogenic atoms are given by eqn 13.4a

$$E_n = -\frac{hcR_\mathrm{N}Z^2}{n^2}$$

Ionisation corresponds to a transition from $n = 1$ to $n = \infty$, so that

$$I = E_\infty - E_1 = -hcR_\mathrm{N}Z^2\left(\frac{1}{\infty^2} - \frac{1}{1^2}\right) = hcR_\mathrm{N}Z^2$$

Thus, ignoring the differences in the mass of the nuclei, which have only a small effect on the value of the Rydberg constant, the ionisation energy is directly proportional to the square of the nuclear charge. Hence,

$$I_{\mathrm{Li}^{2+}} = I_{\mathrm{He}^+} \times (Z_{\mathrm{Li}^{2+}}/Z_{\mathrm{He}^+})^2 = 54.36\ \mathrm{eV} \times (3/2)^2 = \mathbf{122.31\ eV}$$

**E13.9** The longest wavelength, and therefore lowest energy, transition in a series with common lower quantum number $n$ corresponds to the transition from $n + 1 \rightarrow n$. Thus, applying the Rydberg formula, eqn 13.1,

$$\tilde{\nu} = 1/\lambda = R_\mathrm{H}\left(\frac{1}{n_1^2} - \frac{1}{n_2^2}\right)$$

Thus, rearranging,

$$\left(\frac{1}{n_1^2} - \frac{1}{n_2^2}\right) = \frac{1}{\lambda R_\mathrm{H}}$$

$$\left\{\frac{1}{n^2} - \frac{1}{(n+1)^2}\right\} = \frac{(n+1)^2 - n^2}{(n+1)^2 n^2} = \frac{1}{(12368 \times 10^{-9}\ \mathrm{m}) \times (109677 \times 10^2\ \mathrm{m}^{-1})}$$

$$\frac{2n+1}{(n+1)^2n^2} = 7.37 \times 10^{-3}$$

We may solve this equation analytically. However, it is much easier to try different values, starting from $n = 5$, and check which value is consistent with the equation. In doing so, we find that, for the Humphreys series, $n = 6$. Thus, the transition from $n = 7$ to $n = 6$ is that at 12368 nm. Other lines in the series correspond to wavelengths of

$$1/\tilde{\nu}_{8\to6} = 1/\left\{R_{\mathrm{H}}\left(\frac{1}{6^2}-\frac{1}{8^2}\right)\right\} = 1/\left\{\overbrace{(109677 \times 10^2\ \mathrm{m^{-1}})}^{1\ \mathrm{cm^{-1}}=10^2\ \mathrm{m^{-1}}} \times \left(\frac{1}{6^2}-\frac{1}{8^2}\right)\right\}$$
$$= 7503 \times 10^{-9}\ \mathrm{m} = \mathbf{7503\ nm}$$

$$1/\tilde{\nu}_{9\to6} = 1/\left\{R_{\mathrm{H}}\left(\frac{1}{6^2}-\frac{1}{9^2}\right)\right\} = 1/\left\{(109677 \times 10^2\ \mathrm{m^{-1}}) \times \left(\frac{1}{6^2}-\frac{1}{9^2}\right)\right\}$$
$$= 5908 \times 10^{-9}\ \mathrm{m} = \mathbf{5908\ nm}$$

and so on, converging at the ionization limit,

$$1/\tilde{\nu}_{\infty\to6} = 1/\left\{R_{\mathrm{H}}\left(\frac{1}{6^2}-\frac{1}{\infty^2}\right)\right\} = 1/\left\{(109677 \times 10^2\ \mathrm{m^{-1}}) \times \left(\frac{1}{6^2}-\frac{1}{\infty^2}\right)\right\}$$
$$= 3282 \times 10^{-9}\ \mathrm{m} = \mathbf{3282\ nm}$$

which is consistent with the shortest wavelength, highest energy, transition observed.

**E13.10** The longest wavelength transition in the Humphreys series corresponds to a transition from $n = 7$ to $n = 6$. The wavelength of this line is therefore given by eqn 13.1,

$$\nu_{7\to6} = 1/\left\{R_{\mathrm{He}}\left(\frac{1}{6^2}-\frac{1}{7^2}\right)\right\} = 1/\left\{Z_{\mathrm{He}}^2 R_{\mathrm{H}}\left(\frac{1}{6^2}-\frac{1}{7^2}\right)\right\}$$
$$= 1/\left\{2^2 \times \overbrace{(109677 \times 10^2\ \mathrm{m^{-1}})}^{1\ \mathrm{cm^{-1}}=10^2\ \mathrm{m^{-1}}} \times \left(\frac{1}{6^2}-\frac{1}{7^2}\right)\right\}$$
$$= 3093 \times 10^{-9}\ \mathrm{m} = \mathbf{3093\ nm}$$

**E13.11** For a series of transitions with common lower quantum number $n_1$, the longest wavelength transition, which in this case is that with wavelength 656.46 nm, is that from $n_1 + 1$ to $n_1$. We saw in Exercise 13.11, that for this transition,

$$\lambda R_{\mathrm{H}} = \frac{(n_1+1)^2 n_1^2}{2n_1+1}$$

We find, by substituting different values for the common lower quantum number $n_1$ that this expression is satisfied when $n_1 = 2$. The observed wavelengths therefore correspond to lines in the Balmer series, and must correspond to transitions with quantum numbers $3 \to 2$, $4 \to 2$, $5 \to 2$ and $6 \to 2$.

(a) The next line in the series must therefore correspond to the transition 7 → 2, and have a wavelength given by the Rydberg formula, eqn 13.1,

$$\lambda = \left\{R_H\left(\frac{1}{n_1^2}-\frac{1}{n_2^2}\right)\right\}^{-1}$$

$$= \left\{(109677\ \mathrm{cm^{-1}})\left(\frac{1}{2^2}-\frac{1}{7^2}\right)\right\}^{-1} = 3.9713\times10^{-5}\ \mathrm{cm} = \mathbf{397.13\ nm}$$

(b) Ionization may be considered as a transition to a level with quantum number $n_2 = \infty$, and so corresponds to an energy

$$I = hc\tilde{\nu} = hcR_H\left(\frac{1}{n_1^2}-\frac{1}{n_2^2}\right) = hcR_H\left(\frac{1}{2^2}-\frac{1}{\infty^2}\right) = \frac{hcR_H}{4}$$

$$= \frac{(6.626\times10^{-34}\ \mathrm{J\ s})\times(2.998\times10^{8}\ \mathrm{m\ s^{-1}})\times\overbrace{(109677\times10^{2}\ \mathrm{m^{-1}})}^{1\ \mathrm{cm^{-1}}=10^2\ \mathrm{m^{-1}}}}{4}$$

$$= 5.447\times10^{-19}\ \mathrm{J}$$

which is equivalent to an energy in units of eV

$$I = (5.447\times10^{-19}\ \mathrm{J})/(1.602\times10^{-19}\ \mathrm{J\ eV^{-1}}) = \mathbf{3.400\ eV}$$

**E13.12** (a) The energy levels of a hydrogenic atom or ion are given by eqn 13.4a, so that for $Li^{2+}$,

$$E_n = -\frac{hcR_N Z^2}{n^2} = -\frac{hcR_{Li}3^2}{n^2} = -\frac{9hcR_{Li}}{n^2}$$

The wavenumbers of transitions $n_2 \rightarrow n_1$ in the spectrum of $Li^{2+}$ are therefore given by

$$\tilde{\nu} = \frac{\Delta E}{hc} = \frac{E_{n_2}-E_{n_1}}{hc} = \left\{\left(-\frac{9hcR_{Li}}{n_2^2}\right)-\left(-\frac{9hcR_{Li}}{n_1^2}\right)\right\}/hc = \frac{9R_{Li}}{n_1^2}-\frac{9R_{Li}}{n_2^2}$$

so that, for transitions in the Lyman series, $n_1 = 1$,

$$\tilde{\nu} = 9R_{Li} - \frac{9R_{Li}}{n_2^2}$$

This expression has the form of the equation of a straight-line graph

$$\overbrace{\tilde{\nu}}^{y} = \overbrace{-9R_{Li}}^{\text{slope}} \times \overbrace{\frac{1}{n_2^2}}^{x} + \overbrace{9R_{Li}}^{\text{intercept}}$$

Figure 13.1 shows a plot of wavenumber against $(1/n_2^2)$. The graph is indeed a straight line, with a slope of $-987662\ \mathrm{cm^{-1}}$, confirming that the energy levels are indeed described by the Rydberg formula. It follows that the Rydberg constant for lithium has the value

$$R_{Li} = -\frac{\text{slope}}{9} = -\frac{987622\ \mathrm{cm^{-1}}}{9} = \mathbf{109736\ cm^{-1}}$$

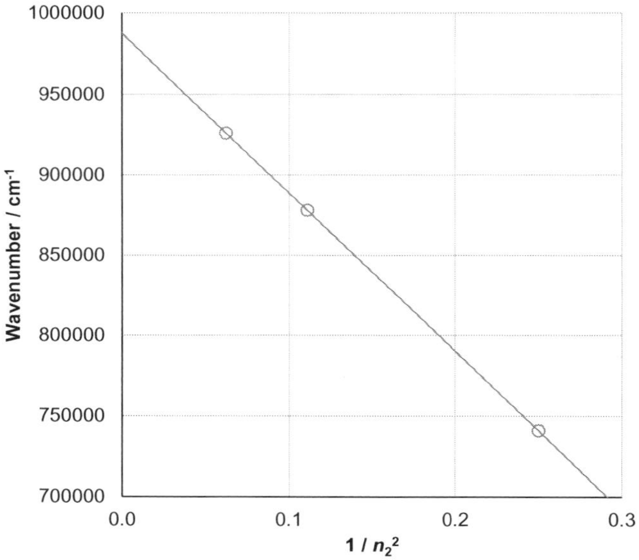


**Figure 13.1**

(b) The Balmer series corresponds to transitions with a common lower state quantum number $n_1 = 2$. The wavenumbers of the transitions are given by the Rydberg formula,

$$\tilde{\nu} = Z_N{}^2 R_N \left(\frac{1}{n_1^2} - \frac{1}{n_2^2}\right)$$

The shortest wavelength, highest energy, transitions in the Balmer series therefore correspond to transitions $3 \rightarrow 2$ and $4 \rightarrow 2$, with wavenumbers

$$\tilde{\nu}_{3\rightarrow 2} = 3^2 R_{Li}\left(\frac{1}{2^2} - \frac{1}{3^2}\right) = 9 \times (109736\ \text{cm}^{-1}) \times \left(\frac{1}{4} - \frac{1}{9}\right) = \mathbf{137170\ cm^{-1}}$$

$$\tilde{\nu}_{4\rightarrow 2} = 3^2 R_{Li}\left(\frac{1}{2^2} - \frac{1}{4^2}\right) = 9 \times (109736\ \text{cm}^{-1}) \times \left(\frac{1}{4} - \frac{1}{16}\right) = \mathbf{185180\ cm^{-1}}$$

(c) Ionization may be considered as a transition to a level with quantum number $n_2 = \infty$. Thus, the ionization energy of the $Li^{2+}$ ion is

$$I = hc\tilde{\nu} = Z_N{}^2 hcR_N\left(\frac{1}{n_1^2} - \frac{1}{n_2^2}\right) = 3^2 hcR_{Li}\left(\frac{1}{1^2} - \frac{1}{\infty^2}\right) = 9hcR_{Li}$$

$$= 9 \times (6.626 \times 10^{-34}\text{J s}) \times (2.998 \times 10^8\ \text{m s}^{-1}) \times (109736 \times 10^2\ \text{m}^{-1})$$

$$= \mathbf{1.962 \times 10^{-17} J}$$

which is equivalent to

$$I = (1.962 \times 10^{-17}\text{J})/(1.602 \times 10^{-19}\ \text{J eV}^{-1}) = \mathbf{122.5\ eV}$$

**E13.13** By analogy with eqn 13.9, the ionization energy of an anion $X^-$, is the energy for the process

$$X^-(g) \rightarrow X(g) + e^-(g) \qquad I_1^-(X^-) = E(X) - E(X^-)$$

The electron affinity of X is the energy **released** when an electron attaches to a gas-phase atom,

$$X(g) + e^-(g) \rightarrow X^-(g) \qquad E_{ea}(X) = -\{E(X^-) - E(X)\} = E(X) - E(X^-)$$

Thus, ionization energy of $X^-$ is equal to the electron affinity of X

$$I_1^-(X^-) = E_{ea}(X)$$

**E13.14** By analogy with the photoelectric effect, the kinetic energy of the ejected photoelectron corresponds to the difference between the energy of the incident photon and the energy required to ionise the atom. Thus, from eqn 12.3,

$$E_k = (hc/\lambda) - I = ½m_e v^2$$

Hence, rearranging, the ionization energy of krypton is

$$\begin{aligned} I &= (hc/\lambda) - ½m_e v^2 \\ &= \frac{(6.626 \times 10^{-34}\,\mathrm{J\,s}) \times (2.998 \times 10^{8}\,\mathrm{m\,s^{-1}})}{(58.4 \times 10^{-9}\,\mathrm{m})} \\ &\qquad - ½ \times (9.109 \times 10^{-34}\,\mathrm{kg}) \times (1.59 \times 10^{6}\,\mathrm{m\,s^{-1}})^2 \\ &= 2.25 \times 10^{-18}\,\mathrm{J} \end{aligned}$$

which is equivalent to

$$I = (2.25 \times 10^{-18}\,\mathrm{J})/(1.602 \times 10^{-19}\,\mathrm{J\,eV^{-1}}) = \mathbf{14.0\,eV}$$

**E13.15** According to the designations given in section 13.3, shell N corresponds to a principal quantum number $n = 4$. In general a shell consists of $n^2$ orbitals. In this particular case, the N shell consists of one 4s, three 4p, five 4d and seven 4f orbitals, giving a total of $n^2 = 4^2 =$ **16** orbitals in total.

**E13.16** The magnitude of the orbital angular momentum of an electron with orbital angular quantum number $l$ is, from eqn 12.23,

$$\mathcal{L} = \{l(l+1)\}^{1/2}\hbar$$

In general, the wavefunction of an electron has $(n - 1)$ nodes. Of these, $l$ are angular nodes and therefore $(n - 1 - l)$ are radial nodes. Thus,

(a) A 1s electron, which has $n = 1$ and $l = 0$, has angular momentum

$$\mathcal{L}_{1s} = \{0(0+1)\}^{1/2}\hbar = 0$$

with no angular nodes and no radial nodes.

(b) A 3s electron has $n = 3$ and $l = 0$, has angular momentum

$$\mathcal{L}_{3s} = \{0(0+1)\}^{1/2}\hbar = 0$$

with no angular nodes and $(3 - 1 - 0) = 2$ radial nodes.

(c) A 3d electron, which has $n = 3$ and $l = 2$ has angular momentum

$$\mathcal{L}_{3d} = \{2(2+1)\}^{1/2}\hbar = 6^{1/2}\hbar$$

and two angular nodes and $(3 - 1 - 2) = 0$ radial nodes.

(d) A 2p electron, which has $n = 2$ and $l = 1$ has angular momentum

$$\mathcal{L}_{2p} = \{1(1+1)\}^{1/2}\hbar = 2^{1/2}\hbar$$

and one angular node and $(2 - 1 - 1) = 0$ radial nodes.

(e) A 3p electron, which has $n = 3$ and $l = 1$ has angular momentum

$$\mathcal{L}_{3p} = \{1(1+1)\}^{1/2}\hbar = 2^{1/2}\hbar$$

and one angular node and $(3 - 1 - 1) = 1$ radial nodes.

**E13.17** Different states are degenerate if they have exactly the same energy. For a hydrogenic atom, all orbitals with the same principal quantum number $n$ have the same energy and are thus degenerate. Each shell has $n^2$ orbitals, so the degeneracy of a shell is also $n^2$.

We may deduce the principal quantum number from the expression for the energy levels of a hydrogenic atom, eqn 13.4a

$$E_n = -\frac{hcR_N Z^2}{n^2}$$

(a) Thus, if the energy is $-hcR_H$, it follows that $n = 1$ and so the degeneracy is $1^2 = \mathbf{1}$. This corresponds to the single 1s orbital.

(b) If the energy is $-hcR_H/9$, it follows that $n = 3$ and so the degeneracy is $3^2 = \mathbf{9}$. This corresponds to the one 3s orbital, three 3p orbitals and five 3d orbitals.

(c) If the energy is $-hcR_H/49$, it follows that $n = 7$ and so the degeneracy is $7^2 = \mathbf{49}$. This corresponds to the one 7s orbital, three 7p orbitals, five 7d orbitals, nine 7f orbitals, eleven 7g orbitals and thirteen 7i orbitals.

**E13.18** The number of orbitals in a subshell with quantum number $l$ is $(2l + 1)$. Each orbital may, however, be doubly occupied by electrons in opposing spin states.

(a) Thus if $l = 0$, $(2l + 1) = 1$, and there is only one s orbital only. The subshell may therefore be occupied by **2** electrons.

(b) If $l = 3$, corresponding to a f subshell, there are $(2l + 1) = 7$ orbitals, which may be occupied by **14** electrons.

(c) If $l = 5$, $(2l + 1) = 11$, and there are eleven h orbitals in the subshell, which may be occupied by **22** electrons.

**E13.19** According to the Born interpretation, the probability of finding an electron at a point is given by the square of the wavefunction. Thus, the probability density for the hydrogen 1s orbital varies as

$$\psi_{1s}^2(r) = \left\{\frac{1}{(\pi a_0^3)^{1/2}} e^{-r/a_0}\right\}^2 = \frac{1}{\pi a_0^3} e^{-2r/a_0}$$

The maximum probability therefore occurs for $r = 0$, and has a value

$$\psi_{1s}^2(0) = \frac{1}{\pi a_0^3}$$

Thus, the radius at which the probability falls to 30 per cent of this value is given by the solution to the equation

$$\frac{1}{\pi a_0^3} e^{-2r/a_0} = 0.30 \times \frac{1}{\pi a_0^3}$$

Rearranging gives

$$r = -(a_0/2)\ln(0.30) = \mathbf{0.602}\ \boldsymbol{a_0}$$

which corresponds to 31.8 pm.

**E13.20** The radial distribution function for the spherically symmetric ground, 1s, state of a hydrogen atom is, from eqn 13.7a,

$$P(r) = 4\pi r^2 \psi_{1s}^2(r)$$
$$= 4\pi r^2 \left\{\frac{1}{(\pi a_0^3)^{1/2}} e^{-r/a_0}\right\}^2 = 4\pi r^2 \times \frac{1}{\pi a_0^3} e^{-2r/a_0} = 4a_0^{-3} r^2 e^{-2r/a_0}$$

We may see from Figure 13.8 of the text occurs for a radius of $a_0$. Substituting $r = a_0$ into the expression for the radial distribution function gives

$$P_{max} = P(a_0) = 4a_0^{-3}\ \overbrace{a_0^2}^{r=a_0}\ e^{-2a_0/a_0} = \frac{4}{e^2 a_0} = 0.541\ a_0^{-1}$$

Thus, the radius at which the radial distribution function falls to 30 per cent, or 5 per cent of this value may be found by solving the equations

$$P(r) = 0.30 \times P_{max} = 0.162\ a_0^{-1} \quad \text{or} \quad 0.05 \times P_{max} = 0.027\ a_0^{-1}$$

Unfortunately, solution of the equations is not straightforward and it is therefore easier to find the solutions by plotting a graph of the variation of the radial distribution function with radius. Figure 13.2 shows that the radial distribution function has (a) 30 per cent of its maximum value at $r =$ **0.262** $\boldsymbol{a_0}$ and **2.530** $\boldsymbol{a_0}$ and (b) 5 per cent of its value at **0.090** $\boldsymbol{a_0}$ and **3.845** $\boldsymbol{a_0}$.

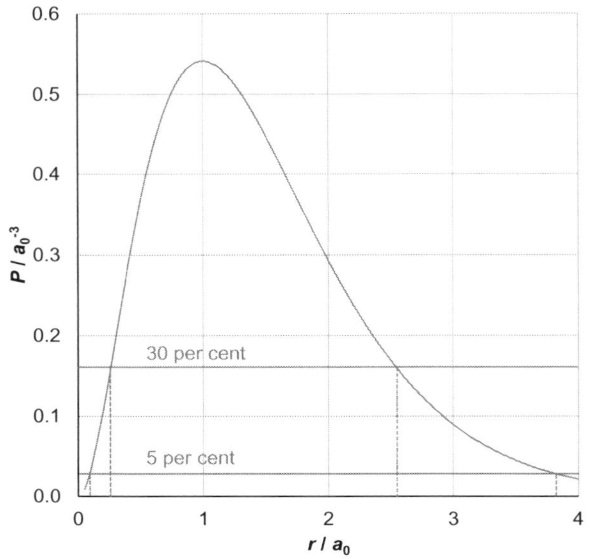


**Figure 13.2**

**E13.21** Following the method adopted in *Brief Illustration 13.5*, the probability of finding an electron in a small element of volume $\delta V$ is

$$\text{Probability} = \psi^2 \delta V$$

Taking the wavefunction for a 1s orbital from Table 13.1, and setting $r = 0$, then

(a) for hydrogen, with $Z = 1$

$$\text{Probability} = \overbrace{\{(Z^3/\pi a_0^3)^{1/2} e^{-Zr/a_0}\}^2}^{\psi_{1s}^2} \delta V = \frac{1}{\pi a_0^3} \times 6.5\ \text{pm}^3 = \mathbf{1.4 \times 10^{-5}}$$

(b) for helium, with $Z = 2$

$$\text{Probability} = \overbrace{\{(Z^3/\pi a_0^3)^{1/2} e^{-Zr/a_0}\}^2}^{\psi_{1s}^2} \delta V = \frac{2^3}{\pi a_0^3} \times 6.5\ \text{pm}^3 = \mathbf{1.1 \times 10^{-4}}$$

**E13.22** A node is a point at which the wavefunction passes through zero. The nodes may therefore be found by solving the equation

$$R_{n,l} = 0$$

(a) For the 3s orbital, we expect $n - l - 1 = 3 - 0 - 1 = 2$ radial nodes. Noting that for hydrogen, $Z = 1$, and writing $\rho = r/3a_0$, the radial wavefunction given in Table 13.1 may be expressed more simply as

$$R_{3s} = k(3 - 6\rho + 2\rho^2)e^{-\rho}$$

where $k$ is a constant. If $R_{3s} = 0$, then either

$$e^{-\rho} = 0$$

or

$$(3 - 6\rho + 2\rho^2) = 0$$

The first condition corresponds to $\rho = \infty$, and implies that the wavefunction decays to zero at an infinite radius from the nucleus. The second condition is a quadratic equation and has two roots that correspond to the two radial nodes in the wavefunction. These solutions may be found using the methods outlined in *The chemist's toolkit 7.1*. The roots are

$$\rho = ½(3 \pm \sqrt{3})$$

and therefore

$$r = ½(9 \pm 3\sqrt{3})a_0 = \mathbf{1.9}\ \boldsymbol{a_0} \text{ and } \mathbf{7.10}\ \boldsymbol{a_0}$$

(b) For a 4s orbital, we expect $n - l - 1 = 4 - 0 - 1 = 3$ radial nodes. Writing $\rho = r/2a_0$, the radial wavefunction may be expressed as

$$R_{4s} = k(\rho^3 - 12\rho^2 + 36\rho - 24)e^{-\rho} = 0$$

This implies that either

$$e^{-\rho} = 0$$

or

$$(\rho^3 - 12\rho^2 + 36\rho - 24) = 0$$

Once again, the nodes are given by the roots to this second equation. This is a cubic equation and so will give rise to the three solutions that we expect. The solutions to a cubic equation cannot be found analytically. Instead, we must use either a scientific calculator or spreadsheet to find the roots

$$\rho = 0.936, 3.305 \text{ and } 7.759$$

corresponding to nodes at

$$r = \mathbf{1.87}\ \boldsymbol{a_0}, \mathbf{6.61}\ \boldsymbol{a_0} \text{ and } \mathbf{15.5}\ \boldsymbol{a_0}$$

**E13.23** There are 2 lobes to a p orbital so the probability that a p electron will be found in one-or-other lobe is ½. However, there are three degenerate orbitals in a p subshell so the probability of finding a p subshell electron in one-or-other p-orbital lobe of the subshell is $^1/_6$.

**E13.24** Nodal planes occur at angles for which the angular wavefunction passes through zero. If the wavefunction is proportional to $\sin\theta\cos\theta$, then for a nodal plane,

$$\sin\theta\cos\theta = 0$$

and so either $\sin\theta = 0$, in which case $\theta =$ **0°** or **180°** or $\cos\theta = 0$, in which case $\theta =$ **90°** or **270°**.

**E13.25** In general, for an atomic orbital with quantum numbers $n$ and $l$, there are (a) $\boldsymbol{(n-l-1)}$ radial nodes, (b) $\boldsymbol{l}$ angular nodes and (c) $\boldsymbol{(n-1)}$ nodes in total.

**E13.26** Fermions are particles with half-integral spin; bosons are particles with integral spin. An electron, proton and neutron all have spin of ½ so are fermions. A photon, however, has spin of 1, so is a boson.

**E13.27** For a one-electron atom, the selection rules are given in section 13.7 of the main text as

$$\Delta n = \text{no restriction}$$
$$\Delta l = \pm 1$$
$$\Delta m_l = 0, \pm 1$$

(a) For 2s → 1s, $\Delta l = 0$, so the transition is **forbidden**.

(b) For 2p → 1s, $\Delta l = -1$, so the transition is **allowed**.

(c) For 3d → 2p, $\Delta l = -1$, so the transition is **allowed**.

(d) For 5d → 2s, $\Delta l = -2$, so the transition is **forbidden**.

(e) For 5p → 3s, $\Delta l = -1$, so the transition is **allowed**.

(f) For 6f → 3s, $\Delta l = -3$, so the transition is **forbidden**.

**E13.28** For a one-electron atom, the selection rules outlined in section 13.7 do not put any restriction upon the change in the principal quantum number. However, the orbital angular momentum quantum number may change only by one,

$$\Delta l = \pm 1$$

so that transitions from an f orbital are only allowed to d or g orbitals. Thus, the allowed transitions are **5f →** $\boldsymbol{n}$**d** and **5f →** $\boldsymbol{n}$**g**.

**E13.29** The yttrium atom has an electronic configuration $[Kr]4d^1 5s^2$ in which the 5s orbital is filled in preference to the 4d orbitals. The average distance of an electron from the nucleus is greater in a 5s orbital than in a 4d orbital. Two electrons in a 5s orbital are therefore, on average, further apart than two electrons in a 4d orbital. Interelectron repulsion is therefore minimised if the electrons preferentially enter the 5s orbital. The effect is sufficient that the reduction in interelectron repulsion overcomes the additional energy necessary to enter the higher energy 5s orbital.

The silver atom, however, has a [Kr]$4d^{10}5s^1$ configuration. The 4d orbitals are filled in preference to the 5s orbital because, in silver, the difference in the energy of these orbitals is much greater than in yttrium; the extra 4d electrons shield the 5s orbital from the nucleus. As a result, the reduction in interelectron repulsion is now no longer sufficient to overcome the additional energy necessary to enter the higher energy 5s orbital.

**E13.30** For a carbon atom in the excited configuration [He]$2s^2$2p3p, we need only consider the contribution to the spin and orbital angular momentum from the 2p and 3p electrons because the [He] core and $2s^2$ subshell have no net angular momentum. The total orbital angular momentum is given by the vector sum of the orbital angular momenta of the individual 2p and 3p electrons. The angular momentum quantum numbers of the electrons are $l_1 = l_2 = 1$, so that using a Clebsch–Gordon series,

$$L = l_1 + l_2, l_1 + l_2 - 1, \ldots |l_1 - l_2| = (1+1), (1+1-1), (1-1) = 2, 1, 0$$

which corresponds to D, P and S terms respectively. In the same way, the total spin angular momentum is given by

$$S = s_1 + s_2, s_1 - s_2 = \tfrac{1}{2} + \tfrac{1}{2}, \tfrac{1}{2} - \tfrac{1}{2} = 1, 0$$

A term with $S = 1$ corresponds to a multiplicity of $(2S + 1) = \{(2 \times 1) + 1\} = 3$, and is therefore designated a triplet, with $S = 0$ corresponding to a multiplicity of $(2S + 1) = \{(2 \times 0) + 1\} = 1$, and is therefore designated a singlet.

The allowed terms are therefore $^3$**D**, $^1$**D**, $^3$**P**, $^1$**P**, $^3$**S** and $^1$**S**.

**E13.31** The four electron spins may be aligned (if they are in different orbitals) giving a maximum total spin angular momentum quantum number $S$ equal to $4 \times s = 4 \times \tfrac{1}{2} = 2$ because each electron has a spin quantum number of $s = \tfrac{1}{2}$. Another possibility is that three of the four electrons are aligned parallel with the remaining electron in an antiparallel alignment. This is equivalent to having two electron spins paired (giving no net spin contribution from the two) with the remaining two aligned (unpaired), thereby, giving $S = 3 \times s - s = 2 \times \tfrac{1}{2} = 1$. Finally, two electrons may have their spins aligned while the remaining two electrons have apposing, antiparallel, spins. This, being equivalent to two sets of paired electrons, gives no net spin. Thus, the possible values for $S$ are **2**, **1**, and **0**. The multiplicity of a term is given by $(2S + 1)$, so that four electrons may give rise to quintet, triplet and singlet states.

**E13.32** (a) A $^1$S term corresponds to a total orbital angular momentum quantum number $L = 0$ and total spin angular momentum quantum number $S = 0$. Thus, the only permitted value for the total angular momentum quantum number is

$$J = L + S, L + S - 1, \ldots |L - S| = 0 + 0 = 0$$

corresponding to a $^1\mathbf{S}_0$ level.

(b) In the same way, a $^3$F term corresponds to $L = 3$ and $S = 1$, giving

$$J = L + S, L + S - 1, \ldots |L - S| = (3 + 1), (3 + 1 - 1), \ldots (3 - 1) = 4, 3, 2$$

and so $^3\mathbf{F}_4$, $^3\mathbf{F}_3$ and $^3\mathbf{F}_2$ levels.

(c) For a $^5$S term, $L = 0$ and $S = 2$, giving

$$J = L + S, L + S - 1, \ldots |L - S| = (0 + 2) = 2$$

and so a $^5\mathbf{S}_2$ level.

(d) For a $^5$P term, $L = 1$ and $S = 2$, giving

$$J = L + S, L + S - 1, \ldots |L - S| = (1 + 2), (1 + 2 - 1) = 3, 2, 1$$

and so $^5\mathbf{P}_3$, $^5\mathbf{P}_2$ and $^5\mathbf{P}_1$ levels.

**E13.33** In deriving the possible levels of the [Ar]3d$^2$ configuration, it is necessary only to consider the angular momentum of the two valence d electrons. The allowed total spin angular momentum quantum number is

$$S = s_1 + s_2, s_1 - s_2 = ½ + ½, ½ - ½ = 1, 0$$

which correspond to triplet and singlet multiplicities. Hund's rules predict that the term with the maximum multiplicity must lie lowest in energy. The lowest energy term must therefore be a triplet.

The 3d electrons have $l = 2$, so the allowed total orbital angular momentum quantum number is therefore

$$L = l_1 + l_2, l_1 + l_2 - 1, \ldots |l_1 - l_2|$$
$$= (2 + 2), (2 + 2 - 1), \ldots (2 - 2) = 4, 3, 2, 1, 0$$

which correspond to G, F, D, P and S terms respectively. According to Hund's rules, the term with the highest orbital angular momentum lies lowest in energy. A $^3$G term is, however, forbidden by the Pauli Exclusion Principle. In order to achieve $L = 4$, two electrons would have to occupy either the $m_l = +2$ or $m_l = -2$ orbital. According to the Pauli Principle, such a configuration is forbidden for a triplet state because the electrons are aligned with their spins parallel. The lowest energy term must therefore be $^3$F, which is allowed under the Pauli Principle.

The permitted values for the total angular momentum quantum number of a $^3$F term, which has $L = 3$ and $S = 1$ are

$$J = L + S, L + S - 1, \ldots |L - S| = (3 + 1), (3 + 1 - 1), \ldots |3 - 1|, = 4, 3, 2$$

The allowed levels are therefore $^3F_4$, $^3F_3$ and $^3F_2$. The valence shell is less than half full, so we should expect that the level with the lowest value of $J$ lies lowest in energy. Thus, the lowest level of the ground configuration of the $Ti^{2+}$ ion is $^3F_2$.

(b) Each level with total angular momentum $J$ corresponds to $(2J + 1)$ states with values of $M_J$ from $+J$ to $-J$. For the $^3F_2$ level, there are therefore $\{(2 \times 2) + 1\} =$ **5** states with $M_J = 2, 1, 0, -1, -2$.

**E13.34** The ground configuration of a $Sc^{2+}$ ion is $[Ar]3d^1$. The [Ar] core makes no net contribution to the total spin and orbital angular momentum of the ion. The only remaining electron has $l = 2$ and $s = ½$. The total orbital angular momentum quantum number of the ion is therefore $L = 2$, resulting in a D term. The total spin angular momentum quantum number is thus $S = ½$, giving rise to a doublet term. Thus, the only allowed term is $\mathbf{^2D}$.

**E13.35** Consideration of the spin–orbit coupling predicts that for an atom with a valence shell that is less than half full, the level with the lowest value of the total angular momentum quantum number, $J$, lies lowest in energy, whereas for an atom with a valence shell that is more than half full, the level with the highest value of the total angular momentum quantum number, $J$, lies lowest in energy. Thus, for Al, for which the valence shell is less than half full, it is the $\mathbf{^2P_{1/2}}$ level that is lowest; in contrast, for Cl, for which the valence shell is more than half full, it is the $\mathbf{^2P_{3/2}}$ level that is lowest in energy.

**E13.36** The ground configurations of iron and its cations are:

Fe: $[Ar]3d^6 4s^2$
$Fe^{2+}$: $[Ar]3d^6$
$Fe^{3+}$: $[Ar]3d^5$

The $\mathbf{Fe^{2+}}$ ion has a greater radius than the radius of $Fe^{3+}$ because the repulsions of six 3d subshell electrons is greater than five. Also, two of the iron(II) cation 3d electrons are paired in a single orbital but none of the 3d electrons are paired in iron(III). Paired electrons repel more strong than unpaired especially when in a single orbital.

**E13.37** The ionization energy of potassium$^-$, is the energy for the process

$$K(g) \rightarrow K^+(g) + e^-(g) \qquad I_1^-(K) = E(K^+) - E(K)$$

The electron affinity of Br is the energy **released** when an electron attaches to a gas-phase atom,

$$Br(g) + e^-(g) \rightarrow Br^-(g) \qquad E_{ea}(Br) = -\{E(Br^-) - E(Br)\} = E(Br) - E(Br^-)$$

The energy change for the reaction

$$K(g) + Br(g) \rightarrow K^+(g) + Br^-(g)$$

is thus given by the difference between the ionization energy of potassium and the electron affinity of bromine,

$$\Delta E = \overbrace{\{E(K^+) + E(Br^-)\}}^{\text{products}} - \overbrace{\{E(K) + E(Br)\}}^{\text{reactants}}$$

$$= \overbrace{\{E(\mathrm{K}^+) - E(\mathrm{K})\}}^{I(\mathrm{K})} - \overbrace{\{E(\mathrm{Br}) - E(\mathrm{Br}^-)\}}^{E_{\mathrm{ea}}(\mathrm{Br})}$$
$$= I(K) - E_{\mathrm{ea}} = 4.34\ \mathrm{eV} - 3.36\ \mathrm{eV} = \mathbf{0.98\ eV}$$

which is equivalent to

$$\Delta E = (0.98\ \mathrm{eV}) \times (1.602 \times 10^{-19}\ \mathrm{J\ eV^{-1}}) \times (6.022 \times 10^{23}\mathrm{mol^{-1}})$$
$$= 95 \times 10^3\ \mathrm{J\ mol^{-1}} = \mathbf{95\ kJ\ mol^{-1}}$$

**E13.38** The selection rules for electronic transitions in many-electron atoms are

$$\Delta S = 0$$
$$\Delta L = 0, \pm 1$$
$$\Delta J = 0, \pm 1 \text{ but } J = 0 \leftrightarrow J = 0 \text{ is forbidden}$$

There is also a requirement that

$$\Delta l = \pm 1$$

but it is not possible to determine whether this condition is fulfilled from the term symbols alone.

(a) For ${}^3\mathrm{D}_2 \rightarrow {}^3\mathrm{P}_1$, $\Delta S = 0$, $\Delta L = -1$ and $\Delta J = -1$. The transition is therefore **allowed**.

(b) For ${}^3\mathrm{P}_2 \rightarrow {}^1\mathrm{S}_0$, $\Delta S = -1$ and the transition is therefore **forbidden**. Transitions between triplet and singlet levels are forbidden in relatively atoms.

(c) For ${}^3\mathrm{F}_4 \rightarrow {}^3\mathrm{D}_3$, $\Delta S = 0$, $\Delta L = -1$ but $\Delta J = -1$. The transition is therefore **allowed**.

**E13.39** The difference in the wavelengths of the two emission lines results from the different energies of the two upper spin–orbit levels of the upper [Ne]3p$^1$ configuration. Relating the energy to the transition wavelength through eqn 0.21b,

$$\Delta E = E({}^2\mathrm{P}_{3/2}) - E({}^2\mathrm{P}_{1/2}) = \{E({}^2\mathrm{P}_{3/2}) - E({}^2\mathrm{S}_{1/2})\} - \{E({}^2\mathrm{P}_{1/2}) - E({}^2\mathrm{S}_{1/2})\}$$
$$= \frac{hc}{\lambda({}^2\mathrm{P}_{3/2} \rightarrow {}^2\mathrm{S}_{1/2})} - \frac{hc}{\lambda({}^2\mathrm{P}_{1/2} \rightarrow {}^2\mathrm{S}_{1/2})}$$
$$= (6.626 \times 10^{-34}\mathrm{J\ s}) \times (2.998 \times 10^8\ \mathrm{m\ s^{-1}})$$
$$\times \left\{\frac{1}{589.0 \times 10^{-9}\ \mathrm{m}} - \frac{1}{589.6 \times 10^{-9}\ \mathrm{m}}\right\}$$
$$= 3.412 \times 10^{-22}\ \mathrm{J}$$

This is equivalent to

$$\Delta E = (3.412 \times 10^{-22}\ \mathrm{J})/(1.602 \times 10^{-19}\ \mathrm{J\ eV^{-1}})$$
$$= 2.130 \times 10^{-3}\ \mathrm{eV} = \mathbf{2.130\ meV}$$

# Answers to projects

**P13.40** (a) The radial distribution function for a 1s electron in hydrogen is

$$P(r) = 4\pi r^2\psi_{1s}^2(r) = 4\pi r^2\{(1/\pi a_0^3)^{1/2}e^{-r/a_0}\}^2 = 4a_0^{-3}r^2e^{-2r/a_0}$$

The maximum in this function may be found by differentiating and setting the derivative to zero.

$$\begin{aligned}\frac{dP(r)}{dr} &= \frac{d}{dr}(4a_0^{-3}r^2e^{-2r/a_0})\\ &= 4a_0^{-3}\frac{d}{dr}(r^2e^{-2r/a_0})\\ &= 4a_0^{-3}\overbrace{\left\{r^2\frac{d}{dr}(e^{-2r/a_0}) + e^{-2r/a_0}\frac{d}{dr}(r^2)\right\}}^{\frac{d}{dx}uv=u\frac{dv}{dx}+v\frac{du}{dx}}\\ &= 4a_0^{-3}\{(r^2\times -2a_0^{-1}e^{-2r/a_0}) + (e^{-2r/a_0}\times 2r)\}\\ &= 8a_0^{-3}r\{1-(r/a_0)\} = 0\end{aligned}$$

This is true if either $r = 0$ or $\{1 - (r/a_0)\} = 0$. The first condition corresponds to the minimum in the radial distribution function at the nucleus. The second condition implies that

$$\begin{aligned}1-(r/a_0) &= 0\\ (r/a_0) &= 1\\ r &= a_0\end{aligned}$$

The most probable distance from the nucleus for an electron in a ground-state hydrogen atom is therefore $\boldsymbol{r = a_0}$, where $a_0$ is the Bohr radius, which has a value 52.9 pm.

(b) The probability of finding an electron in a small element of volume $\delta V$ is

$$P = \psi^2(r)\delta V$$

Substituting the expression for the wavefunction of a 2s electron in a hydrogen atom, and assuming that the element of volume is sufficiently small that the value of the wavefunction is constant,

$$P = \left\{\left(\frac{1}{32\pi a_0^3}\right)^{1/2}\left(2-\frac{r}{a_0}\right)e^{-r/2a_0}\right\}^2\delta V = \left(\frac{1}{32\pi a_0^3}\right)\left(2-\frac{r}{a_0}\right)^2 e^{-r/a_0}\delta V$$

(i) If $r = 0$, so that the element of volume is centred upon the nucleus,

$$\begin{aligned}P &= \left(\frac{1}{32\pi a_0^3}\right)\left(2-\frac{0}{a_0}\right)^2 e^{-0/a_0}\delta V = \left(\frac{1}{8\pi a_0^3}\right)\delta V\\ &= \frac{1}{8\pi\times(52.9\ \text{pm})^3}\times 1\ \text{pm}^3 = \mathbf{2.68\times 10^{-7}}\end{aligned}$$

(ii) If $r = a_0$,

$$P = \left(\frac{1}{32\pi a_0^3}\right)\left(2 - \frac{a_0}{a_0}\right)^2 e^{-a_0/a_0}\delta V = \left(\frac{1}{8\pi a_0^3}\right)\delta V$$
$$= \frac{e^{-1}}{32\pi \times (52.9\text{ pm})^3} \times 1\text{ pm}^3 = \mathbf{2.47 \times 10^{-8}}$$

(iii) If $r = 2a_0$,

$$P = \left(\frac{1}{32\pi a_0^3}\right)\left(2 - \frac{2a_0}{a_0}\right)^2 e^{-2a_0/a_0}\delta V = 0$$

The probability is zero because, for a 2s orbital in hydrogen, there is a radial node at $r = 2a_0$.

(c) The radial distribution function for a 2s orbital is

$$P(r) = 4\pi r^2 \psi_{2s}^2(r)$$
$$= 4\pi r^2 \times \left\{\left(\frac{1}{32\pi a_0^3}\right)^{1/2}\left(2 - \frac{r}{a_0}\right) e^{-r/2a_0}\right\}^2$$
$$= \left(\frac{1}{8a_0}\right)(r/a_0)^2\left(2 - \frac{r}{a_0}\right)^2 e^{-r/a_0}$$

Figure 13.3 shows a plot of this function. The maximum in the function, which represents the most probable distance for the electron from the nucleus in a 2s orbital in hydrogen, occurs at **5.24 $a_0$**.

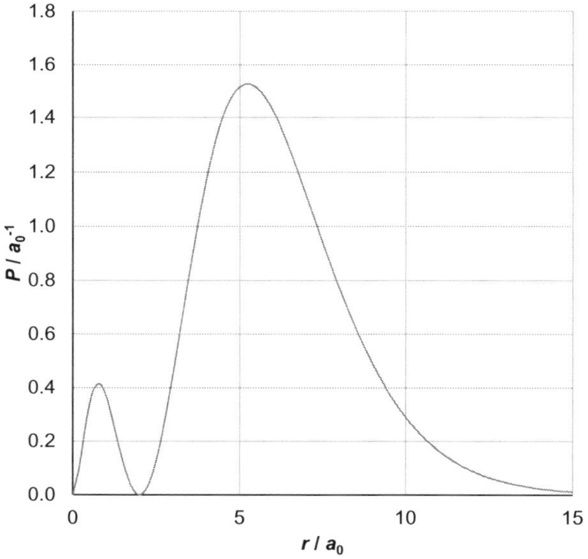


**Figure 13.3**

(d) The most probable distance may also be found by differentiating the radial distribution function and setting the derivative to zero. It is mathematically convenient to make the substitution

$$\rho = r/a_0$$

Thus,

$$\begin{aligned}\frac{\mathrm{d}P(r)}{\mathrm{d}r} = \frac{\mathrm{d}P(\rho)}{\mathrm{d}\rho} &= \frac{\mathrm{d}}{\mathrm{d}\rho}\left\{\left(\frac{1}{8a_0}\right)\rho^2(2-\rho)^2\mathrm{e}^{-\rho}\right\}\\
&= \left(\frac{1}{8a_0}\right)\frac{\mathrm{d}}{\mathrm{d}\rho}\{\rho^2(2-\rho)^2\mathrm{e}^{-\rho}\}\\
&= \left(\frac{1}{8a_0}\right)\left\{\rho^2(2-\rho)^2\frac{\mathrm{d}}{\mathrm{d}\rho}(\mathrm{e}^{-\rho}) + \rho^2\mathrm{e}^{-\rho}\frac{\mathrm{d}}{\mathrm{d}\rho}(2-\rho)^2\right.\\
&\qquad \left. + (2-\rho)^2\mathrm{e}^{-\rho}\frac{\mathrm{d}}{\mathrm{d}\rho}(\rho^2)\right\}\\
&= \left(\frac{1}{8a_0}\right)[\{\rho^2(2-\rho)^2 \times (-\mathrm{e}^{-\rho})\} + \{\rho^2\mathrm{e}^{-\rho} \times -2(2-\rho)\}\\
&\qquad + \{(2-\rho)^2\mathrm{e}^{-\rho} \times 2\rho\}]\\
&= -\left(\frac{1}{8a_0}\right)(\rho^4 - 8\rho^3 + 16\rho^2 - 8\rho)\mathrm{e}^{-\rho}\\
&= -\left(\frac{1}{8a_0}\right)(\rho^3 - 8\rho^2 + 16\rho - 8)\rho\mathrm{e}^{-\rho} = 0\end{aligned}$$

This implies that either

$\rho = 0$, and therefore $r = 0$
$\mathrm{e}^{-\rho} = 0$, and therefore $r = \infty$

or

$$(\rho^3 - 8\rho^2 + 16\rho - 8) = 0$$

The first two conditions correspond to the limiting behaviour at the nucleus and at an infinite distance from the nucleus. The roots to the third condition correspond to the maxima and minima in the radial distribution function. We may factorise this cubic expression

$$(\rho^3 - 8\rho^2 + 16\rho - 8) = (2-\rho)(\rho^2 - 6\rho + 4) = 0$$

Using the methods outlined in in *The chemist's toolkit 7.1* to solve the quadratic factor, gives solutions

$\rho = 2, 3 \pm \sqrt{5}$, and therefore $r = 2a_0, (3 \pm \sqrt{5})a_0$

We may differentiate again to find which of these solutuions correspond to maxima and which to minima. However, having plotted the function, it is clear that the solution

$$r = (3 + \sqrt{5})a_0 = 5.236\ a_0$$

corresponds to a maximum, and thus to the most probable distance from the nucleus in a 2s orbital in hydrogen.

**P13.41** Figure 13.4 shows the variation of the first, second and third ionization energies with atomic number for the elements of group 13.

It can be seen that in each case, $I_1 < I_2 < I_3$. The nuclear shielding decreases as each successive electron is removed, so that more energy is required to remove successive electrons.

The ionization energies of boron are much larger than those of the remaining group elements because the valence shell of boron is very small and compact with little nuclear shielding. The boron atom is much smaller than the aluminum atom.

The ionization energies of aluminium, gallium, indium, and thallium are comparable even though successive valence shells are further from the nucleus because the decrease in ionization energy expected from large atomic radii is balanced by an increase in effective nuclear charge.

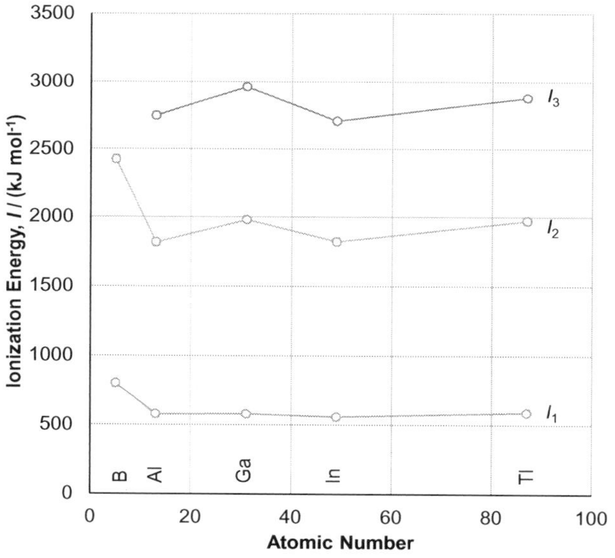


**Figure 13.4**

**P13.42** (a) Frequency and wavelength are related through eqn 0.19, $c = \nu\lambda$. In each case, the wavelength of the observed transitions from the star are longer than those observed from a stationary source. This implies that the frequency of transitions observed from the star is lower than from a stationary source. This is the case for a receding source,

$$\nu_{\text{receding}} = \nu f = \nu \overbrace{\left\{\frac{(1 - s/c)}{(1 + s/c)}\right\}^{1/2}}^{f}$$

because $f < 1$. We may calculate the speed of the star by determining the average value of the factor $f$

$$f = \frac{\nu_{\text{star}}}{\nu} = \frac{\lambda}{\lambda_{\text{star}}} = \overbrace{\frac{438.392\ \text{nm}}{438.882\ \text{nm}}}^{0.99884} = \overbrace{\frac{440.510\ \text{nm}}{441.000\ \text{nm}}}^{0.99889} = \overbrace{\frac{441.510\ \text{nm}}{442.020\ \text{nm}}}^{0.99885}$$

Thus, taking

$$f = 0.99885$$

$$\left\{\frac{(1 - s/c)}{(1 + s/c)}\right\}^{1/2} = 0.99885$$

$$\frac{(1 - s/c)}{(1 + s/c)} = 0.99772$$

$$s/c = \frac{1 - 0.99772}{1 + 0.99772} = 1.14 \times 10^{-3}$$

Thus, the star is receding at a speed of

$$s = (1.14 \times 10^{-3})c = 3.42 \times 10^{5}\ \text{ms}^{-1} = \mathbf{342\ km\ s^{-1}}$$

(b) We could compute the star's radial velocity with respect to the sun if we knew the Earth's speed with respect to the sun along the sun–star vector at the time of the spectral observation. This could be estimated from quantities available through astronomical observation: the Earth's orbital velocity times the cosine of the angle between that velocity vector and the Earth–star vector at the time of the spectral observation. The Earth–star direction, which is observable by Earth-based astronomers, is practically identical to the sun–star direction, which is technically the direction needed. Alternatively, repeat the experiment half a year later. At that time, the Earth's motion with respect to the sun is approximately equal in magnitude and opposite in direction compared to the original experiment. Averaging $f$ values over the two experiments would yield $f$ values in which the Earth's motion is effectively averaged out.

# Chapter 14

# Quantum chemistry: the chemical bond

## Answers to discussion questions

**D14.1** Our comparison of the two theories focusses on the manner of construction of the trial wavefunctions for the hydrogen molecule in the simplest versions of both theories. In the valence-bond method, the trial function is a linear combination of two simple product wavefunctions, in which one electron resides totally in an atomic orbital (AO) on atom A, and the other totally in an orbital on atom B.

$$\psi_{\mathrm{H-H}}(1,2) = \psi_{\mathrm{A}}(1)\psi_{\mathrm{B}}(2) + \psi_{\mathrm{A}}(2)\psi_{\mathrm{B}}(1)$$

This approach is illustrated in *Derivation 14.1* and Figure 14.3 of the text. There is no contribution to the wavefunction from products in which both electrons reside on either atom A or B. So the valence bond approach undervalues, by totally neglecting, any ionic contribution to the trial function. It is a totally covalent function.

The modern one-electron molecular orbital (MO) extends throughout the molecule and is written as a linear combination of atomic orbitals (LCAO).

$$\psi_{\mathrm{MO}}(1) = c_{\mathrm{A}}\psi_{\mathrm{A}}(1) + c_{\mathrm{B}}\psi_{\mathrm{B}}(1)$$

The squares of the coefficients give the relative proportions of the AO contributing to the MO.

The two-electron molecular orbital function for the hydrogen molecule is a product of two one-electron MOs. That is

$$\begin{aligned}\psi &= \{c_{\mathrm{A}}\psi_{\mathrm{A}}(1) + c_{\mathrm{B}}\psi_{\mathrm{B}}(1)\}\{c_{\mathrm{A}}\psi_{\mathrm{A}}(2) + c_{\mathrm{B}}\psi_{\mathrm{B}}(2)\} \\ &= c_{\mathrm{A}}^2\psi_{\mathrm{A}}(1)\psi_{\mathrm{A}}(2) + c_{\mathrm{B}}^2\psi_{\mathrm{B}}(1)\psi_{\mathrm{B}}(2) + c_{\mathrm{A}}c_{\mathrm{B}}\psi_{\mathrm{A}}(1)\psi_{\mathrm{A}}(2) + c_{\mathrm{A}}c_{\mathrm{B}}\psi_{\mathrm{A}}(2)\psi_{\mathrm{A}}(1)\end{aligned}$$

The first two terms are ionic forms for which both electrons on either on atom A or on atom B. The molecular orbital approach greatly overvalues the ionic contributions. At these crude levels of approximation, the valence-bond method gives dissociation energies closer to the experimental values. However, more sophisticated versions of the molecular orbital approach are the method of choice for obtaining quantitative results on both diatomic and polyatomic molecules.

**D14.2** Consider the case of the carbon atom. Mentally we break the process of hybridization into two steps. The first is promotion, in which we imagine that one of the electrons in the 2s orbital of carbon ($2s^2 2p^2$) is promoted to the empty 2p orbital giving the configuration $2s2p^3$. In the second step we mathematically mix the four orbitals by way of the specific linear combinations in eqn 14.4 corresponding to the $sp^3$ hybrid orbitals shown in Figure 14.6 of the main text. If we mix four unhybridized atomic orbitals we must end up with four hybrid orbitals. In the construction of the $sp^2$ hybrids we start with the 2s orbital and two of the 2p orbitals, and after mixing we end up with three $sp^2$ hybrid orbitals. In the sp case we start with the 2s orbital and one of the 2p orbitals. Eqns 14.5 and 14.6 present the LCAO for the $sp^2$ and sp hybrid orbitals; Figure 14.7 of the main text shows the orientations of the $sp^2$ hybrid orbitals. The justification for all of this is in a sense the first law of thermodynamics. Energy is a state function and therefore its value is determined only by the final state of the system, not by the path taken to achieve that state, and the path can even be imaginary.

**D14.3** In valence-bond (VB) theory, a bond is regarded as forming when an electron in a valence atomic orbital (AO) on one atom overlaps with a valence AO on an adjacent atom to form a wavefunction orbital that is more diffuse than the individual AO. If constructive interference occurs in the overlap, the wavefunction orbital is a bonding orbital that is lower in total energy than the AO. If the overlap gives destructive interference, the wavefunction is antibonding and higher in total energy than the AO. Sigma bonding orbitals ($\sigma$) and sigma antibonding orbitals ($\sigma^*$) have cylindrical symmetry around the internuclear axis; pi bonding orbitals ($\pi$) and pi antibonding orbitals ($\pi^*$) have a nodal plane along the internuclear axis. Two electrons at most may occupy any one of these orbitals and their spins must be paired (Pauli exclusion principle).

In addition to the overlap of combinations of s, p, and d orbitals, valence-bond theory introduces the $sp^3$, $sp^2$, and sp hybrid atomic orbitals and envisions their overlap with adjacent atomic orbital. Simple alkanes exhibit $sp^3$ hybridization (text Figure 14.6) while alkenes exhibit $sp^2$ hydridization (text Figure 14.7) and alkynes exhibit sp hybridization (text Figure 14.9). These valence-bond concepts are powerful tools that often provide insight into bond strengths, bond lengths, bond angles, and bonding sites of high and low reactivity within molecules.

Molecular orbital theory provides a perspective in which each molecular orbital extends throughout the molecule. This removes the restriction that a bonding electron pair be localized at two adjacent atoms. They are now spread over the whole molecule. This is illustrated in Figure 14.38 of the text, which shows some of the molecular orbitals of benzene. Every electron in a molecular orbital contributes to the strength of every bond and the total energy determines whether the bonded chemical species will be stable with respect to another bonding pattern, a consideration that gives emphasis to the molecular orbital energy-level diagram and the electron configuration.

In the discussion of diatomic molecules and ions, the sigma and pi bonding and antibonding descriptors are common to both valence-bond theory and molecular orbital theory because the molecule consists of two adjacent atoms only. However, the MOs of larger molecules cannot usually employ these descriptors. For examples of the symmetry-based molecular orbital descriptors see text Figures 14.34, 14.35, and 14.37. Even when discussing diatomic molecules, molecular orbital theory does not employ valence-bond terms like single bond and double bond. Molecular orbital theory uses the **bond order**, $b$, which is defined through eqn 14.12 as

$$b = ½(N - N^*)$$

where $N$ is the number of electrons in bonding orbitals and $N^*$ is the number of electrons in antibonding orbitals.

**D14.4** The **Pauli exclusion principle** indicates that a bonding orbital can only exist if the two electrons it describes have opposite spins. It follows that the merging of atomic orbitals that gives rise to a bond is accompanied by the pairing of the two electrons that contribute to it. Bonds do not form because electrons tend to pair: bonds are allowed to form by the electrons pairing their spins.

**D14.5** Both the Pauling and Mulliken methods for measuring the attracting power of atoms for electrons seem to make good chemical sense.

If we look at the Pauling scale,

$$|\chi_A - \chi_B| = 0.102 \times \{\Delta E / (\text{kJ mol}^{-1})\}$$
$$\text{with } \Delta E = E(\text{A}-\text{B}) - ½\{E(\text{A}-\text{A}) + E(\text{B}-\text{B})\}$$

we see that if $E$(A–B) is equal to ½[$E$(A–A) + $E$(B–B)], then the calculated electronegativity difference would be zero, as expected for completely non-polar bonds. Hence, any increased strength of the A–B bond over the average of the A–A and B–B bonds, can reasonably be thought of as being due to the polarity of the A–B bond, which in turn is due to the difference in electronegativity of the atoms involved. Therefore, this difference in bond strengths can be used as a measure of electronegativity difference. To obtain numerical values for individual atoms, a reference state (atom) for electronegativity must be established. The value for fluorine is arbitrarily set at 4.0.

The Mulliken scale

$$\chi = ½(I + E_{ea})$$

may be more intuitive than the Pauling scale because we are used to thinking of ionization energies and electron affinities as measures of the electron attracting powers of atoms. The choice of factor ½, however, is arbitrary, though reasonable, and no more arbitrary than the specific form that defines the Pauling scale.

**D14.6** Consider the simple molecular orbital (MO) wavefunction given by eqn 14.9a for the $H_2^+$ ion

$$\psi = c_A\psi_A + c_B\psi_B$$

where $\psi_A$ and $\psi_B$ are atomic orbitals centred on A and B respectively. Consider that the atomic orbitals constructively interfer and, thereby, form a bonding molecular orbital that has a lower energy than the separated atoms. The probability density is

$$\psi^2 = (c_A\psi_A + c_B\psi_B)^2 = c_A^2\psi_A^2 + c_B^2\psi_B^2 + 2c_A\psi_A c_B\psi_B$$

The term $\psi_A^2$ is the probability density if the electron is confined to atomic orbital A and $\psi_B^2$ is the probability density if the electron is confined to atomic orbital B. Since these two isolated-atom probability-density terms cannot explain the electron sharing of a covalent bond, the extra contribution that $2\psi_A\psi_B$ gives to the density must be the origin of bonding. This is called the **overlap density** because it represents an enhancement of the probability of finding the electron in the internuclear region due to orbital overlap. As the two atoms approach from infinite separation the overlap density increases from zero as the orbital energy decreases to the minimum value at the equilibrium nuclear separation of the stable molecular species. Thus, orbital overlap is the guide to assessing the bond strength. Figure 14.1 in the main text shows, however, that as the atoms approach more closely, severe nuclear repulsion causes the orbital energy to rapidly increase to a greater value than that of the separate atoms, and overlap is no longer an indicator of bond strength.

**D14.7** In the simple Hückel theory of hydrocarbon $\pi$-electron systems:

Only the carbon $p_z$ valence orbitals of $sp^2$ hybridized carbon atoms contribute to the LCAO of the $\pi$ system. This is justified to an extent because the hybrization approximation gives reasonable estimates in many instances and $p_z$ orbitals do not overlap with $sp^2$ hybridized orbitals.

All overlap integrals are set equal to zero. Overlap integrals have small values and their neglect eases the mathematics so that an indication of the molecular orbital energy level diagram can be obtained.

All terms of the form $H_{AA}$ equal $\alpha$ (a negative quantity). The electronic environments of each $sp^2$ hybridized carbon are very similar, thereby, making all $p_z$ valence orbitals equal in size and energy.

All terms of the form $H_{AB}$ equal $\beta$ (a negative quantity) if the atoms are neighbours and to zero otherwise. In addition to a justification similar to that for $H_{AA}$, when A and B are not neighbours the $p_{zA}$ orbital overlap with the $p_{zB}$ orbital is negligibly small.

These approximations are obviously very severe, but they let us calculate at least a general picture of the molecular orbital energy levels with very little work.

**D14.8** In *ab initio* methods an attempt is made to evaluate the Schrödinger equation numerically without employing empirical information. Approximations are employed, but these are mainly associated with the construction of the wavefunctions involved in the integrals of the computation. *ab initio* computations are iterative in that each cycle of the computation gives an improved estimate of the energy and wavefunction that is used in the next calculation cycle. The computation is **self-consistent** in that the iteration of energy and wavefunction are repeated (after an initial approximation is made about the mathematical form of the wavefunction) until the energy and wavefunction, are unchanged to within some acceptable tolerance.

In semi-empirical methods, many of the integrals are expressed in terms of spectroscopic data or physical properties. Semi-empirical methods exist at several levels. At some levels, in order to simplify the calculations, many of the integrals are set equal to zero.

## Solutions to exercises

**E14.1** Figure 14.1 shows a plot of the Morse potential function for the parameters $R_e = 0.30$ nm and $D_e = 50$ kJ mol$^{-1}$ and the two values $a = 0.15$ nm$^{-1}$ and $0.30$ nm$^{-1}$.

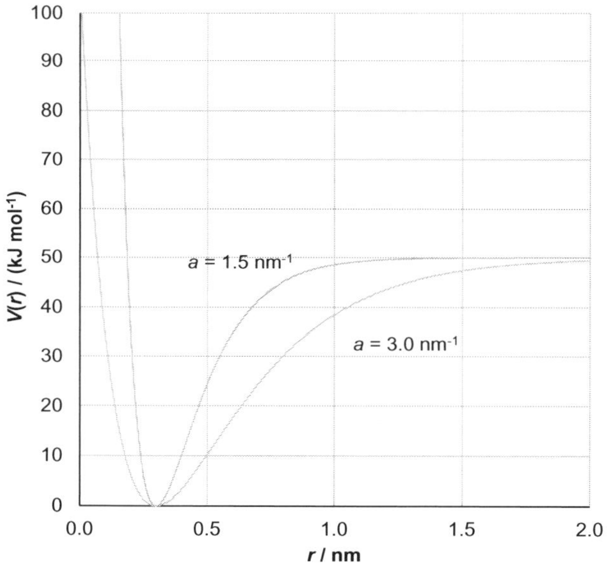


**Figure 14.1**

**E14.2** The energy of the Coulombic repulsion between the two nuclei is given by eqn 14.3,

$$V = \frac{Z_A Z_B e^2}{4\pi\epsilon_0 R}$$

$$= \frac{(+1)(+1)(1.602 \times 10^{-19}\ \text{C})^2}{4\pi \times (8.854 \times 10^{-12}\ \text{J}^{-1}\ \text{C}^2\ \text{m}^{-1}) \times (74.1 \times 10^{-12}\ \text{m})} = 3.11 \times 10^{-18}\ \text{J}$$

which is equivalent to a molar energy of

$$V_{\mathrm{m}} = N_A V = (6.022 \times 10^{23}\ \mathrm{mol}^{-1}) \times (3.11 \times 10^{-18}\ \mathrm{J})$$
$$= 1870 \times 10^{3}\ \mathrm{J\ mol}^{-1} = \mathbf{1870\ kJ\ mol^{-1}}$$

The value is positive, indicating that the interaction is repulsive.

**E14.3** The valence bond description of a C–H group in a molecule is a σ bond formed from the constructive overlap of the hydrogen 1s orbital with a hybridized carbon valence orbital. The unnormalised valence-bond description of a C–H group is thus

$$\psi_{\mathrm{C-H}} = \psi_{\mathrm{C}}(1)\psi_{\mathrm{H}}(2) + \psi_{\mathrm{C}}(2)\psi_{\mathrm{H}}(1)$$

When the carbon atom is bonded with four σ bonds, it is $sp^3$ hybridized and so we may write the wavefunction $\psi_{\mathrm{C}}$ as one of the linear combinations given in eqn 14.4. If the carbon is bonded with three σ bonds and one π bond, it is $sp^2$ hydridized and the appropriate linear combinations are given in eqn 14.5. Finally, when bonded with two σ bonds and two π bonds, it is sp hydridized and the appropriate functions are given in eqn 14.6.

**E14.4** The valence bond description of $P_2$ is similar to that of $N_2$: one $\sigma(2p_{zA}, 2p_{zB})$, one $\pi(2p_{xA}, 2p_{xB})$, and one $\pi(2p_{yA}, 2p_{yB})$ bond, along with their antibonding counterparts.

Elemental white phosphorus exists as a tetrahedral $P_4$ molecule, shown in Figure 14.2. There are six single P–P bonds each with a bond enthalpy of roughly 200 kJ mol$^{-1}$ so that, the total bonding enthalpy is approximately 1200 kJ mol$^{-1}$.

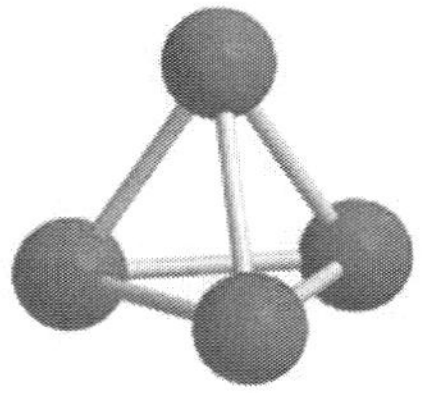

**Figure 14.2**

In the transformation

$$P_4 \rightarrow 2P_2$$

there is a loss of about 800 kJ mol$^{-1}$ in σ bond enthalpy. This loss is not likely to be made up by the formation of 4 P–P π bonds. Period 3 atoms, such as phosphorus, are too large to get close enough to each other to form strong π bonds. Thus, $P_4$ is more stable than $P_2$. White phosphorus is, however, unstable with respect to its oxides and it spontaneously combusts in air and must be stored under water.

**E14.5** The three valence-bond wavefunctions for $N_2$ are of the form described by eqn 14.2.

$$\psi_1(\sigma\text{-bond}) = \psi_{2p_zA}(1)\psi_{2p_zB}(1) + \psi_{2p_zA}(2)\psi_{2p_zB}(1)$$
$$\psi_2(\pi\text{-bond}) = \psi_{2p_xA}(1)\psi_{2p_xB}(1) + \psi_{2p_xA}(2)\psi_{2p_xB}(1)$$
$$\psi_3(\sigma\text{-bond}) = \psi_{2p_yA}(1)\psi_{2p_yB}(1) + \psi_{2p_yA}(2)\psi_{2p_yB}(1)$$

**E14.6** The six valence electrons from the sulfur atom plus two from each oxygen atoms gives ten electrons, and therefore five pairs, altogether. We may consider two of these pairs as being involved in pi bonding, leaving three $sp^2$ hybridised sigma pairs. Thus, the shape might be expected to be trigonal planar with a lone pair occupying one of the three positions. This prediction is consistent with the observed bond angle for $SO_2$, which is indeed 120°.

The exercise is a good example of the deficiencies of valence-bond theory. Although the explanation does predict the right shape, it does not give a good picture of the pi bonding.

**E14.7** The carbon atom in $CH_4$ is $sp^3$ hybridized and these four equivalent hybrid orbitals are given by the four linear combinations, $h_i$ ($i = 1$ to 4) in eqn 14.4. Numbering the hydrogen atoms from 1 to 4, and the two electrons in each bond as 1 and 2, the four valence-bond, C–H σ bonds are

$$\psi_{\sigma1} = \overbrace{h_1(1)}^{\substack{sp^3\\ \text{hybrid}}}\psi_{1sH1}(2) + h_1(2)\psi_{1sH1}(1)$$
$$\psi_{\sigma2} = h_2(1)\psi_{1sH2}(2) + h_2(2)\psi_{1sH2}(1)$$
$$\psi_{\sigma3} = h_3(1)\psi_{1sH3}(2) + h_3(2)\psi_{1sH3}(1)$$
$$\psi_{\sigma4} = h_4(1)\psi_{1sH4}(2) + h_4(2)\psi_{1sH4}(1)$$

**E14.8** Numbering the carbon atoms as shown in Figure 14.3, carbon atoms 5–15 each have three $sp^2$ hybrid atomic orbitals which form σ bonds with their neighbouring atoms.

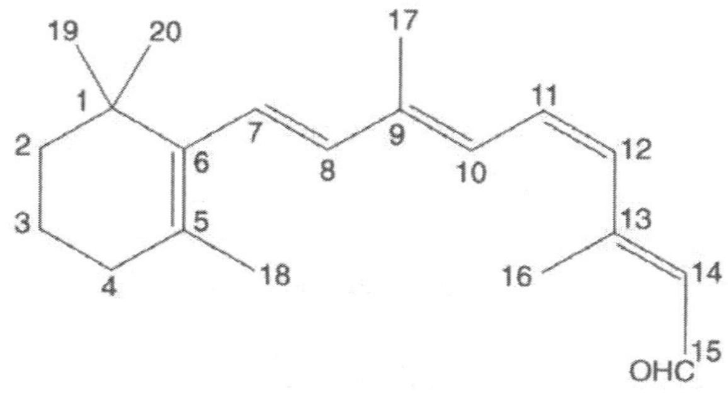


**Figure 14.3**

There are six conjugated π bonds between these eleven C atoms and the one O atom. These six π bonds are formed from twelve $p_x$ atomic orbitals, one on each of the twelve atoms. All are resonance hybrids of the form

$$\psi(\pi\text{-bond}) = \sum_{i=5}^{15} \psi_{2p_x C_i} + \psi_{2p_x O}$$

The remaining C atoms, 1–4, each have four $sp^3$ hybrid atomic orbitals which form σ bonds with their neighbouring atoms.

**E14.9** The structure of naphthalene, $C_{10}H_8$, may be represented by the three covalent resonance forms shown in Figure 14.4.

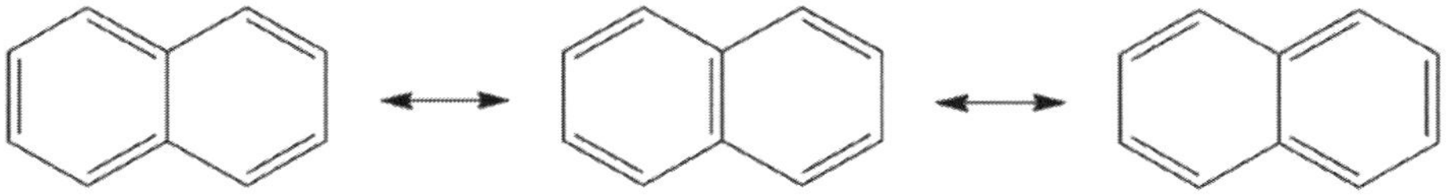

**Figure 14.4**

**E14.10** The normalized two-electron wavefunction is of the form

$$\psi = c_{cov}\psi_{cov} + c_{ion}\psi_{ion}$$

where $c_{cov} = 0.889$ and $c_{ion} = 0.458$. The probability density of the electron pair is given by the square of the wavefunction

$$\psi^2 = c_{cov}^2\psi_{cov}^2 + c_{ion}^2\psi_{ion}^2 + c_{cov}c_{ion}\psi_{cov}\psi_{ion}$$

The coefficient $c_{cov}^{\;2}$ is the probability density if the pair were confined to the covalent bond, $c_{ion}^{\;2}$ is the probability density if the pair were confined to one atom as an ionic bond and $c_{cov}c_{ion}$ is an extra contribution to the density due to overlap. Thus, the ionic probability, where both electrons are confined to one atom, is

$$c_{ion}^2 = 0.458^2 = 0.210$$

In 1000 inspections, both electrons will be observed on one atom 210 times.

**E14.11** Figure 14.5 represents three structures that involve only covalent sigma and pi bonds and Figure 14.6 shows two structures that also involve ionic bonding, although there are many more. These structures can be safely ignored in simple descriptions of the molecule because the coefficients of the wavefunction representing these structures in the linear combination of wavefunctions for the entire resonance hybrid are very small. Benzene is a very symmetrical molecule, and we expect that all the carbon atoms will be equivalent. Hence, those structures in which the carbon atoms are not equivalent should contribute little to the resonance hybrid.

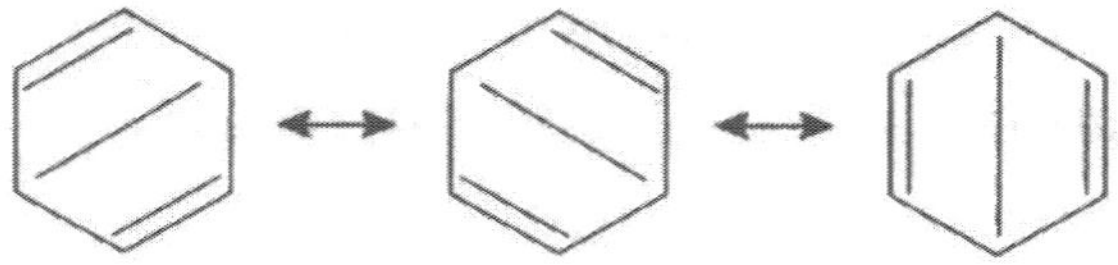

Figure 14.5

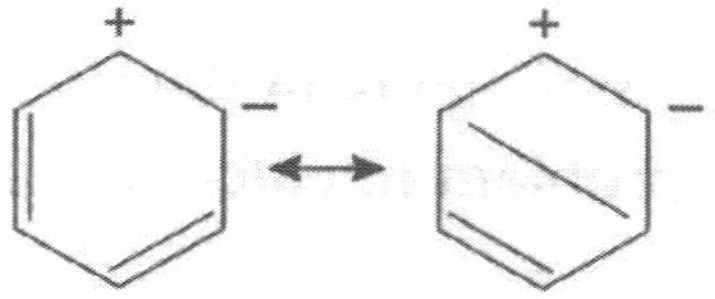


Figure 14.6

**E14.12** The wavefunctions of a particle in a box are given by eqn 12.8

$$\psi_n = N \sin\frac{n\pi x}{L}, \qquad \text{with } n = 1, 2, 3, \ldots$$

and are shown in Figure 14.7.

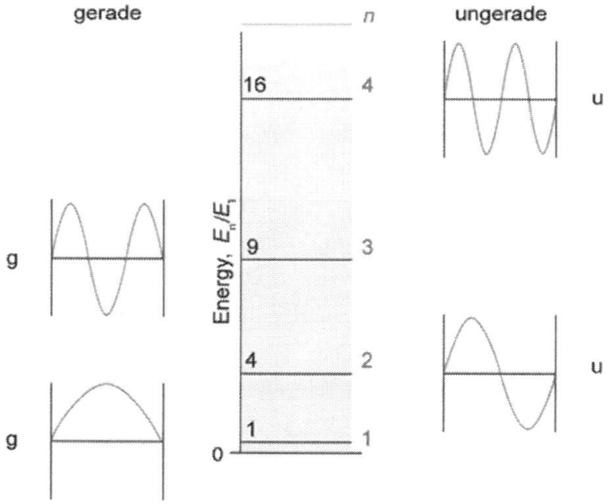


Figure 14.7

It can be seen from the figure that wavefunctions for odd values of the quantum number $n$ are symmetric with respect to inversion through the centre of the box and are therefore designated as gerade, or of g symmetry. In contrast, wavefunctions with even values of $n$

are antisymmetric with respect to inversion and are therefore of ungerade, or of u symmetry.

**E14.13** The unnormalised vibrational wavefunctions for the first four levels of a harmonic oscillator are shown in Figure 14.8. As for the particle in a box, wavefunctions for odd values of the quantum number $v$ are symmetric with respect to inversion through the centre of the box and are therefore designated as gerade, or of g symmetry. In the same way, wavefunctions with even values of $v$ are antisymmetric with respect to inversion and are therefore of ungerade, or of u symmetry.

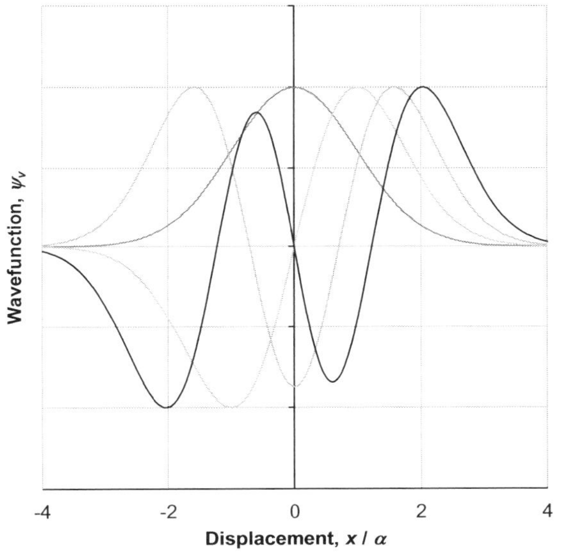


**Figure 14.8**

**E14.14** For a particle in a two-dimensional rectangular box, the wavefunction for each state may be expressed as the product of two one-dimensional wavefunctions, according to eqn 12.14

$$\psi_{n_X,n_Y}(x,y) = X_{n_X}(x)Y_{n_Y}(y)$$

The two one-dimensional wavefunctions have even parity when their respective quantum numbers, $n_X$ and $n_Y$, are odd and odd parity when their respective quantum numbers are even. A state will have odd parity when one of the wavefunctions has odd parity while the other has even parity. Similarly, a state will have even parity when either both of the wavefunctions have odd parity or both have even parity.

The structure of naphthalene is shown in Figure 14.9. It can be seen that the molecule has five pi bonds, and therefore ten pi electrons. Each quantum state may be occupied by two electrons. Thus, we need to consider the parity of the first five states.

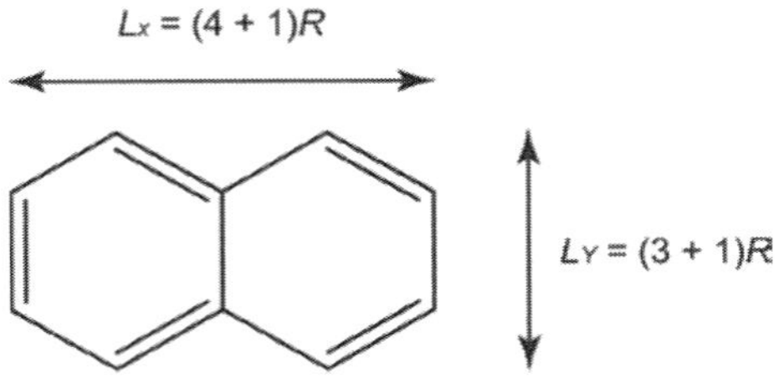


**Figure 14.9**

The energies of the states are given by eqn 12.14b

$$E_{n_X,n_Y} = E_{n_X} + E_{n_Y} = \left(\frac{n_X^2}{L_X^2} + \frac{n_Y^2}{L_Y^2}\right)\frac{h^2}{8m}$$

Taking the length of each bond as $R$ and allowing for the box to extend beyond the molecule, then the dimensions of the box may be taken as $L_X = 5R$ and $L_Y = 4R$. The five lowest energy states are thus those with quantum numbers $(n_X, n_Y) = (1, 1), (2, 1), (1, 2), (2, 2)$ and $(3, 1)$. The parities of these states are therefore even, odd, odd, odd, even, even respectively.

| | | | | | | |
|---|---|---|---|---|---|---|
| | $n_X$ | 1 | 2 | 1 | 2 | 3 |
| | $n_Y$ | 1 | 1 | 2 | 2 | 1 |
| Energy / $(h^2 / 3200m_e)$ | | 41 | 89 | 116 | 164 | 169 |
| Parity | $\psi_X$ | even | odd | even | odd | even |
| | $\psi_Y$ | even | even | odd | odd | odd |
| | $\psi_X\psi_Y$ | even | odd | odd | even | odd |

**E14.15** Figure 14.10 gives two examples of bonding interactions between d and p orbitals. The equivalent antibonding orbitals may be derived by reversing the phase of the p orbitals.

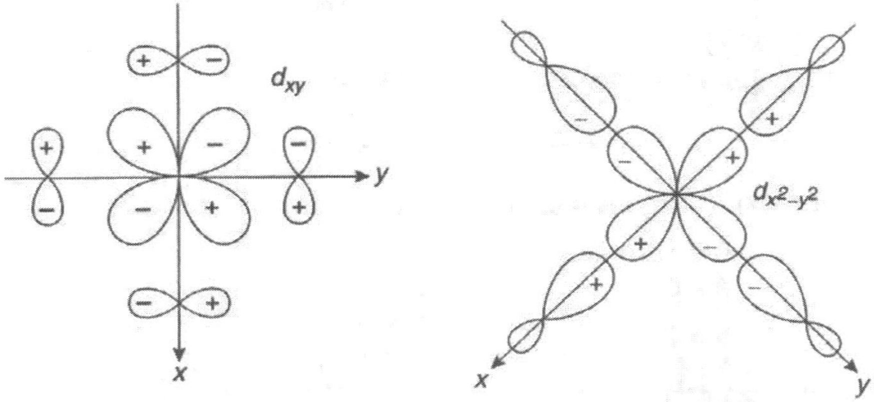


**Figure 14.10**

**E14.16** In order to anticipate the form that the bonding and antibonding $\phi$ orbitals that could be constructed from two neighbouring f atomic orbitals, we must first deduce the shape and parity of the seven f orbitals. An atomic orbital with angular momentum quantum number $l$ has $l$ angular nodes. We therefore expect f orbitals to possess $l = 3$ angular nodes. Furthermore, atomic orbitals with even values of $l$ are of gerade parity and those with odd values are of ungerade parity. Thus, we may conclude that f orbitals have ungerade parity. We may therefore predict that f orbitals are represented either by functions, or by linear combinations of functions, that consist of six lobes. The shapes of the f orbitals are shown in Figure 14.11.

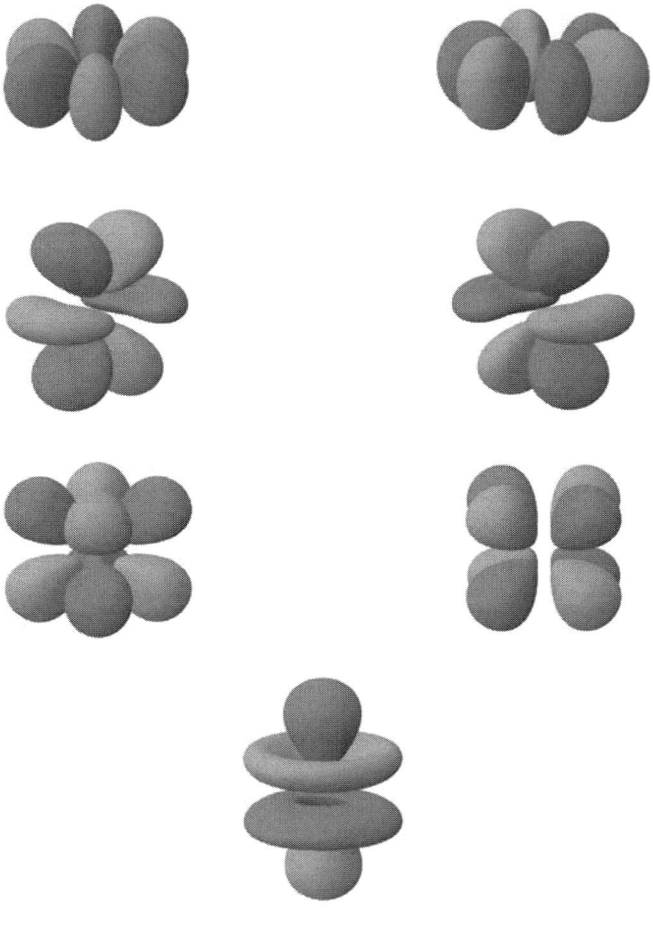

**Figure 14.11**

These f orbitals may overlap to give $\sigma$, $\pi$, $\delta$ and $\phi$ bonds, which are characterized by 0, 1, 2 and 3 nodal planes along the internuclear axis respectively. Figure 14.12 shows the form of a bonding and an antibonding $\phi$ orbital formed between two f atomic orbitals.

Combinations of other f orbitals may also give rise to $\phi$ bonds. The shapes of these $\phi$ bonds are more complicated, but are still characterised by having three nodal planes.

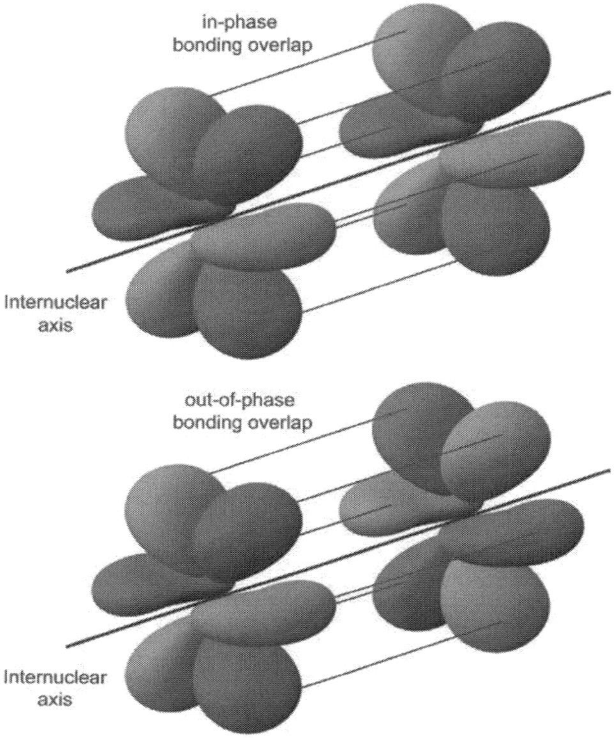


**Figure 14.12**

**E14.17** Using molecular orbital theory to write the electronic configurations of the various species allows us to predict the bond order of each. For example, for $F_2^-$, the electronic configuration is

$$F_2^-:\ 1\sigma_g^2\,1\sigma_u^2\,2\sigma_g^2\,1\pi_u^4\,1\pi_g^4\,2\sigma_u^1$$

so that there are $N = 8$ bonding electrons and $N^* = 7$ antibonding electrons giving a bond order of

$$b = \tfrac{1}{2}(8 - 6) = \tfrac{1}{2}$$

In the same way, we find that for the other species, removing an electron from an antibonding orbital to form $F_2$ strengthens the bond

$$F_2:\ 1\sigma_g^2\,1\sigma_u^2\,2\sigma_g^2\,1\pi_u^4\,1\pi_g^4 \qquad b = \tfrac{1}{2}(8 - 6) = 1$$

and removing a further electron from a bonding orbital weakens the bond once more.

$$F_2^+:\ 1\sigma_g^2\,1\sigma_u^2\,2\sigma_g^2\,1\pi_u^4\,1\pi_g^3 \qquad b = \tfrac{1}{2}(7 - 6) = \tfrac{1}{2}$$

**E14.18** We may identify the bond order of each species using the approach adopted in the previous exercise. Thus, the electronic configurations and bond orders of the various species are

$O_2^+$: $1\sigma_g^2\,1\sigma_u^2\,2\sigma_g^2\,1\pi_u^4\,1\pi_g^1$ $\quad b = ½(8-3) = 2½$
$O_2$: $1\sigma_g^2\,1\sigma_u^2\,2\sigma_g^2\,1\pi_u^4\,1\pi_g^2$ $\quad b = ½(8-4) = 2$
$O_2^-$: $1\sigma_g^2\,1\sigma_u^2\,2\sigma_g^2\,1\pi_u^4\,1\pi_g^3$ $\quad b = ½(8-5) = 1½$
$O_2^{2-}$: $1\sigma_g^2\,1\sigma_u^2\,2\sigma_g^2\,1\pi_u^4\,1\pi_g^4$ $\quad b = ½(8-6) = 1$

We expect the species with the highest bond order to have the strongest bond and thus the shortest bond length. Hence the bond lengths are predicted to increase in the order

$$O_2^+ < O_2 < O_2^- < O_2^{2-}$$

**E14.19** Using molecular orbital theory, and considering only the valence orbitals:

(a) $H_2^-$: $1\sigma_g^2 1\sigma_u^1$
(b) $Li_2$: $1\sigma_g^2$
(c) $Be_2$: $1\sigma_g^2\,1\sigma_u^2$
(d) $C_2$: $1\sigma_g^2\,1\sigma_u^2\,2\sigma_g^2\,1\pi_u^2$
(e) $N_2$: $1\sigma_g^2\,1\sigma_u^2\,2\sigma_g^2\,1\pi_u^4$
(f) $O_2$: $1\sigma_g^2\,1\sigma_u^2\,2\sigma_g^2\,1\pi_u^4\,1\pi_g^2$

**E14.20** Considering only the valence orbitals, the ground-state electronic configurations, and bond orders, of $B_2$ and $C_2$ are

$B_2$: $1\sigma_g^2\,1\sigma_u^2\,2\sigma_g^2$ $\quad b = ½(N - N^*) = ½(4-2) = 1$
$C_2$: $1\sigma_g^2\,1\sigma_u^2\,2\sigma_g^2\,1\pi_u^2$ $\quad b = ½(N - N^*) = ½(6-2) = 2$

Thus, because $C_2$ has a bond order of 2, and $B_2$ a bond order of 1, we might expect $C_2$ to have the strongest bond and thus the highest dissociation energy.

**E14.21** The total number of atomic orbitals in a single set of s, p, d, and f subshells is

$$1 + 3 + 5 + 7 = 16$$

In a diatomic molecule there would therefore be $2 \times 16 = 32$ atomic orbitals from which 32 molecular orbitals can be constructed.

**E14.22** The parity of a system represents the symmetry of the wavefunction with respect to inversion through a centre of symmetry. We may see from Figures 14.18 and 14.26 of the text that, in general, $\sigma$ and $\pi^*$ orbitals are of gerade symmetry and $\sigma^*$ and $\pi$ orbitals are of ungerade symmetry. We may extend this pattern to predict that $\delta$ orbitals will be of gerade symmetry and $\delta^*$ orbitals of ungerade symmetry. It therefore follows that:

(a) the $2\pi^*$ orbital in $F_2$ is symmetric with respect to inversion through the centre of the molecule, so is of **gerade** symmetry;

(b) NO is a heteronuclear diatomic molecule and thus does not possess a centre of symmetry and thus the concept of parity is thus not valid for NO,

(c) the 1δ bonding orbital of $Tl_2$ is is symmetric with respect to inversion through the centre of the molecule, and thus of **gerade** symmetry;

(d) the $2\delta^*$ antibonding orbital of $Fe_2$ is antisymmetric with respect to inversion through the centre of symmetry and thus is of **ungerade** symmetry.

**E14.23** Molecules will be stabilized if an electron is added to a bonding orbital or removed from an antibonding orbital. The electronic configurations of $C_2$, CN, $N_2$, NO, $O_2$, and $F_2$ are

$$C_2\!: 1\sigma_g^2\, 1\sigma_u^2\, 2\sigma_g^2\, 1\pi_u^2$$
$$CN\!: 1\sigma^2\, 2\sigma^2\, 3\sigma^2\, 1\pi^3$$
$$N_2\!: 1\sigma_g^2\, 1\sigma_u^2\, 2\sigma_g^2\, 1\pi_u^4$$
$$NO\!: 1\sigma_g^2\, 1\sigma_u^2\, 2\sigma_g^2\, 1\pi_u^4\, 1\pi_g^1$$
$$O_2\!: 1\sigma_g^2\, 1\sigma_u^2\, 2\sigma_g^2\, 1\pi_u^4\, 1\pi_g^2$$
$$F_2\!: 1\sigma_g^2\, 1\sigma_u^2\, 2\sigma_g^2\, 1\pi_u^4\, 1\pi_g^4$$

CN is a heteronuclear diatomic molecule and so does not possess a centre of symmetry. the molecular orbitals cannot, therefore, be assigned a gerade or ungerade parity.

Consideration of the configurations shows that only for $C_2$ and CN, does an additional electron enter a bonding orbital and make the anion more stable than the neutral molecule. For NO, $O_2$ and $F_2$, if an electron is removed, it is lost from an antibonding orbital, and thus the cations are more stable than the neutral molecule.

**E14.24** Using molecular orbital theory to deduce the electronic configurations and thus bond orders of NO and $N_2$ gives

$$N_2\!: 1\sigma_g^2\, 1\sigma_u^2\, 2\sigma_g^2\, 1\pi_u^4 \qquad b = \tfrac{1}{2}(N - N^*) = \tfrac{1}{2}(8 - 2) = 3$$
$$NO\!: 1\sigma^2\, 2\sigma^2\, 3\sigma^2\, 1\pi^4\, 2\pi^1 \qquad b = \tfrac{1}{2}(N - N^*) = \tfrac{1}{2}(8 - 3) = 2\tfrac{1}{2}$$

Note that because NO is a heteronuclear diatomic molecule, it does not possess a centre of symmetry and the orbitals cannot be assigned a gerade or ungerade parity. We expect the species with the highest bond order to have the strongest, and therefore the shortest bond. Thus, we predict that the length of the bond in $N_2$ is shorter than that in NO. This is indeed the case: the equilibrium bond lengths of $N_2$ and NO have been found experimentally to be 109 and 115 pm respectively.

**E14.25** The electronic configurations of CO, NO and $CN^-$ are, by analogy with the equivalent isoelectronic homonuclear diatomic molecules,

$$CN^-\!: 1\sigma^2\, 2\sigma^2\, 3\sigma^2\, 1\pi^4$$
$$CO\!: 1\sigma^2\, 2\sigma^2\, 3\sigma^2\, 1\pi^4$$
$$NO\!: 1\sigma^2\, 2\sigma^2\, 3\sigma^2\, 1\pi^4\, 2\pi^1$$

Note that $CN^-$ and CO have the same electronic configuration.

**E14.26** Figure 14.13 shows the molecular orbital energy-level diagram for XeF. The electronic configuration is $1\sigma^2\, 2\sigma^2\, 1\pi^4\, 3\sigma^2\, 2\pi\, 4\sigma^1$, and has a bond order of ½.

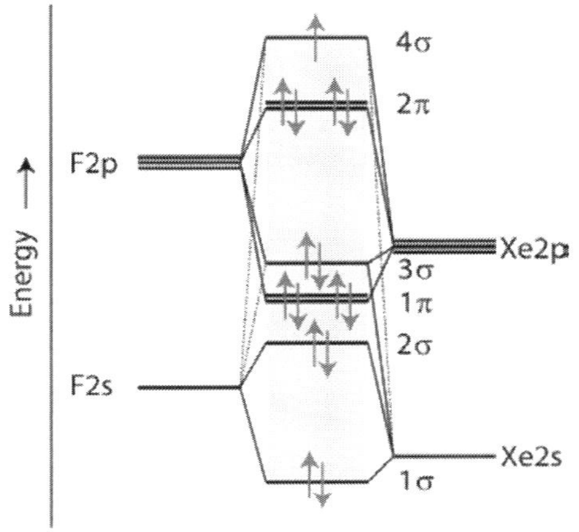


**Figure 14.13**

The molecular orbital diagram shows that an electron is removed from an antibonding orbital upon ionisation. The bond order is therefore increased when $XeF^+$ is formed from XeF and $XeF^+$ will have a shorter bond length than XeF.

**E14.27** (a) The molecular orbital energy level diagram of the hybridized $CH_2$ fragments and ethene, $CH_2{=}CH_2$, is shown in Figure 14.14. Only the C–C bonding is shown; the remaining two $sp^2$ hydrids within each fragment form σ C–H bonds. The σ and π symmetry labels are appropriate only for the C–C fragment. The energies, and therefore the order, of the molecular orbitals will depend upon the exact strength of these interactions, which are not drawn to scale. Note, however, that the π-bonding orbital must be lower in energy than the σ-antibonding orbital for π-bonding to exist in ethene.

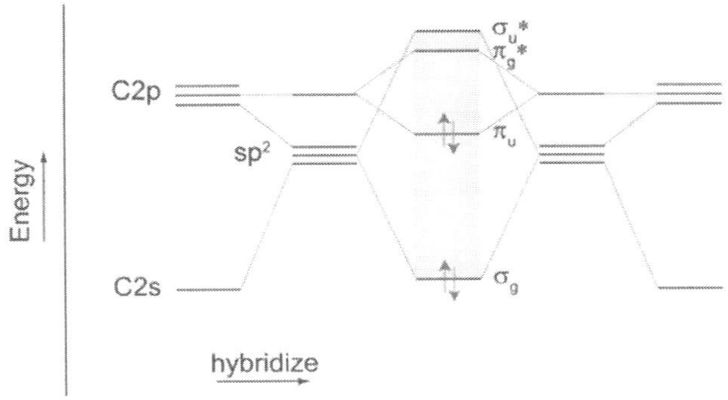


**Figure 14.14**

(b) The molecular orbital energy level diagram of the hybridized CH fragments and ethyne, CH≡CH is shown in Figure 14.15. Once again, only the C–C bonding is shown; the remaining sp hydrids form σ C–H bonds.

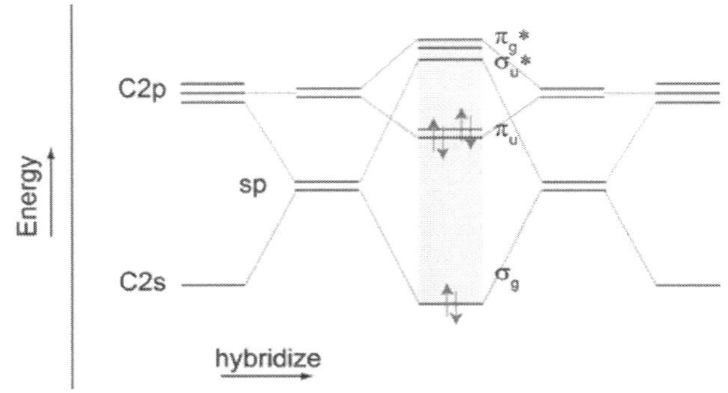


**Figure 14.15**

**E14.28** The Pauling electronegativities given in Table 14.2 are $\chi_H = 2.1$, $\chi_B = 2.0$, and $\chi_P = 2.1$.

(a) The P–H bond should be nonpolar as the electronegativities of P and H are identical.

(b) The B–H bond should be slightly polarized toward H as the electronegativity of H is slightly larger.

**E14.29** Using Figure 14.37 of the text, we can see that the symmetries of the six π-orbitals of benzene are, in order of increasing energy, $a_{2u}$, $e_{1g}$, $e_{2u}$ and $b_{2g}$. The parities of these orbitals may be confirmed by considering whether the wavefunction is symmetric or antisymmetric with respect to inversion through the centre of the molecule.

**E14.30** (a) According to free-electron molecular orbital theory, the orbitals are represented by the wavefunctions for a particle in a box, eqn 12.8

$$\psi_n(x) = (2/L)^{1/2} \sin\frac{n\pi x}{L}, \text{ with } n = 0, 1, 2, 3 \ldots$$

Butadiene has four π-electrons, which occupy the two lowest energy molecular orbitals in pairs. These orbitals are represented by the wavefunctions $\psi_1$ and $\psi_2$, which are shown in Figure 14.16. Superimposed on the wavefunction are the p orbitals that together make up the π system.

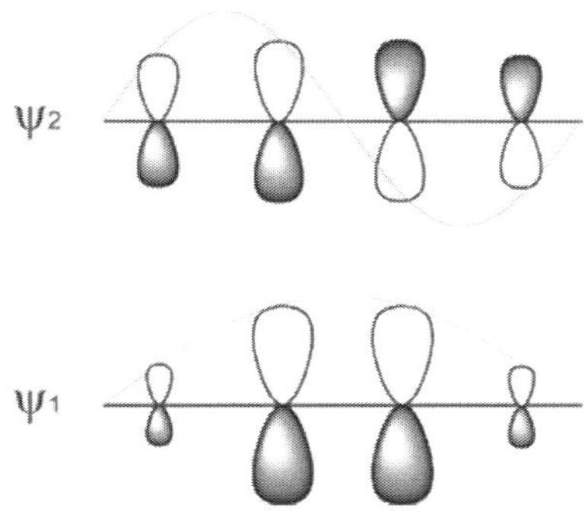


**Figure 14.16**

The figure shows that for the ground state, all of the atomic orbitals are in phase. For the first excited state, however, only pairs of orbitals are in phase, with an out-of-phase overlap between the pairs.

The energy levels of a particle in a box are also given by eqn 12.8

$$E_n = \frac{n^2h^2}{8m_eL^2}$$

The energy of the levels depends quadratically on the quantum number $n$, so that the lowest energy, longest wavelength excitation must correspond to the transition of an electron from the highest occupied molecular orbital (HOMO), $\psi_2$, to the lowest unoccupied molecular orbital (LUMO), $\psi_3$. For butadiene, with the length of the box given by $L = 4R$ to allow for the extension by half a bond length at each end of the molecule, and $R = 140$ pm,

$$\begin{aligned}\Delta E = E_3 - E_2 &= \frac{(3^2 - 2^2)h^2}{8m_e(4R)^2} = \frac{5h^2}{128m_eL^2}\\ &= \frac{5 \times (6.626 \times 10^{-34}\,\mathrm{J\ s})^2}{128 \times (9.109 \times 10^{-31}\ \mathrm{kg}) \times (140 \times 10^{-12}\mathrm{m})^2}\\ &= 9.61 \times 10^{-19}\ \mathrm{J}\end{aligned}$$

which is equivalent to

$$\Delta E = (1.92 \times 10^{-18}\ \mathrm{J})/(1.602 \times 10^{-19}\ \mathrm{J\ eV^{-1}}) = \mathbf{6.00\ eV}$$

or a wavelength of

$$\begin{aligned}\lambda = hc/\Delta E &= (6.626 \times 10^{-34}\mathrm{J\ s}) \times (2.998 \times 10^{8}\ \mathrm{m\ s^{-1}})/(1.92 \times 10^{-18}\ \mathrm{J})\\ &= 103 \times 10^{-9}\mathrm{m} = \mathbf{103\ nm}\end{aligned}$$

(b) In the same way for a tetraene with eight $\pi$ electrons, the first four molecular orbitals are doubly occupied. The lowest energy excitation is thus from the highest occupied molecular orbital, $\psi_4$, to the lowest unoccupied molecular orbital, $\psi_5$. The wavefunctions representing these orbitals are shown in Figure 14.17.

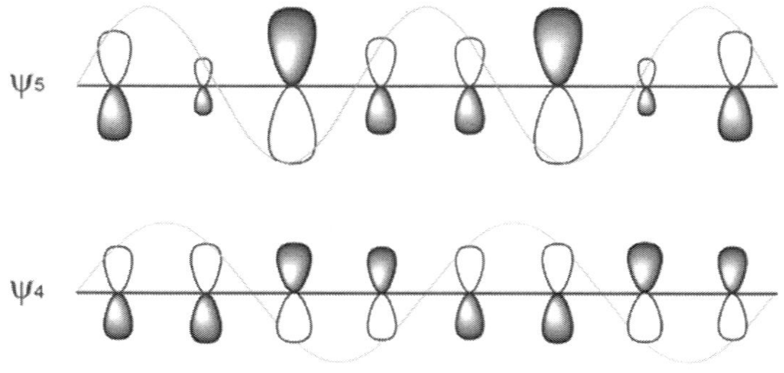


**Figure 14.17**

$$\Delta E = E_5 - E_4 = \frac{(5^2 - 4^2)h^2}{8m_e(8R)^2} = \frac{9h^2}{512m_eL^2}$$
$$= \frac{9 \times (6.626 \times 10^{-34}\text{J s})^2}{512 \times (9.109 \times 10^{-31}\text{ kg}) \times (140 \times 10^{-12}\text{m})^2}$$
$$= 4.32 \times 10^{-19}\text{ J}$$

which is equivalent to

$$\Delta E = (4.32 \times 10^{-19}\text{ J})/(1.602 \times 10^{-19}\text{ J eV}^{-1}) = \mathbf{2.70\ eV}$$

or a wavelength of

$$\lambda = hc/\Delta E = (6.626 \times 10^{-34}\text{J s}) \times (2.998 \times 10^8\text{ m s}^{-1})/(4.32 \times 10^{-19}\text{ J})$$
$$= 460 \times 10^{-9}\text{m} = \mathbf{460\ nm}$$

The example demonstrates that as the number of conjugated atoms within the $\pi$-system increases, the wavelength of the lowest energy transition increases. Thus, for butadiene, with four carbon atoms, this transition falls in the vacuum ultraviolet region of the spectrum, whereas for tetraene with eight carbon atoms, the transition is observed in the visible region of the spectrum.

**E14.31** For a conjugated alkene, each atom contributes one electron to the $\pi$ electron system. Thus, for an alkene consisting of $N$ carbon atoms and therefore $N$ $\pi$ electrons, because the electrons enter the orbitals in pairs, then numbering the orbitals in order of increasing energy, the highest occupied molecular orbital (HOMO) is that with $N/2$, and the lowest unoccupied molecular orbital is that with $N/2+1$. The difference in energy between these two orbitals is therefore

$$\Delta E = E_{\text{LUMO}} - E_{\text{HOMO}} = \left\{\alpha + 2\beta\cos\frac{(N/2+1)\pi}{N+1}\right\} - \left\{\alpha + 2\beta\cos\frac{(N/2)\pi}{N+1}\right\}$$
$$= 2\beta\left\{\cos\frac{(N/2+1)\pi}{N+1} - \cos\frac{(N/2)\pi}{N+1}\right\}$$

The transition wavenumber is related to this difference in energy through eqn 0.21b

$$\Delta E = hc\tilde{\nu}$$

Thus, rearranging and solving for $\beta$ for each polyene yields the values shown in the table.

| Species | $N$ | $\tilde{\nu}$ / cm$^{-1}$ | ($\beta_{\text{FEMO}}$ / $hc$) / cm$^{-1}$ |
|---|---|---|---|
| ethene, $C_2H_4$ | 2 | 61500 | −30750 |
| butadiene, $C_4H_6$ | 4 | 46080 | −37280 |
| hexatriene, $C_6H_8$ | 6 | 39750 | −44660 |
| octatetraene $C_8H_{10}$ | 8 | 32900 | −47370 |

Examination of the table reveals that $\beta_{\text{FEMO}}$ is not a constant for the series. However, it is reasonable to estimate that $\beta/hc \approx$ **−40000 cm$^{-1}$**, which is equivalent to −5.0 eV for the homologous series.

(b) The total energy of the π electron system is the sum of the energies of the occupied orbitals weighted by the number of electrons that occupy them. In octatetraene, $C_8H_{10}$, each of the first four orbitals are doubly occupied, so that

$$E_{\pi} = 2\sum_{k=1}^{4} E_k = 2\sum_{k=1}^{4}\left(\alpha + 2\beta\cos\frac{k\pi}{N+1}\right) = 8\alpha + 4\beta\sum_{k=1}^{4}\cos\frac{k\pi}{9} = 8\alpha + 9.518\beta$$

The delocalization energy is the difference between this quantity and that of four isolated double bonds

$$E_{\text{deloc}} = E_{\pi} - 4\times 2(\alpha+\beta) = (8\alpha + 9.518\beta) - (8\alpha + 8\beta) = 1.518\beta$$

Using the estimate of $\beta$ for octatetraene from the above table yields

$$E_{\text{deloc}}/hc = 1.518 \times (-47370\ \text{cm}^{-1}) = \mathbf{60720\ cm^{-1}}$$

which is equivalent to 7.35 eV.

**E14.32** (a) According to the Hückel model, the energy levels of monocyclic conjugated polyenes, such as cyclobutadiene, benzene and cyclooctaene, which have even numbers of carbon atoms $N$, are given by

$$E_k = \alpha + 2\beta\cos\frac{2k\pi}{N}, \text{ with } k = 0, \pm1, \pm2, \pm3, \ldots \pm (N/2)$$

For benzene, $N = 6$, the energies of the π orbitals are

$$E_0 = \alpha + 2\beta$$
$$E_{\pm1} = \alpha + \beta$$
$$E_{\pm2} = \alpha - \beta$$
$$E_{\pm3} = \alpha - 2\beta$$

and for cyclooctaene with $N = 8$

$$\begin{aligned}
E_0 &= \alpha + 2\beta \\
E_{\pm 1} &= \alpha + \sqrt{2}\beta \\
E_{\pm 2} &= \alpha \\
E_{\pm 3} &= \alpha - \sqrt{2}\beta \\
E_{\pm 4} &= \alpha - 2\beta
\end{aligned}$$

In each case, the lowest and highest energy levels are non-degenerate, while the other energy levels are doubly degenerate. The degeneracy is clear for all energy levels except, perhaps, the highest: each value of the quantum number $k$ corresponds to a separate molecular orbital, and positive and negative values of $k$ therefore give rise to a pair of molecular orbitals of the same energy. This is not the case for the highest energy level, though, because there are only as many molecular orbitals as there were atomic orbitals input to the calculation, which is the same as the number of carbon atoms. Thus, for benzene, we expect six, and for cyclooctaene, we expect eight molecular orbitals.

(b) The delocalisation energy is defined as the difference between the energy of the conjugated π system and the energy of the equivalent number of separate π bonds. Thus, for benzene, in which the first three orbitals are doubly occupied,

$$\begin{aligned}
E_{\text{deloc}} &= (2E_0 + 2E_1 + 2E_{-1}) - (3 \times 2 \times E_\pi) \\
&= \{2 \times (\alpha + 2\beta) + 2 \times (\alpha + \beta) + 2 \times (\alpha + \beta)\} - \{6 \times (\alpha + \beta)\} \\
&= (6\alpha + 8\beta) - (6\alpha + 6\beta) = \mathbf{2\beta}
\end{aligned}$$

The energy levels of the equivalent linear conjugated polyene, hexatriene are given by the expression from the previous exercise

$$E_k = \alpha + 2\beta \cos\frac{k\pi}{N+1}, \text{ with } k = 1, 2, 3, \ldots N$$

and so the energies of the three doubly occupied orbitals are

$$\begin{aligned}
E_1 &= \alpha + 1.802\beta \\
E_2 &= \alpha + 1.247\beta \\
E_3 &= \alpha + 0.445\beta
\end{aligned}$$

The delocalisation energy for hexatriene is thus

$$\begin{aligned}
E_{\text{deloc}} &= (2E_1 + 2E_2 + 2E_3) - (3 \times 2 \times E_\pi) \\
&= \{2 \times (\alpha + 1.802\beta) + 2 \times (\alpha + 1.247\beta) + 2 \times (\alpha + 0.445\beta)\} \\
&\qquad - \{6 \times (\alpha + \beta)\} \\
&= (6\alpha + 6.988\beta) - (6\alpha + 6\beta) = \mathbf{0.988\beta}
\end{aligned}$$

The delocalisation energy of benzene is thus considerable greater than that for hexatriene. We may therefore infer that, for polyenes with six electrons, the delocalisation energy for the cyclic system is considerably greater than for the linear system.

(c) In cyclooctaene, there are eight π electrons. The first three orbitals, which are the non-degenerate lowest orbital with energy $E_0$ and the doubly degenerate pair of orbitals with energy $E_1 = E_{-1}$, will all be doubly occupied. We know, in general, that electrons tend to occupy degenerate orbitals separately, rather than in pairs. This implies that the next two electrons singly occupy each of the next doubly degenerate pair of orbitals with energy $E_2 = E_{-2}$ rather than doubly occupying just one of the orbitals. However, Hückel theory does not take account this difference in energy due to the spins of the electrons. Thus, at this level of theory these two configurations have the same energy. The delocalisation energy of cycloocatene is thus

$$\begin{aligned} E_{\text{deloc}} &= (2E_0 + 2E_1 + 2E_{-1} + E_2 + E_{-2}) - (3 \times 2 \times E_\pi) \\ &= \{2 \times (\alpha + 2\beta) + 4 \times (\alpha + \sqrt{2}\beta) + 2 \times (\alpha)\} - \{8 \times (\alpha + \beta)\} \\ &= \{8\alpha + 4(1 + \sqrt{2})\beta\} - (8\alpha + 8\beta) = \mathbf{1.657\beta} \end{aligned}$$

For octatetrene, the energies of the four double occupied orbitals are

$$\begin{aligned} E_1 &= \alpha + 1.879\beta \\ E_2 &= \alpha + 1.532 \\ E_3 &= \alpha + \beta \\ E_4 &= \alpha + 0.437\beta \end{aligned}$$

so that the delocalisation energy is

$$\begin{aligned} E_{\text{deloc}} &= (2E_1 + 2E_2 + 2E_3 + 2E_4) - (4 \times 2 \times E_\pi) \\ &= \{2 \times (\alpha + 1.879\beta) + 2 \times (\alpha + 1.532) + 2 \times (\alpha + \beta) + 2 \times \alpha + 0.437\beta\} \\ &\qquad - \{8 \times (\alpha + \beta)\} \\ &= \{8\alpha + 9.517\beta\} - (8\alpha + 8\beta) = \mathbf{1.517\beta} \end{aligned}$$

Thus, for systems with eight electrons, there is little difference between the delocalisation energy for the cyclic and linear molecules.

This exercise is an illustration of the Huckel $4n + 2$ rule. Compounds, such as benzene, that possess planar, cyclic conjugated π systems with $4n + 2$ electrons are described as aromatic. The delocalisation energy for such compounds is greater than for those such as cyclooctaene, with conjugated π systems with $4n + 4$ electrons. It is this extra delocalisation energy that is the explanation for the special stability of aromatic compounds.

**E14.33** The symmetries of the six π orbitals of benzene are given in Figure 14.37 as, in order of increasing energy, $1a_{2u}$, $1e_{1g}$, $1e_{2u}$ and $1b_{2g}$. The $1a_{2u}$ and $1b_{2g}$ levels are singly degenerate and may be occupied by two electrons, whereas the $1e_{1g}$ and $1e_{2u}$ levels are doubly degenerate and so may accommodate four electrons. The energies of the orbitals are given in the following table. The $1a_{2u}$ and $1e_{1g}$ orbitals have energies of $\alpha + 2\beta$ and $\alpha + \beta$ respectively and may therefore be considered to be bonding. The $1e_{2u}$ and $1b_{2g}$ orbitals have energies of $\alpha - \beta$ and $\alpha - 2\beta$ respectively are antibonding.

The electronic configurations of the benzene anion is therefore

$$C_6H_6^-: 1a_{2u}^2\ 1e_{1g}^4\ 1e_{1u}^1$$

with a delocalisation energy

$$E_{\text{deloc}} = 2E_{1a_{2u}} + 4E_{1e_{1g}} + E_{1e_{2u}} = 2(\alpha + 2\beta) + 4(\alpha + \beta) + (\alpha - \beta) = \mathbf{7\alpha + 7\beta}$$

and the benzene cation is

$$C_6H_6^+: 1a_{2u}^2\ 1e_{1g}^3$$

with a delocalisation energy

$$E_{\text{deloc}} = 2E_{1a_{2u}} + 3E_{1e_{1g}} = 2(\alpha + 2\beta) + 3(\alpha + \beta) = \mathbf{5\alpha + 7\beta}$$

## Answers to projects

**P14.34** (a) For two functions, such as orbitals, to be orthogonal then the integral of their product must be zero. For the hybrid orbitals, $h_1$ and $h_2$,

$$\begin{aligned}\int h_1h_2\,dV &= \int (s + p_x + p_y + p_z)(s - p_x - p_y + p_z)\,dV \\ &= \overbrace{\int s^2\,dV}^{1} - \overbrace{\int s.p_x\,dV}^{0} - \overbrace{\int s.p_y\,dV}^{0} + \overbrace{\int s.p_z\,dV}^{0} \\ &\quad + \overbrace{\int p_x.s\,dV}^{0} - \overbrace{\int p_x^2\,dV}^{1} - \overbrace{\int p_x.p_y\,dV}^{0} + \overbrace{\int p_x.p_z\,dV}^{0} \\ &\quad + \overbrace{\int p_y.s\,dV}^{0} - \overbrace{\int p_y.p_x\,dV}^{0} - \overbrace{\int p_y^2\,dV}^{1} + \overbrace{\int p_y.p_z\,dV}^{0} \\ &\quad + \overbrace{\int p_z.s\,dV}^{0} - \overbrace{\int p_z.p_x\,dV}^{0} - \overbrace{\int p_z.p_y\,dV}^{0} + \overbrace{\int p_z^2\,dV}^{1} \\ &= \mathbf{0}\end{aligned}$$

demonstrating that the two orbitals are indeed orthogonal.

(b) A wavefunction is normalised if the integral of its square is equal to 1. Thus, for an $sp^2$ hybrid function,

$$\begin{aligned}\int \{(s + 2^{1/2}p)/3^{1/2}\}^2\,dV &= \frac{1}{3}\int \{s + 2^{1/2}p\}^2\,dV \\ &= \frac{1}{3}\int (s^2 + 4sp + 2p^2)\,dV \\ &= \frac{1}{3}\left(\overbrace{\int s^2\,dV}^{1} + \overbrace{\int 4sp\,dV}^{0} + \overbrace{\int 2p^2\,dV}^{2}\right) \\ &= \mathbf{1}\end{aligned}$$

(c) The $sp^2$ hybrid orbitals are linear combinations of the s and in-plane $p_x$ and $p_y$ functions, and may be written in the form

$$h_i = N_i(s + a_i p_x + b_i p_y)$$

The orbitals are identical in everything but orientation and may be superimposed upon one another following a rotation about the $z$ axis through an angle of $2\pi/3$. The s orbital is spherically symmetric, so its coefficient will be unchanged by the rotation. However, the coefficients of the $p_x$ and $p_y$ orbitals will change. A clockwise rotation through $2\pi/3$ corresponds to a transformation of coordinates

$$\begin{aligned} x' &= x\cos(2\pi/3) + y\sin(2\pi/3) = -\tfrac{1}{2}x + \tfrac{1}{2}\sqrt{3}y \\ y' &= -x\sin(2\pi/3) + y\cos(2\pi/3) = -\tfrac{1}{2}\sqrt{3}x + \tfrac{1}{2}x \end{aligned}$$

Successive application of such a transformation to one of the $sp^2$ hybrid orbitals should, therefore, generate the other orbitals. Thus, taking

$$h_1 = \frac{1}{\sqrt{3}}(s + \sqrt{2}p_x)$$

so that $N_1 = 1/\sqrt{3}$, $a_1 = \sqrt{2}$ and $b_1 = 0$, then an anticlockwise rotation will convert the $p_x$ orbital to $\tfrac{1}{2}p_x - \tfrac{1}{2}\sqrt{3}p_y$ and so transform the hybrid orbital into

$$h_2 = \frac{1}{\sqrt{3}}\left\{s + \sqrt{2}\overbrace{\left(-\tfrac{1}{2}p_x + \tfrac{1}{2}\sqrt{3}p_y\right)}^{p_x \to p_{x'}}\right\} = \frac{1}{\sqrt{3}}\left(s - \frac{1}{\sqrt{2}}p_x + \frac{\sqrt{3}}{\sqrt{2}}p_y\right)$$

A successive rotation generates the third $sp^2$ orbital, with the $p_x$ orbital once again becoming $-\tfrac{1}{2}p_x + \tfrac{1}{2}\sqrt{3}p_y$ and the $p_y$ orbital becoming $-\tfrac{1}{2}\sqrt{3}p_x + \tfrac{1}{2}p_y$. Thus,

$$\begin{aligned} h_3 &= \frac{1}{\sqrt{3}}\left\{s - \frac{1}{\sqrt{2}}\overbrace{\left(-\tfrac{1}{2}p_x + \tfrac{1}{2}\sqrt{3}p_y\right)}^{p_x \to p_{x'}} + \frac{\sqrt{3}}{\sqrt{2}}\overbrace{\left(-\tfrac{1}{2}\sqrt{3}p_x + \tfrac{1}{2}p_y\right)}^{p_y \to p_{y'}}\right\} \\ &= \frac{1}{\sqrt{3}}\left(s + \frac{1}{\sqrt{2}}p_x + \frac{\sqrt{3}}{\sqrt{2}}p_y\right) \end{aligned}$$

We can confirm, by integration, that these two new $sp^2$ hybrid orbitals are normalised and orthogonal, both to one another and to the original orbital. For example, we may show that the orbitals $h_1$ and $h_2$ are indeed orthogonal by evaluating the integral

$$\begin{aligned} \int h_1 . h_2\, dV &= \int \frac{1}{\sqrt{3}}(s + \sqrt{2}p_x).\frac{1}{\sqrt{3}}\left(s - \frac{1}{\sqrt{2}}p_x + \frac{\sqrt{3}}{\sqrt{2}}p_y\right) dV \\ &= \frac{1}{3}\left\{\overbrace{\int s^2\, dV}^{1} - \frac{1}{\sqrt{2}}\overbrace{\int s.p_x\, dV}^{0} + \frac{\sqrt{3}}{\sqrt{2}}\overbrace{\int s.p_y\, dV}^{0} + \sqrt{2}\overbrace{\int s.p_x\, dV}^{0} \right. \\ &\qquad \left. - \overbrace{\int p_x^2\, dV}^{1} + \sqrt{3}\overbrace{\int p_x.p_y\, dV}^{0}\right\} = 0 \end{aligned}$$

**P14.35** (a) We may write a linear combination of two orbitals as

$$\psi = c_1\psi_1 + c_2\psi_2$$

where, in order that the resulting wavefunction satisfies the Born interpretation, the coefficients $c_1$ and $c_2$ have values between $-1$ and $+1$. For the wavefunction to be normalised

$$\int \psi^2 \, dV = 1$$

and so

$$\begin{aligned}\int (c_1\psi_1 + c_2\psi_2)^2 \, dV &= \int (c_1^2\psi_1^2 + 2c_1c_2\psi_1\psi_2 + c_2^2\psi_2^2) \, dV \\ &= c_1^2 \overbrace{\int \psi_1^2 \, dV}^{1} + 2c_1c_2 \overbrace{\int \psi_1\psi_2 \, dV}^{0} + c_2^2 \overbrace{\int \psi_2^2 \, dV}^{1} \\ &= c_1^2 + c_2^2 = 1\end{aligned}$$

This is the equation for a circle of radius 1

$$x^2 + y^2 = 1$$

We may describe any point on this circle using polar coordinates in terms only of an angle so that

$$c_1 = \cos\theta$$
$$c_2 = \sin\theta$$

(b) We may demonstrate that the linear combination is normalised by evaluating the integral

$$\begin{aligned}\int \psi^2 \, dV &= \int (\cos\theta\,\psi_A + \sin\theta\,\psi_B)^2 \, dV \\ &= \cos^2\theta \overbrace{\int \psi_A^2 \, dV}^{1} + 2\sin\theta\cos\theta \overbrace{\int \psi_A\psi_B dV}^{0} + \sin^2\theta \overbrace{\int \psi_B^2 \, dV}^{1} \\ &= \sin^2\theta + \cos^2\theta = 1\end{aligned}$$

(c) For a homonuclear diatomic molecule the contribution to the electron density from the two functions must, by symmetry, be equal, so that

$$c_1^2 = c_2^2$$
$$c_1 = \pm c_2$$

with the positive sign corresponding to the bonding orbital and the negative sign the antibonding orbital. We have, however, already established that

$$c_1^2 + c_2^2 = 1$$

implying that for the bonding orbital, $c_1 = c_2 = 1/\sqrt{2}$, and therefore

$$\theta = \cos^{-1}\overbrace{(1/\sqrt{2})}^{c_1} = \sin^{-1}\overbrace{(1/\sqrt{2})}^{c_2} = \boldsymbol{\pi/4}$$

and for the antibonding orbital, $c_1 = -c_2 = 1/\sqrt{2}$, and therefore

$$\theta = \cos^{-1}\overbrace{(1/\sqrt{2})}^{c_1} = \sin^{-1}\overbrace{(-1/\sqrt{2})}^{c_2} = \boldsymbol{-\pi/4}$$

**P14.36** (a) Consider the overlap between an s orbital and a $2p_z$ orbital such as that found in σ bonding. Note that there is no net overlap between an s orbital and either a $2p_x$ or $2p_y$ orbital. The interaction between the s orbital and one lobe of the p orbital is exactly cancelled by that with the other lobe of the p orbital for all separations.

(b) Figure 14.18 shows how the value of the overlap integral between an s and $p_z$ orbital varies with separation. The separation for which the overlap is maximised may be found by differentiating the function given and finding the value of $R$ for which the derivative is zero. Writing the function in terms of $(R / a_0)$,

$$\begin{aligned}
\frac{dS}{dR} &= \frac{dS}{d(R/a_0)} \\
&= \frac{d}{d(R/a_0)}\left[(R/a_0)\{1 + (R/a_0) + 1/3(R/a_0)^2\}e^{-(R/a_0)}\right] \\
&= (R/a_0)\{1 + (R/a_0) + 1/3(R/a_0)^2\}\frac{d}{d(R/a_0)}e^{-(R/a_0)} \\
&\qquad + (R/a_0)e^{-(R/a_0)}\frac{d}{d(R/a_0)}\{1 + (R/a_0) + 1/3(R/a_0)^2\} \\
&\qquad + \{1 + (R/a_0) + 1/3(R/a_0)^2\}e^{-(R/a_0)}\frac{d}{d(R/a_0)}(R/a_0) \\
&= \left[(R/a_0)\{1 + (R/a_0) + 1/3(R/a_0)^2\} \times -e^{-(R/a_0)}\right] \\
&\qquad + \left[(R/a_0)e^{-(R/a_0)} \times \{1 + 2/3(R/a_0)\}\right] \\
&\qquad + \left[\{1 + (R/a_0) + 1/3(R/a_0)^2\}e^{-(R/a_0)} \times 1\right] \\
&= \{-1/3(R/a_0)^3 - 3(R/a_0) + 1\}e^{-(R/a_0)} = 0
\end{aligned}$$

Thus, either

$$e^{-(R/a_0)} = 0$$
$$\{-1/3(R/a_0)^3 + 3(R/a_0) + 1\} = 0$$

The first factor corresponds to the asymptote at infinite separation. The second factor is a cubic equation. Use of mathematical software, or a calculator, to solve the equation gives the maximum at

$$(R/a_0) = \mathbf{2.11}$$

which corresponds to the maximum in the plot shown in Figure 14.18.

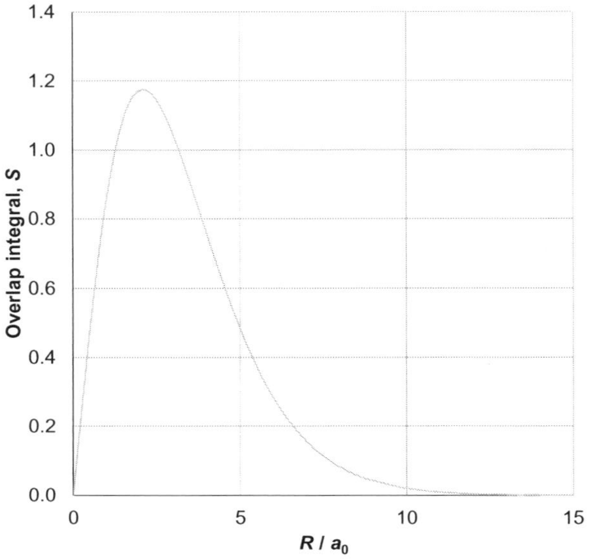


**Figure 14.18**

(c) If we label the linear combinations as

$$\psi_1 = N(0.245A + 0.644B)$$
$$\psi_2 = N(c_A A + c_B B)$$

The linear combinations must be normalised, so that

$$\int \psi_1^2 \,\mathrm{d}V = \int \psi_2^2 \,\mathrm{d}V = 1$$

But,

$$\int \psi_1^2 \,\mathrm{d}V = \int \{N(0.245A + 0.644B)\}^2 \mathrm{d}V$$
$$= N^2 \left\{ 0.245^2 \overbrace{\int A^2 \,\mathrm{d}V}^{1} + (2 \times 0.245 \times 0.644) \overbrace{\int AB \,\mathrm{d}V}^{0} + 0.644^2 \overbrace{\int B^2 \,\mathrm{d}V}^{1} \right\}$$
$$= N^2(0.245^2 + 0.644^2)$$
$$= 0.475N^2 = 1$$

Thus,

$$N = \pm 1.451$$

The wavefunctions must be orthogonal,

$$\begin{aligned}\int \psi_1\psi_2\,\mathrm{d}V &= 0\\ &= \int\{N(0.245A + 0.644B) \times N(c_\mathrm{A}A + c_\mathrm{B}B)\}\mathrm{d}V\\ &= N^2\left\{0.245c_\mathrm{A}\overbrace{\int A^2\,\mathrm{d}V}^{1} + 0.245c_\mathrm{B}\overbrace{\int AB\,\mathrm{d}V}^{0} + 0.644c_\mathrm{A}\overbrace{\int AB\,\mathrm{d}V}^{0}\right.\\ &\qquad\left. + 0.644c_\mathrm{B}\overbrace{\int B^2\,\mathrm{d}V}^{1}\right\}\end{aligned}$$

Thus, the coefficients $c_\mathrm{A}$ and $c_\mathrm{B}$ must satisfy the equation

$$0.245c_\mathrm{A} + 0.644c_\mathrm{B} = 0$$

so that

$$c_\mathrm{B} = -\frac{0.245}{0.644}c_\mathrm{A} = -0.380\ c_\mathrm{A}$$

In the same way for the second linear combination,

$$\begin{aligned}\int \psi_2^2\,\mathrm{d}V &= \int\{N(c_\mathrm{A}A - 0.380\ c_\mathrm{A}B)\}^2\mathrm{d}V\\ &= N^2\left\{{c_\mathrm{A}}^2\overbrace{\int A^2\,\mathrm{d}V}^{1} - (2\times 0.380\times c_A)\overbrace{\int AB\,\mathrm{d}V}^{0} + 0.380^2c_\mathrm{A}^2\overbrace{\int B^2\,\mathrm{d}V}^{1}\right\}\\ &= N^2({c_\mathrm{A}}^2 + 0.144\ c_\mathrm{A}^2)\\ &= 1.451^2(1.144\ c_\mathrm{A}^2) = 1\end{aligned}$$

Thus,

$$\begin{aligned}c_\mathrm{A} &= \pm\mathbf{0.644}\\ c_\mathrm{B} &= -0.380\times\pm 0.644 = \mp\mathbf{0.245}\end{aligned}$$

and

$$\begin{aligned}\psi_1 &= \pm 1.451(0.245A + 0.644B) = \pm(\mathbf{0.356}\boldsymbol{A} + \mathbf{0.934}\boldsymbol{B})\\ \psi_2 &= \pm 1.451(0.644A - 0.245B) = \pm(\mathbf{0.934}\boldsymbol{A} - \mathbf{0.356}\boldsymbol{B})\end{aligned}$$

(d) Assuming that the individual wavefunctions $\psi_\mathrm{cov}$ and $\psi_\mathrm{ion}$ are independently normalised, then

$$\begin{aligned}\int \psi^2\mathrm{d}V &= \int\{N(\psi_\mathrm{cov} + \lambda\psi_\mathrm{ion})\}^2\mathrm{d}V\\ &= N^2\left\{\overbrace{\int \psi_\mathrm{cov}^2\,\mathrm{d}V}^{1} + 2\lambda\overbrace{\int \psi_\mathrm{cov}\psi_\mathrm{ion}\mathrm{d}V}^{S} + \lambda^2\overbrace{\int \psi_\mathrm{ion}^2\,\mathrm{d}V}^{1}\right\}\end{aligned}$$

$$= N^2(1 + 2\lambda S + \lambda^2) = 1$$

Hence, the wavefunction is normalised when

$$N = \pm 1/(1 + 2\lambda S + \lambda^2)^{1/2}$$

# Chapter 15

# Molecular interactions

## Answers to discussion questions

**D15.1** Molecules with a permanent separation of electric charge have a **permanent dipole moment** $\mu$. In molecules containing atoms of differing electronegativity, the bonding electrons may be displaced in such a way as to produce a net separation of charge in the molecule. Separation of charge may also arise from a difference in atomic radii of the bonded atoms. The separation of charges in the bonds is usually, though not always, in the direction of the more electronegative atom but depends on the precise bonding situation in the molecule. A heteronuclear diatomic molecule necessarily has a dipole moment if there is a difference in electronegativity between the atoms, but the situation in polyatomic molecules is more complex. A polyatomic molecule has a permanent dipole moment only if at least one of its $\mu_x$, $\mu_y$, $\mu_z$ components is non-zero. Thus, the tetrahedral $CCl_4$ molecule has polar bonds but the sum of the polar components balance so as to cancel and give $\mu = 0$. Molecular symmetry is reduced in $CHCl_3$, a molecule that has a permanent dipole moment because the C–H bond does not balance the polarity of the C–Cl bonds. Similarly, 1,4-dichlorobenzene is nonpolar while 1,2-dichlorobenzene is a polar molecule. Carbon monoxide is a very important example of a molecule that has a dipole moment in the opposite direction to that expected from electronegativity considerations alone because the polarity of the highest occupied molecular orbital, which is an antibonding orbital, is reversed from the electronegativity expectation, provides a large contribution to the observed polarity.

Both nonpolar and polar molecules may acquire a temporary **induced dipole moment** $\mu^*$ as a result of the influence of an **electric field** $\mathcal{E}$ generated by a nearby ion or polar molecule. The field distorts the electron distribution of the molecule, and gives rise to an electric dipole. The induced dipole moment is proportional to the field and the constant of proportionality is called the **polarizability** $\alpha$. Features of the molecular structure that affect polarizabilty include: molecular size, nuclear control, ionization energy, and the relative orientation of the molecule with the external electric field.

**D15.2** The progression from a $1/r$ separation dependence for the interaction energy between two point charges (the Coulomb potential) to a more rapidly declining $1/r^6$ dependence observed for many attractive interactions between molecules is a very important feature of molecular science. Theoretical analysis, beginning with the Coulomb potential, concludes that the potential energy of dipole $\mu_1$ in the presence of a point charge $Q_2$ is given by eqn 15.6b

$$V(r) = -\frac{\mu_1 Q_2 \cos\theta}{4\pi\epsilon_0 r^2}$$

From the viewpoint of the point charge, the partial charges of the dipole seem to merge and cancel as the distance $r$ increases, thereby, causing the observed potential to vary as $1/r^2$, a more rapid decline than the Coulomb $1/r$ potential.

The theoretical analysis of the interaction energy between two dipoles $\mu_1$ and $\mu_2$ in a stationary orientation, which is not time-averaged as the molecules rotate, is given by eqn 15.7

$$V(r) = -\frac{\mu_1\mu_2(1-3\cos^2\theta)}{4\pi\epsilon_0 r^3}$$

The potential energy decreases even more rapidly (as $1/r^3$ instead of $1/r^2$) because the charges of both dipoles seem to merge as the separation of the dipoles increases.

When a dipole rotates under the influence of a neighbouring dipole (either permanent or induced), lower energy orientations are favoured and the average orientation yields an average interaction potential given by the Keesom interaction, eqn 15.8

$$V(r) = -\frac{\mu_1^2\mu_2^2}{3(4\pi\epsilon_0)^2 kTr^6}$$

The $1/r^6$ dependence originates from the product of the dipole–dipole potential energy of interaction that goes as $1/r^3$ and a weighting factor for favoured orientations that also goes as $1/r^3$ (because it depends upon the dipole–dipole energy). Additional van der Waals type interactions that depend upon distance as $1/r^6$ include the permanent-dipole–induced-dipole-interaction, and the induced-dipole–induced-dipole, or London dispersion, interaction. In each case, we can visualize the distance dependence of the potential energy as arising from the $1/r^3$ dependence of the orienting field (and hence the magnitude of the induced dipole) and the $1/r^3$ dependence of the potential energy of interaction of the dipoles (either permanent or induced).

**D15.3** Molecular energy interactions that are proportional to the inverse sixth power of the separation are called **van der Waals interactions**. They include the rotating permanent-dipole-permanent-dipole interaction, the permanent-dipole–induced-dipole-interaction, and the induced-dipole–induced-dipole, or London dispersion, interaction. Each depends upon the structure of the molecule through the questions of whether the molecule has a dipole and whether the electronic structure is polarizable.

**D15.4** The attractive interaction between atoms of the noble gases arises because of dispersion interactions. Random fluctuations in the electron density distribution result in transient dipoles. The strength of these dipoles depends upon the polarizability, $\alpha$, and ionization energy, $I$, of the atoms through the London formula, eqn 15.12

$$V(r) = -\frac{2}{3} \times \frac{\alpha_1' \alpha_2'}{r^6} \times \frac{I_1 I_2}{I_1 + I_2}$$

which for interactions between atoms of the same element reduces to

$$V(r) = -\frac{1}{3} \times \frac{\alpha'^2}{r^6} \times I$$

The polarizability and ionization energy of an atom are not independent. As the size of an atom increases, polarizability increases. The valence electrons are also more effectively shielded by the core electrons and the ionization energy therefore decreases. Thus, polarizability increases and ionization energy decreases down a group. If we assume that polarizability is inversely proportional to ionization energy, we can deduce that the potential energy of interaction is inversely proportional to ionization energy

$$V(r) \propto \frac{1}{I}$$

Hence, we should expect the strength of the attractive interaction between radon, at the bottom of group 18, to be greater than that for helium at the top. Thus, the magnitude of the Lennard-Jones parameter $\varepsilon$ increases down the group. Furthermore, as the size of the atoms increases, the separation at which the attractive and repulsive interactions balance, which is indicated by the parameter $\sigma$, increases. This effect is illustrated by Figure 15.13 of the text, which shows the Lennard-Jones curves for argon and xenon.

**D15.5** A **hydrogen bond** ($\cdots$) is an attractive interaction between two species that arises from a link of the form A–H···B, where A and B are highly electronegative elements (usually nitrogen, oxygen, or fluorine) and B possesses a lone pair of electrons. It is a contact-like attraction that requires AH to touch B. Experimental evidences supports a linear or near-linear structural arrangement and a bond strength of about 20 kJ $mol^{-1}$. The hydrogen bond strength is considerably weaker than a covalent bond but it is larger than, and dominates, other intermolecular attractions such as dipole–dipole attractions. Its formation can be understood in terms of either the (a) electrostatic interaction model or with (b) molecular orbital calculations.

(a) A and B, being highly electronegative, are viewed as having partial negative charges ($\delta^-$) in the electrostatic interaction model of the hydrogen bond. Hydrogen, being less electronegative than A, is viewed as having a partial positive ($\delta^+$). A linear, A–H···B structure maximizes the electrostatic attraction between H and B. This model is conceptually very useful. However, it is impossible to calculate exactly the interaction strength with this model because the partial atomic charges cannot be precisely defined. There is no way to define which fraction of the electrons of the AB covalent bond should be assigned to one or the other nucleus.

(b) Ab initio molecular orbital quantum calculations are needed in order to explore questions about the linear structure, the role of the lone pair, the shape of the potential energy surface, and the extent to which the hydrogen bond has covalent sigma-bond character. The hydrogen bond appears to have some sigma bond character. This was initially suggested by Linus Pauling in the 1930's and more recent experiments with Compton scattering of x-rays and NMR techniques indicate that the covalent character may provide as much as 20% of the hydrogen bond strength. A three-centre molecular orbital model provides a degree of insight. A linear combination of an appropriate sigma orbital on A, the 1s hydrogen orbital, and an appropriate orbital for the lone pair on B yields a total of three molecular orbitals:

$$\psi = c_1\psi_A + c_2\psi_H + c_3\psi_B$$

As can be seen in Figure 15.8 of the text, one of the MOs is bonding, one is almost nonbonding, and the third is antibonding. Both the bonding MO and the almost nonbonding orbital are occupied by two electrons (the sigma bonding electrons of A–H and the lone pair of B). The antibonding MO is empty. Thus, depending on the precise location of the almost nonbonding orbital, the nonbonding orbital may lower the total energy and account for the hydrogen bond.

**D15.6** The increase in entropy of a solution when hydrophobic molecules or groups in molecules cluster together and reduce their structural demands on the water solvent is the origin of the hydrophobic interaction that tends to stabilize clustering of hydrophobic groups in solution. A manifestation of the hydrophobic interaction is the clustering together of hydrophobic groups in biological macromolecules. For example, the side chains of amino acids that are used to form the polypeptide chains of proteins are hydrophobic, and the hydrophobic interaction is a major contributor to the tertiary structure of polypeptides. At first thought, this clustering would seem to be a nonspontaneous process as the clustering of the solute results in a decrease in entropy of the solute. However, the clustering of the solute results in greater freedom of movement of the solvent molecules and an accompanying increase in disorder and entropy of the solvent. The total entropy of the system has increased and the process is spontaneous.

**D15.7** In the Monte Carlo method, the particles in the box are moved through small but otherwise random distances, and the change in total potential energy of the $N$ particles in the box, $\Delta V_N$, is calculated using one of the intermolecular potentials discussed in this chapter. Whether this new configuration is accepted is then judged by considering:

If the potential energy is not greater than before the change, then the configuration is accepted.

If the potential energy is greater than before the change, the Boltzmann factor $e^{-\Delta V_N/kT}$ is compared with a random number between 0 and 1; if the factor is larger than the random number, the configuration is accepted; if the factor is not larger, the configuration is rejected. This procedure ensures that at equilibrium the probability of occurrence of any configuration is proportional to the Boltzmann factor.

In the molecular dynamics approach, the history of an initial arrangement is followed by calculating the trajectories of all the particles under the influence of the intermolecular potentials. Newton's laws are used to predict where each particle will be after a short time interval (about 1 fs which is shorter than the average time between collisions), and then the calculation is repeated for tens of thousands of such steps. The time-consuming part of the calculation is the evaluation of the net force on the molecule arising from all the other molecules present in the system. The calculation gives a series of snapshots of the liquid.

## Solutions to exercises

**E15.1** The potential energy of interaction between charged particles is given by the Coulomb potential, eqn 15.2,

$$V(r) = \frac{Q_1 Q_2}{4\pi \epsilon r}$$

For a medium other than a vacuum, the permittivity is given by $\epsilon = \epsilon_R \epsilon_0$ where the relative permittivity $\epsilon_R = 78$ for water at 25 °C. Thus,

$$V(r) = \frac{Q_1 Q_2}{4\pi \epsilon_R \epsilon_0 r} = \frac{(+e)(-e)}{4\pi \times 78 \times (8.854 \times 10^{-12}\ \mathrm{J^{-1}\ C^2\ m^{-1}}) \times (50 \times 10^{-9}\ \mathrm{m})}$$
$$= -5.9 \times 10^{-23}\ \mathrm{J}$$

which is equivalent to a molar potential energy of

$$V_{\mathrm{m}}(r) = V(r) \times N_{\mathrm{A}} = (-5.9 \times 10^{-23}\mathrm{J}) \times (6.022 \times 10^{23}\mathrm{mol^{-1}}) = \mathbf{-36\ J\ mol^{-1}}$$

The negative sign indicates that the interaction between a positive and negative ion is attractive.

**E15.2** We may calculate the dipole moment of a diatomic molecule from the electronegativities of the atoms using eqn 15.3. Thus, for HF,

$$\mu/D = \Delta\chi = \chi(\mathrm{F}) - \chi(\mathrm{H}) = 4.0 - 2.1 = 1.9$$

which is equivalent to

$$\mu = 1.9 \times (3.336 \times 10^{-30}\mathrm{C\ m}) = \mathbf{6.3 \times 10^{-30}C\ m}$$

The calculated dipole moment of 1.9 D compares well with the experimental value of 1.82 D.

**E15.3** We may describe the bonding in $PCl_5$ using valence-bond theory as consisting of five P–Cl sigma bonds. These bonds use all of the valence electrons of the phosphorus atom, so that there are no lone pairs. The repulsions between the bonding pairs are minimised if the molecule adopts a trigonal bipyramidal structure as shown in Figure 15.1, with equatorial bond angles of 120° and axial bond angles of 90°. The polarity of the axial P–Cl bonds cancel as they point in opposite directions. Also, the vector sum of the three equatorial P–Cl bond polarities cancels to zero. Thus, the molecule is **nonpolar**.

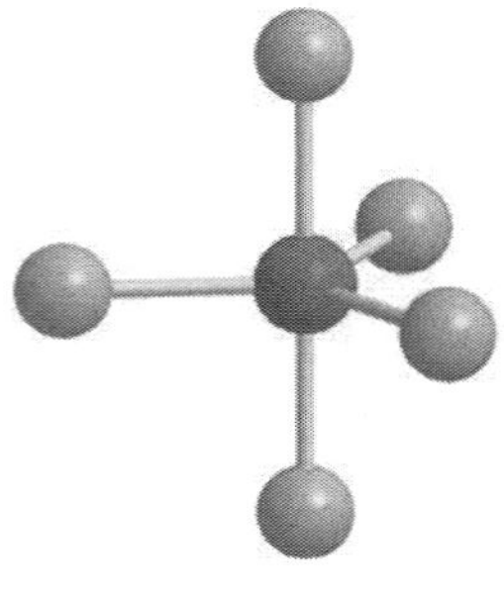

Figure 15.1

**E15.4** The dipole moment in methylbenzene arises because of the polarity of the methyl group. If we assume that the dipole moments in the dimethylbenzenes may be treated independently, then the overall dipole moment in these molecules may be estimated by vector addition using eqn 15.4. In this special case when the magnitudes of the two dipole moments are equal, then the resultant is

$$\mu_{res} = (\mu_1^2 + \mu_2^2 + 2\mu_1\mu_2 \cos\theta)^{1/2} = 2^{1/2}\mu(1+\cos\theta)^{1/2}$$

It can be seen from the structures shown in Figure 15.2 that for 1,2-dimethylbenzene, the angle between the two methylbenzene dipole moments is $\theta = \pi/3$, so that

$$\mu_{res} = 2^{1/2} \times (0.40\ \mathrm{D}) \times \{1+\cos(\pi/3)\}^{1/2} = \mathbf{0.69\ D}$$

and in 1,3-dimethylbenzene with $\theta = 2\pi/3$

$$\mu_{res} = 2^{1/2} \times (0.40\ \mathrm{D}) \times \{1+\cos(2\pi/3)\}^{1/2} = \mathbf{0.40\ D}$$

In 1,4-dimethylbenzene, the two methylbenzene dipoles oppose one another so that the resultant dipole moment is zero. Thus, we can be sure that this xylene is nonpolar.

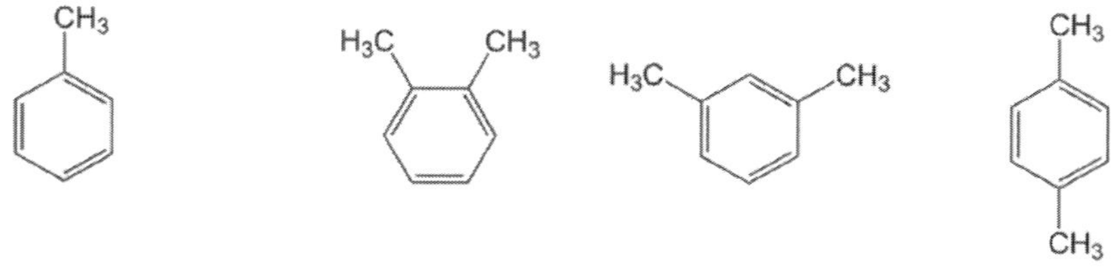


methylbenzene 1,2-dimethylbenzene 1,3-dimethylbenzene 1,4-dimethylbenzene

Figure 15.2

**E15.5** From eqn 15.4,

$$\begin{aligned}\mu_{\text{res}} &= (\mu_1^2 + \mu_2^2 + 2\mu_1\mu_2 \cos\theta)^{1/2} \\ &= \{(1.20\ \text{D})^2 + (0.60\ \text{D})^2 + 2 \times (1.20\ \text{D}) \times (0.60\ \text{D}) \times \cos 107°\}^2 \\ &= \mathbf{1.26\ D}\end{aligned}$$

**E15.6** It may be seen from Figure 15.3a that for 1,2,3-trimethylbenzene, the dipole moment may be considered as the resultant formed by from the dipole moments of 1,3-dimethylbenzene and methylbenzene. The component dipole moments are aligned along the same axis. Thus, if we assume that the dipole moments are independent, the resultant may be estimated simply as the sum of dipole moments for the two separate molecules. Hence, taking the value of the dipole moment for 1,3-dimethylbenzene from Exercise 15.4,

$$\mu_{\text{res}} = \mu_1 + \mu_2 = 0.40\ \text{D} + 0.40\ \text{D} = \mathbf{0.80\ D}$$

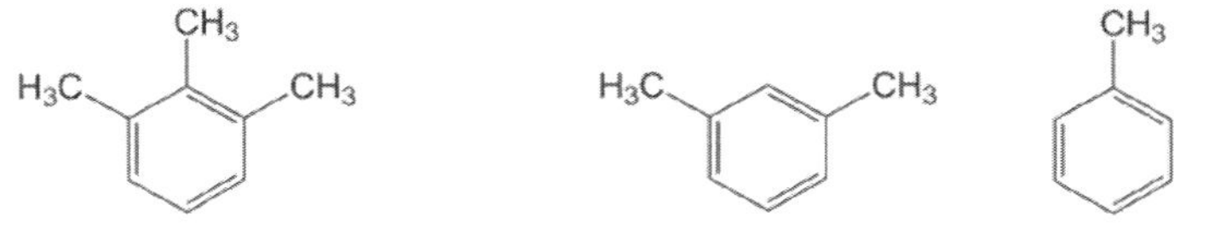

1,2,3-trimethylbenzene 1,3-dimethylbenzene methylbenzene

**Figure 15.3a**

Figure 15.3b shows that the dipole moment in 1,2,4-trimethylbenzene may be also be considered as the resultant of that from 1,3-dimethylbenzene and methylbenzene. In this case, however, the component dipole moments are arranged at an angle of $2\pi/3$ to one another. The resultant is therefore given using eqn 15.4,

$$\begin{aligned}\mu_{\text{res}} &= (\mu_1^2 + \mu_2^2 + 2\mu_1\mu_2 \cos\theta)^{1/2} \\ &= [(0.40\ \text{D})^2 + (0.40\ \text{D})^2 + \{2 \times (0.40\ \text{D})^2 \times (0.40\ \text{D})^2 \times \cos(2\pi/3)\}]^{1/2} \\ &= \mathbf{0.40\ D}\end{aligned}$$

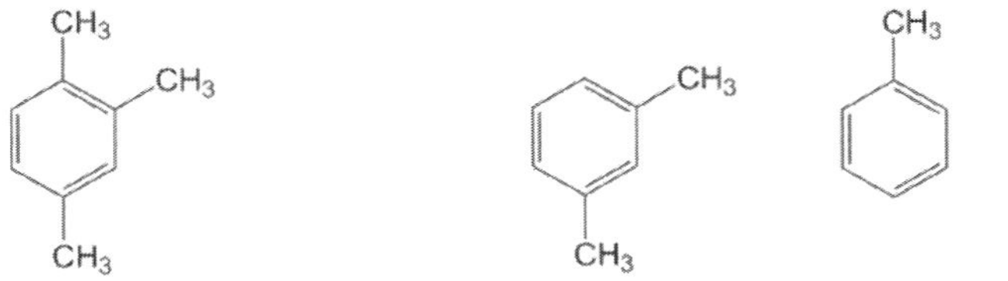

1,2,4-trimethylbenzene 1,3-dimethylbenzene methylbenzene

**Figure 15.3b**

For 1,3,5-trimethylbeneczne, Figure 15.3c shows that the dipole moments resulting from the three methyl groups are symmetrically arranged around the aromatic ring so that the dipole moments cancel. Thus, 1,3,5-trimethylbenzene is non polar. We can be sure about this result because by symmetry the polarities of all equivalent bonds are opposed and cancel.

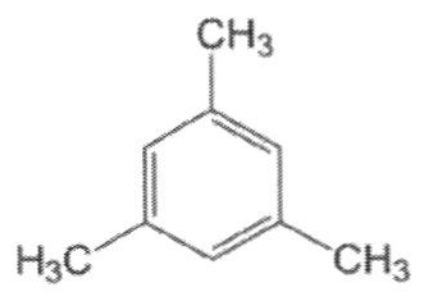


**Figure 15.3c**

**E15.7** In order to calculate the mean dipole moment, we must first calculate the dipole moments of each of the conformers. It is useful to resolve the dipole moment for the C–Cl bond into a component that lies in the plane perpendicular to the C–C bond, and a component that is parallel to the C–C bond. If we assume that the bonds around the carbon atoms are arranged tetrahedrally, so that the interbond angles are all 109.5°, then we may see from Figure 15.4 that the component of the dipole moment lying in the plane perpendicular to the C–C bond is

$$\mu_{\text{perp}} = \mu_{\text{C-Cl}} \sin(180° - 109.5°) = (1.50 \text{ D}) \times 0.943 = 1.41 \text{ D}$$

and that parallel to the bond is

$$\mu_{\text{llel}} = \mu_{\text{C-Cl}} \cos(180° - 109.5°) = (1.50 \text{ D}) \times 0.33 = 0.50 \text{ D}$$

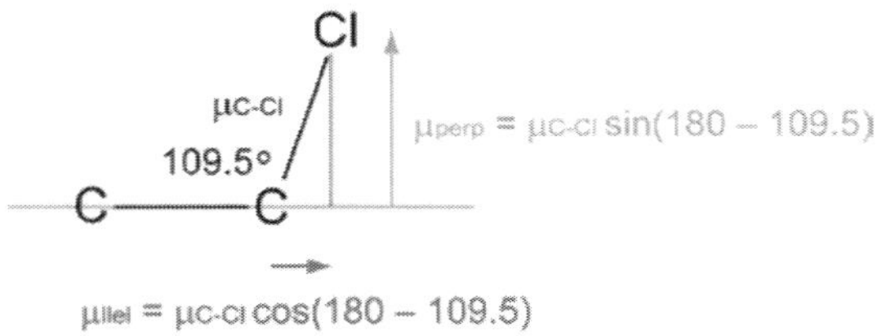


**Figure 15.4**

For each conformation **16**, the C–Cl are diametrically opposed; all of the component dipoles that result from these polar bonds therefore cancel. This conformation is therefore nonpolar, so that $\mu_{16} = \mathbf{0}$. For conformations **17** and **18**, however, the two bonds are arranged with a dihedral angle of 60°. Thus, the component of the resultant dipole moment perpendicular to the internuclear axis is given by eqn 15.4,

$$\begin{aligned}\mu_{\text{res}} &= (\mu_1^2 + \mu_2^2 + 2\mu_1\mu_2 \cos\theta)^{1/2} = 2^{1/2}\mu_{\text{perp}}(1 + \cos\theta)^{1/2} \\ &= 2^{1/2} \times (1.41 \text{ D}) \times (1 + \cos 60°)^{1/2} = 2.44 \text{ D}\end{aligned}$$

By symmetry, there is no component of the dipole moment along the axis parallel to the C–C bond. Thus, the magnitude of the total dipole moment is $\mu_{17} = \mu_{18} = \mathbf{2.44\ D}$.

Although the dipole moments of the two conformations are equal in magnitude, their directions are different, making an angle of 60° to one another.

The average dipole moment is given by the weighted vector average of the individual dipole moments. Following the notation introduced in *The chemist's toolkit 13.1*, and denoting vectors in bold, then

$$\mu_{\text{average}} = \frac{1}{N}(n_{16}\boldsymbol{\mu}_{\mathbf{16}} + n_{17}\boldsymbol{\mu}_{\mathbf{17}} + n_{18}\boldsymbol{\mu}_{\mathbf{18}})$$

where $n_{16}$, $n_{17}$ and $n_{18}$ are the weightings for each conformation and $N = n_{16} + n_{17} + n_{18}$ is the total weighting.

(a) When all three conformations are equally likely, then $n_{16} = n_{17} = n_{18}$. Furthermore, we have already established that conformation **16** is non-polar and makes no contribution to the average. Thus,

$$\mu_{\text{average}} = \tfrac{1}{3}(\boldsymbol{\mu}_{\mathbf{16}} + \boldsymbol{\mu}_{\mathbf{17}} + \boldsymbol{\mu}_{\mathbf{18}}) = \tfrac{1}{3}(\boldsymbol{\mu}_{\mathbf{17}} + \boldsymbol{\mu}_{\mathbf{18}})$$

The magnitude of the average is, then, from eqn 15.4

$$\begin{aligned}\mu_{\text{average}} &= \tfrac{1}{3}(\mu_{\mathbf{17}}^2 + \mu_{\mathbf{18}}^2 + 2\mu_{\mathbf{17}}\mu_{\mathbf{18}}\cos\theta) = \tfrac{1}{3}\{2^{1/2}\mu(1+\cos\theta)^{1/2}\} \\ &= \tfrac{1}{3}\{2^{1/2} \times (2.44\ \text{D}) \times (1+\cos 60°)^{1/2}\} = \mathbf{1.41\ D}\end{aligned}$$

(b) If only conformation **17** is present, then dipole moment is simply **2.44 D**.

(c) If the conformations are present in a ratio of 2:1:1, then the vector average is

$$\begin{aligned}\mu_{\text{average}} &= \frac{1}{(2+1+1)}(2 \times \boldsymbol{\mu}_{\mathbf{16}} + 1 \times \boldsymbol{\mu}_{\mathbf{17}} + 1 \times \boldsymbol{\mu}_{\mathbf{18}}) \\ &= \tfrac{1}{4}(\boldsymbol{\mu}_{\mathbf{17}} + \boldsymbol{\mu}_{\mathbf{18}}) = \tfrac{1}{4}\{2^{1/2} \times (2.44\ \text{D}) \times (1+\cos 60°)^{1/2}\} = \mathbf{1.06\ D}\end{aligned}$$

(d) In the same way for probabilities in the ratio 1:2:2

$$\begin{aligned}\mu_{\text{average}} &= \frac{1}{(1+2+2)}(1 \times \boldsymbol{\mu}_{\mathbf{16}} + 2 \times \boldsymbol{\mu}_{\mathbf{17}} + 2 \times \boldsymbol{\mu}_{\mathbf{18}}) \\ &= \tfrac{2}{5}(\boldsymbol{\mu}_{\mathbf{17}} + \boldsymbol{\mu}_{\mathbf{18}}) = \tfrac{1}{5}\{2^{1/2} \times (2.44\ \text{D}) \times (1+\cos 60°)^{1/2}\} = \mathbf{1.69\ D}\end{aligned}$$

**E15.8** Using eqn 15.5b to find the magnitude of the components of the total dipole moment, in terms of the partial charges, $Q_J$, and the coordinates $x_J$, $y_J$ and $z_J$ of the atoms

$$\begin{aligned}\mu_x = \sum_J Q_J x_J &= \{3e \times 0\} + \{-e \times (0.32\ \text{nm})\} + \{-2e \times (0.23\cos 20°)\text{nm}\} \\ &= -(0.752\ \text{nm})e\end{aligned}$$

$$\begin{aligned}\mu_y = \sum_J Q_J y_J &= \{3e \times 0\} + \{-e \times 0\} + \{-2e \times (0.23\sin 20°)\text{nm}\} \\ &= -(0.157\ \text{nm})e\end{aligned}$$

The magnitude of the dipole moment is thus

$$\mu = \left(\mu_x^2 + \mu_y^2\right)^{1/2} = (0.752^2 + 0.157^2)^{1/2} \times e \text{ nm}$$
$$= 0.768 \times (1.602 \times 10^{-19}\text{ C}) \times (10^{-9}\text{m}) = 1.23 \times 10^{-29}\text{ C m}$$

which is equivalent to

$$\mu = (1.23 \times 10^{-29}\text{ C m})/(3.336 \times 10^{-30}\text{ C m D}^{-1}) = \mathbf{3.7\ D}$$

The direction of the dipole moment may also be calculated from the relative magnitudes of the components. Thus, the angle that the dipole makes to the $x$ axis is given by

$$\theta = \tan^{-1}\left(\mu_y/\mu_x\right)$$
$$= \tan^{-1}[\{-(0.157\text{ nm})e\}/\{-(0.752\text{ nm})e\}] = \tan^{-1}(0.157/0.752) = \mathbf{17.8°}$$

**E15.9** We may use eqn 15.5b to calculate the magnitude of the components of the total dipole moment, in terms of the partial charges, $Q_J$, and the coordinates $x_J$, $y_J$ and $z_J$ of the atoms. Thus,

$$\mu_x = \sum_J Q_J x_J$$
$$= \{0.02e \times (-86\text{ pm})\} + \{0.02e \times (34\text{ pm})\} + \{0.06e \times (-195\text{ pm})\}$$
$$+ \{0.18e \times (-199\text{ pm})\} + \{-0.36e \times (-101\text{ pm})\} + \{0.45e \times (82\text{ pm})\}$$
$$+ \{-0.38e \times (199\text{ pm})\} + \{0.18e \times (-80\text{ pm})\} + \{-0.38e \times (49\text{ pm})\}$$
$$+ \{0.42e \times (129\text{ pm})\}$$
$$= -29.76e\text{ pm}$$

$$\mu_y = \sum_J Q_J y_J$$
$$= \{0.02e \times (118\text{ pm})\} + \{0.02e \times (146\text{ pm})\} + \{0.06e \times (70\text{ pm})\}$$
$$+ \{0.18e \times (-1\text{ pm})\} + \{-0.36e \times (-11\text{ pm})\} + \{0.45e \times (-15\text{ pm})\}$$
$$+ \{-0.38e \times (16\text{ pm})\} + \{0.18e \times (-110\text{ pm})\} + \{-0.38e \times (-107\text{ pm})\}$$
$$+ \{0.42e \times (-146\text{ pm})\}$$
$$= -40.03e\text{ pm}$$

$$\mu_z = \sum_J Q_J z_J$$
$$= \{0.02e \times (37\text{ pm})\} + \{0.02e \times (-98\text{ pm})\} + \{0.06e \times (-38\text{ pm})\}$$
$$+ \{0.18e \times (-100\text{ pm})\} + \{-0.36e \times (-126\text{ pm})\} + \{0.45e \times (34\text{ pm})\}$$
$$+ \{-0.38e \times (-38\text{ pm})\} + \{0.18e \times (111\text{ pm})\} + \{-0.38e \times (88\text{ pm})\}$$
$$+ \{0.42e \times (126\text{ pm})\}$$
$$= +53.10e\text{ pm}$$

The magnitude of the dipole moment is thus

$$\mu = \left(\mu_x^2 + \mu_y^2 + \mu_z^2\right)^{1/2} = \{(-29.76)^2 + (-40.03)^2 + 53.10^2\}e\text{ pm}$$

$$= 72.85e\text{ pm} = 72.85 \times (1.602 \times 10^{-19}\text{ C}) \times (10^{-12}\text{m}) = \mathbf{1.17 \times 10^{-29}\ C\ m}$$

which is equivalent to

$$\mu = (1.17 \times 10^{-29}\text{ C m})/(3.336 \times 10^{-30}\text{ C m D}^{-1}) = \mathbf{3.50\ D}$$

**E15.10** We must first determine the dipole moment of the OH fragment, $\mu_{O-H}$. The total dipole moment of the $H_2O$ molecule, may be considered to be the resultant of the dipoles of two identical OH fragments aligned at an angle $\theta$ equal to 104.5° with respect to each other. The dipole moment of $H_2O$ is known to be $\mu_{H-O-H}$ = 1.85 D. Thus, from eqn 15.4,

$$\mu_{H-O-H} = (\mu_{O-H}^2 + \mu_{O-H}^2 + 2\mu_{O-H}\mu_{O-H}\cos\theta)^{1/2} = 2^{1/2}\mu_{O-H}(1+\cos\theta)^{1/2}$$

Hence, rearranging,

$$\mu_{O-H} = \frac{\mu_{H-O-H}}{2^{1/2}(1+\cos\theta)^{1/2}} = \frac{1.85\text{ D}}{2^{1/2}\{1+\cos(104.5°)\}^{1/2}} = 1.51\text{ D}$$

Then, using $\phi$ to represent the angle between the two O–H bond dipoles in $H_2O_2$, we have

$$\mu_{H-O-O-H} = (\mu_{O-H}^2 + \mu_{O-H}^2 + 2\mu_{O-H}\mu_{O-H}\cos\phi)^{1/2} = 2^{1/2}\mu_{O-H}(1+\cos\phi)^{1/2}$$

Figure 15.5 shows a plot of the total dipole moment of $H_2O_2$, $\mu_{H-O-O-H}$, plotted as function of dihedral angle $\phi$. The continuous line shows the magnitude of the dipole moment; the dashed line shows how the dipole moment changes sign as its direction changes. At 90°, the dipole moment is 2.13 D, which is the experimental value.

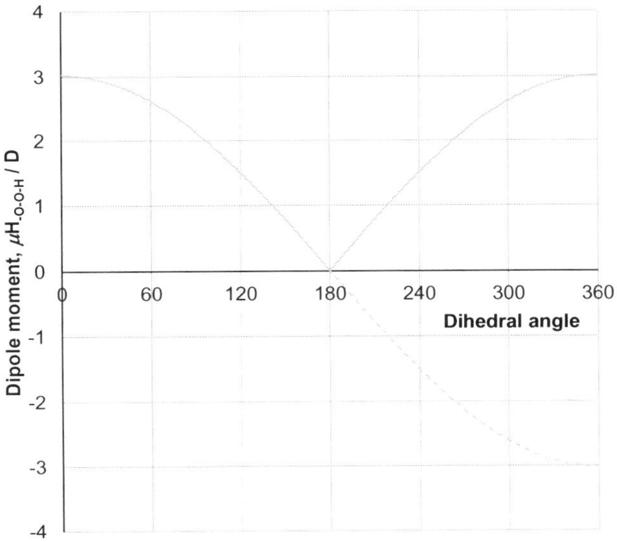


**Figure 15.5**

**E15.11** We assume that the dipole of the $H_2O$ molecule and the $Li^+$ ion are collinear and that the separation of charges in the dipole is smaller than the distance to the ion. With these assumptions we can use eqn 15.6a to calculate the express the interaction energy between the dipole and the point charge. To flip the water molecule over requires twice the energy of interaction.

(a) Thus, for a separation of 150 pm,

$$\begin{aligned}\Delta E &= 2 \times \frac{\mu_1 Q_2}{4\pi\epsilon_0 r^2} \\ &= \frac{2 \times (1.85\ \mathrm{D}) \times (3.336 \times 10^{-30}\ \mathrm{C\,m\,D^{-1}}) \times (1.602 \times 10^{-19}\ \mathrm{C})}{4\pi \times (8.854 \times 10^{-12}\ \mathrm{J^{-1}\,C^2\,m^{-1}}) \times (150 \times 10^{-12}\ \mathrm{m})^2} \\ &= 7.90 \times 10^{-19}\ \mathrm{J}\end{aligned}$$

which is equivalent to a molar energy

$$\begin{aligned}\Delta E_\mathrm{m} &= N_\mathrm{A}\Delta E = (6.022 \times 10^{23}\mathrm{mol^{-1}}) \times (7.90 \times 10^{-19}\ \mathrm{J}) \\ &= 476 \times 10^3\ \mathrm{J\,mol^{-1}} = \mathbf{476\ kJ\ mol^{-1}}\end{aligned}$$

(b) and for a separation of 350 pm,

$$\begin{aligned}\Delta E &= 2 \times \frac{\mu_1 Q_2}{4\pi\epsilon_0 r^2} \\ &= \frac{2 \times (1.85\ \mathrm{D}) \times (3.336 \times 10^{-30}\ \mathrm{C\,m\,D^{-1}}) \times (1.602 \times 10^{-19}\ \mathrm{C})}{4\pi \times (8.854 \times 10^{-12}\ \mathrm{J^{-1}\,C^2\,m^{-1}}) \times (350 \times 10^{-12}\ \mathrm{m})^2} \\ &= 1.45 \times 10^{-19}\ \mathrm{J}\end{aligned}$$

which is equivalent to a molar energy

$$\begin{aligned}\Delta E_\mathrm{m} &= N_\mathrm{A}\Delta E = (6.022 \times 10^{23}\mathrm{mol^{-1}}) \times (1.45 \times 10^{-19}\ \mathrm{J}) \\ &= 476 \times 10^3\ \mathrm{J\,mol^{-1}} = \mathbf{87.4\ kJ\ mol^{-1}}\end{aligned}$$

**E15.12** The potential energy of two parallel dipole moments is given by the sum of the interactions between the partial charges

$$V(r) = \sum_{i,j} \frac{Q_i Q_j}{4\pi\epsilon_0 r_{ij}}$$

where $i$ and $j$ represent partial charges on different dipoles. Consider the arrangement shown in Figure 15.6, where we have assumed, for mathematical simplicity, that the lengths of the two dipoles, AB and CD, are the same.

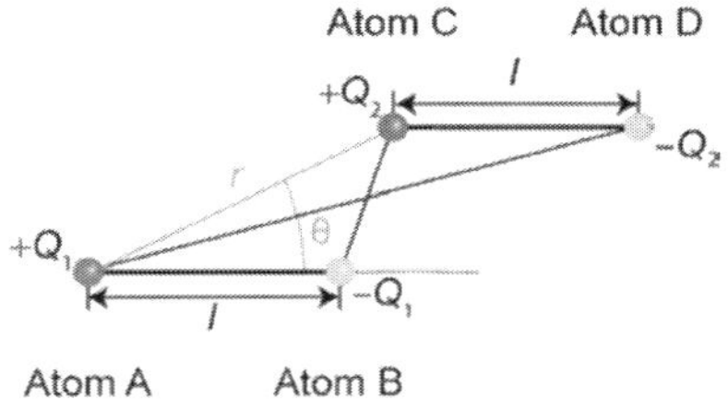


**Figure 15.6**

The separation between like charges

$$r_{AC} = r$$
$$r_{BD} = r$$

and, by trigonometry, the separation between opposing charges is

$$\begin{aligned} r_{BC} &= (r^2 + l^2 - 2rl\cos\theta)^{1/2} \\ &= r\{1 + (l/r)^2 - 2(l/r)\cos\theta\}^{1/2} \\ r_{AD} &= \{r^2 + l^2 - 2rl\cos(180° - \theta)\}^{1/2} = (r^2 + l^2 + 2rl\cos\theta)^{1/2} \\ &= r\{1 + (l/r)^2 + 2(l/r)\cos\theta\}^{1/2} \end{aligned}$$

Thus,

$$\begin{aligned} V(r,\theta) &= \overbrace{\frac{Q_1Q_2}{4\pi\epsilon_0 r_{AC}}}^{\text{Interaction between A and C}} + \overbrace{\frac{Q_1Q_2}{4\pi\epsilon_0 r_{BD}}}^{\text{Interaction between B and D}} + \overbrace{\frac{Q_1 \times (-Q_2)}{4\pi\epsilon_0 r_{AD}}}^{\text{Interaction between A and D}} + \overbrace{\frac{Q_2 \times (-Q_1)}{4\pi\epsilon_0 r_{BC}}}^{\text{Interaction between B and C}} \\ &= \frac{Q_1Q_2}{4\pi\epsilon_0 r}\left\{1 + 1 - \frac{1}{\{1 + (l/r)^2 + 2(l/r)\cos\theta\}^{1/2}} \right. \\ &\qquad \left. - \frac{1}{\{1 + (l/r)^2 - 2(l/r)\cos\theta\}^{1/2}}\right\} \end{aligned}$$

We may expand a function of the form $(1 + x)^{-1/2}$ as a Taylor series if $x \ll 1$

$$(1 + x)^{-1/2} = 1 - \tfrac{1}{2}x + \tfrac{3}{8}x^2 - \tfrac{5}{16}x^3 + \cdots$$

so that

$$\begin{aligned} &[1 + \{(l/r)^2 + 2(l/r)\cos\theta\}]^{1/2} \\ &\qquad = 1 - \frac{1}{2}\overbrace{\{(l/r)^2 + 2(l/r)\cos\theta\}}^{x} + \frac{3}{8}\overbrace{\{(l/r)^2 + 2(l/r)\cos\theta\}^2}^{x^2} \ldots \end{aligned}$$

Expanding, and collecting together the terms in $(l/r)$, $(l/r)^2$ and so on,

$$[1 + \{(l/r)^2 \pm 2(l/r)\cos\theta\}]^{1/2} = 1 \mp (l/r)\cos\theta + ½(l/r)^2(3\cos^2\theta - 1) - \cdots$$

Hence, substituting,

$$V(r,\theta) = \frac{Q_1Q_2}{4\pi\epsilon_0 r} \times$$
$$[2 - \{1 - (l/r)\cos\theta + ½\,(l/r)^2(3\cos^2\theta - 1)\}$$
$$- \{1 + (l/r)\cos\theta + ½\,(l/r)^2(3\cos^2\theta - 1)\}]$$
$$= \frac{Q_1Q_2}{4\pi\epsilon_0 r}(l/r)^2(3\cos^2\theta - 1)$$
$$= \frac{(Q_1l)(Q_2l)}{4\pi\epsilon_0 r^3}(3\cos^2\theta - 1)$$
$$= \frac{\mu_1\mu_2}{4\pi\epsilon_0 r^3}(3\cos^2\theta - 1)$$

which, as required, is eqn 15.7.

**E15.13** (a) From the equipartition theorem explained in *Foundations*, we know that the average molar kinetic energy of the molecules in a gas is

$$E_{\text{k.m}} = N_A \times E_K = N_A \times (3/2)kT = (3/2)\overbrace{R}^{R=N_Ak}\,T$$
$$= 3/2 \times (8.3145\ \text{J K}^{-1}\text{mol}^{-1}) \times (298\ \text{K}) = 3.72 \times 10^3\text{J mol}^{-1}$$
$$= \mathbf{3.72\ kJ\ mol^{-1}}$$

(b) We may calculate the average potential energy of interaction between the HCl molecules using eqn 15.8

$$V(r) = -\frac{2\mu_1^2\mu_2^2}{3(4\pi\epsilon_0)^2kTr^6}$$

For 0.50 mol of molecules in a 1.0 $\text{dm}^3$ volume, the volume occupied per molecule is, on average,

$$v = (2.00 \times 10^{-3}\ \text{m}^3\ \text{mol}^{-1})/(6.022 \times 10^{23}\ \text{mol}^{-1})$$

This places the molecules at an average distance of $r = v^{1/3}$ with respect to each other, so that

$$r = v^{1/3} = \{(2.00 \times 10^{-3}\ \text{m}^3\ \text{mol}^{-1})/(6.022 \times 10^{23}\ \text{mol}^{-1})\}^{1/3}$$
$$= 1.49 \times 10^{-9}\ \text{m} = 1.49\ \text{nm}$$

The dipole moment of an HCl molecule is, from Table 15.2, $\mu = 1.08$ D. Thus,

$$V = -\frac{2\ \overbrace{\mu_{\text{HCl}}^4}^{\mu_1=\mu_2=\mu_{\text{HCl}}}}{3(4\pi\epsilon_0)^2kTr^6}$$
$$= -\frac{2 \times \{(1.08\ \text{D}) \times (3.336 \times 10^{-30}\ \text{C m D}^{-1})\}^4}{[3 \times \{4\pi \times (8.854 \times 10^{-12}\ \text{J}^{-1}\ \text{C}^2\ \text{m}^{-1})\}^2 \times (1.38 \times 10^{-23}\ \text{J K}^{-1}) \times (298\ \text{K}) \times (1.49 \times 10^{-12}\ \text{m})^6]}$$
$$= -2.02 \times 10^{-25}\text{J}$$

Each molecule has an average of 6 nearest neighbours, but we count a pair interaction only once. Thus, the total molar potential energy of interaction in this sample is

$$V_m = -3N_A \times V$$
$$= -3 \times 6.022 \times 10^{23}\text{mol}^{-1} \times (-2.02 \times 10^{-25}\text{J}) = \mathbf{-0.365\ J\ mol^{-1}}$$

The negative sign indicates that the interaction between the HCl molecules is attractive. This potential energy is exceedingly small compared to the kinetic energy, so the kinetic theory of gases is justifiable for this sample.

**E15.14** (a) Polarizability is defined through eqn 15.8, $\alpha = \mu^*/\mathcal{E}$, where $\mu^*$ is the dipole moment induced by an electric field of strength, $\mathcal{E}$. The units of dipole moment are C m, and of electric field strength are V m = J C$^{-1}$ m$^{-1}$. is the force per unit charge experienced by a charge. It has the unit N C$^{-1}$ or J C$^{-1}$ m$^{-1}$. Consequently, polarizability has the SI unit (C m) / (J C$^{-1}$ m$^{-1}$) = $\mathbf{C^2\ m^2\ J^{-1}}$.

(b) Polarizability volume, is related to the polarizability through eqn 15.10, $\alpha' = \alpha / 4\pi\varepsilon_0$ We have already established that $\alpha$ has the SI unit C$^2$ m$^2$ J$^{-1}$; $\varepsilon_0$ has the units C$^2$ J$^{-1}$ m$^{-1}$ unit. Consequently, polarizability volume has the SI unit (C$^2$ m$^2$ J$^{-1}$) / (C$^2$ J$^{-1}$ m$^{-1}$) = $\mathbf{m^3}$.

**E15.15** The magnitude of the dipole induced by an electric field is given by eqn 15.9, so that

$$\mu^* = \alpha\mathcal{E} = (4\pi\epsilon_0\alpha')\mathcal{E}$$

We may define the strength of an electric field as the electrostatic force experienced per unit charge. For an ion, the magnitude of the force is given by Coulomb's law, so that for a charge $Q_1$, the resulting electric field is

$$\mathcal{E} = F/Q_2 = \left(\frac{Q_1Q_2}{4\pi\epsilon_0 r^2}\right)/Q_2 = \frac{Q_1}{4\pi\epsilon_0 r^2}$$

Combining these two expressions,

$$\mu^* = (4\pi\epsilon_0\alpha') \times \frac{Q_1}{4\pi\epsilon_0 r^2}$$

and so, rearranging, for an ion with charge $Q_1 = e$,

$$r = \left(\frac{e\alpha'}{\mu^*}\right)^{1/2}$$
$$= \left\{\frac{(1.602 \times 10^{-19}\ \text{C}) \times (1.48 \times 10^{-30}\ \text{m}^3)}{(1.85\ \text{D}) \times (3.336 \times 10^{-30}\ \text{C m D}^{-1})}\right\}^{1/2} = 1.96 \times 10^{-10}\ \text{m} = \mathbf{196\ pm}$$

**E15.16** For argon atoms, the polarizability volume is, from Table 15.2, $\alpha' = 1.66 \times 10^{-30}$ m$^3$, and ionization energy 15.76 eV. Applying the London formula, eqn 15.12, for the potential energy resulting from dispersion forces, then for interactions between the same species, so that $\alpha_1' = \alpha_2' = \alpha$ and $I_1 = I_2 = I$,

$$V(r) = -\frac{2}{3}\times\frac{\alpha_1'\alpha_2'}{r^6}\times\frac{I_1I_2}{I_1+I_2} = -\frac{2}{3}\times\frac{\alpha'^2}{r^6}\times\frac{I^2}{2I} = -\frac{\alpha'^2}{3r^6I}$$
$$= -\frac{(1.66\times10^{-30}\ \mathrm{m^3})^2}{3\times(1.00\times10^{-9}\ \mathrm{m})^6\times(15.76\ \mathrm{eV})\times(1.602\times10^{-19}\ \mathrm{J\ eV^{-1}})}$$
$$= \mathbf{-2.32\times10^{-24}\ J}$$

**E15.17** The interaction between the phenylalanine ring and the neighbouring peptide group is a dipole–induced-dipole interaction. The energy is thus given by eqn 15.11

$$V(r) = -\frac{\mu_1^2\alpha_2'}{4\pi\epsilon_0 r^6}$$
$$= -\frac{\{(2.7\ \mathrm{D})\times(3.336\times10^{-30}\ \mathrm{C\ m\ D^{-1}})\}^2\times(1.04\times10^{-29}\ \mathrm{m^3})}{4\pi\times(8.854\times10^{-12}\ \mathrm{J^{-1}\ C^2\ m^{-1}})\times(4.0\times10^{-9}\ \mathrm{m})^2}$$
$$= -1.8\times10^{-27}\ \mathrm{J}$$

which is equivalent to a molar energy

$$V_\mathrm{m}(r) = N_\mathrm{A}V(r) = (6.022\times10^{23}\mathrm{mol^{-1}})\times(-1.8\times10^{-27}\ \mathrm{J})$$
$$= -1.10\times10^{3}\mathrm{J\ mol^{-1}} = \mathbf{-1.10\ kJ\ mol^{-1}}$$

The energy is negative, because the interaction is attractive.

**E15.18** Applying the London formula, eqn 15.12, then for interactions between the same species, so that $\alpha_1' = \alpha_2' = \alpha$ and $I_1 = I_2 = I$,

$$V(r) = -\frac{2}{3}\times\frac{\alpha_1'\alpha_2'}{r^6}\times\frac{I_1I_2}{I_1+I_2} = -\frac{2}{3}\times\frac{\alpha'^2}{r^6}\times\frac{I^2}{2I} = -\frac{\alpha'^2}{3r^6I}$$
$$= -\frac{(10.4\times10^{-30}\ \mathrm{m^3})^2}{3\times(4.0\times10^{-9}\ \mathrm{m})^6\times(5.0\ \mathrm{eV})\times(1.602\times10^{-19}\ \mathrm{J\ eV^{-1}})}$$
$$= \mathbf{-7.1\times10^{-27}\ J}$$

where the value for the polarizability volume comes from Table 15.2. This energy is equivalent to a molar energy

$$V_\mathrm{m}(r) = N_\mathrm{A}V(r) = (6.022\times10^{23}\mathrm{mol^{-1}})\times(-7.1\times10^{-27}\ \mathrm{J})$$
$$= \mathbf{-4.2\times10^{-3}J\ mol^{-1}}$$

The energy is negative, because the interaction is attractive.

**E15.19** We may assume that the geometry at the hydrogen bond between the tyrosine and histidine residues is linear. Distances in structure (**22**) are not given, but we may take $r_{\mathrm{O\text{–}H}}$ to be 100 pm, $r_{\mathrm{O\cdots N}}$ to be 300 pm and hence $r_{\mathrm{H\cdots N}}$ to be $r_{\mathrm{O\cdots N}} - r_{\mathrm{O\text{–}H}}$ = (300 – 100) pm = 200 pm. Partial charges for polypeptides are given in Table 15.1, so that we may take $Q_\mathrm{O} = -0.38e$ $Q_\mathrm{H} = +0.42e$ and $Q_\mathrm{H} = +0.42e$. Thus, from Coulomb's law, eqn 15.2a

$$V(r) = \frac{Q_1Q_2}{4\pi\epsilon_0 r}$$

the total potential energy of interaction is given by the sum of the energy of interaction between the oxygen and nitrogen atoms and the hydrogen and nitrogen atoms

$$V(r) = V(r)_{\mathrm{O\cdots N}} + V(r)_{\mathrm{H\cdots N}} = \frac{Q_\mathrm{O}Q_\mathrm{N}}{4\pi\epsilon_0 r_{\mathrm{O\cdots N}}} + \frac{Q_\mathrm{H}Q_\mathrm{N}}{4\pi\epsilon_0 r_{\mathrm{H\cdots N}}} = \frac{1}{4\pi\epsilon_0}\left(\frac{Q_\mathrm{O}Q_\mathrm{N}}{r_{\mathrm{O\cdots N}}} + \frac{Q_\mathrm{H}Q_\mathrm{N}}{r_{\mathrm{H\cdots N}}}\right)$$

$$= \frac{(1.602\times10^{-19}\ C)^2}{4\pi\times(8.854\times10^{-12}\ \mathrm{J^{-1}\ C^2\ m^{-1}})} \times \left\{\frac{(-0.38)\times(-0.36)}{300\times10^{-12}\ \mathrm{m}} + \frac{(-0.36)\times(0.42)}{200\times10^{-12}\ \mathrm{m}}\right\}$$

$$= -7.0\times10^{-20}\ \mathrm{J}$$

which is equivalent to a molar energy of

$$V_\mathrm{m}(r) = N_\mathrm{A}V(r) = (6.022\times10^{23}\mathrm{mol^{-1}})\times(-7.0\times10^{-20}\ \mathrm{J})$$

$$= -42\times10^{3}\mathrm{J\ mol^{-1}} = \mathbf{-42\ kJ\ mol^{-1}}$$

**E15.20** Individual acetic acid molecules have a non-zero dipole moment. At low temperature, however, a significant fraction of molecules are a part of a dimer in which the two dipoles are exactly opposed and so cancel. This means that their individual dipole moments will not be observed. However, as temperature is increased, hydrogen bonds of the dimer are broken, thereby, releasing individual molecules and the apparent dipole moment increases.

**E15.21** The potential energy resulting from the Coulombic interaction between atoms is given by eqn 15.2a

$$V(r) = \frac{Q_1Q_2}{4\pi\epsilon_0 r}$$

We may calculate the separations between the atoms using the coordinates given. For atoms with coordinates $(x, y)$ and $(x', y')$, the separation is

$$r = \{(x-x')^2 + (y-y')^2\}^{1/2}$$

The coordinates and partial charges of the atoms of interest are shown in Figure 15.7.

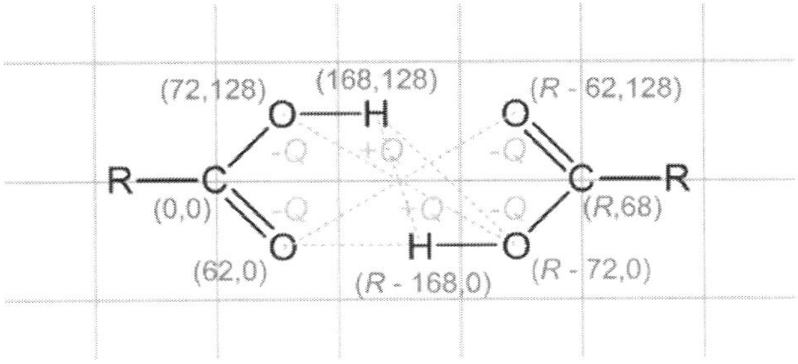


**Figure 15.7**

Hence,

$$\begin{aligned}
r_{\text{O}\cdots\text{O}} &= [\overbrace{\{(R-72)-72\}^2}^{(x-x')^2} + \overbrace{\{128-0\}^2}^{(y-y')^2}]^{1/2} = \{(R-144)^2+128^2\}^{1/2}\\
r_{\text{O}'\cdots\text{O}'} &= [\{(R-62)-62\}^2 + \{128-0\}^2]^{1/2} = \{(R-124)^2+128^2\}^{1/2}\\
r_{\text{H}\cdots\text{H}} &= [\{(R-168)-168\}^2 + \{128-0\}^2]^{1/2} = \{(R-336)^2+128^2\}^{1/2}\\
r_{\text{O}\cdots\text{O}'} &= [\{(R-72)-62\}^2 + \{0-0\}^2]^{1/2} = \{(R-134)^2+0^2\}^{1/2}\\
r_{\text{H}\cdots\text{O}} &= [\{(R-72)-168\}^2 + \{128-0\}^2]^{1/2} = \{(R-240)^2+128^2\}^{1/2}\\
r_{\text{O}'\cdots\text{H}} &= [\{(R-168)-62\}^2 + \{0-0\}^2]^{1/2} = \{(R-230)^2+0^2\}^{1/2}
\end{aligned}$$

Thus, summing the contributions from each pairwise interaction

$$\begin{aligned}
V(R) &= V_{\text{O}\cdots\text{O}} + V_{\text{O}'\cdots\text{O}'} + V_{\text{H}\cdots\text{H}} + 2V_{\text{O}'\cdots\text{O}} + 2V_{\text{H}\cdots\text{O}} + 2V_{\text{O}'\cdots\text{H}}\\
&= \frac{1}{4\pi\epsilon_0}\left[\frac{(-Qe)^2}{\{(R-144)^2+128^2\}^{1/2}} + \frac{(-Qe)^2}{\{(R-124)^2+128^2\}^{1/2}}\right.\\
&\qquad + \frac{(+Qe)^2}{\{(R-336)^2+128^2\}^{1/2}} + 2\frac{(-Qe)(-Qe)}{(R-134)}\\
&\qquad \left. + 2\frac{(-Qe)(+Qe)}{\{(R-240)^2+128^2\}^{1/2}} + 2\frac{(-Qe)(+Qe)}{(R-230)}\right]\\
&= \frac{Q^2e^2}{4\pi\epsilon_0}\left[\frac{1}{\{(R-144)^2+128^2\}^{1/2}} + \frac{1}{\{(R-124)^2+128^2\}^{1/2}}\right.\\
&\qquad + \frac{1}{\{(R-336)^2+128^2\}^{1/2}} + \frac{2}{(R-134)}\\
&\qquad \left. - \frac{2}{\{(R-240)^2+128^2\}^{1/2}} - \frac{2}{(R-230)}\right]\\
&= \frac{Q^2e^2}{4\pi\epsilon_0}f(R)
\end{aligned}$$

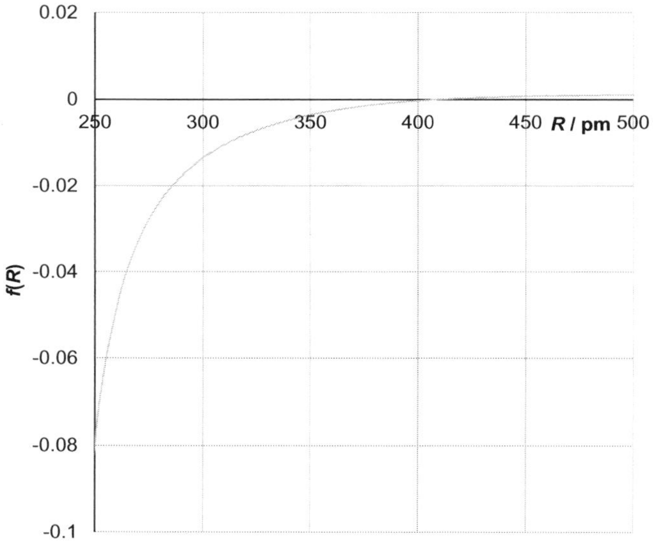


Figure 15.8

The most simple way of finding the value of $R$ for which the potential energy becomes negative, and thus the interaction attractive, is to plot the function. Figure 15.8 shows a plot of the function in square brackets, $f(R)$. It can be seen that for values of $R$ from 230 to 410 pm the value of the function is negative and thus the potential energy resulting from the electrostatic interactions is negative.

**E15.22** Considering the atoms within the hydrogen bond as point charges, the potential energy is given by the sum of the pairwise contributions resulting from the electrostatic interactions. We may ignore the interaction between the atoms of the covalent O–H bond because the contribution that this makes to the total energy is constant and does not vary with angle. Using trigonometry to calculate the distance between the atoms within the hydrogen bond in terms of the coordinates $r$, $R$ and $\theta$,

$$r_{\mathrm{HO'}} = (R^2 + r^2 - 2Rr\cos\theta^{1/2}) = R\{1 + (r/R)^2 - 2(r/R)\cos\theta\}^{1/2}$$
$$r_{\mathrm{OO'}} = R$$

Thus, applying Coulomb's law, eqn 15.2a, the molar potential energy is

$$\begin{aligned} V_{\mathrm{m}}(R,\theta) &= N_{\mathrm{A}}\left(\frac{Q_{\mathrm{O}}Q_{\mathrm{O'}}}{4\pi\epsilon_0 r_{\mathrm{OO'}}} + \frac{Q_{\mathrm{H}}Q_{\mathrm{O'}}}{4\pi\epsilon_0 r_{\mathrm{HO'}}}\right) \\ &= \frac{N_{\mathrm{A}}}{4\pi\epsilon_0}\left[\frac{(-0.83e)(-0.83e)}{R} + \frac{(+0.45e)(-0.83e)}{R\{1 + (r/R)^2 - 2(r/R)\cos\theta\}^{1/2}} + \right] \\ &= \frac{N_{\mathrm{A}}e^2}{4\pi\epsilon_0 R}\left[0.6889 - \frac{0.3735}{\{1 + (r/R)^2 - 2(r/R)\cos\theta\}^{1/2}}\right] \end{aligned}$$

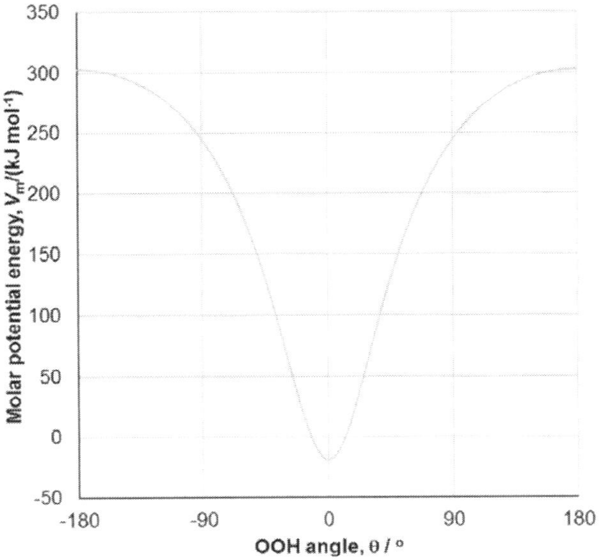


Figure 15.9

Figure 15.9 shows a plot of this function for $r = 95.7$ pm and $R = 200$ pm. As indicated in the text, the molar potential energy is negative only for angles of ±12° about the linear configuration.

**E15.23** The minimum in the Lennard-Jones potential function occurs for a separation $r = 2^{1/6}\sigma$. Thus, using the value for bromine from Table 15.4,

$$r = 2^{1/6}\sigma = 2^{1/6} \times 427 \text{ pm} = \mathbf{479\ pm}$$

**E15.24** Comparing the two forms of the Lennard-Jones potential function,

$$V(r) = \frac{A}{r^{12}} - \frac{B}{r^6} = 4\epsilon\left\{\left(\frac{\sigma}{r}\right)^{12} - \left(\frac{\sigma}{r}\right)^6\right\}$$

we may see that

$$A = 4\epsilon\sigma^{12}$$
$$B = 4\epsilon\sigma^6$$

Thus, rearranging,

$$\sigma = (A/B)^{1/6} = \{(7.31 \times 10^{13}\ \text{J pm}^{12})/(1.24 \times 10^{-3}\ \text{J pm}^6)\}^{1/6} = 623 \text{ pm}$$
$$\epsilon = (B^2/4A) = \{(1.24 \times 10^{-3}\ \text{J pm}^6)^2/(7.31 \times 10^{13}\ \text{J pm}^{12})\} = 2.10 \times 10^{-20}\ \text{J}$$

The depth of the well is thus

$$N_A\epsilon = (6.022 \times 10^{23}\text{mol}^{-1}) \times (2.10 \times 10^{-20}\ \text{J})$$
$$= 12.7 \times 10^3\ \text{J mol}^{-1} = \mathbf{12.7\ kJ\ mol^{-1}}$$

and the separation at which the potential energy is lowest is

$$r = 2^{1/6}\sigma = 2^{1/6} \times 623 \text{ pm} = \mathbf{699\ pm}$$

**E15.25** (a) The trans configuration corresponds to an azimuthal angle $\phi = \pi/3$ and an eclipsed configuration $\phi = 0$. Thus, the difference in potential energy between these two configurations is

$$\Delta V = ½V_0\{1 + \cos 0\} - ½V_0\{1 + \cos 3(\pi/3)\} = V_0 = \mathbf{11.6\ kJ\ mol^{-1}}$$

(b) The minimum in the potential energy occurs for the staggered conformation with an azimuthal angle $\phi = \pi/3$. Thus, considering the potential energy at angles close to this minimum, for small deviations $\delta\phi$, we may write

$$V = ½V_0\{1 + \cos 3\phi\} = ½V_0\{1 + \cos(\pi + \delta\phi)\} = ½V_0\{1 - \cos\delta\phi\}$$

because

$$\cos(x + \pi) = -\cos x$$

Using the MacLaurin expansion

$$\cos x = 1 - x^2/2! + x^4/4! - x^6/6! + \cdots$$

so that, if we neglect terms of order $\delta\phi^4$ and higher,

$$V = \tfrac{1}{2}V_0\{1 - (1 - (\delta\phi)^2/2! + (\delta\phi)^4/4! - (\delta\phi)^6/6! + \cdots)\}$$
$$\approx \tfrac{1}{2}V_0 \times \{(\delta\phi)^2/2!\} = V_0(\delta\phi)^2/4$$

The quadratic dependence upon the coordinate $\delta\phi$ confirms that the twisting motion follows the characteristics of a harmonic oscillator.

(c) We discovered in *Chapter 12* that for a harmonic oscillator with a potential function $V = \tfrac{1}{2}kx^2$, the vibrational frequency is

$$\nu = (1/2\pi)\sqrt{k/m}$$

By analogy, for angular motion, we should expect that for a potential function $V = \tfrac{1}{2}k\theta^2$, the vibrational frequency is

$$\nu = (1/2\pi)\sqrt{k/I}$$

with the moment of inertia $I$ taking the place of the mass $m$. For the torsional oscillation of a methyl group, the moment of inertia is

$$I = 3m_{\mathrm{H}}r^2$$

where $r$ is the length of a C–H bond which for ethane, we may take as 104 pm. Thus, comparison of the expressions for the potential function shows that for this example $k = \tfrac{1}{2}V_0$ and so the vibrational frequency is

$$\nu = (1/2\pi)\sqrt{\underbrace{(\tfrac{1}{2}V_0/N_{\mathrm{A}})}_{k}/\underbrace{(3m_{\mathrm{H}}r^2)}_{I}} = (1/2\pi)\sqrt{V_0/(6N_{\mathrm{A}}m_{\mathrm{H}}r^2)}$$
$$= \frac{1}{2\pi}\sqrt{\frac{(11.6\times10^3\ \mathrm{J\ mol^{-1}})}{6\times(1.673\times10^{-27}\ \mathrm{kg})\times(6.022\times10^{23}\mathrm{mol^{-1}})\times(104\times10^{-12}\mathrm{m})^2}}$$
$$= \mathbf{2.11\times10^{12}\ s^{-1}}$$

## Answers to projects

**P15.26** We may assume that the interactions between the chains are described by a Lennard-Jones potential function,

$$V(R) = 4\epsilon\left\{\left(\frac{\sigma}{R}\right)^{12} - \left(\frac{\sigma}{R}\right)^{6}\right\}$$

(a) The separation at which the force is zero is the point of mechanical equilibrium which to the minimum in the potential function.

(b) Thus, writing

$$F(R) = -\frac{\delta V}{\delta R} = -\frac{V(R+\delta R) - V(R)}{\delta R}$$
$$= -\left[4\epsilon\left\{\left(\frac{\sigma}{R+\delta R}\right)^{12} - \left(\frac{\sigma}{R+\delta R}\right)^{6}\right\} - 4\epsilon\left\{\left(\frac{\sigma}{R}\right)^{12} - \left(\frac{\sigma}{R}\right)^{6}\right\}\right]/\delta R$$

$$= -4\epsilon\left(\left(\frac{\sigma}{R}\right)^{12}\left[\frac{1}{\{1+(\delta R/R)\}^{12}}-1\right]-\left(\frac{\sigma}{R}\right)^{6}\left[\frac{1}{\{1+(\delta R/R)\}^{6}}-1\right]\right)/\delta R$$

For simplicity, we may write $x = \delta R/R$, so that the expression for the force becomes

$$F(R) = 4\epsilon\left[\left(\frac{\sigma}{R}\right)^{12}\left\{\frac{1-(1+x)^{12}}{(1+x)^{12}}\right\}-\left(\frac{\sigma}{R}\right)^{6}\left\{\frac{1-(1+x)^{6}}{(1+x)^{6}}\right\}\right]/\delta R$$

Noting that because $x \ll 1$

$$(1+x)^{12} = 1 + 12x + \cdots$$
$$(1+x)^{6} = 1 + 6x + \cdots$$

we may write

$$F(R) = -4\epsilon\left[\left(\frac{\sigma}{R}\right)^{12}\left\{\frac{1-(1+12x+\cdots)}{1+12x+\cdots}\right\}-\left(\frac{\sigma}{R}\right)^{6}\left\{\frac{1-(1+6x+\cdots)}{1+6x+\cdots}\right\}\right]/\delta R$$
$$\approx -4\epsilon\left[\left(\frac{\sigma}{R}\right)^{12}\left\{\frac{-12x+\cdots}{1+12x+\cdots}\right\}-\left(\frac{\sigma}{R}\right)^{6}\left\{\frac{-6x}{1+6x+\cdots}\right\}\right]/\delta R$$

Then, because $x \ll 1$, we may make the approximations $1 + 12x + \cdots \approx 1$ and $1 + 6x + \cdots \approx 1$, so that

$$F(R) = -4\epsilon\left[\left(\frac{\sigma}{R}\right)^{12}\left\{\frac{1-(1+12x+\cdots)}{1+12x+\cdots}\right\}-\left(\frac{\sigma}{R}\right)^{6}\left\{\frac{1-(1+6x+\cdots)}{1+6x+\cdots}\right\}\right]/\delta R$$
$$\approx 4\epsilon[(\sigma/R)^{12}\{12x\} - (\sigma/R)^{6}\{6x\}]/\delta R$$
$$= 4\epsilon[(\sigma/R)^{12}\{12x\} - (\sigma/R)^{6}\{6x\}]/\delta R$$
$$= 24x\epsilon(\sigma/R)^{6}\{2(\sigma/R)^{6} - 1\}/\delta R$$

We established in part (a) that at the minimum in the potential function, $F(R_e) = 0$. This is true if

$$\{2(\sigma/R_e)^6 - 1\} = 0$$

which may be rearranged to give

$$R_e = 2^{1/6}\sigma$$

(c) We may derive the same result rather more straightforwardly using calculus. Thus

$$F(R) = -\frac{dV}{dR} = -\frac{d}{dR}4\epsilon\left\{\left(\frac{\sigma}{R}\right)^{12}-\left(\frac{\sigma}{R}\right)^{6}\right\} = -4\epsilon\left\{\left(\sigma^{12}\frac{d}{dR}R^{-12}\right)-\left(\sigma^{6}\frac{d}{dR}R^{-6}\right)\right\}$$
$$= -4\epsilon\{(\sigma^{12}\times -12R^{-13}) - (\sigma^{6}\times -6R^{-7})\}$$
$$= 24\epsilon\sigma^{6}R^{-7}\{2(\sigma/R)^{6} - 1\}$$

At equilibrium, $F(R_e) = 0$. This condition is satisfied if

$$\{2(\sigma/R_e)^6 - 1\} = 0$$

so that

$$R_e = 2^{1/6}\sigma$$

**P15.27** The drug Crixivan, shown in Figure 15.10 with some of its hydrogen-bonding interactions with HIV protease, is a competitive inhibitor of HIV protease and has several molecular features that optimize binding to the enzyme's active site. First, the highlighted hydroxyl group displaces a $H_2O$ molecule that acts as the nucleophile in the hydrolysis of the substrate. Second, the carbon atom to which the key OH group is bound has a tetrahedral geometry that mimics the structure of the transition state of the peptide hydrolysis reaction. However, the tetrahedral moiety in the drug is not cleaved by the enzyme. Third, the inhibitor is anchored firmly to the active site via a network of hydrogen bonds involving the carbonyl groups of the drug, a water molecule, and peptide NH groups from the enzyme.

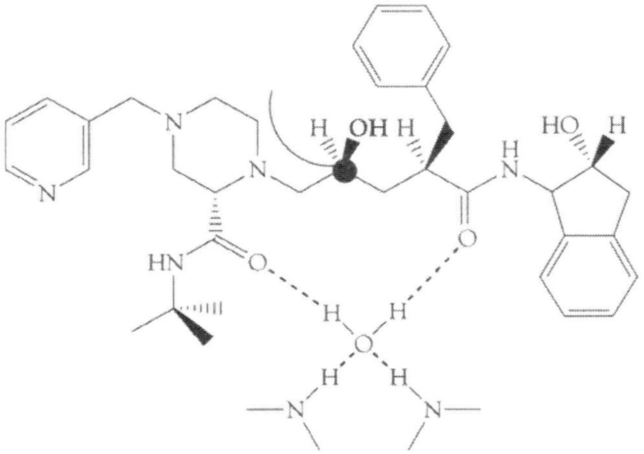

Figure 15.10

# Chapter 16

# Macromolecules and aggregates

## Answers to discussion questions

**D16.1** **Number-average molar mass,** $\bar{M}_n$, is the value obtained by weighting each molar mass by the number of molecules of that mass and is defined through eqn 16.9a and 16.9b

$$\bar{M}_n = \frac{1}{N}\sum_i N_i M_i = \frac{1}{n}\sum_i n_i M_i$$

where $N_i$ is the number of molecules of molar mass $M_i$ and $N$ is the total number of molecules. We may also express the definition in terms of the amount of molecules of a given molar mass $n_i$ and total mass $n$ because $N_i = N_A n_i$ and $N = N_A n$. Measurements of the osmotic pressures of macromolecular solutions yield the number-average molar mass.

**Weight-average molar mass,** $\bar{M}_w$, is the value obtained by weighting each molar mass by the mass of each one present. Thus, from eqn 16.9c

$$\bar{M}_w = \frac{1}{m}\sum_i m_i M_i = \Bigg(1/\underbrace{\sum_i n_i M_i}_{\text{total mass},m}\Bigg)\sum_i \overbrace{(n_i M_i)}^{m_i} \times M_i = \sum n_i M_i^2 / \sum_i n_i M_i$$

Laser light scattering measures $\bar{M}_w$.

The number and weight-average molar masses are identical for molar mass distributions that are very narrow or monodisperse. However, the weight-average molar mass is greater than the number-average molar mass for a polydisperse sample and the difference between the two becomes greater for very wide molar mass distributions. The **heterogeneity index**, $(\bar{M}_w/\bar{M}_n)$, is an indicator of the distribution width. If the index is less than 1.1, the polymer sample is 'monodisperse'. Larger values indicate a wide, or polydisperse, molar mass distribution, which is considered to be heterogeneous.

**D16.2** The **contour length,** $R_c$ is the length of the macromolecule measured along its backbone, that is, the length of all its monomer units placed end to end. This is the stretched-out length of the macromolecule with bond angles maintained within the monomer units and 180° angles at unit links. The conotur length is thus equal to the number of monomer units, $N$, and to the length of each unit, eqn 16.1a.

$$R_c = Nl$$

The **root mean square separation, $R_{rms}$** is one measure of the average separation of the ends of a random coil. It is the square root of the mean value of $R^2$, where $R$ is the separation of the two ends of the coil. The root mean square separation is given by eqn 16.1b,

$$R_{rms} = N^{1/2}l$$

The **radius of gyration**, $R_g$, is the radius of a thin hollow spherical shell of the same mass and moment of inertia as the macromolecule. In general, it is not easy to visualize this distance geometrically. However, for the simple case of a molecule consisting of a chain of identical atoms this quantity can be visualized as the root mean square distance of the atoms from the centre of mass. We can see from eqn 16.1c that the radius of gyration also depends on $N^{1/2}$, but is smaller than the root mean square separation by a factor of $(1/6)^{1/2}$

$$R_g = (N/6)^{1/2}l$$

**D16.3** The random coil model ignores the role of the solvent: a poor solvent will tend to cause the coil to tighten; a good solvent does the opposite. Therefore, calculations based on this model are best regarded as lower bounds to the dimensions of a polymer in a good solvent and as an upper bound for a polymer in a poor solvent. The model is most reliable for a polymer in a bulk solid sample, where the coil is likely to have its natural dimensions.

**D16.4** In **matrix-assisted laser desorption/ionization (MALDI)** the macromolecule sample is embedded in a solid matrix composed of an organic material and inorganic salt. This is irradiated with a pulsed laser, which ejects excited matrix ions, cations, and neutral macromolecules into a dense gas plume above the matrix surface. The macromolecule is ionized by collisions and complexation with small cations and the masses of the resulting ions are determined in a mass spectrometer. Molar mass averages are calculated from the data of the mass spectrum.

In the **ultracentrifuge** technique a column of macromolecule in solution is spun to produce accelerations equivalent to about $10^5$ g. The rate at which the macromolecules recede is related to the number-average molar mass.

**Laser light scattering** by macromolecules in solution is a convenient method for determination of the weight-average molar mass of a polydisperse sample. It is used to characterize polymers, colloids, and biological systems from proteins to viruses. The method involves measuring the dependence of the intensity of scattered light on the angle between the incident and scattered beams.

A **viscometer** is often used to measure the viscosity, which is proportional to the drainage time through a capillary in the basic instrument, of a macromolecule solution over a range of concentrations in order to deduce the viscosity-average molar mass.

**D16.5** **Elastomers** are polymers with numerous crosslinks that pull them back into their original shape when a stress is removed. The internal energy of a **perfect elastomer** is independent of the extension of the random coil; it acts like a coil spring because for small displacements from the random coil, it spontaneously returns to a random coil conformation with a force that is proportional to the displacement. This is driven by an increase in entropy of the perfect elastomer while the entropy of the surroundings remains unchanged as no energy has been released, or absorbed, by the coil.

**D16.6** Molecular interactions of polymeric materials include hydrogen bonding, ionic interactions), van der Waals interactions, hydrophobic interactions, and disulfide links. Physical entanglement of long polymeric chains also plays an important role in determining the thermal stability and mechanical strength of these materials.

**D16.7** A surfactant is a species that is active at the interface of two phases or substances, such as the interface between hydrophilic and hydrophobic phases. A surfactant accumulates at the interface and modifies the properties of the surface, in particular, decreasing its surface tension. A typical surfactant consists of a long hydrocarbon tail and other non-polar materials, and a hydrophilic head group, such as the carboxylate group, $-CO_2^-$, that dissolves in a polar solvent, typically water. In other words, a surfactant is an amphipathic substance, meaning that it has both hydrophobic and hydrophilic regions.

Surface tension is a result of cohesive forces and the solute molecules must weaken the attractive forces between solvent molecules. Thus, molecules with bulky hydrophobic regions such as fatty acids can decrease the surface tension because they attract solvent molecules less strongly than solvent molecules attract each other.

**D16.8** The surface of a disperse, colloidal particle shows two distinctive regions of charge. First, there is a fairly immobile layer of solvated ions and water molecules that stick tightly to the surface. The radius of the sphere that captures this rigid layer is call the **radius of shear**, and it is the major factor determining the mobility of the particle. The electric potential at the radius of shear relative to its value in the distant, bulk medium is called the **electrokinetic potential,** $\zeta$. The charged unit attracts an oppositely charged ionic atmosphere. The inner shell of charge and outer atmosphere jointly constitute the **electric double layer**.

The electric double layer is the major source of colloidal kinetic non-lability and physical stability. Colliding colloidal particles break through the double layer and coalesce only if the collision is sufficiently energetic to disrupt the layers of ions and solvating molecules, or if thermal motion has stirred away the surface accumulation of charge.

# Solutions to exercises

**E16.1** Applying eqn 16.1, the contour length is

$$R_c = Nl = 800 \times (1.10 \times 10^{-9}\ \text{m}) = 8.8 \times 10^{-7}\ \text{m} = \mathbf{0.880\ \mu m}$$

and the root-mean-square separation

$$R_{rms} = N^{1/2}l = 800^{1/2} \times (1.10 \times 10^{-9}\ \text{m}) = 3.11 \times 10^{-7}\ \text{m} = \mathbf{0.311\ \mu m}$$

The equivalent radius of gyration is

$$R_g = (N/6)^{1/2}l = (800/6)^{1/2} \times (1.10 \times 10^{-9}\ \text{m}) = 1.27 \times 10^{-8}\ \text{m} = \mathbf{12.7\ nm}$$

**E16.2** The monomeric repeat unit in polyethene is $-\!(CH_2\text{–}CH_2)\!-$ which has a molar mass of 28.06 g mol$^{-1}$. The number of repeating units, $N$, is therefore

$$N = (250 \times 10^3\ \text{g mol}^{-1})/(28.06\ \text{g mol}^{-1})$$

The monomeric length is the equivalent of the C–C bond length, plus half a bond length at each end

$$l = \tfrac{1}{2}R + R + \tfrac{1}{2}R = 2R$$

Assuming a C–C bond length of 154 pm, and applying eqn 16.1, the contour length is

$$\begin{aligned} R_c &= Nl \\ &= \overbrace{\{(250 \times 10^3\ \text{g mol}^{-1})/(28.06\ \text{g mol}^{-1})\}}^{N} \times \overbrace{\{2 \times (154 \times 10^{-12}\ \text{m})\}}^{l} \\ &= 2.75 \times 10^{-6}\ \text{m} = \mathbf{2.75\ \mu m} \end{aligned}$$

and the root mean square separation

$$\begin{aligned} R_{rms} &= N^{1/2}l \\ &= \overbrace{\{(250 \times 10^3\ \text{g mol}^{-1})/(28.06\ \text{g mol}^{-1})\}^{1/2}}^{N} \times \overbrace{\{2 \times (154 \times 10^{-12}\ \text{m})\}}^{l} \\ &= 2.91 \times 10^{-8}\ \text{m} = \mathbf{29.1\ nm} \end{aligned}$$

**E16.3** The radius of gyration of a long chain molecule is defined through eqn 16.1c

$$R_g = (N/6)^{1/2}l$$

Thus, assuming the length of each link in the chain to be the length of a typical C–C bond, 154 pm, and rearranging,

$$N = 6\left(R_g/l\right)^2 = 6 \times \{(7.3 \times 10^{-9}\text{m})/(154 \times 10^{-12}\text{m})\}^2 = \mathbf{14000}$$

**E16.4** The change in the conformational entropy when a random coli is extended or compressed by a length $nl$, where $l$ is the length of an individual link, is given by eqn 16.2

$$\Delta S = -\tfrac{1}{2}kN[\ln\{(1+\nu)^{1+\nu}(1-\nu)^{1-\nu}\}], \qquad \text{with } \nu = n/N$$

If the length of the random coil is extended by 10 per cent, so that $\nu = 0.1$, then the change in the molar entropy per link in the coil is

$$\begin{aligned}\Delta S_m/N &= -\tfrac{1}{2}kN_A\{\ln(1+0.1)^{1+0.1}(1-0.1)^{1-0.1}\}\\ &= -\tfrac{1}{2}(1.38\times10^{-23}\,\mathrm{J\,K^{-1}})\times(6.022\times10^{23}\,\mathrm{mol^{-1}})\\ &\qquad\times[\ln\{(1.1)^{1.1}(0.9)^{0.9}\}]\\ &= \mathbf{-0.042\ J\,K^{-1}mol^{-1}}\end{aligned}$$

**E16.5** Treating the polybutadiene molecule as a one-dimensional chain, we may apply the approximate form of eqn 16.3 to calculate the restoring force when the molecule is extended by 5.0 per cent of its length. Thus,

$$\mathcal{F} = \frac{kT}{2l}\left(\frac{1+\nu}{1-\nu}\right) = \frac{\nu kT}{l} = \frac{0.05\times(1.38\times10^{-23}\,\mathrm{J\,K^{-1}})\times(25+273.15)\mathrm{K}}{(150\times10^{-12}\mathrm{m})}$$
$$= 4.1\times10^{-10}\,\mathrm{J\,m^{-1}} = \mathbf{0.41\ nN}$$

**E16.6** The glass transition temperature $T_g$ is the temperature at which internal bond rotations freeze. In effect, the easier such rotations are, the lower $T_g$. Internal rotations are more difficult for polymers that have bulky side chains than for polymers without such chains because the side chains of neighbouring molecules can impede each others' motion. Of the four polymers in this problem, polystyrene has the largest side chain (phenyl) and the largest $T_g$. The chlorine atoms in poly(vinyl chloride) interfere with each other's motion more than the smaller hydrogen atoms that hang from the carbon backbone of polyethylene. Poly(oxymethylene), like polyethylene, has only hydrogen atoms protruding from its backbone; however, poly(oxymethylene) has fewer hydrogen protrusions and a still lower $T_g$ than polyethylene.

**E16.7** We may confirm whether a protein molecule has a globular structure by comparing the observed value for the radius of gyration with that calculated by modelling the protein molecule as a sphere. The moment of inertia of the molecule is

$$I = mr_g^2$$

However, the moment of inertia for a sphere of mass $m$ and radius $r$ for rotation about an axis through the centre is

$$I = 2mr^2/5$$

Thus, combining these two equations, we may assume that the protein molecule is globular rather than rod-like if

$$\begin{aligned}mr_g^2 &= 2mr^2/5\\ r_g &= (2r/5)^{1/2}\end{aligned}$$

We may calculate the effective radius of an individual molecule from the specifc volume, $v_s$, which is the reciprocal of the mass density. Thus

$$v_s = 1/\rho = \frac{V}{m} = \frac{V}{(M/N_A)} = \frac{\overbrace{(4\pi r^3/3)}^{\text{volume of a sphere}}}{(M/N_A)}$$

Rearranging,

$$r = \left(\frac{3Mv_s}{4\pi N_A}\right)^{1/3}$$

so that

$$r_g = (2r/5)^{1/2} = \left[2\overbrace{\{(3Mv_s)/(4\pi N_A)\}^{1/3}}^{r}/5\right]^{1/2} = (2/5)^{1/2}\{(3Mv_s)/(4\pi N_A)\}^{1/3}$$

Using the data for serum albumin, we find the calculated value for the radius of gyration, based on the assumption that the molecule is globular, to be

$$r_g = \left(\frac{2}{5}\right)^{1/2} \times \left\{\frac{3 \times \overbrace{(66 \times 10^3 \times 10^{-3}\,\text{kg mol}^{-1})}^{M} \times \overbrace{(0.752 \times 10^{-6} \times 10^3\,\text{m}^3\,\text{kg}^{-1})}^{v_s}}{4\pi \times \underbrace{(6.022 \times 10^{23}\,\text{mol}^{-1})}_{N_A}}\right\}^{1/3}$$
$$= 1.71 \times 10^{-9}\,\text{m} = 1.71\,\text{nm}$$

Given the approximations used, the result is in relatively good agreement with the observed value of 2.98 nm, suggesting that serum albumin does indeed form a globular structure. Performing the same calculation for the bushy stunt virus gives a calculated value for the radius of gyration of 9.22 nm. Once again, this appears to be consistent with the observed value of 12.0 nm, implying that the virus forms a globular structure. For DNA, however, the calculated value for the radius of gyration is 6.11 nm. This is significantly different from the obesrved value of 117.0 nm. We may therefore infer that DNA does not adopt a spherical structure.

**E16.8** The work that is done when the area of a surface changes is given by eqn 16.5. The surface area of a sphere is $\sigma = 4\pi r^2$, so that when the radius doubles, from $r$ to $2r$, the change in surface area is

$$\Delta\sigma = 4\pi(2r)^2 - 4\pi r^2 = 12\pi r^2$$

Hence, the work that must be done in doubling the radius of the spherical cavity is

$$w = \Delta G = \gamma\Delta\sigma = 12\pi\gamma r^2$$
$$= 12\pi \times (72 \times 10^{-3}\,\text{N m}^{-1}) \times (5.0 \times 10^{-3})^2 = 68 \times 10^{-6}\,\text{J} = \mathbf{68\,\mu J}$$

**E16.9** The height through which a column of liquid rises as a result of capillary action is given by eqn 16.7. Thus,

$$h = \frac{2\gamma}{\rho g r}$$
$$= \frac{2 \times (22.39 \times 10^{-3}\ \mathrm{N\ m^{-1}})}{(789\ \mathrm{kg\ m^{-3}}) \times (9.81\ \mathrm{m\ s^{-2}}) \times (0.10 \times 10^{-3}\ \mathrm{m})} = 0.058\ \mathrm{m} = \mathbf{5.8\ cm}$$

**E16.10** Rearranging eqn 16.7, the surface tension of methanol at 298 K is

$$\gamma = h\rho g r/2 = h\rho g \overbrace{(d/2)}^{\text{diameter},d}/2 = h\rho g d/4$$
$$= (5.8 \times 10^{-2}\ \mathrm{m}) \times (791\ \mathrm{kg\ m^{-3}}) \times (9.81\ \mathrm{m\ s^{-2}}) \times (0.20 \times 10^{-3}\ \mathrm{m})/4$$
$$= 23 \times 10^{-3}\ \mathrm{kg\ s^{-2}} = \mathbf{23\ mN\ m^{-1}}$$

**E16.11** According to the Laplace equation, eqn 16.6, the difference in pressure between the concave and convex sides of a spherical surface is

$$\Delta p = p_{\text{concave}} - p_{\text{convex}} = 2\gamma/r$$

(a) Thus, for a curved surface of water with radius 0.10 mm,

$$\Delta p = 2 \times (72 \times 10^{-3}\ \mathrm{N\ m^{-1}})/(0.10 \times 10^{-3}\ \mathrm{m}) = 1400\ \mathrm{N\ m^{-2}} = \mathbf{1.4\ kPa}$$

(b) and 1.0 mm,

$$\Delta p = 2 \times (72 \times 10^{-3}\ \mathrm{N\ m^{-1}})/(1.0 \times 10^{-3}\ \mathrm{m}) = 140\ \mathrm{N\ m^{-2}} = \mathbf{0.14\ kPa}$$

**E16.12** The surface excess of solute molecules is defined through eqn 16.8 as

$$\Gamma = \frac{n_{\text{total}} - n_{\text{solution}}}{\sigma}$$

The amount of solute molecules, both in total and in the bulk solution, may be expressed in terms of the concentrations and volume of the beaker as $n = cV$. If we assume that the beaker is cylindrical, then the surface area is $\sigma = \pi r^2$. Hence,

$$\Gamma = \frac{c_{\text{total}}V - c_{\text{solution}}V}{\pi r^2} = \frac{(c_{\text{total}} - c_{\text{solution}})V}{\pi r^2}$$
$$= \frac{\{(0.100 - 0.0981) \times 10^3\ \mathrm{mol\ m^{-3}}\} \times (100 \times 10^{-6}\ \mathrm{m^3})}{\pi \times (2.6 \times 10^{-2}\ \mathrm{m})^2}$$
$$= 9.7 \times 10^{-2}\ \mathrm{mol\ m^{-2}} = \mathbf{97\ mmol\ m^{-2}}$$

**E16.13** The definitions of the number-average and weight average molar mass are given in eqn 16.9. If the amounts of the two types of polymer are equal, $n_1 = n_2 = \tfrac{1}{2}n$, and so the number-average molar mass is

$$\bar{M}_n = \frac{1}{N}\sum_i N_i M_i = \frac{1}{n}\sum_i n_i M_i$$

$$= \frac{1}{n}\{½n(82\text{ kg mol}^{-1}) + ½n(108\text{ kg mol}^{-1})\} = \mathbf{95\ kg\ mol^{-1}}$$

From eqn 16.9,

$$\bar{M}_w = \frac{1}{m}\sum_i m_i M_i = \left(1/\underbrace{\sum_i n_i M_i}_{\text{total mass},m}\right)\sum_i \overbrace{(n_i M_i)}^{m_i} \times M_i = \sum n_i M_i^2 \Big/ \sum_i n_i M_i$$

Because $n_1 = n_2$, the weight-average molar mass is thus

$$\bar{M}_w = \frac{n_1 M_1^2 + n_2 M_2^2}{n_1 M_1 + n_2 M_2} = \frac{M_1^2 + M_2^2}{M_1 + M_2}$$
$$= \frac{(82\text{ kg mol}^{-1})^2 + (102\text{ kg mol}^{-1})^2}{(82\text{ kg mol}^{-1}) + (102\text{ kg mol}^{-1})} = \mathbf{97\ kg\ mol^{-1}}$$

**E16.14** Measurements of the osmotic pressures of macromolecular solutions yield the number-average molar mass. Thus, if the solution consists of 30 per cent dimer with molar mass 30 kg $\text{mol}^{-1}$, and therefore 70 per cent monomer with molar mass 15 kg $\text{mol}^{-1}$, from eqn 16.9,

$$\bar{M}_n = \frac{1}{N}\sum_i N_i M_i = \sum_i x_i M_i$$
$$= 0.30 \times (30\text{ kg mol}^{-1}) + 0.70 \times (15\text{ kg mol}^{-1}) = \mathbf{18\ kg\ mol^{-1}}$$

Light scattering yields the weight-average molar mass. Thus, from eqn 16.9

$$\bar{M}_w = \frac{1}{m}\sum_i m_i M_i = \left(1/\underbrace{\sum_i n_i M_i}_{\text{total mass},m}\right)\sum_i \overbrace{(n_i M_i)}^{m_i} \times M_i = \sum x_i M_i^2 \Big/ \sum_i x_i M_i$$
$$= \frac{0.30 \times (30\text{ kg mol}^{-1})^2 + 0.70 \times (15\text{ kg mol}^{-1})^2}{0.30 \times (30\text{ kg mol}^{-1}) + 0.70 \times (15\text{ kg mol}^{-1})} = \mathbf{20\ kg\ mol^{-1}}$$

**E16.15** The heterogeneity index of a sample of polymer is given by the ratio of the number-average and weight-average molar masses. Thus, following the method used in Example 16.1, we must first calculate the amount of each component

$$n_i = m_i/M_i$$

Thus, for each component, the amount is

$$n_1 = (16.0\text{ g})/(6.5 \times 10^3\text{ g mol}^{-1}) = 2.5 \times 10^{-3}\text{ mol}$$
$$n_2 = (27.1\text{ g})/(11.5 \times 10^3\text{ g mol}^{-1}) = 2.36 \times 10^{-3}\text{ mol}$$
$$n_3 = (29.5\text{ g})/(19.5 \times 10^3\text{ g mol}^{-1}) = 1.51 \times 10^{-3}\text{ mol}$$
$$n_4 = (13.4\text{ g})/(23.5 \times 10^3\text{ g mol}^{-1}) = 0.570 \times 10^{-3}\text{ mol}$$
$$n_5 = (8.7\text{ g})/(28.5 \times 10^3\text{ g mol}^{-1}) = 0.310 \times 10^{-3}\text{ mol}$$
$$n_6 = (3.5\text{ g})/(35.5 \times 10^3\text{ g mol}^{-1}) = 0.099 \times 10^{-3}\text{ mol}$$

The number-average molar mass is thus

$$\bar{M}_n = \frac{1}{N}\sum_i N_i M_i = \frac{1}{n}\sum_i n_i M_i = \sum_i n_i M_i \Big/ \sum_i n_i$$
$$= [\{(2.5 \times 6.5) + (2.36 \times 11.5) + (1.51 \times 19.5)$$
$$+(0.570 \times 23.5) + (0.310 \times 28.5) + (0.099 \times 35.5)\}$$
$$/(2.5 + 2.36 + 1.51 + 0.570 + 0.310 + 0.099)]\ \text{kg mol}^{-1}$$
$$= 13.4\ \text{kg mol}^{-1}$$

The weight-average molar mass is

$$\bar{M}_w = \frac{1}{m}\sum_i m_i M_i = \sum_i m_i M_i \Big/ \sum_i m_i =$$
$$= [\{(16.0 \times 6.5) + (27.1 \times 11.5) + (29.5 \times 19.5)$$
$$+(13.4 \times 23.5) + (8.7 \times 28.5) + (3.5 \times 35.5)\}$$
$$/(16.0 + 27.1 + 29.5 + 13.4 + 8.7 + 3.5)]\ \text{kg mol}^{-1}$$
$$= 17.1\ \text{kg mol}^{-1}$$

The heterogeneity index is thus

$$\bar{M}_w/\bar{M}_n = (17.1\ \text{kg mol}^{-1})/(13.4\ \text{kg mol}^{-1}) = \mathbf{1.27}$$

**E16.16** The peaks are separated by104 g mol$^{-1}$, so this must be the molar mass of the repeating unit of the polymer. This peak separation is consistent with the identification of the polymer as polystyrene, for the repeating group of $-(CH_2CH(C_6H_5))-$ (8 C atoms and 8 H atoms) has a molar mass of 8 × (12.01 + 1.01) g mol$^{-1}$ = 104.08 g mol$^{-1}$. A consistent difference between peaks suggests a pure system and points away from different numbers of subunits of different molecular weight (such as the *t*-butyl initiators) being incorporated into the polymer molecules. The most intense peak has a molar mass equal to that of *n* repeating groups plus that of a silver cation plus that of terminal groups:

$$M(\text{peak}) = nM(\text{repeat}) + M(\text{Ag}^+) + M(\text{terminal})$$

If both ends of the polymer have terminal *t*-butyl $(CH_3)_3C-$, groups, then

$$M(\text{terminal}) = 2\text{M}(t\text{-butyl})$$
$$= 2 \times \{(4 \times 12.01) + (9 \times 1.01)\ \text{g mol}^{-1}\} = 114.12\ \text{g mol}^{-1}$$

and so the number of repeat units in the molecules that gives rise to the most intense peak is

$$n = \frac{M(\text{peak}) - M(\text{Ag}^+) - M(\text{terminal})}{M(\text{repeat})}$$
$$= \frac{(25578 - 108 - 114)\ \text{g mol}^{-1}}{(104\ \text{g mol}^{-1})} = \mathbf{244}$$

**E16.17** We may rearrange eqn 16.10

$$\ln c_2 = \frac{\bar{M}_w(r_2^2 - r_1^2)b\omega}{2RT} + \ln c_1$$

Let the pair ($c_2$,$r_2$) be any unspecified pair ($c$,$r$) and let the pair ($c_1$,$r_1$) be the reference pair ($c_{\text{ref}}$,$r_{\text{ref}}$), then the expression can be written in the linear form

$$\overbrace{\ln c}^{y} = \overbrace{\left(\frac{\bar{M}_w b\omega}{2RT}\right)}^{\text{slope}} \overbrace{r^2}^{x} + \overbrace{\left(\ln c_{\text{ref}} - \frac{\bar{M}_w b\omega r_{\text{ref}}{}^2}{2RT}\right)}^{\text{intercept}}$$

Thus, the slope of a graph of ln $c$ against $r^2$ should allow us to determine the value of the weight-average molar mass. Noting that the centrifuge rotates at a frequency of 55000 revolutions per minute, and thus an angular velocity of

$$\omega = 2\pi \times (55000 \text{ min}^{-1})/(60 \text{ s min}^{-1})$$

then

$$\begin{aligned}\bar{M}_w &= \frac{2RT}{(1-\rho v_s)\omega^2} \times \text{slope} \\ &= \left[\frac{2 \times (8.3145 \text{ J K}^{-1}\text{mol}^{-1}) \times (300 \text{ K})}{\{1-(0.996 \text{ g cm}^{-3}) \times (0.61 \text{ cm}^3 \text{ g}^{-1})\} \times \{2\pi \times (55000/60) \text{ s}^{-1}\}^2}\right] \\ &\qquad \times (659 \times 10^4 \text{ m}^{-2}) \\ &= \mathbf{2.5 \times 10^3 \text{ kg mol}^{-1}}\end{aligned}$$

## Answers to projects

**P16.18** (a) In general, for a variable $x$, with the probability distribution $P(x)$, the mean value of a continuous function, $f(x)$, is given by the integral

$$\langle f(x)\rangle = \int_{-\infty}^{\infty} f(x)P(x)\,\mathrm{d}x \Big/ \int_{-\infty}^{\infty} P(x)\,\mathrm{d}x = \int_{-\infty}^{\infty} f(x)P(x)\,\mathrm{d}x$$

The mean value of the squared separation of the ends of the polymer chain is therefore given by the integral

$$\int_0^{\infty} R^2 f(R)\,\mathrm{d}R$$

where $f(R)$ is the probability function

$$f(R) = 4\pi(a/\pi^{1/2})^3 R^2 \mathrm{e}^{-a^2R^2} \text{ with } a = \{3/(2Nl^2)\}^{1/2}$$

Hence,

$$\langle R^2\rangle = \int_0^{\infty} R^2 4\pi(a/\pi^{1/2})^3 R^2 \mathrm{e}^{-a^2R^2}\,\mathrm{d}R$$

$$= 4\pi(a/\pi^{1/2})^3 \int_0^\infty R^4 e^{-a^2R^2}\, dR$$

The integral is a standard integral of the form

$$\int_0^\infty x^{2n} e^{-bx^2}\, dx = \frac{(2n)!}{n!\, 2^{2n+1}}\left(\frac{\pi}{b^{2n+1}}\right)^{1/2}$$

with $n = 2$ and $b = a^2$ so that

$$\begin{aligned}\langle R^2\rangle &= 4\pi(a/\pi^{1/2})^3 \times \frac{(2\times 2)!}{2!\, 2^{\{(2\times 2)+1\}}}\left\{\frac{\pi}{(a^2)^{\{(2\times 2)+1\}}}\right\}^{1/2}\\ &= 4\pi(a/\pi^{1/2})^3 \times \frac{4!}{2!\, 2^5}\left(\frac{\pi}{a^{10}}\right)^{1/2}\\ &= \frac{3}{2a^2} = \frac{3}{2\times[\{3/(2Nl^2)\}^{1/2}]^2} = Nl^2\end{aligned}$$

Thus, the root mean-square separation is

$$\langle R^2\rangle^{1/2} = N^{1/2}l = 5000^{1/2} \times (154\text{ pm}) = 10.9\times 10^{-9}\text{ m} = \mathbf{10.9\ nm}$$

(b) In the same way, the mean separation is

$$\begin{aligned}\langle R\rangle &= \int_0^\infty R\, 4\pi(a/\pi^{1/2})^3 R^2 e^{-a^2R^2}\, dR\\ &= 4\pi(a/\pi^{1/2})^3 \int_0^\infty R^3 e^{-a^2R^2}\, dR\end{aligned}$$

The integral is a standard integral of the form

$$\int_0^\infty x^{2n+1} e^{-bx^2}\, dx = \frac{n!}{2b^{n+1}}$$

with $n = 1$ and $b = a^2$ so that

$$\begin{aligned}\langle R\rangle &= 4\pi(a/\pi^{1/2})^3 \times \frac{1!}{2(a^2)^{(1+1)}}\\ &= 4\pi(a/\pi^{1/2})^3 \times \frac{1}{2a^4}\\ &= \frac{2}{a\pi^{1/2}} = \left(\frac{8N}{3\pi}\right)^{1/2} l\end{aligned}$$

Thus, the mean separation is

$$\langle R\rangle = (8\times 5000/3\pi)^{1/2} \times (154\text{ pm}) = 10.0\times 10^{-9}\text{ m} = \mathbf{10.0\ nm}$$

(c) The most probable separation is given by the maximum in the probability function for which

$$\frac{df(R)}{dR} = 0$$

Thus,

$$\begin{aligned}\frac{d}{dR}4\pi(a/\pi^{1/2})^3R^2e^{-a^2R^2} &= 4\pi(a/\pi^{1/2})^3\frac{d}{dR}R^2e^{-a^2R^2}\\ &= 4\pi(a/\pi^{1/2})^3\left\{R^2\frac{d}{dR}e^{-a^2R^2}+e^{-a^2R^2}\frac{d}{dR}R^2\right\}\\ &= 4\pi(a/\pi^{1/2})^3\{R^2\times\left(-2a^2R\,e^{-a^2R^2}\right)+e^{-a^2R^2}\times 2R\}\\ &= 4\pi(a/\pi^{1/2})^3R\,e^{-a^2R^2}\{-a^2R^2+1\}\\ &= 0\end{aligned}$$

This expression is satisfied if

$$R = 0$$
$$e^{-a^2R^2} = 0$$

which correspond to the asymptotic limits, rather than a true maximum or minimum, and

$$1 - a^2R^2 = 0$$
$$R = a^{-1}$$

The most probable separation is thus

$$R^* = (2Nl^2/3)^{1/2} = \{2\times 5000\times(154\text{ pm})^2/3\}^{1/2} = \mathbf{8.89\ nm}$$

**P16.19** Group project

**P16.20** (a) We may estimate the force required for a 10 per cent expansion from the coiled state with the one-dimensional perfect elastomer model, eqn 16.3a. Assuming $l$ = 154 pm, which is the C–C bond length in a typical polymer

$$\begin{aligned}\mathcal{F} = \frac{kT}{2l}\ln\left(\frac{1+\nu}{1-\nu}\right) &= \frac{(1.38\times10^{-23}\text{ J K}^{-1})\times(300\text{ K})}{2\times(154\times10^{-12}\text{ m})}\ln\left(\frac{1+0.1}{1-0.1}\right)\\ &= 2.70\times10^{-12}\text{ J m}^{-1} = \mathbf{2.70\ pN}\end{aligned}$$

(b) If the restoring force,

$$\mathcal{F} = -T\frac{dS}{dx}$$

then because the conformational entropy for the equilibrium conformation is constant, we may write

$$\mathcal{F} = -T\frac{d(S-S_e)}{dx} = -T\frac{d\Delta S}{dx}$$

But, our expression for the change in entropy, $\Delta S$, eqn 16.2, is written in terms of the relative extension or compression, $\nu = n/N$. However, if the extension or compression is equivalent to a change of $n$ bond lengths, $x = nl = \nu Nl$, so that $\delta x = Nl\delta\nu$. For an infinitesimally small change in length, $dx = Nld\nu$, and so

$$\mathcal{F} = -T\frac{d\Delta S}{(Nld\nu)} = -\frac{T}{Nl}\frac{d\Delta S}{d\nu} = -\frac{T}{Nl}\frac{d}{d\nu} - \tfrac{1}{2}kN[\ln\{(1+\nu)^{1+\nu}(1-\nu)^{1-\nu}\}]$$

$$= \frac{½kNT}{Nl}\frac{\mathrm{d}}{\mathrm{d}\nu}\{\ln(1+\nu)^{1+\nu} + \ln(1-\nu)^{1-\nu}\}$$
$$= \frac{kT}{2l}\frac{\mathrm{d}}{\mathrm{d}\nu}\{(1+\nu)\ln(1+\nu) + (1-\nu)\ln(1-\nu)\}$$
$$= \frac{kT}{2l}\frac{\mathrm{d}}{\mathrm{d}\nu}\left\{(1+\nu)\frac{\mathrm{d}}{\mathrm{d}\nu}\ln(1+\nu) + \ln(1+\nu)\frac{\mathrm{d}}{\mathrm{d}\nu}(1+\nu) + (1-\nu)\frac{\mathrm{d}}{\mathrm{d}\nu}\ln(1-\nu) + \ln(1-\nu)\frac{\mathrm{d}}{\mathrm{d}\nu}(1-\nu)\right\}$$

Then, because

$$\frac{\mathrm{d}}{\mathrm{d}x}\ln(1+ax) = \frac{a}{1+ax}$$

It follows that

$$\mathcal{F} = \frac{kT}{2l}\frac{\mathrm{d}}{\mathrm{d}\nu}\left\{(1+\nu)\times\frac{1}{(1+\nu)} + \ln(1+\nu) + (1-\nu)\times-\frac{1}{(1-\nu)} - \ln(1-\nu)\right\}$$
$$= \frac{kT}{2l}\{\ln(1+\nu) - \ln(1-\nu)\} = \frac{kT}{2l}\ln\left(\frac{1+\nu}{1-\nu}\right)$$

which is eqn 16.3a.

**P16.21** Considering eqn 16.4b, and taking $N = 2$ and $K = 1$, then

$$K = \frac{[\mathrm{M}_N]}{([\mathrm{M}]_{\mathrm{total}} - N[\mathrm{M}_N])^N} = \frac{[\mathrm{M}_2]}{([\mathrm{M}]_{\mathrm{total}} - 2[\mathrm{M}_2])^2} = 1$$

so that

$$([\mathrm{M}]_{\mathrm{total}} - 2[\mathrm{M}_2])^2 = [\mathrm{M}_2]$$
$$4[\mathrm{M}_2]^2 - 4[\mathrm{M}_2][\mathrm{M}]_{\mathrm{total}} + [\mathrm{M}]_{\mathrm{total}}^2 = [\mathrm{M}_2]$$
$$4[\mathrm{M}_2]^2 - (4[\mathrm{M}]_{\mathrm{total}} + 1)[\mathrm{M}_2] + [\mathrm{M}]_{\mathrm{total}}^2 = 0$$

This is a quadratic equation of the form $ax^2 + bx + c = 0$, with $a = 4$, $b = -(4[\mathrm{M}]_{\mathrm{total}} + 1)$ and $c = [\mathrm{M}]_{\mathrm{total}}^2$, which has solutions

$$x = \frac{-b \pm \sqrt{b^2 - 4ac}}{2a}$$

and may be solved

$$[\mathrm{M}_2] = \frac{(4[\mathrm{M}]_{\mathrm{total}} + 1) \pm \sqrt{(4[\mathrm{M}]_{\mathrm{total}} + 1)^2 - (4\times 4\times[\mathrm{M}]_{\mathrm{total}}^2)}}{2\times 4}$$
$$= \frac{(4[\mathrm{M}]_{\mathrm{total}} + 1) \pm \sqrt{(8[\mathrm{M}]_{\mathrm{total}} + 1)}}{8}$$

Because $[\mathrm{M}_2] < [\mathrm{M}]_{\mathrm{total}}$, we may ignore the larger of the two roots. Figure 16.1 shows a plot of the function

$$[\mathrm{M}_2] = \frac{(4[\mathrm{M}]_{\mathrm{total}} + 1) - \sqrt{(8[\mathrm{M}]_{\mathrm{total}} + 1)}}{8}$$

Plots of $[M_{50}]$, $[M_{100}]$ and $[M_{200}]$ as a function of total monomer concentration under the same conditions show how the transition becomes sharper as $N$ increases.

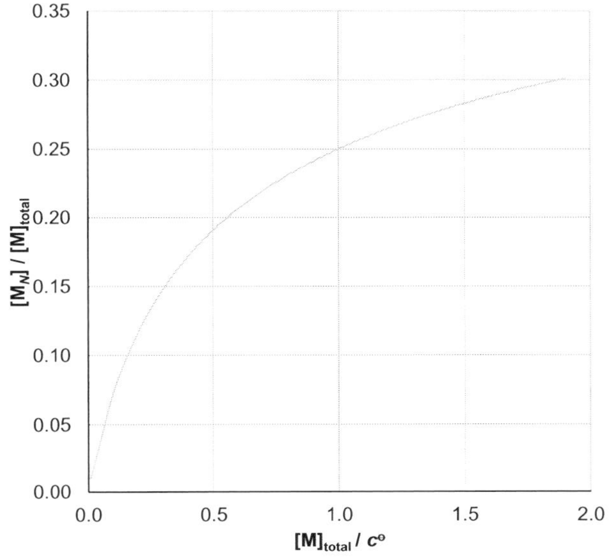


**Figure 16.1**

# Chapter 17

# Metallic, ionic, and covalent solids

## Answers to discussion questions

**D17.1** A **metallic conductor** is a substance with a conductivity that decreases as the temperature is raised. A **semiconductor** is a substance with a conductivity that increases as the temperature is raised. A semiconductor generally has a lower conductivity than that typical of metals, but the magnitude of the conductivity is not the criterion of the distinction. It is conventional to classify semiconductors with very low electrical conductivities, such as most synthetic polymers and diamond, as **insulators**. We shall use this term. But it should be appreciated that it is one of convenience rather than one of fundamental significance.

The conductivity of these three kinds of materials is explained by **band theory**. When each of $N$ atoms of a metallic element contributes one atomic orbital to the formation of molecular orbitals, the resulting $N$ molecular orbitals form an almost continuous band of levels. The orbital at the bottom of the band is fully bonding between all neighbours, and the orbital at the top of the band is fully antibonding between all immediate neighbours. If the atomic orbitals are s-orbitals, then the resulting band is called an s-band; if the original orbitals are p-orbitals, then they form a p band. In a typical case, there is so large an energy difference between the s and p atomic orbitals that the resulting s and p bands are separated by a region of energy in which there are no orbitals. This region is called the band gap, and its width is denoted $E_g$.

When electrons occupy the orbitals in the bands, they do so in accord with the Pauli principle. If insufficient electrons are present to fill the band, the electrons close to the top of the band are mobile and the solid is a metallic conductor. An unfilled band is called a **conduction band** and the energy of the highest occupied orbital at $T = 0$ K is called the **Fermi level**. Only the electrons close to the Fermi level can contribute to conduction and to the heat capacity of a metal. If the band is full, then the electrons cannot transport a current readily, and the solid is an insulator; more formally, it is a species of semiconductor with a large band gap. A full band is called a **valence band**. The detailed population of the levels in a band taking into account the role of temperature is expressed by the Fermi–Dirac distribution.

The distinction between metallic conductors and semiconductors can be traced to their band structure: a metallic conductor has an incomplete band, its conductance band, and a semiconductor has full bands, and hence lacks a conductance band. The decreasing conductance of a metallic conductor with temperature stems from the scattering of electrons by the vibrating atoms of the metal lattice. The increasing conductance of a semiconductor arises from the increasing population of an upper empty band as the temperature is increased. Many substances, however, have such large band gaps that their ability to conduct an electric current remains very low at all temperatures: it is conventional to refer to such solids as insulators. The ability of a semiconductor to transport charge is enhanced by doping it, or adding substances in controlled quantities. If the dopant provides additional electrons, then the semiconductor is classified as n-type. If it removes electrons from the valence band and thereby increases the number of positive holes, it is classified as p-type.

Diamond and graphite are **covalent solids** in which covalent bonds in a definite spatial orientation link the atoms in a network extending through the crystal. In diamond each $sp^3$ hybridized carbon is covalently bonded tetrahedrally to its four neighbours. Each bond involves a low energy, localized σ electron pair. This means that there is a large gap between the filled σ band and the empty π band above it; it is a large band gap semiconductor, an insulator. In graphite, σ bonds between $sp^2$ hybridized carbon atoms form hexagonal rings that repeat throughout a graphene sheet to which each carbon contributes one $p_z$ orbital and one electron. Neighbouring $p_z$ orbitals overlap to produce a π band that extends throughout the graphene sheet and is half full; it is, therefore, a conduction band that lies within the graphene sheets alone.

**D17.2** Lattice planes are labelled by their Miller indices $h$, $k$, and $l$, where $h$, $k$, and $l$ refer respectively to the reciprocals of the smallest intersection distances (in units of the lengths of the unit cell, $a$, $b$ and $c$) of the plane with the $\boldsymbol{a}$, $\boldsymbol{b}$, and $\boldsymbol{c}$ axes of the unit cell. The axes may be, but are not always, orthogonal. Examples of the labelling of planes are shown in text Figures 17.24 and 17.25..

**D17.3** The phase problem arises with the analysis of X-ray diffraction data to determine a crystal structure. The analysis requires knowledge of the so called **structure factor**, $F_{hkl}$, which is related to the measured intensity, $I_{hkl}$, of the diffracted radiation by the expression $I_{hkl} \propto |F_{hkl}|^2$ (i.e., the modulus square $F_{hkl}{}^*F_{hkl}$). In the simplest case, even though we have measured $I_{hkl}$, we do not know whether $F_{hkl}$ is positive or negative. Thus, when we attempt to compute the electron density distribution, $\rho(\boldsymbol{r})$, with the **Fourier synthesis**, which has the form

$$\rho(x) = \frac{1}{V}\left\{F_0 + 2\sum_{h=1}^{\infty} F_h \cos(2h\pi x)\right\}$$

in a simple case, we do not know the sign of each term in the sum. Things are even more difficult in the general case because the structure factor has the general form $F_{hkl} \propto |F_{hkl}|e^{i\alpha}$ where $i = (-1)^{1/2}$ and $\alpha$ is the **phase** of $F_{hkl}$. Upon taking the modulus square of $F_{hkl}$, information about the phase is completely lost. Thus, measurement of radiation intensity gives no information about the phase and it is not available for use in the Fourier synthesis. This is the phase problem.

The phase problem may be evaded by the use of a **Patterson synthesis** or tackled directly by using the so-called **direct methods of phase allocation**. The Patterson synthesis is a technique of data analysis in X-ray diffraction which helps to circumvent the phase problem. In it, a function $P$ is formed by calculating the Fourier transform of the squares of the structure factors (which are proportional to the intensities):

$$P(r) = \frac{1}{V}\sum_{hkl}|F_{hkl}|^2 e^{-2\pi i(hx+ky+lz)}$$

The outcome is a map of the *separations* of the atoms in the unit cell of the crystal. If some atoms are heavy (perhaps because they have been introduced by isomorphous replacement), they dominate the Patterson function, and their locations can be deduced quite simply. Their locations can then be used in the determination of the locations of lighter atoms. Direct methods dominate modern X-ray diffraction analysis. These methods use statistical techniques, and the considerable computational capacity of the modern computer, to compute the probabilities that the phases have a particular value.

**D17.4** The majority of metals crystallize in structures that can be interpreted as the closest packing arrangements of hard spheres. These are the cubic close-packed (ccp) and hexagonal close-packed (hcp) structures. In these models, 74 per cent of the volume of the unit cell is occupied by the atoms (packing fraction = 0.74). Most of the remaining metallic elements crystallize in the body-centered cubic (bcc) arrangement, which is not too much different from the close-packed structures in terms of the efficiency of the use of space (packing fraction 0.68 in the hard sphere model). Polonium is an exception; it crystallizes in the simple cubic structure, which has a packing fraction of 0.52. If atoms were truly hard spheres, we would expect that all metals would crystallize in either the cubic or hexagonal close-packed structures. The fact that a significant number crystallize in other structures is proof that a simple hard sphere model is an inaccurate representation of the interactions between the atoms. Covalent bonding between the atoms may influence the structure. Text Figures 17.36–39 illustrate the difference between cubic, hexagonal and body-centred close packed structures.

**D17.5** The caesium-chloride and rock-salt structures are illustrated and described in text Figures 17.41 and 17.42. The **radius ratio**, $\gamma = r_{\text{smaller ion}} / r_{\text{larger ion}}$, eqn 17.10, is an aid in the classification of ionic compound structure. If $\gamma > 0.732$, the caesium chloride structure is indicated. If $0.414 < \gamma < 0.732$, the rock salt structure is indicated. If $\gamma < 0.414$, the zinc blend (ZnS) structure is indicated.

The structures can also be described in terms of the occupation of holes in expanded closed-packed lattices. In a face-centred cubic close-packed lattice, there is an octahedral hole in the centre. The rock-salt structure can be thought of as being derived from a face-centred cubic structure of $Cl^-$ ions in which $Na^+$ ions have filled the octahedral holes.

The caesium-chloride structure can be considered to be derived from the cubic close packed structure by having $Cl^-$ ions occupy all the primitive lattice points and octahedral sites, with all tetrahedral sites occupied by $Cs^+$ ions. This is exceedingly difficult to visualize and describe without carefully constructed figures or models. Appropriate diagrams are, however, shown in S.-M. Ho and B. E. Douglas, *J. Chem. Educ.* **46**, 208, 1969.

**D17.6** **Diamagnetic** substances have negative magnetic susceptibilities and they tend to move out of a magnetic field. Most molecules with no unpaired electron spins are diamagnetic because the magnetic field induces the circulation of electronic currents, which give rise to a magnetic field that opposes the applied field, in the substance. **Paramagnetic** substances have positive magnetic susceptibilities and they tend to move into a magnetic field. Molecules with unpaired electrons are paramagnetic because the spin of the electron has an associated magnetic field that lines up in parallel with the applied field so as to lower energy. Some paramagnetic solid substances, like iron and cobalt, have microscopic domains in which many unpaired electrons are aligned parallel. They can undergo a transition in which the spin of many domains align to give rise to the strong magnetism called **ferromagnetism**. Some paramagnetic substances have structures that cause domains to orient with alternating up-down spins; this low-magnetization arrangement is called **anti-ferromagnetism**. Chromium exhibits this behavior.

## Solutions to exercises

**E17.1** The resistance of metals increases with increasing temperature; the opposite is true of semiconductors; therefore, this substance is a metallic conductor.

**E17.2** We discovered in *Chapter 12* that a wavefunction must: be continuous; have a continuous slope, which is indicated as $\psi'$ in our discussion; be single-valued and cannot become infinite over a finite region of space; and be square-integrable.

This means that, when a line of $N$ tight-bonding identical atoms are wrapped into a ring, the wavefunction must satisfy the conditions: $\psi(\text{left end}) = \psi(\text{right end})$ and $\psi'(\text{left end}) = \psi'(\text{right end})$. These boundary conditions are more restrictive than those required for the line of atoms: $\psi(\text{left end}) = \pm\psi(\text{right end})$ and $\psi'(\text{left end}) = \pm\psi'(\text{right end})$. As the line is wrapped into a ring, the states for which $\psi(\text{left end}) = -\psi(\text{right end})$ become forbidden and only alternate quantum numbers for which $\psi(\text{left end}) = \psi(\text{right end})$ are allowed. This explains the appearance of the factor of 2 within the cosine term of the allowed ring energies. Additionally, the quantum number for the electron moving around the ring of atoms may be either positive of negative because the angular momentum may be in either direction around the axis of the ring. Thus, each energy level for the ring is doubly degenerate. Figure 17.1 shows the energy levels for a system with six atoms.

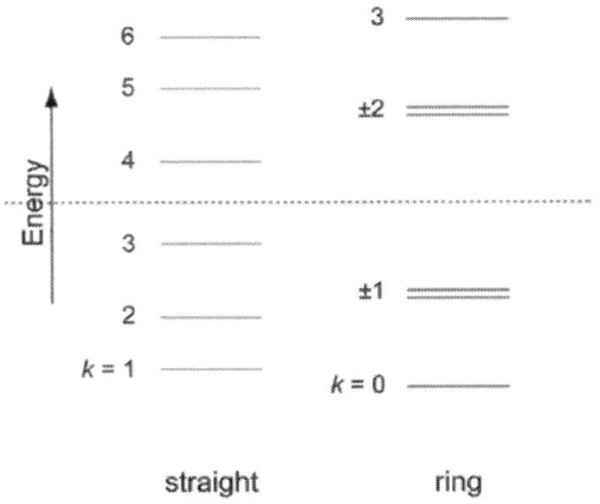


**Figure 17.1**

**E17.3** (a) Phosphorus of group 15 has one more valence electron than germanium of group 14; therefore germanium doped with phosphorus forms an n-type semiconductor.

(b) Indium of group 13 has one fewer valence electron than germanium of group 14; therefore germanium doped with indium forms an p-type semiconductor.

**E17.4** The relationship between critical temperature and critical magnetic field is given by

$$\mathcal{H}_c(T) = \mathcal{H}_c(0)\left(1 - \frac{T^2}{T_c^2}\right)$$

Solving for $T$ gives the critical temperature for a given magnetic field

$$T = T_c\left(1 - \frac{\mathcal{H}_c(T)}{\mathcal{H}_c(0)}\right)^{1/2} = (7.19\text{ K}) \times \left(1 - \frac{20.0\text{ kA m}^{-1}}{63.9\text{ kA m}^{-1}}\right) = \mathbf{6.0\ K}$$

**E17.5** The valence electrons of Ca of Group 2, are 4s electrons, and those of O, Group 16 are 2p electrons. We therefore expect that the oxygen 2p electrons will be much lower in energy than the calcium 4s electrons. The energy band diagram of CaO is thus expected to be similar to that shown in Figure 17.2. There are three degenerate oxygen 2p orbitals available for band formation for each of $N$ oxygen atoms, which results in a p band that can hold $3 \times 2 \times N = 6N$ electrons. Each oxygen atom contributes 4 electrons to the p band while each calcium atom also contributes 2 electrons. Thus, the p band is filled with $6N$ electrons leaving no electrons to occupy the s band. The gap between the filled p band and empty s band is large, so that CaO is a large-gap semiconductor, and thus effectively an insulator. We may view this model as the transfer of two electrons from each calcium atom to each oxygen atom, to create $Ca^{2+}$ and $O^{2-}$ ions, as in the ionic model.

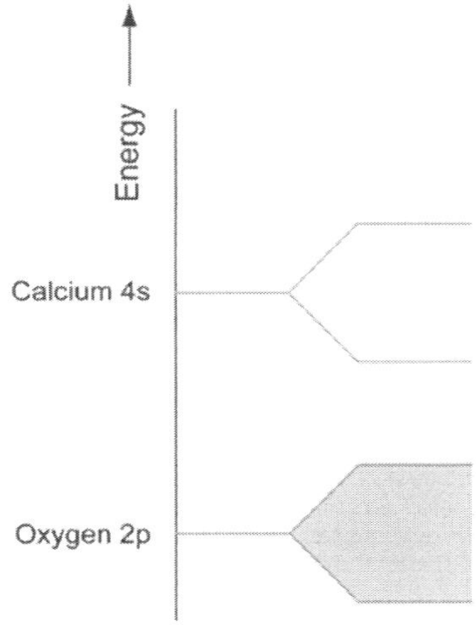


Figure 17.2

**E17.6** The standard lattice enthalpy, which is the difference in enthalpy between an ionic solid and the corresponding isolated ions

$$CaO(s) \rightarrow Ca^{2+}(g) + O^{2-}(g)$$

can be calculated from the standard enthalpies given in the exercise by considering the formation of CaO(s)

$Ca(s) + \tfrac{1}{2} O_2(g) \rightarrow CaO(s)$ formation of CaO, $\Delta_f H^\ominus$

Treating the formation as occuring through the following steps:

$Ca(s) + \tfrac{1}{2} O_2(g) \rightarrow Ca(g) + \tfrac{1}{2} O_2(g)$ sublimation of Ca, $\Delta_{sub}H^\ominus(Ca)$
$Ca(g) + \tfrac{1}{2} O_2(g) \rightarrow Ca^{2+}(g) + \tfrac{1}{2} O_2(g)$ ionisation of Ca, $\{\Delta_{ion}H^\ominus(Ca) + \Delta_{ion}H^\ominus(Ca^+)\}$
$Ca^{2+}(g) + \tfrac{1}{2} O_2(g) \rightarrow Ca^{2+}(g) + O(g)$ atomization of $O_2$, $\tfrac{1}{2}H^\ominus_{O-O}$
$Ca^{2+}(g) + O(g) \rightarrow Ca^{2+}(g) + O^{2-}(g)$ electron gain of O, $\Delta_{eg}H^\ominus(O) + \Delta_{eg}H^\ominus(O^-)$
$Ca^{2+}(g) + O^{2-}(g) \rightarrow CaO(s)$ reverse of lattice enthalpy, $-\Delta_L H^\ominus(CaO)$

then

$$\Delta_f H^\ominus(CaO) = \Delta_{sub}H^\ominus(Ca) + \{\Delta_{ion}H^\ominus(Ca) + \Delta_{ion}H^\ominus(Ca^+)\}$$
$$\tfrac{1}{2}H^\ominus_{O-O} + \Delta_{eg}H^\ominus(O) + \Delta_{eg}H^\ominus(O^-) - \Delta_L H^\ominus(CaO)$$

Hence, rearranging,

$$\begin{aligned}\Delta_L H^\ominus(CaO) &= \Delta_{sub}H^\ominus(Ca) + \{\Delta_{ion}H^\ominus(Ca) + \Delta_{ion}H^\ominus(Ca^+)\} + \\ &\quad \tfrac{1}{2}H^\ominus_{O-O} + \Delta_{eg}H^\ominus(O) + \Delta_{eg}H^\ominus(O^-) - \Delta_f H^\ominus(CaO) \\ &= \{178 + 1735 + 249 + (-141) + 844 - (-635)\}\ \text{kJ mol}^{-1} \\ &= \mathbf{+3500\ kJ\ mol^{-1}}\end{aligned}$$

**E17.7** The standard lattice enthalpy, which is the enthalpy change for the process

$$MgBr_2(s) \rightarrow Mg^{2+}(g) + 2\,Br^-(g)$$

can be calculated from the standard enthalpies given in the exercise by considering the formation of $MgBr_2(s)$

$$Mg(s) + Br_2(l) \rightarrow MgBr_2(s) \qquad \text{formation of } MgBr_2,\ \Delta_f H^\ominus$$

Treating the formation as occuring through the following steps:

| | |
|---|---|
| $Mg(s) + Br_2(l) \rightarrow Mg(g) + Br_2(g)$ | sublimation of Mg, $\Delta_{sub}H^\ominus(Mg)$ |
| $Mg(g) + Br_2(l) \rightarrow Mg^{2+}(g) + Br_2(g)$ | ionisation of Mg, $\{\Delta_{ion}H^\ominus(Mg) + \Delta_{ion}H^\ominus(Mg^+)\}$ |
| $Mg(g) + Br_2(l) \rightarrow Mg^{2+}(g) + Br_2(g)$ | vaporization of $Br_2$, $\Delta_{vap}H^\ominus(Br_2)$ |
| $Mg^{2+}(g) + Br_2(g) \rightarrow Mg^{2+}(g) + 2\,Br(g)$ | atomization of $Br_2$, $H^\ominus_{Br-Br}$ |
| $Mg^{2+}(g) + 2\,Br(g) \rightarrow Mg^{2+}(g) + 2\,Br^-(g)$ | electron gain of Br, $2\,\Delta_{eg}H^\ominus(Br)$ |
| $Mg^{2+}(g) + 2\,Br^-(g) \rightarrow MgBr_2(s)$ | reverse of lattice enthalpy, $-\Delta_L H^\ominus$ |

then

$$\begin{aligned}\Delta_f H^\ominus(MgBr_2) = {} & \Delta_{sub}H^\ominus(Mg) + \{\Delta_{ion}H^\ominus(Mg) + \Delta_{ion}H^\ominus(Mg^+)\} \\ & + \Delta_{vap}H^\ominus(Br_2) + H^\ominus_{Br-Br} + 2\Delta_{eg}H^\ominus(Br) - \Delta_L H^\ominus(MgBr_2)\end{aligned}$$

Hence, rearranging,

$$\begin{aligned}\Delta_L H^\ominus(MgBr_2) &= \Delta_{sub}H^\ominus(Mg) + \{\Delta_{ion}H^\ominus(Mg) + \Delta_{ion}H^\ominus(Mg^+)\} \\ &\quad + \Delta_{vap}H^\ominus(Br_2) + H^\ominus_{Br-Br} + 2\Delta_{eg}H^\ominus(Br) - \Delta_f H^\ominus(MgBr_2) \\ &= \{148 + 2187 + 31 + 193 + (-331) - (-635)\}\ \text{kJ mol}^{-1} \\ &= \mathbf{+1593\ kJ\ mol^{-1}}\end{aligned}$$

**E17.8** Using the Born–Mayer equation, eqn 17.5, the ratio of the lattice energies of SrO and CaO is

$$\frac{\Delta_L H^\ominus(SrO)}{\Delta_L H^\ominus(CaO)} = \frac{\dfrac{|z_{Sr^{2+}}z_{O^{2-}}|}{d_{SrO}} \times \dfrac{N_A e^2}{4\pi\epsilon_0} \times \left(1 - \dfrac{d^*}{d_{SrO}}\right) A_{SrO}}{\dfrac{|z_{Ca^{2+}}z_{O^{2-}}|}{d_{CaO}} \times \dfrac{N_A e^2}{4\pi\epsilon_0} \times \left(1 - \dfrac{d^*}{d_{CaO}}\right) A_{CaO}}$$

Both Sro and Cao adopt a rock salt crystal structure, so that the Madelung constant, $A$, as well as many other terms, cancel, so that

$$\frac{\Delta_L H^\ominus(SrO)}{\Delta_L H^\ominus(CaO)} = \frac{d_{CaO}\left(1 - \dfrac{d^*}{d_{SrO}}\right)}{d_{SrO}\left(1 - \dfrac{d^*}{d_{CaO}}\right)}$$

Using the data for ionic radii from Table 17.2,

$$d_{SrO} = r_{Sr^{2+}} + r_{O^{2-}} = 116\ \text{pm} + 140\ \text{pm} = 256\ \text{pm}$$
$$d_{CaO} = r_{Ca^{2+}} + r_{O^{2-}} = 100\ \text{pm} + 140\ \text{pm} = 240\ \text{pm}$$

and so

$$\frac{\Delta_L H^{\ominus}(\text{SrO})}{\Delta_L H^{\ominus}(\text{CaO})} = \frac{(240\ \text{pm})\left(1 - \dfrac{34.5\ \text{pm}}{256\ \text{pm}}\right)}{(256\ \text{pm})\left(1 - \dfrac{34.5\ \text{pm}}{240\ \text{pm}}\right)} = \mathbf{0.947}$$

**E17.9** Let us assume that the ion at the centre of the diffuse spherical crystal has a charge *ze*. Then, let there be *N* charges –*ze* on the first sphere, which is of radius *d*. We may imagine then that there will by *N*/2 of charge *ze* on the second sphere of radius 2*d*, *N*/3 of charge -*ze* on the third sphere of radius 3*d*, and so on. The total Coulomb potential energy for the interaction of the ion, treated as a point charge *Q* at the centre with the alternating charges in the spherical layers is therefore the sum

$$\begin{aligned} V &= \frac{ze}{4\pi\epsilon_0}\left\{\frac{-Nze}{d} + \frac{(N/2)ze}{2d} + \frac{-(N/3ze)}{3d} + \frac{(N/4)ze}{4d} + \cdots\right\} \\ &= -\frac{Nz^2e^2}{4\pi\epsilon_0 d}\left\{1 - \frac{1}{4} + \frac{1}{9} - \frac{1}{16} + \cdots\right\} \\ &= -\frac{Nz^2e^2}{4\pi\epsilon_0 d}\left(\frac{\pi^2}{12}\right) = -\frac{\boldsymbol{Nz^2e^2\pi}}{\boldsymbol{48\epsilon_0 d}} \end{aligned}$$

**E17.10** Consider the array of anions and cations shown in Figure 17.3. The potential energy of the cation on top of the array may be calculated as a summation of the Coulombic interactions with the anions and cations.

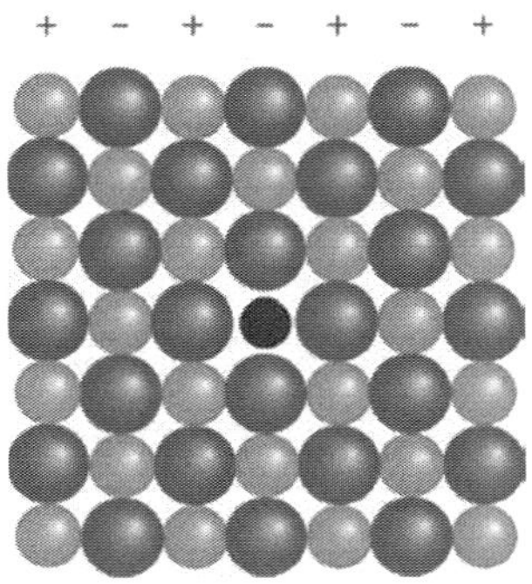


**Figure 17.3**

The Coulombic potential energy resulting from the interaction with the four nearest anions is, by Pythagoras' theorem, $2^{1/2}d$, so that the potential energy of interaction is

$$4 \times \frac{-e^2}{4\pi\epsilon_0 d}$$

where the energy is negative, because the interaction is attractive.

In the same way, the distance to each of the next four nearest cations is, $2^{1/2}d$, so that the potential energy of interaction is

$$4 \times \frac{e^2}{4\pi\epsilon_0(2^{1/2}d)}$$

It follows that the total energy is the sum of these, and the terms arising from the interactions with more distant ions,

$$V = -4 \times \frac{e^2}{4\pi\epsilon_0 d}\left\{1 - \frac{1}{2^{1/2}} - \frac{1}{4^{1/2}} + \frac{2}{5^{1/2}} + \frac{1}{6^{1/2}} - \frac{1}{8^{1/2}} + \frac{1}{9^{1/2}} - \frac{2}{10^{1/2}} - \frac{2}{13^{1/2}} \cdots\right\}$$

The terms in brackets sum to 1.768, so that

$$\begin{aligned} V &= -1.768 \times \frac{e^2}{4\pi\epsilon_0 d} \\ &= -1.768 \times \frac{(1.602 \times 10^{-19}\ \mathrm{C})^2}{4\pi \times (8.854 \times 10^{-12}\ \mathrm{J^{-1}\ C^2\ m^{-1}}) \times (200 \times 10^{-12}\mathrm{m})} \\ &= \mathbf{-2.04 \times 10^{-18}\ J} \end{aligned}$$

**E17.11** In general, the volume of a unit cell is

$$V = abc$$

where $a$, $b$ and $c$ are the cell parameters. For a tetragonal unit cell, $a = b$, so that for $Rb_3TlF_6$,

$$V = a^2c = (651\ \mathrm{pm})^2 \times (934\ \mathrm{pm}) = 396 \times 10^6\ \mathrm{pm}^6 = \mathbf{0.396\ nm^3}$$

If we assume a simple tetragonal unit cell, then there is one formula unit per unit cell. Thus, the mass contained within this volume is $m = 574.79m_u$, so that the mass density is

$$\begin{aligned} \rho = m/V &= 574.79 \times (1.661 \times 10^{-27}\ \mathrm{kg}) \times (0.396 \times 10^{-27}\ \mathrm{m^3}) \\ &= 2.41 \times 10^6\ \mathrm{g\ m^{-3}} = \mathbf{2.41 \times 10^3 kg\ m^{-3}} \end{aligned}$$

**E17.12** The number of formula units in each unit cell, $N$, may be calculated from the ratio of the mass of a unit cell, $m$, to the mass of one formula unit, $m_{\mathrm{NiSO_4}}$

$$N = m/m_{\mathrm{NiSO_4}}$$

The mass of the unit cell may be calculated from the mass density, $\rho$, and volume, $V = abc$. Hence,

$$\begin{aligned} N &= \rho V/m_{\mathrm{NiSO_4}} = \rho \times abc/m_{\mathrm{NiSO_4}} \\ &= \frac{\overbrace{(3.9 \times 10^3 \mathrm{kg\ m^{-3}})}^{1\ \mathrm{g\ cm^{-3}} = 1\ \mathrm{kg\ m^{-3}}} \times (634 \times 10^{-12}\ \mathrm{m}) \times (784 \times 10^{-12}\mathrm{m}) \times (516 \times 10^{-12}\mathrm{m})}{\underbrace{154.77 \times (1.661 \times 10^{-27}\ \mathrm{kg})}_{m_{\mathrm{NiSO_4}} = 154.77 m_u}} \\ &= \mathbf{3.9} \end{aligned}$$

We may therefore reasonably assume that there are four formula units in each unit cell. The discrepancy between the observed and theoretical value is the result of defects in the crystal. The density of a defect-free crystal is thus

$$\rho = Nm_{NiSO_4}/abc$$
$$= \frac{4 \times 154.77 \times (1.661 \times 10^{-27}\ \text{kg})}{(634 \times 10^{-12}\text{m}) \times (784 \times 10^{-12}\text{m}) \times (516 \times 10^{-12}\text{m})}$$
$$= \mathbf{4.01 \times 10^3\ kg\ m^{-3}}$$

**E17.13** The separation, $d$, between crystal planes with Miller indices ($hkl$) is given by eqn 17.7,

$$\frac{1}{d^2} = \frac{h^2}{a^2} + \frac{k^2}{b^2} + \frac{l^2}{c^2}$$

(a) Thus, for the (321) planes in $SbCl_3$

$$\frac{1}{d^2} = \frac{3^2}{(812\ \text{pm})^2} + \frac{2^2}{(947\ \text{pm})^2} + \frac{1^2}{(637\ \text{pm})^2} = 2.05 \times 10^{-5}\ \text{pm}^{-2}$$

so that $d$ = **221 pm**.

(b) For the (642) planes,

$$\frac{1}{d^2} = \frac{6^2}{(812\ \text{pm})^2} + \frac{4^2}{(947\ \text{pm})^2} + \frac{2^2}{(637\ \text{pm})^2} = 8.23 \times 10^{-5}\ \text{pm}^{-2}$$

so that $d$ = **110 pm**. As expected, the separation between the (642) planes is half that between the (321) planes.

**E17.14** The crystal planes are shown in Figure 17.4. The Miller indices are the reciprocals of the minimum intersection distances on each axis. The figure illustrates that the smaller the value of the Miller index, the more closely parallel the plane is to that axis.

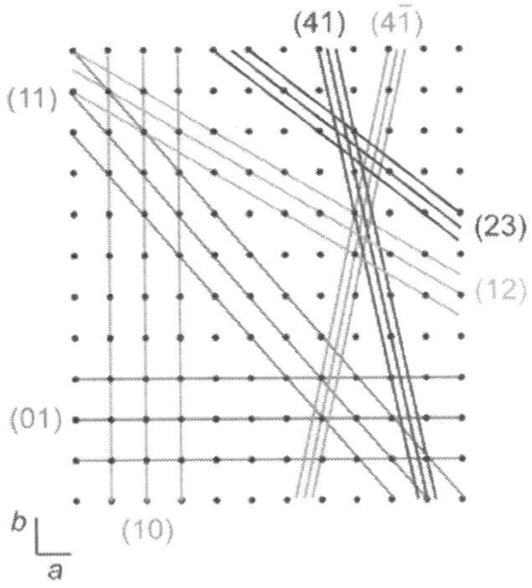


**Figure 17.4**

**E17.15** A two-dimensional crystal in which the axes are arranged at 60° to one another corresponds to a hexagonal system. The crystal planes are shown in Figure 17.5.

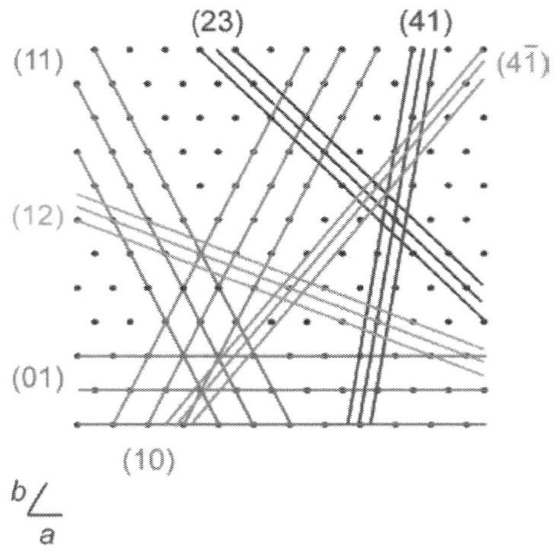


**Figure 17.5**

**E17.16** The Miller indices of a plane are given by finding the reciprocals of the intersections on each axis and then scaling to eliminate any fractions. Thus, a plane that intersects axes at ($2a$, $3b$, $c$) corresponds to reciprocals (1/2, 1/3, 1) or, if multiplied through so that all of the indices are integers, Miller indices of **(321)**. In the same way, planes that intersect the axes at ($a$, $b$, $c$) correspond to **(111)**. Intercepts of ($6a$, $3b$, $3c$) correspond to reciprocals of (1/6, 1/3, 1/3), and therefore Miller indices of **(122)**. Finally, planes that interesct the axes at ($2a$, $-3b$, $-3c$) correspond to reciprocals of (1/2, −1/3, −1/3) and therefore **(3$\bar{2}\bar{2}$)**.

**E17.17** An orthorhomic unit cell is one in which the axes are orthogonal to one another, but the unit-cell dimensions, $a$, $b$ and $c$ are all different. An example of such a unit cell, together with the various crystal planes is shown in Figure 17.6.

**E17.18** A triclinic unit cell possesses no essential symmetry elements. Thus, none of the angles , $\alpha$, $\beta$ and $\gamma$, between the axes are equal to 60°, 90° or 120°, and the unit-cell dimensions, $a$, $b$ and $c$ are all different. Figure 17.7 shows such a triclinic unit cell, together with the various crystal planes.

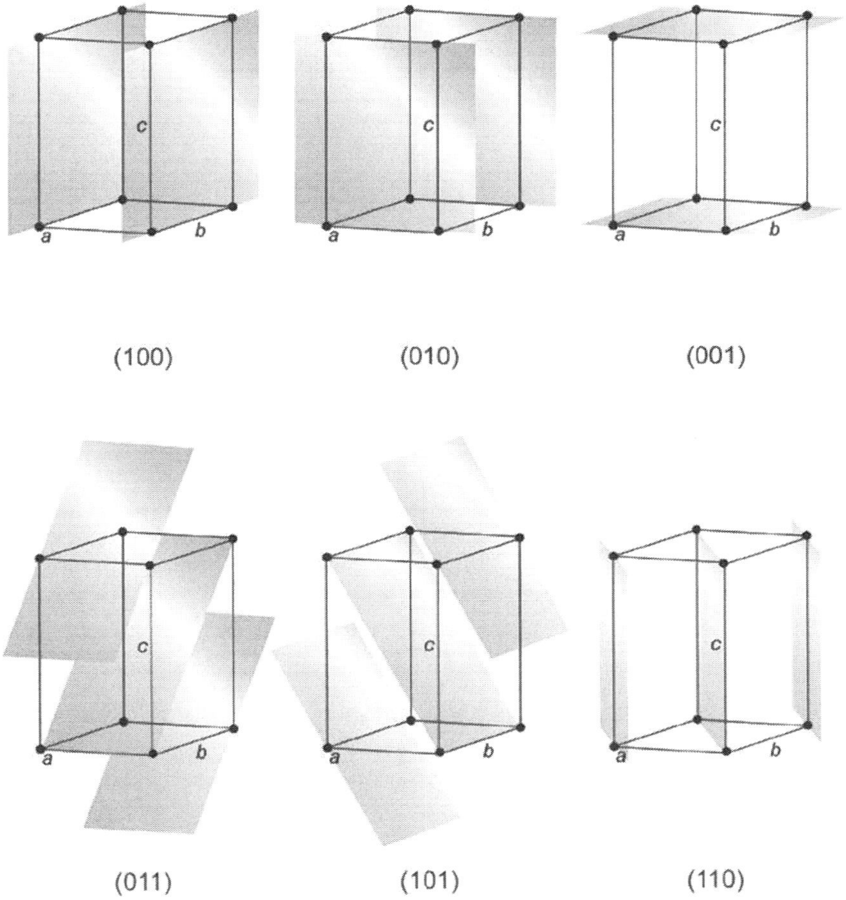


Figure 17.6

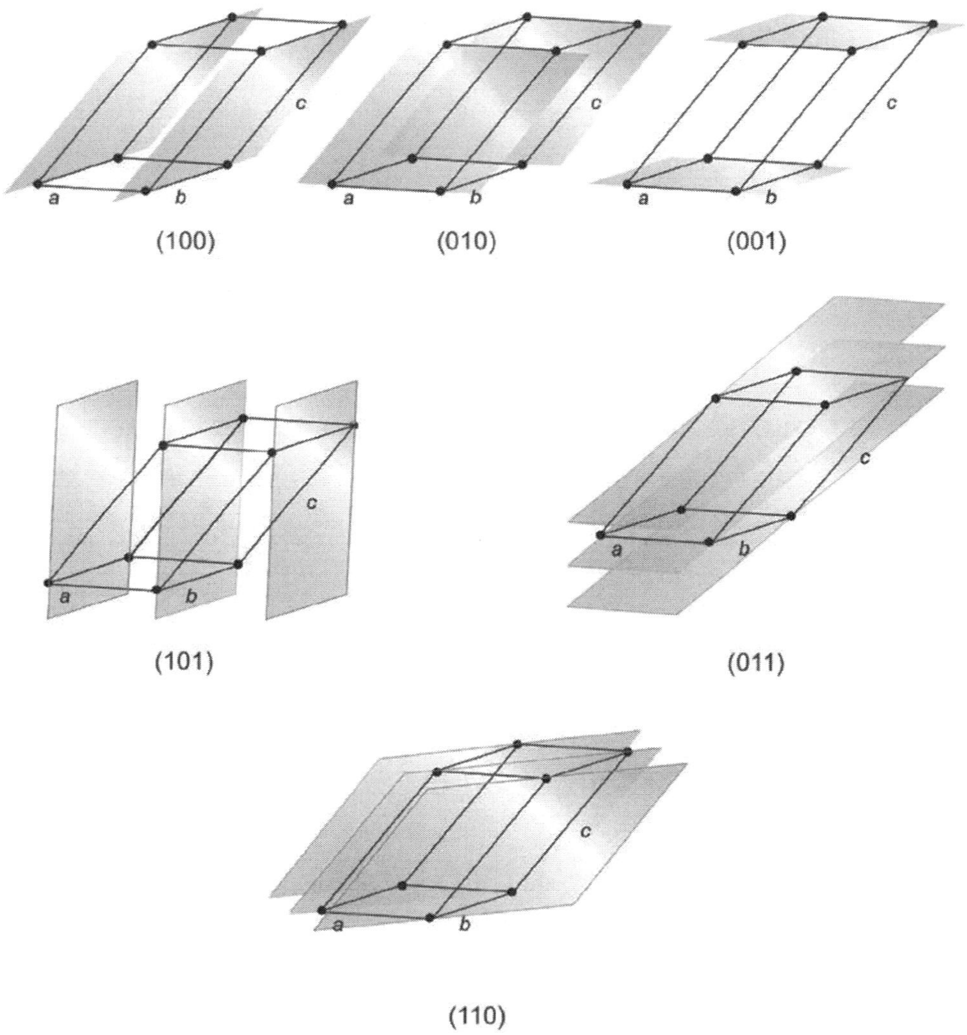


Figure 17.7

**E17.19** The separation between crystal planes is given by eqn 17.7. For a cubic crystal system, $a = b = c$ so that

$$\frac{1}{d^2} = \frac{h^2}{a^2} + \frac{k^2}{b^2} + \frac{l^2}{c^2} = \frac{h^2 + k^2 + l^2}{a^2}$$

(a) Thus for the (111) planes,

$$d = a(h^2 + k^2 + l^2)^{-1/2}$$
$$= (572\ \text{pm}) \times (1^2 + 1^2 + 1^2)^{-1/2} = (572\ \text{pm})/3^{1/2} = \mathbf{330\ pm}$$

(b) and for (211),

$$d = a(h^2 + k^2 + l^2)^{-1/2}$$
$$= (572\ \text{pm}) \times (2^2 + 1^2 + 1^2)^{-1/2} = (572\ \text{pm})/6^{1/2} = \mathbf{233\ pm}$$

(c) and for (100),

$$d = a(h^2 + k^2 + l^2)^{-1/2} = (572\ \text{pm}) \times (1^2 + 0^2 + 0^2)^{-1/2} = \mathbf{572\ pm}$$

**E17.20** (a) Applying eqn 17.7, the separation between the (123) planes is given by

$$\frac{1}{d^2} = \frac{h^2}{a^2} + \frac{k^2}{b^2} + \frac{l^2}{c^2} = \frac{1^2}{(784\ \text{pm})^2} + \frac{2^2}{(633\ \text{pm})^2} + \frac{3^2}{(454\ \text{pm})^2}$$

so that $d =$ **135 pm**.

(b) In the same way, the separation between the (236) planes is given by

$$\frac{1}{d^2} = \frac{h^2}{a^2} + \frac{k^2}{b^2} + \frac{l^2}{c^2} = \frac{2^2}{(784\ \text{pm})^2} + \frac{3^2}{(633\ \text{pm})^2} + \frac{6^2}{(454\ \text{pm})^2}$$

so that $d =$ **70 pm**.

**E17.21** From the Bragg law, eqn 17.8, the wavelength of the X-rays is

$$\lambda = 2d\sin\theta = 2 \times (97.3\ \text{pm}) \times \sin(19.85°) = \mathbf{66.1\ pm}$$

**E17.22** We may use the Bragg law, eqn 17.7 to calculate the separation between the planes, from which diffraction occurs,

$$d = \frac{\lambda}{2\sin\theta}$$

For a tetragonal system, $a = b \neq c$, and for (110) planes, eqn 17.7 therefore simplifies to

$$\frac{1}{d^2} = \frac{h^2}{a^2} + \frac{k^2}{b^2} + \frac{l^2}{c^2} = \frac{h^2 + k^2}{a^2} + \frac{l^2}{c^2} = \frac{1^2 + 1^2}{a^2} + \frac{0^2}{c^2}$$

so that for

$$d = a/2^{1/2}$$

Hence, equating these two expressions and rearranging,

$$a = \frac{\lambda}{2^{1/2}\sin\theta} = \frac{179\text{ pm}}{2^{1/2}\times\sin 9.13°} = \mathbf{798\ pm}$$

**E17.23** The electron density may be reconstructed from the structure factors using the Fourier series, eqn 17.9. Thus,

$$\rho(x) = \frac{1}{V}\left\{F_0 + 2\sum_{h=1}^{\infty} F_h\cos(2\pi hx)\right\}$$

$$= \frac{1}{V}\left[30.0 + 2\times\left\{\overbrace{(8.2\times\cos 2\pi x)}^{h=1} + \overbrace{(6.5\times\cos 4\pi x)}^{h=2}\right\} + \cdots\right]$$

The result is plotted, as the dimensionless function $\rho(x)V$, in Figure 17.8. The electron density peaks at $x = 0$ and $x = 1$, implying a build up of charge at this lattice point.

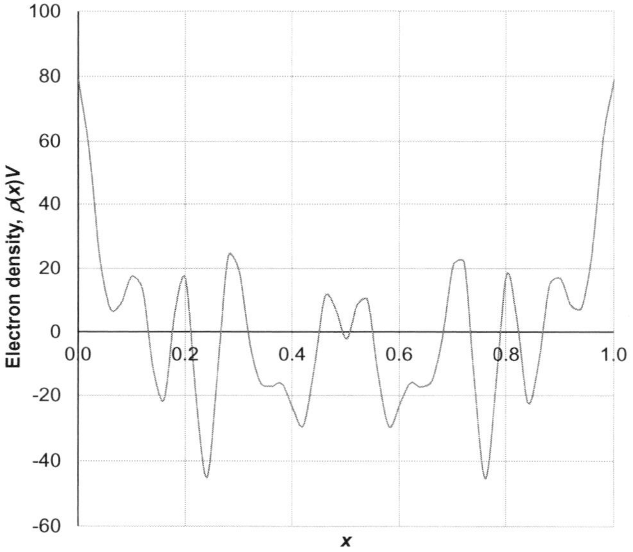


**Figure 17.8**

**E17.24** Mass density is the ratio of mass to volume. Thus, if there are $N$ lithium atoms in the units cell, and the volume of the unit cell is $V = a^3$, the mass density is

$$\rho = \frac{Nm_{\text{Li}}}{V} = \frac{N(M_{\text{Li}}/N_{\text{A}})}{a^3}$$

Rearranging, and noting that if the (100) planes are separated by 350 pm, then the unit cell parameter $a = 350$ pm

$$N = \frac{N_{\text{A}}\rho a^3}{M_{\text{Li}}}$$

$$= \frac{(6.022 \times 10^{23}\text{mol}^{-1}) \times \overbrace{(0.53 \times 10^{3}\ \text{kg m}^{-3})}^{1\ \text{g cm}^{-3}=10^{3}\text{kg m}^{-3}} \times (350 \times 10^{-12}\ \text{m})^{3}}{6.94 \times 10^{-3}\text{kg mol}^{-1}}$$

$$= 2$$

A face-centred cubic crystal has $N = 4$, and a body-centred crystal has $N = 2$, atoms in each unit cell. The calculation therefore implies that lithium has a **body-centred cubic** structure.

**E17.25** (a) Applying eqn 17.7, the separation between crystal planes with Miller indices (*hkl*) is given by

$$\frac{1}{d^2} = \frac{h^2}{a^2} + \frac{k^2}{b^2} + \frac{l^2}{c^2} = \frac{(h^2 + k^2 + l^2)}{a^2}$$

However, according to Bragg's law, eqn 17.8, diffraction is observed at angles for which

$$\lambda = 2d \sin\theta$$

Combining these two equations and rearranging,

$$\theta = \sin^{-1}\left(\frac{\lambda}{2d}\right) = \sin^{-1}\left\{\frac{\lambda(h^2 + k^2 + l^2)^{1/2}}{2a}\right\}$$

Using this relationship and the values $a = 361$ pm and $\lambda = 154$ pm, we may compile a table of angles of diffraction for planes with various Miller indices. In practice, diffraction is only observed for a face-centred cubic crystal from planes for which the Miller indices are either all even, or all odd. Thus, diffraction is not observed for the (100), (110), (210), (300), (310), (320), and (321) planes because for these planes, the structure factors equal zero by symmetry. These missing diffraction spots constitue systematic absences in the diffraction pattern.

| (*hkl*) | (111) | (200) | (220) | (311) | (222) | (400) |
|---|---|---|---|---|---|---|
| $\theta_{hkl}$ | 21.7° | 25.3° | 37.1° | 45.0° | 47.6° | 58.6° |

(b) For a face-centred cubic crystal, there are $N = 4$ atoms in each unit cell. The volume of the unit cell is $V = a^3$, so that the mass density is

$$\rho = \frac{m}{V} = \frac{Nm_{\text{Cu}}}{a^3} = \frac{N(M_{\text{Cu}}/N_{\text{A}})}{a^3}$$

$$= \frac{4 \times \overbrace{(63.55 \times 10^{-3}\ \text{kg mol}^{-1})}^{\text{Molar mass, } M_{\text{Cu}}}}{\underbrace{(361 \times 10^{-12}\ \text{m})^3}_{a^3} \times \underbrace{(6.022 \times 10^{23}\ \text{mol}^{-1})}_{N_{\text{A}}}} = \mathbf{8.97 \times 10^{3}\ kg\ m^{-3}}$$

**E17.26** Considering the cylinders shown in Figure 17.9, the shaded area shown, which is equivalent to the base of the unit cell, has an area

$$\{2R\sin(\pi/3)\}\times 2R = 2\sqrt{3}R^2$$

The unit cell thus has a volume $2\sqrt{3}R^2c$. Each unit cell contains a net total of one cylinder. The area of each cylinder's base is $\pi R^2$. Hence, the packing fraction, which is the ratio of the volume of the cylinders to the volume of the unit, is

$$f = \frac{\text{volume of cylinders}}{\text{volume of unit cell}} = \frac{\pi R^2 c}{2\sqrt{3}R^2 c} = \frac{\pi}{2\sqrt{3}} = \mathbf{0.907}$$

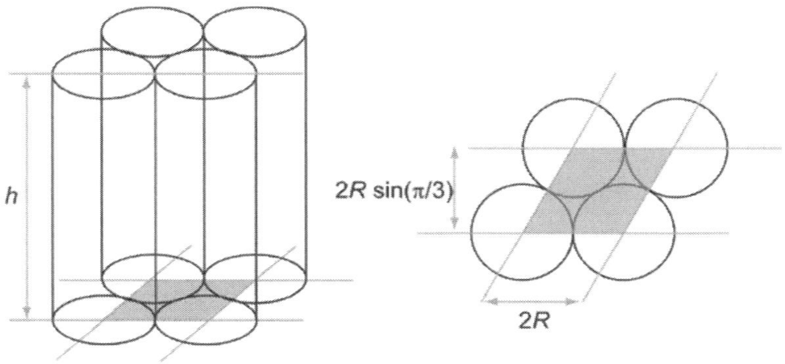


**Figure 17.9**

**E17.27** To calculate the packing fraction of a cubic close packed structure, we must first calculate the volume of the unit cell shown in Figure 17.10, and then calculate the total volume of the spheres that fully or partial occupy it. The first part of the calculation is a straightforward exercise in geometry. The second part involves counting the fraction of spheres that occupy the cell. Refer to the figure.

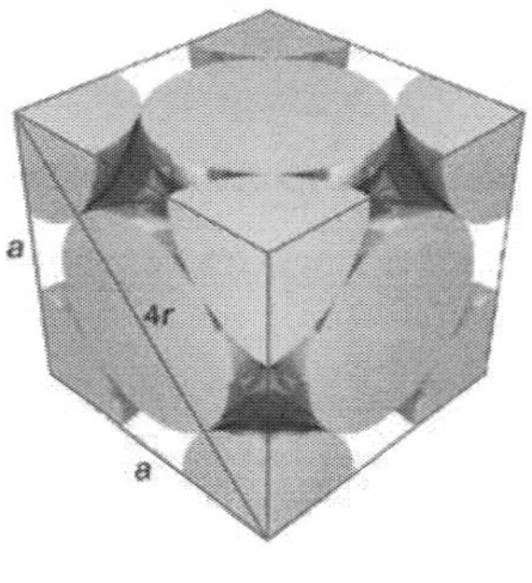


**Figure 17.10**

Because a diagonal of any face passes completely through one sphere and halfway through two other spheres, its length is $4R$. The length of a side is therefore $8^{1/2}R$ and the volume of the unit cell is

$$(8^{1/2}R)^3 = 8^{3/2}R^3$$

Because each cell contains the equivalent of $(6 \times \frac{1}{2}) + (8 \times \frac{1}{8}) = 4$ spheres, and the volume of each sphere is $4/3\pi R^3$ the total occupied volume is

$$4 \times \{(4/3)\pi R^3\} = (16/3)\pi R^3$$

The fraction of space occupied is therefore

$$\frac{(16/3)\pi R^3}{8^{3/2}R^3} = \mathbf{0.740}$$

Because a hexagonal close-packed structure has the same coordination number, its packing fraction is the same.

**E17.28** The packing fraction for hexagonal close-packing is 0.740. Therefore the density of the solid virus sample is

$$0.740 \times 1.00\ \text{g cm}^{-3} = \mathbf{0.740\ g\ cm^{-3}}$$

**E17.29** Referring to Figure 17.39 of the text, it can be seen that each atom has (a) eight nearest neighbours and (b) six next-nearest neighbours. Nearest neighbours touch each along the body diagonal of the cube. If the side of the cube is $a$, then the length of the body diagonal is $3^{1/2}a$. As there are two atoms along the body diagonal, the distance between nearest neighbours is given by

$$d = \tfrac{1}{2} \times 3^{1/2}a = \tfrac{1}{2} \times 3^{1/2} \times 600\ \text{nm} = \mathbf{520\ nm}$$

The next nearest neighbours are the length of a side away, 600 nm.

**E17.30** In the same way, and referring to Figure 17.38 of the text, each atom has (a) 12 nearest neighbours and (b) 6 next nearest neighbours. Nearest neighbours touch each other along the diagonal of a face; therefore if the length of one side of the cubic unit cell is $a$, then, by Pythagoras' theorem, the distance between neighbours is

$$d = a/2^{1/2} = 600\ \text{nm}/2^{1/2} = \mathbf{424\ nm}$$

For next nearest neighbours, the separation is again the length of one side, **600 nm**.

**E17.31** The packing fraction for cubic close-packing is 0.74, and that for body-centred structures is 0.68. (a) Therefore, the solid becomes less dense, as a result of the transition from cubic close packed to body-centred cubic packing. (b) Its density would decrease to $0.68/0.74 = 0.92$, or **92 per cent** of its former value.

**E17.32** Applying the radius ratio rule, eqn 17.10, for magnesium oxide,

$$\gamma = \frac{r_{\text{smaller}}}{r_{\text{larger}}} = \frac{r_{\text{Mg}^{2+}}}{r_{\text{O}^{2-}}} = \frac{72\ \text{pm}}{140\ \text{pm}} = 0.51$$

where the values of the radii have been taken from Table 17.6. This ratio falls within the limits predicted in Table 17.5 for rock salt structure.

## Answers to projects

**P17.33** (a) If the energies of the levels are given by eqn 17.1, then the separation between levels is

$$\Delta E_k = E_{k+1} - E_k = \overbrace{\left[\alpha + 2\beta\cos\left\{\frac{(k+1)\pi}{N+1}\right\}\right]}^{E_{k+1}} - \overbrace{\left[\alpha + 2\beta\cos\left\{\frac{k\pi}{N+1}\right\}\right]}^{E_k}$$
$$= 2\beta\left[\cos\left\{\frac{(k+1)\pi}{N+1}\right\} - \cos\left\{\frac{k\pi}{N+1}\right\}\right]$$

In the limit as $N \to \infty$, the denominator of each cosine term becomes infinite and, therefore, each cosine term becomes cos(0), which equals 1. Thus,

$$\lim_{N\to\infty} \Delta E_k = 2\beta \times \lim_{N\to\infty}\left[\cos\left\{\frac{(k+1)\pi}{N+1}\right\} - \cos\left\{\frac{k\pi}{N+1}\right\}\right]$$
$$= 2\beta \times [\cos(0) - \cos(0)] = 0$$

This means that the separation between neighbouring levels goes to zero as $N$ increases to infinity.

(b) We may derive an expression for the density of states by differentiating eqn 17.1. Thus,

$$\rho(k) = \frac{\mathrm{d}E}{\mathrm{d}k} = \frac{\mathrm{d}}{\mathrm{d}k}\left\{\alpha + 2\beta\cos\left(\frac{k\pi}{N+1}\right)\right\} = 2\beta\frac{\mathrm{d}}{\mathrm{d}k}\cos\left(\frac{k\pi}{N+1}\right)$$
$$= 2\beta \times \frac{\pi}{N+1} \times -\sin\left(\frac{k\pi}{N+1}\right) = -\frac{2\beta\pi}{N+1}\sin\left(\frac{k\pi}{N+1}\right)$$

We may simplify this expression by using the trigonometric identity

$$\sin^2 x + \cos^2 x = 1$$

and by noting that we may rearrange eqn 17.1 to give

$$\cos\left(\frac{k\pi}{N+1}\right) = \frac{E_k - \alpha}{2\beta}$$

Thus,

$$\sin\left(\frac{k\pi}{N+1}\right) = \left\{1 - \cos^2\left(\frac{k\pi}{N+1}\right)\right\}^{1/2} = \left\{1 - \left(\frac{E_k - \alpha}{2\beta}\right)^2\right\}^{1/2}$$

and so

$$\rho(k) = -\frac{2\beta\pi}{N+1} \times \left\{1 - \left(\frac{E_k - \alpha}{2\beta}\right)^2\right\}^{1/2}$$

A plot of $\rho(k)$ against $k$ is shown in Figure 17.11. It can be seen, both fropm the expression derived and the plot, that the density of states is greatest when $E_k = \alpha$.

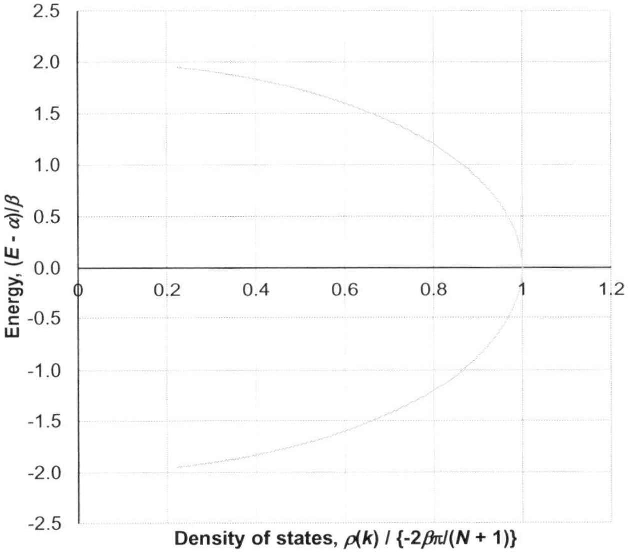


**Figure 17.11**

(c) Permitted states at the low-energy edge of the band must have a relatively long characteristic wavelength while the permitted states at the high energy edge of the band must have a relatively short characteristic wavelength. There are few wavefunctions that have these characteristics so the density of states is lowest at the edges. This is analogous to the MO picture that shows a few bonding MOs that lack nodes and a few antibonding MOs that have the maximum number of nodes.

An electron within a three-dimensional crystal experiences a spatially periodic potential. By analogy with a particle in a three-dimensional box, we might expect the wavefunction to be of the form

$$\psi \propto \sin\frac{n_x\pi x}{L_x}\sin\frac{n_y\pi y}{L_y}\sin\frac{n_z\pi z}{L_z}$$

with quantun numbers $n_x, n_y$ and $n_z$ taking values 0, ±1, ±2, etc. and energies

$$E = \left(\frac{n_x^2}{L_x^2} + \frac{n_y^2}{L_y^2} + \frac{n_z^2}{L_z^2}\right)\frac{h^2}{8m_e}$$

The lengths $L_x$, $L_y$ and $L_z$ depend upon the symmetry and dimensions of the unit cell of the crsytal. If, for simplicity, we assume that the crystal is cubic, so that $L_x = L_y = L_z = L$ then

$$E = \left(n_x^2 + n_y^2 + n_z^2\right)\frac{h^2}{8m_e}$$

This equation suggests that the density of states for energy level $E$ can be visually evaluated by looking at a plot of permitted $n_x$, $n_y$, $n_z$ values. The number of $n_x$, $n_y$, $n_z$ values within a thin, spherical shell around the origin equals the density of states which have energy $E$. A cross section through such a plot is shown in Figure 17.12. Three spherical shells, labelled 1, 2, and 3, are shown in the graph. All have the same width but their energies increase with their distance from the origin, as $n_x$ and $n_y$ increase. It is obvious that the low energy shell 1 contains fewer states than the intermediate energy shell 2. The sphere of shell 3 has been cut into the shape determined by the periodic potential pattern of the crystal and, because of this phenomena, it also has a lower density of states than the intermediate energy shell 2. The general concept is that the low-energy and high-energy edges of a band have lower density of states than that of the band centre.

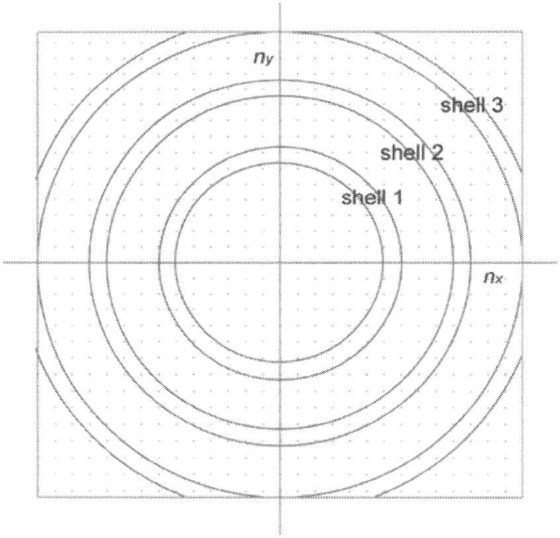


**Figure 17.12**

**P17.34** Special time-resolved X-ray diffraction techniques have become available in recent years and it is now possible to make exquisitely detailed measurements of atomic motions during chemical and biochemical reactions. Time-resolved X-ray diffraction techniques make use of synchrotron sources, which can emit intense polychromatic pulses of X-ray radiation with pulse widths varying from 100 ps to 200 ps. Instead of the Bragg method, the Laue method is used because many reflections can be collected simultaneously, rotation of the sample is not required, and data acquisition times are short. However, good diffraction data cannot be obtained from a single X-ray pulse and reflections from several pulses must be averaged together. In practice, this averaging dictates the time resolution of the experiment, which is commonly tens of microseconds or less.

**P17.35** Tans and coworkers (*Nature*, **393**, 49 (1998)) have draped a semiconducting carbon nanotube (CNT) over metal electrodes that are 400 nm apart atop a silicon surface coated with silicon dioxide. A bias voltage between the electrodes provides the source and drain of the molecular field-effect transistor (FET). The silicon serves as a gate electrode and the thin silicon oxide layer (at least 100 nm thick) insulates the gate from the CNT circuit. By adjusting the magnitude of an electric field applied to the gate, current flow across the CNT may be turned on and off.

Wind and coworkers (*Appl. Phys. Letters*, **80**, 3817 (2002)) have designed a CNT-FET of improved current carrying capability. The gate electrode is above the conduction channel and separated from the channel by a thin oxide dielectric. In this manner the CNT-to-air contact is eliminated, an arrangement that prevents the circuit from acting like a p-type transistor. This arrangement also reduces the gate oxide thickness to about 15 nm, allowing for much smaller gate voltages and a steeper subthreshold slope, which is a measure of how well a transistor turns on or off.

A single-electron transistor (SET) has been prepared by Cees Dekker and coworkers (*Science*, **293**, 76, (2001)) with a CNT. The SET is prepared by putting two bends in a CNT with the tip of an AFM (Fig. 17.17). Bending causes two buckles that, at a distance of 20 nm, serves as a conductance barrier. When an appropriate voltage is applied to the gate below the barrier, electrons tunnel one at a time across the barrier.

Weitz et al. (*Phys. Stat. Sol.* (b) **243**, 13, 3394 (2006)) report on the construction of a single-wall CNT using a silane-based organic self-assembled monolayer (SAM) as a gate dielectric on top of a highly doped silicon wafer. The organic SAM is made of 18-phenoxyoctadecyltrichlorosilane. This ultrathin layer ensures strong gate coupling and therefore low operation voltages. Single-electron transistors (SETs) were obtained from individual metallic SWCNTs. Field-effect transistors made from individual semiconducting SWCNTs operate with gate-source voltages of −2 V, show good saturation, small hysteresis (200 mV) as well as a low subthreshold swing (290 mV/dec).

Rodgers and researchers at the University of Illinois (*J. Phys. Chem. C*, **111**, 17879 (2007)) have reported a technique for producing near perfect alignment of CNT transistors. The array is prepared by patterning thin strips of an iron catalyst on quartz crystals and then growing nanometre-wide CNTs along those strips using conventional carbon vapor deposition. The quartz crystal aligns the nanotubes. Transistor development then includes depositing source, drain, and gate electrodes using conventional photolithography. Transistors made with about 2,000 nanotubes can carry currents of one ampere, which is several orders of magnitude larger than the current possible with single nanotubes. The research group also developed a technique for transferring the nanotube arrays onto any substrate, including silicon, plastic, and glass.

# Chapter 18

# Solid surfaces

## Answers to discussion questions

**D18.1** Characterizing the composition and structure of a surface requires that the cleanliness of a freshly prepared surface be assured with **ultrahigh vacuum** (UHV) techniques, which provide low pressures in the range of 1 μPa to 1 nPa. At these pressures collision fluxes may be as low as once a day.

One technique that may be used to characterize a solid surface is **photoemission spectroscopy**, in which X-rays (for XPS) or hard (short-wavelength) ultraviolet (for UPS) ionizing radiation is used to eject electrons from adsorbed species. The kinetic energies of the electrons ejected from their orbitals are measured and the pattern of energies is used to identify the material present. UPS, which examines electrons ejected from valence shells, is also used to establish the bonding characteristics and the details of electronic structures of substances on the surface. Its usefulness is its ability to reveal which orbitals of the adsorbate are involved in the bond to the substrate.

A technique, which is widely used in the microelectronics industry, is **Auger electron spectroscopy** (AES). The **Auger effect** (pronounced oh-zhey) is the emission of a second electron after high-energy radiation has expelled another electron. The first electron to depart leaves a hole in a low lying orbital, and an upper electron falls into it. The energy released in this transition may result either in the generation of radiation, which is called **X-ray fluorescence** or in the ejection of another electron. The latter is the secondary electron of the Auger effect. The energies of the secondary electrons are characteristic of the material present. In practice, the Auger spectrum is normally obtained by irradiating the sample with an electron beam rather than electromagnetic radiation. In **scanning Auger electron microscopy** (SAM), the finely focused electron beam is scanned over the surface and a map of composition is compiled; the resolution can reach to below about 50 nm.

A technique for determining the arrangement of the atoms close to and adsorbed on the surface is **low-energy electron diffraction** (LEED). This technique is like X-ray diffraction but uses the wave character of electrons. The use of low-energy electrons (with energies in the range 10–200 eV, corresponding to wavelengths in the range 100–400 pm) ensures that the diffraction is caused only by atoms on and close to the surface. The presence of terraces, steps, and kinks in a surface shows up in LEED patterns, and their surface density (the number of defects in a region divided by the area of the region) can be estimated.

Terraces, steps, kinks, and dislocations on a surface may be observed by **scanning tunnelling microscopy** (STM), and **atomic force microscopy** (AFM). In scanning tunnelling microscopy a platinum–rhodium or tungsten needle is scanned across the surface of a conducting solid. When the tip of the needle is brought very close to the surface, electrons tunnel across the intervening space. In the *constant-current mode* of operation, the stylus moves up and down corresponding to the form of the surface, and the topography of the surface, including any adsorbates, can be mapped on an atomic scale. The vertical motion of the stylus is achieved by fixing it to a piezoelectric cylinder, which contracts or expands according to the potential difference it experiences. In the *constant-z mode*, the vertical position of the stylus is held constant and the current is monitored. Because the tunnelling probability is very sensitive to the size of the gap, the microscope can detect tiny, atom-scale variations in the height of the surface.

In *atomic force microscopy* (AFM) a sharpened stylus attached to a beam is scanned across the surface. The force exerted by the surface and any adsorbate pushes or pulls on the stylus and deflects the beam. The deflection is monitored by using a laser beam. Because no current is needed between the sample and the probe, the technique can be applied to nonconducting surfaces too.

**D18.2** The **Langmuir isotherm** applies under the following conditions:

Adsorption cannot proceed beyond monolayer coverage. This is justified when the initial adsorbed layer cannot act as a substrate for the adsorption of multilayers because the pressure is much lower than the vapour pressure of the adsorbate.

All sites are equivalent and the surface is uniform, so that the incidence of steps, kinks, and dislocations on a surface is minimal. This implies that the enthalpy of adsorption is the same for all sites.

The ability of a molecule to adsorb at a given site is independent of the occupation of neighbouring sites. Thus, the enthalpy of adsorption is independent of the extent of surface coverage.

**D18.3** Multilayer adsorption is indicated by when $V/V_{mon} > 1$. For a given value of the constant $c$, which equals $K_0/K_1$ where $K_0$ is the equilibrium constant for adsorption on to the substrate and $K_1$ is the equilibrium constant for physisorption on to the overlaying layers already present, the ratio $V/V_{mon}$ becomes greater than 1 at a pressure that is less than the vapour pressure of the liquid, $p^*$. To find a relationship for $z = p/p^*$ at the point for which $V/V_{mon} = 1$ on the BET isotherm, we may set $V/V_{mon} = 1$ in eqn 18.7 and solve for $z$. Thus,

$$\frac{V}{V_{\text{mon}}} = \frac{cz}{(1-z)\{1-(1-c)z\}} = 1$$

$$cz = (1-z)\{1-(1-c)z\}$$

$$cz = 1 - z + cz - z + z^2 - cz^2$$
$$(c-1)z^2 + 2z - 1 = 0$$

This expression is a second-order polynomial in $z$ and application of the solution of the quadratic equation using the method outlined in *The chemist's toolkit 7.1* gives

$$z = \frac{1 \pm \sqrt{c}}{1-c}, \qquad \text{where } c \neq 1$$

The solution is valid if $z$ is in the range $0 < z < 1$ and the range of $c$ is $0 < c < \infty$. These ranges imply that of the two possible solutions to the above equation only the negative sign in the numerator provides a physically reasonable value. Thus,

$$z = \frac{1 - \sqrt{c}}{1-c}, \qquad \text{where } c \neq 1$$

The following table gives the calculated value of $z$ at $V/V_{mon} = 1$, and hence at which multilayer formation begins to occur, on the BET isotherm over a range of values of $c$. The solution is not valid when $c = 1$, but direct examination of the BET isotherm under these conditions reveals that $z = 0.50$.

| $c$ | 0.001 | 0.01 | 0.1 | 1 | 10 | 100 | 1000 |
|---|---|---|---|---|---|---|---|
| $z$ | 0.9693 | 0.9090 | 0.7597 | 0.5000 | 0.2403 | 0.09091 | 0.03065 |

The results therefore give an indication of the vapour pressure required for multilayer formation as a function of the ratio of the equilibrium constants for adsorption onto the substrate and onto an existing monolayer. The results indicate that if $K_1 \ll K_0$, so that $c \ll 1$, relatively large pressures are required before a second layer begins to form. If, however, $K_1 \gg K_0$, so that $c \gg 1$, multilayer formation occurs even at low pressure.

**D18.4** In the **Langmuir–Hinshelwood mechanism** of surface-catalysed reactions, the reaction takes place by encounters between molecular fragments and atoms already adsorbed on the surface. We therefore expect the rate law for the process

$$A + B \rightarrow P$$

to be second-order in the extent of surface coverage

$$v = k_r \theta_A \theta_B$$

Insertion of the appropriate isotherms for A and B then gives the reaction rate in terms of the partial pressures of the reactants. For example, if A and B follow Langmuir isotherms, eqn 18.5, and adsorb without dissociation, then it follows that the rate law is

$$v = \frac{k_r \alpha_A \alpha_B p_A p_B}{(1 + \alpha_A p_A + \alpha_B p_B)^2}$$

The parameters $\alpha_A$ and $\alpha_B$ in the isotherms and the rate constant $k_r$ are all temperature dependent, so the overall temperature dependence of the rate may be strongly non-Arrhenius (in the sense that the reaction rate is unlikely to be proportional to $e^{-E_a/RT}$.

In the **Eley-Rideal mechanism** of a surface-catalysed reaction, a gas phase molecule collides with another molecule already adsorbed on the surface. The rate of formation of product is expected to be proportional to the partial pressure, $p_B$ of the non-adsorbed gas B and the extent of surface coverage, $\theta_A$, of the adsorbed gas A. It follows that the rate law should be

$$v = k_r p_B \theta_A$$

The rate constant, $k_r$, might be much larger than for the uncatalysed gas-phase reaction because the reaction on the surface has a low activation energy and the adsorption itself is often not activated.

If we know the adsorption isotherm for A, we can express the rate law in terms of its partial pressure, $p_A$. For example, if the adsorption of A follows a Langmuir isotherm in the pressure range of interest, then the rate law would be

$$v = \frac{k_r \alpha_A p_A p_B}{1 + \alpha_A p_A}$$

According to eqn 18.18, when the partial pressure of A is high, in the sense that $\alpha_A p_A \gg 1$, there is almost complete surface coverage, and the rate is equal to $k_r p_B$. Now the rate-determining step is the collision of B with the adsorbed fragments. When the pressure of A is low, so that $ap_A \ll 1$, perhaps because of its reaction, the rate is equal to $k_r \alpha_A p_A p_B$; and now the extent of surface coverage is important in the determination of the rate.

The Lindemann–Hinshelwood and Eley–Rideal mechanism have distinctive isotherms that can be distinguished with plots of measured rates against a full range of $p_A$ at constant $p_B$. The prediction of the Lindemann–Hinshelwood mechanism with competition for the same surface site is shown in Figure 18.1. The rate is limited by the low fractional coverage of A at low values of $\alpha_A p_A$ while the rate is limited by low fractional coverage of B at high values of $\alpha_A p_A$. Thus, the Lindemann–Hinshelwood isotherm goes through a maximum when $\alpha_A p_A = 1 + \alpha_B p_B$.

The Eley–Rideal prediction is shown in Figure 18.2. The rate is limited only by the low fractional coverage of A at low values of $\alpha_A p_A$ while the rate reaches a plateau, equal to $k_r^{-1} p_B$, as $\alpha_A p_A$ becomes large. Almost all thermal surface-catalysed reactions are thought to take place by the Lindemann–Hinshelwood mechanism.

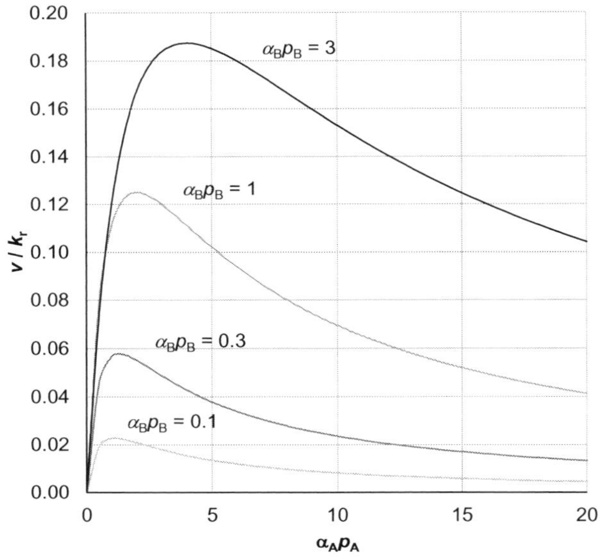


Figure 18.1

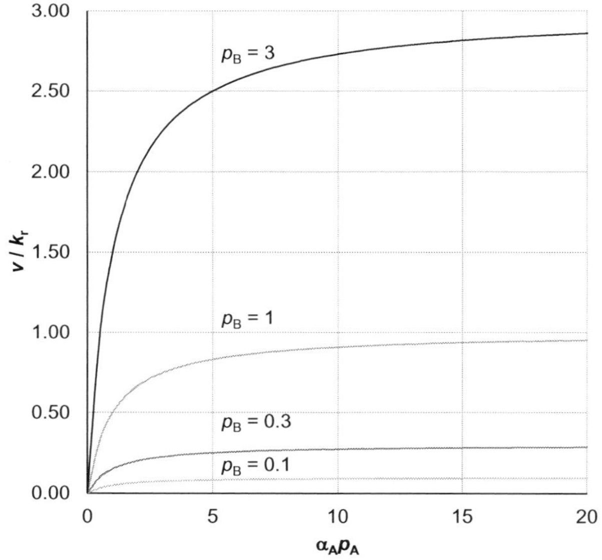


Figure 18.2

**D18.5** In the **Mars van Krevelen mechanism of catalytic oxidation** (MvK), for example in the partial oxidation of propene to propenal, the first stage is the adsorption of the propene molecule with loss of a hydrogen to form the allyl radical, $CH_2{=}CHCH_2$. An O atom in the surface can now transfer to this radical, leading to the formation of acrolein (propenal, $CH_2{=}CHCHO$) and its desorption from the surface. The H atom also escapes with a surface O atom, and goes on to form $H_2O$, which leaves the surface. The surface is left with vacancies and metal ions in lower oxidation states. These vacancies are attacked by $O_2$ molecules in the overlying gas, which then chemisorb as $O_2^-$ ions, so reforming the catalyst. This sequence of events involves great upheavals of the surface, and some materials break up under the stress.

The MvK mechanism can be identified by finding that a product leaves the catalytic surface with a constituent of the surface lattice. The lattice contributes an atom, or molecular fragment, to formation of an intermediate product and is more than a substrate alone. For example an oxygen atom of the lattice may be carried away as product and the resulting oxygen vacancies are refilled by gas phase oxygen in a separate reaction. Changes in the surface structure may be observed along with changes in both the coordination numbers and oxidation states of transition metals on the catalytic surface.

**D18.6** The **electrical double layer** model of the electrode–electrolyte interface consists of a sheet of positive charge at the surface of the electrode and a sheet of negative charge next to it in the solutions (or vice versa). This creates the **Galvani potential difference** between the bulk of the electrode and the bulk of the solution. In the **Helmholtz layer model** of the interface the solvated ions arrange themselves along the surface of the electrode but are held away from it by their hydration spheres. The plane running through the solvated ions is called the outer Helmholtz plane. The model results in an electrical potential that changes linearly between the electrode and the outer Helmholtz plane. In a refinement of this model, ions that have discarded their solvating molecules and have become attached to the electrode surface by chemical bonds are regarded as forming the **inner Helmholtz plane**. In the **Gouy–Chapman model** of the **diffuse double layer**, the disordering effect of thermal motion is taken into account by replacing the outer Helmholtz plane with a diffuse counter ionic atmosphere.

**D18.7** In cyclic voltammetry, the current at a working electrode is monitored as the applied potential difference is changed back and forth at a constant rate between pre-set limits. As the potential difference approaches the standard potential, $E^\ominus(\text{Ox, Red})$, for a solution that contains the reduced component (Red), current begins to flow as Red is oxidized. When the potential difference is swept beyond $E^\ominus(\text{Ox, Red})$, the current passes through a maximum and then falls as all the Red near the electrode is consumed and converted to Ox, the oxidized form. When the direction of the sweep is reversed and the potential difference passes through $E^\ominus(\text{Ox, Red})$, current flows in the reverse direction. This current is caused by the reduction of the Ox formed near the electrode on the forward sweep. It passes through the maximum as Ox near the electrode is consumed. The forward and reverse current maxima bracket $E^{\ominus}$(Ox, Red), so the species present can be identified. Furthermore, the forward and reverse peak currents are proportional to the concentration of the couple in the solution, and vary with the sweep rate. If the electron transfer at the electrode is rapid, so that the ratio of the concentrations of Ox and Red at the electrode surface have their equilibrium values for the applied potential (that is, their relative concentrations are given by the Nernst equation), the voltammetry is said to be *reversible*. In this case, the peak separation is independent of the sweep rate and equal to $(59\,\text{mV})/n$ at room temperature, where $n$ is the number of electrons transferred. If the rate of electron transfer is low, the voltammetry is said to be *irreversible*. Now, the peak separation is greater than $(59\,\text{mV})/n$ and increases with increasing sweep rate. If homogeneous chemical reactions accompany the oxidation or reduction of the couple at the electrode, the shape of the voltammogram changes, and the observed changes give valuable information about the kinetics of the reactions as well as the identities of the species present.

## Solutions to exercises

**E18.1** The collisional flux is, from eqn 18.1,

$$Z_W = \frac{p}{(2\pi mkT)^{1/2}} = \frac{p}{\{2\pi(M/N_A)kT\}^{1/2}}$$

(a) (i)Thus, for hydrogen, with molar mass $M_{H_2}$=2.02 g mol$^{-1}$, at 100 Pa

$$Z_W = \frac{100\ \text{Pa} \times (6.022 \times 10^{23}\text{mol}^{-1})^{1/2}}{[2\pi \times (2.02 \times 10^{-3}\text{kg mol}^{-1}) \times (1.38 \times 10^{-23}\ \text{J K}^{-1}) \times (25+273)\ \text{K}]^{1/2}}$$
$$= \mathbf{1.075 \times 10^{25}\ m^2\ s^{-1}}$$

(ii) and at 0.10 μTorr

$$Z_W = \frac{(0.10\ \mu\text{Torr}) \times (133.32\ \text{Pa Torr}^{-1}) \times (6.022 \times 10^{23}\text{mol}^{-1})^{1/2}}{[2\pi \times (2.02 \times 10^{-3}\text{kg mol}^{-1}) \times (1.38 \times 10^{-23}\ \text{J K}^{-1}) \times (25+273)\ \text{K}]^{1/2}}$$
$$= \mathbf{1.433 \times 10^{18}\ m^2\ s^{-1}}$$

where we have used the conversion factor, 1 Torr = 133.32 Pa, from Table 0.1.

(b) (i) In the same way for propane, $C_3H_8$, with molar mass $M_{C_3H_8}$=44.09 g mol$^{-1}$

$$Z_W = \frac{100\ \text{Pa} \times (6.022 \times 10^{23}\text{mol}^{-1})^{1/2}}{[2\pi \times (44.09 \times 10^{-3}\text{kg mol}^{-1}) \times (1.38 \times 10^{-23}\ \text{J K}^{-1}) \times (25+273)\ \text{K}]^{1/2}}$$
$$= \mathbf{2.298 \times 10^{24}\ m^2\ s^{-1}}$$

(ii) and at 0.10 μTorr

$$Z_W = \frac{(0.10\ \mu\text{Torr}) \times (133.32\ \text{Pa Torr}^{-1}) \times (6.022 \times 10^{23}\text{mol}^{-1})^{1/2}}{[2\pi \times (44.09 \times 10^{-3}\text{kg mol}^{-1}) \times (1.38 \times 10^{-23}\ \text{J K}^{-1}) \times (25+273)\ \text{K}]^{1/2}}$$
$$= \mathbf{3.064 \times 10^{17}\ m^2\ s^{-1}}$$

**E18.2** The collisional flux is the number of molecules hitting a surface divided by the time interval and the area of the surface. Thus, given the collisional rate, $Z$

$$Z_W = Z/A$$

For a circular surface with radius $r$ and diameter $d$, the area is $A = \pi r^2 = \pi d^2/4$. Thus, rearranging eqn 18.1, the pressure required for a particular collisional flux is

$$\begin{aligned} p &= Z_W(2\pi mkT)^{1/2} = (Z/A) \times (2\pi mkT)^{1/2} = \left(\frac{4Z}{\pi d^2}\right) \times \{2\pi(M_{Ar}/N_A)kT\}^{1/2} \\ &= \frac{4 \times (8.5 \times 10^{20}\,\text{s}^{-1})}{\pi \times (2.5 \times 10^{-3}\,\text{m})} \\ &\quad \times \frac{\{2\pi \times (39.95 \times 10^{-3}\,\text{kg mol}^{-1}) \times (1.38 \times 10^{-23}\,\text{J K}^{-1}) \times (450\,\text{K})\}^{1/2}}{(6.022 \times 10^{23}\,\text{mol}^{-1})} \\ &= \mathbf{8.8 \times 10^3\ Pa} \end{aligned}$$

**E18.3** The rate at which molecules hit a surface is given by the product of the collisional flux and the area. Thus, from eqn 18.1,

$$Z = Z_W A = \frac{p}{(2\pi mkT)^{1/2}} A = \frac{pA}{\{2\pi(M/N_A)kT\}^{1/2}}$$

For a face-centred cubic structure, there is the equivalent of two atoms on each face of the unit cell. The (100) plane corresponds to just such a face, so that if the unit cell has a dimension $a$, the area of one copper atom may be assumed to be $A = \tfrac{1}{2}a^2$. Hence,

$$\begin{aligned} Z &= \frac{p \times (\tfrac{1}{2}a^2) \times N_A^{1/2}}{\{2\pi M_{He} kT\}^{1/2}} \\ &= \frac{(25\,\text{Pa}) \times \{\tfrac{1}{2} \times (361 \times 10^{-12}\,\text{m})^2\} \times (6.022 \times 10^{23}\,\text{mol}^{-1})^{1/2}}{\{2\pi \times (4.02 \times 10^{-3}\text{kg mol}^{-1}) \times (1.38 \times 10^{-23}\,\text{J K}^{-1}) \times (100\,\text{K})\}^{1/2}} \\ &= \mathbf{2.14 \times 10^5\ s^{-1}} \end{aligned}$$

**E18.4** At first sight, it appears from eqn 18.1 that collisional flux is inversely proportional to the square root of temperature. However, the pressure of the gas is also dependent upon temperature, and so, substituting using the perfect gas equation of state, eqn 1.2,

$$Z_W = \frac{p}{(2\pi mkT)^{1/2}} = \frac{nRT/V}{(2\pi mkT)^{1/2}} = \frac{nR}{(2\pi mk)^{1/2}V} T^{1/2}$$

Thus, the collisional flux is, in fact, proportional to the square root of temperature. Hence, if the temperature increases from 300 K to 400 K, the collisional flux changes by a factor of

$$\left\{\frac{(400\,\text{K})}{(300\,\text{K})}\right\}^{-1/2} = \mathbf{1.15}$$

**E18.5** We may calculate the amount of gas, and hence the number of molecules adsorbed using the perfect gas equation of state, eqn 1.2. Thus,

$$N = nN_A = N_A pV/RT$$

We may take the area, $\sigma$, of an individual CO molecule to be equal to that for $N_2$, and use the value from Table 1.4. Thus, the total area of the catalyst is

$$A = N\sigma = \frac{N_A pV\sigma}{RT}$$
$$= \frac{(6.022 \times 10^{23}\ \text{mol}^{-1}) \times \overbrace{(1.00 \times 10^5\ \text{Pa})}^{1\ \text{bar}=10^5\,\text{Pa}} \times \overbrace{(4.25 \times 10^{-6}\ \text{m}^3)}^{1\ \text{cm}^3=10^{-6}\text{m}^3} \times \overbrace{(0.43 \times 10^{-18}\ \text{m}^2)}^{1\ \text{nm}^2=10^{-18}\text{m}^2}}{(8.3145\ \text{J K}^{-1}\text{mol}^{-1}) \times (273\ \text{K})}$$
$$= \mathbf{48.5\ m^2}$$

**E18.6** Rearranging the Langmuir isotherm, eqn 18.3,

$$\theta = \frac{\alpha p}{1 + \alpha p}$$
$$(1 + \alpha p)\theta = \alpha p$$
$$\alpha p(1 - \theta) = \theta$$
$$p = \frac{\theta}{\alpha(1 - \theta)}$$

(a) Hence, for a ratio of forward and backward rate constants, $\alpha = 1.85\ \text{kPa}^{-1}$ and fractional surface coverage $\theta = 0.10$,

$$p = \frac{0.10}{(1.85\ \text{kPa}^{-1})(1 - 0.10)} = 0.060\ \text{kPa} = \mathbf{60\ Pa}$$

(b) And for a fractional surface coverage, $\theta = 0.90$,

$$p = \frac{0.90}{(1.85\ \text{kPa}^{-1})(1 - 0.90)} = \mathbf{4.9\ kPa}$$

**E18.7** Suppose that the sticking probability, $s$, which is defined through eqn 18.12, has the form $s = (1 - \theta)s_0$ where $s_0$ is the sticking probability on a perfectly clean surface and $\theta$ is the fractional coverage. Then, using the rate of adsorption for a Langmuir isotherm and a collision rate that equals $Z_W \times N$, where $N$ is the number of adsorption sites, we may write

$$s = (1 - \theta)s_0 = \frac{\overbrace{k_a N(1 - \theta)p}^{\text{rate of adsorption on surface}}}{\underbrace{Z_W N}_{\text{rate of collision with surface}}}$$

Solving for the rate constant for adsorption, $k_a$

$$k_a = \frac{s_0 Z_W}{p} = \frac{s_0}{(2\pi mkT)^{1/2}}$$

We may assume that the rate constant for desorption is given by eqn 18.13

$$k_\text{d} = A\,\text{e}^{-E_\text{d}/RT}$$

so that

$$\alpha = \frac{k_a}{k_d} = \frac{s_0/(2\pi mkT)^{1/2}}{A\,\text{e}^{-E_\text{d}/RT}} = \frac{s_0\text{e}^{E_\text{d}/RT}}{A(2\pi mkT)^{1/2}}$$

**E18.8** Following the method used in Example 18.2, we may rewrite the Langmuir isotherm as

$$\overbrace{\frac{p}{V}}^{y} = \overbrace{\frac{1}{\alpha V_\infty}}^{\text{intercept}} + \overbrace{\frac{1}{V_\infty}}^{\text{slope}}\overbrace{p}^{x}$$

Thus, if the Langmuir isotherm is obeyed, a graph of $(p/V)$ against $p$ should be a straight line with a slope of $1/V_\infty$, and intercept of $1/\alpha V_\infty$. Figure 18.3 shows that for the data given, such a plot is indeed a straight line, so that the chemisorption of hydrogen on copper powder at 25 °C does indeed follow the Langmuir isotherm. The graph has a gradient of 1.767 $\text{cm}^{-3}$ and intercept 629.1 Pa $\text{cm}^{-3}$.

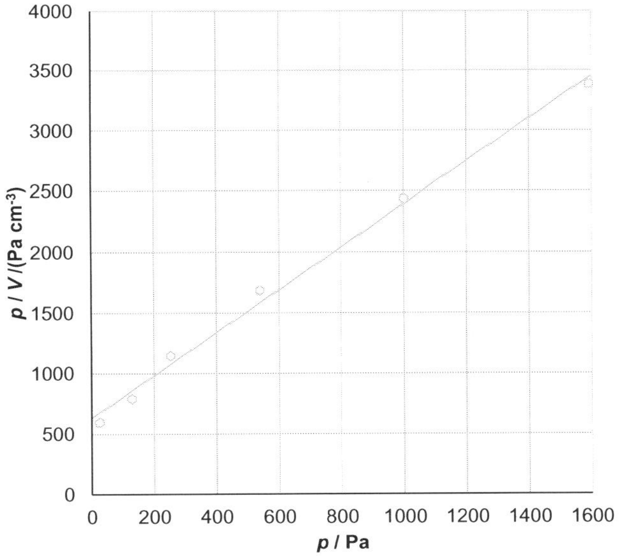


**Figure 18.3**

The parameter $\alpha$, is given by the ratio of slope to the intercept

$$\frac{\text{slope}}{\text{intercept}} = \frac{1/V_\infty}{1/\alpha V_\infty} = \alpha = \frac{1.767\ \text{cm}^{-3}}{629.1\ \text{Pa cm}^{-3}} = \mathbf{2.808\ Pa^{-1}}$$

The adsorption volume corresponding to complete coverage, $V_\infty$, is given by the reciprocal of the slope,

$$\frac{1}{\text{slope}}=\frac{1}{1/V_\infty}=V_\infty=\frac{1}{1.767\text{cm}^{-3}}=\mathbf{0.5660\ cm^3}$$

**E18.9** Rearranging the van't Hoff equation, eqn 18.4, the enthalpy of adsorption is

$$\begin{aligned}\Delta_{\text{ads}}H^\ominus &= -\frac{R(\ln\alpha-\ln\alpha')}{\{(1/T)-(1/T')\}}=-\frac{R\ln(\alpha/\alpha')}{\{(1/T)-(1/T')\}}\\ &= -\frac{(8.3145\ \text{J K}^{-1}\text{mol}^{-1})\times\{\ln(1.0\times10^{-3}\text{Torr}^{-1})/(2.7\times10^{-3}\ \text{Torr}^{-1})\}}{(1/273\ \text{K})-(1/250\ \text{K})}\\ &= -24.5\times10^3\ \text{J mol}^{-1}=\mathbf{-24.5\ kJ\ mol^{-1}}\end{aligned}$$

**E18.10** Following the method used in Example 18.3, the van 't Hoff equation may be rearranged into the form of a straight-line graph

$$\overbrace{\ln p}^{y}=\overbrace{\left(\ln p'-\frac{\Delta_{\text{ads}}H^\ominus}{RT'}\right)}^{\text{intercept}}+\overbrace{\frac{\Delta_{\text{ads}}H^\ominus}{R}}^{\text{slope}}\times\overbrace{\frac{1}{T}}^{x}$$

Figure 18.4 shows a plot of $\ln p$ against $1/T$. The graph has a slope of $-1.0868\times10^3\ \text{K}^{-1}$, so that the enthalpy of adsorption is

$$\begin{aligned}\Delta_{\text{ads}}H^\ominus &= R\times\text{slope}=(8.3145\ \text{J K}^{-1}\text{mol}^{-1})\times(-1.0868\times10^3\ \text{K}^{-1})\\ &= -15.02\times10^3\ \text{J mol}^{-1}=\mathbf{-15.02\ kJ\ mol^{-1}}\end{aligned}$$

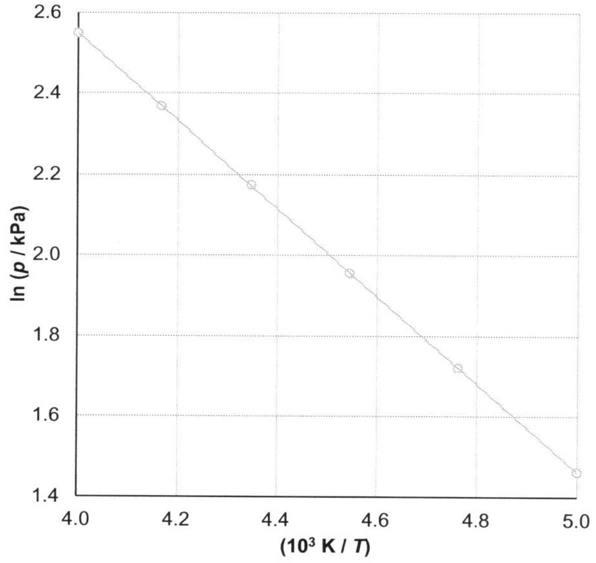


**Figure 18.4**

**E18.11** If, from eqn 18.5, the fraction of surface covered is

$$\theta = \frac{(\alpha p)^{1/2}}{1+(\alpha p)^{1/2}}$$

then, rearranging,

$$\theta\{1+(\alpha p)^{1/2}\} = (\alpha p)^{1/2}$$
$$(\alpha p)^{1/2} = \frac{\theta}{1-\theta}$$

so that

$$p = \frac{1}{\alpha}\left(\frac{\theta}{1-\theta}\right)^2$$

**E18.12** For adsorption with dissociation,

$$O_3(g) + M(\text{surface}) \rightleftharpoons 3\ O\text{–}M(\text{surface})$$

the rate of adsorption is proportional to the pressure and to the probability that all three atoms of ozone will find sites, which is proportional to the cube of the number of vacant sites. Thus,

$$\text{Rate of adsorption} = k_a p\{N(1-\theta)\}^3$$

The rate of desorption is proportional to the frequency of encounters of three atoms on the surface, and is therefore third-order in the number of atoms present:

$$\text{Rate of desorption} = k_d(N\theta)^3$$

At equilibrium, the two rates are equal, so we can write

$$k_a p\{N(1-\theta)\}^3 = k_d(N\theta)^3$$
$$\frac{k_a}{k_d}p = \left(\frac{\theta}{1-\theta}\right)^3$$
$$\alpha p = \left(\frac{\theta}{1-\theta}\right)^3$$

Solving for $\theta$ gives the isotherm

$$\theta = \frac{(\alpha p)^{1/3}}{1+(\alpha p)^{1/3}}$$

At low pressures, $1 \gg (\alpha p)^{1/3}$ and so $1 + (\alpha p)^{1/3} \approx 1$. Thus, a plot of $\theta$ against $p$ at low pressures shows a weaker pressure dependence for the dissociation than that shown by a Langmuir isotherm without dissociation.

**E18.13** *Derivation 18.1* provides a model for deriving eqn 18.6. However, with A and B competing for $N$ adsorption sites, the number of sites not occupied equals $(1 - \theta_A - \theta_B)N$ where $\theta_A$ and $\theta_B$ are the fraction of sites occupied by A and B, respectively. The rate at which A adsorbs to the surface is proportional to the partial pressure of A, $p_A$, and to $(1 - \theta_A - \theta_B)N$.

$$\text{Rate of adsorption of A} = k_{a,A}N(1 - \theta_A - \theta_B)p_A$$

The rate at which adsorbed A molecules leave the surface is proportional to the number currently on the surface, $N\theta_A$.

$$\text{Rate of desorption of A} = k_{d,A}\, N\theta_A$$

At equilibrium the two rates are equal:

$$k_{a,A}N\,(1 - \theta_A - \theta_B)p_A = k_{d,A}\, N\theta_A$$

Using $\alpha_A = k_{a,A}/\,k_{d,A}$, this rearranges to

$$\alpha_A(1 - \theta_A - \theta_B)p_A = \theta_A$$

Similarly,

$$\alpha_B(1 - \theta_A - \theta_B)p_B = \theta_B$$

Division of one equation by the other yields

$$\theta_B = \left(\frac{\alpha_B p_B}{\alpha_A p_A}\right)\theta_A$$

and, upon substitution of this expression for $\theta_B$ into the expression for $\theta_A$, it is found that

$$\theta_A = \frac{\alpha_A p_A}{1 + \alpha_A p_A + \alpha_B p_B}$$

and in the same way,

$$\theta_B = \frac{\alpha_B p_B}{1 + \alpha_A p_A + \alpha_B p_B}$$

**E18.14** Example 18.4 shows how the BET isotherm, eqn 18.9,

$$\frac{V}{V_{mon}} = \frac{cz}{(1-z)\{1-(1-c)z\}}$$

with $z = p\,/\,p^*$, may be rearranged into

$$\overbrace{\frac{z}{(1-z)V}}^{y} = \overbrace{\frac{1}{cV_{mon}}}^{\text{intercept}} + \overbrace{\frac{(c-1)}{cV_{mon}}}^{\text{slope}}\overbrace{z}^{x}$$

This expression has the same form as that of a straight-line graph. Figure 18.5 shows a plot of $z\,/\,\{(1-z)V\}$ against $z$. The graph is indeed a straight line, with a slope of $7.61 \times 10^{-2}$ cm$^{-3}$ and intercept $4.64 \times 10^{-4}$ cm$^{-3}$. The ratio

$$\frac{\text{slope}}{\text{intercept}} = \frac{(c-1)/cV_{mon}}{1/cV_{mon}} = c - 1 = \frac{7.61 \times 10^{-3}\text{cm}^{-3}}{4.64 \times 10^{-4}\text{cm}^{-3}} = 164$$

so that

$$c = 164 + 1 = \mathbf{165}$$

and

$$\frac{1}{(c \times \text{intercept})} = \frac{1}{c \times 1/(cV_{\text{mon}})} = V_{\text{mon}}$$

$$= \frac{1}{165 \times (4.64 \times 10^{-4}\text{cm}^{-3})} = \mathbf{13.1\ cm^3}$$

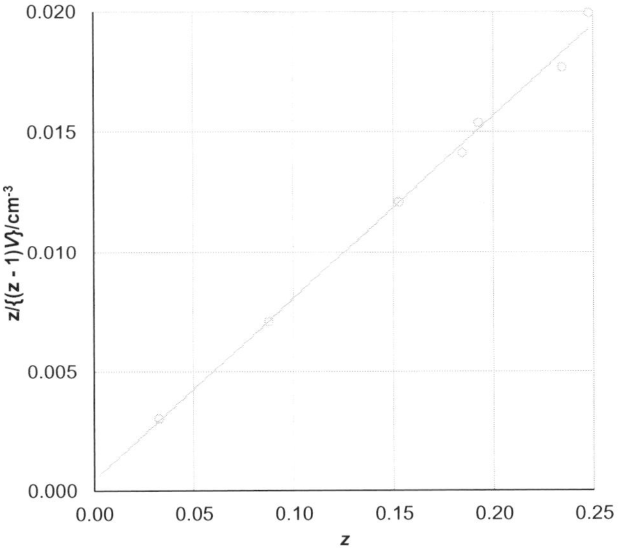


**Figure 18.5**

**E18.15** The residence half life of a molecule on a surface is given by eqn 18.14. The magnitude of the enthalpy of adsorption is indicative of chemisorption rather than physisorption. It is thus reasonable to assume that the vibrational frequency of the molecule–surface bond is of the order of $10^{-14}\ \text{s}^{-1}$, so that $\tau_0 = 1/(10^{-14}\ \text{s}^{-1}) = 10^{14}$ s. We may assume that the activation energy for desorption is approximately equal, in magnitude, to the enthalpy of desorption, $E_{\text{d}} = -\Delta_{\text{ads}}H^{\circ}$. Hence, the residence half life for an ammonia molecule ona nickel surface at 600 K is

$$t_{1/2} = \tau_0 e^{E_{\text{d}}/RT} = (10^{14}\ \text{s}) \times e^{(+155\times10^3\ \text{J mol}^{-1})/\{(8.3145\ \text{J K}^{-1}\text{mol}^{-1})\times(600\ \text{K})\}} = \mathbf{3.2\ s}$$

**E18.16** We may express the residence half life of a molecule on a surface as a function of temperature using eqn 18.14.

(a) Thus, for two different temperatures, $T$ and $T'$

$$t_{1/2}(T) = \tau_0 e^{E_{\text{d}}/RT}$$

$$t_{1/2}(T') = \tau_0 e^{E_d/RT'}$$

Combining the two expressions,

$$\frac{t_{1/2}(T)}{t_{1/2}(T')} = e^{E_d/R\{(1/T)-(1/T')\}}$$

so that, taking logarithms and rearranging,

$$E_d = \frac{R\ln\{t_{1/2}(T)/t_{1/2}(T')\}}{(1/T)-(1/T')} = \frac{(8.3145\ \mathrm{J\,K^{-1}mol^{-1}}) \times \ln\{(0.36\ \mathrm{s})/(3.49\ \mathrm{s})\}}{(2548\ \mathrm{K})^{-1} - (2362\ \mathrm{K})^{-1}}$$
$$= 611 \times 10^3\ \mathrm{J\,mol^{-1}} = \mathbf{611\ kJ\,mol^{-1}}$$

The activation energy for desorption is high, and therefore characteristic of a tightly bound, chemisorbed molecule.

(b) Rearranging eqn 18.14, and substituting, the pre-exponential factor is

$$\tau_0(T) = t_{1/2}e^{-E_d/RT}$$
$$= 0.36 \times e^{-(611\times10^3\ \mathrm{J\,mol^{-1}})/\{(8.3145\ \mathrm{J\,K^{-1}mol^{-1}})\times(2548\ \mathrm{K})\}} = \mathbf{1.1 \times 10^{-13}\ s}$$

**E18.17** By analogy with eqn 18.14, we may express the time taken for a certain amount of gas to desorb as

$$t(T) = t_0 e^{E_d/RT}$$

Following the same approach as in the previous exercise, we may express the activation energy for desorption in terms of the time for the gas to desorb at different temperatures

$$E_d = \frac{R\ln\{t(T)/t(T')\}}{(1/T)-(1/T')} = \frac{(8.3145\ \mathrm{J\,K^{-1}mol^{-1}}) \times \ln\{(27\ \mathrm{min})/(2.0\ \mathrm{min})\}}{(1856\ \mathrm{K})^{-1} - (1978\ \mathrm{K})^{-1}}$$
$$= 651 \times 10^3\mathrm{J\,mol^{-1}} = \mathbf{651\ kJ\,mol^{-1}}$$

It follows, by rearrangement and substitution, that

$$t_0 = t(T)e^{-E_d/RT}$$
$$= (27\ \mathrm{min}) \times e^{-(651\times10^3\ \mathrm{J\,mol^{-1}})/\{(8.3145\ \mathrm{J\,K^{-1}mol^{-1}})\times(1856\ \mathrm{K})\}} = 1.29 \times 10^{-17}\ \mathrm{min}$$

Thus, the time taken for the same amount to desorb (a) at 298 K is

$$t(298\ \mathrm{K}) = (1.29 \times 10^{-17}\ \mathrm{min}) \times e^{(651\times10^3\ \mathrm{J\,mol^{-1}})/\{(8.3145\ \mathrm{J\,K^{-1}mol^{-1}})\times(298\ \mathrm{K})\}}$$
$$= \mathbf{1.4 \times 10^{97}\ min}$$

implying that at this temperature, the molecules remain bound to the surface and do not desorb. (b) In the same way at 3000 K,

$$t(3000\ \mathrm{K}) = (1.29 \times 10^{-17}\ \mathrm{min}) \times e^{(651\times10^3\ \mathrm{J\,mol^{-1}})/\{(8.3145\ \mathrm{J\,K^{-1}mol^{-1}})\times(3000\ \mathrm{K})\}}$$
$$= \mathbf{2.8 \times 10^{-6}\ min}$$

**E18.18** The sticking probability is defined, through eqn 18.12, as the ratio of the rate at which molecules are adsorbed on a surface to the rate at which they collide with the surface. We may, however, express the rate at which molecules strike the surface as the product of the collisional flux, which is given by eqn 18.1, and the surface area. Thus,

$$s = \frac{\overbrace{\text{Rate of adsorption of particles by the surface}}^{vN_A}}{\underbrace{\text{Rate of collision of particles with the surface}}_{Z_W A}} = \frac{vN_A}{p/(2\pi mkT)^{1/2}A}$$

$$= \frac{vN_A\{2\pi(M/N_A)kT\}^{1/2}}{pA} = \frac{v(2\pi M_{NH_3}N_AkT)^{1/2}}{pA} = \frac{v(2\pi M_{NH_3}RT)^{1/2}}{pA}$$

$$= \frac{(0.33\times10^{-3}\,\text{mol s}^{-1})\times\{2\pi\times(17.03\times10^{-3}\,\text{kg mol}^{-1})\times(8.3145\,\text{J K}^{-1}\text{mol}^{-1})\times(210\,\text{K})\}^{1/2}}{(10.0\,\text{Pa})\times\underbrace{(10\times10^{-4}\text{m}^2)}_{1\,\text{cm}^2=10^{-4}\,\text{m}^2}}$$

$$= \mathbf{0.45}$$

**E18.19** Desorption is a first-order process so that, using the Langmuir isotherm, eqn 18.3, to express the fraction of the surface covered,

$$\text{Rate of desorption} = k_d\theta = k_d\frac{\alpha p}{1+\alpha p}$$

Hydrogen iodide is very strongly adsorbed on gold, so we may assume that $\alpha p \gg 1$. Thus, $1+\alpha p \approx 1$, so that

$$\text{Rate of desorption} \approx k_d\frac{\alpha p}{\alpha p} = k_d$$

The rate of desorption of hydrogen iodide on gold is therefore zeroth order.

In contrast, hydrogen iodide is very weakly adsorbed on platinum. Thus, assuming that $\alpha p \ll 1$ so that $1+\alpha p \approx \alpha p$,

$$\text{Rate of desorption} \approx k_d\frac{\alpha p}{1} = k_d\alpha p$$

The rate of desorption of hydrogen iodide on platinum is therefore proportional to pressure and thus first order.

**E18.20** (a) The rate law for the Langmuir–Hinshelwood mechanism for surface-catalyzed reactions is given by eqn 18.16,

$$\text{Rate} = v = \frac{k_r\alpha_A\alpha_B p_A p_B}{(1+\alpha_A p_A+\alpha_B p_B)^2}$$

(b) In the limit that the pressures of both species are low, so that $p_A \to 0$ and $p_B \to 0$ and therefore $(1+\alpha_A p_A+\alpha_B p_B) \approx 1$, the rate law becomes

$$\text{Rate} = v = \frac{k_r\alpha_A\alpha_B p_A p_B}{\underbrace{(1+\alpha_A p_A+\alpha_B p_B)^2}_{\approx 1}} = k_r\alpha_A\alpha_B p_A p_B$$

which is first order with respect to the pressure of species A and species B.

(c) The rate law is highly non-linear and is not zeroth order for any limiting conditions. Only for the very particular case in which $\alpha_A p_A = \alpha_B p_B \gg 1$ so that

$$\text{Rate} = v = \frac{k_r \alpha_A \alpha_B p_A p_B}{(1 + \alpha_A p_A + \alpha_B p_B)^2} = \frac{k_r(\alpha_A p_A)^2}{(1 + 2\alpha_A p_A)^2} \approx \frac{k_r(\alpha_A p_A)^2}{(2\alpha_A p_A)^2} = \frac{k_r}{4}$$

is the rate law zeroth order.

**E18.21** In the limit of a large positive overpotential, the Butler–Volmer equation, eqn 18.18, may be simplified to

$$j = j_0\{e^{(1-\alpha)f\eta} - e^{\alpha f\eta}\} \approx j_0 e^{(1-\alpha)f\eta}$$

because the contribution from the second exponential term becomes negligible. Rearranging, we may write an expression for the overpotential required for different current densities

$$\eta = \frac{\ln(j/j_0)}{(1-\alpha)f} = \frac{\ln j - \ln j_0}{(1-\alpha)f}$$
$$\eta' = \frac{\ln(j'/j_0)}{(1-\alpha)f} = \frac{\ln j' - \ln j_0}{(1-\alpha)f}$$

Thus, combining these two equations,

$$\eta - \eta' = \frac{\ln j - \ln j_0}{(1-\alpha)f} - \frac{\ln j' - \ln j_0}{(1-\alpha)f} = \frac{\ln j - \ln j'}{(1-\alpha)f} = \frac{\ln(j/j')}{(1-\alpha)f}$$

Hence,

$$\eta = \eta' + \frac{\ln(j/j')}{(1-\alpha)f}$$
$$= (115 \times 10^{-3}\ \text{V}) + \frac{\ln\{(38\ \text{mA cm}^{-2})/(17.0\ \text{mA cm}^{-2})\}}{(1-0.48) \times (38.9\ \text{V}^{-1})} = 0.154\ \text{V} = \mathbf{154\ mV}$$

**E18.22** We may determine the value of the exchange current density from the data given, by rearranging the simplified form of the Butler–Volmer equation

$$j_0 = j/e^{(1-\alpha)f\eta} = je^{-(1-\alpha)f\eta}$$
$$= (17.0\ \text{mA cm}^{-2}) \times e^{-(1-0.48)\times(38.9\ \text{V}^{-1})\times(115\times10^{-3}\ \text{V})} = \mathbf{1.66\ mA\ cm^2}$$

**E18.23** Applying the Butler–Volmer equation, eqn 18.18,

$$j = j_0\{e^{(1-\alpha)f\eta} - e^{\alpha f\eta}\}$$

(a) for an overpotential of 10 mV,

$$j = (0.79\ \text{mA cm}^{-2}) \times \{e^{(1-0.5)\times(38.9\ \text{V}^{-1})\times(10\times10^{-3}\ \text{V})} - e^{0.5\times(38.9\ \text{V}^{-1})\times(10\times10^{-3}\ \text{V})}\}$$
$$= \mathbf{0.31\ mA\ cm^{-2}}$$

(b) for an overpotential of 100 mV,

$$j = (0.79\ \text{mA cm}^{-2}) \times \{e^{(1-0.5)\times(38.9\ \text{V}^{-1})\times(100\times10^{-3}\ \text{V})} - e^{0.5\times(38.9\ \text{V}^{-1})\times(100\times10^{-3}\ \text{V})}\}$$
$$= \mathbf{5.41\ mA\ cm^{-2}}$$

(c) for an overpotential of −5.0 V,

$$j = (0.79\ \text{mA cm}^{-2}) \times \{e^{(1-0.5)\times(38.9\ \text{V}^{-1})\times(-5\ \text{V})} - e^{0.5\times(38.9\ \text{V}^{-1})\times(-5\ \text{V})}\}$$
$$= \mathbf{4.6\times10^{-43}A\ cm^{-2}}$$

**E18.24** The rate at which electrons (or protons) are transported the double layer is given

$$v = j_0A/e$$

where $j_0$ is the exchange current density, which is the flux of electrons per unit area, and $A$ is the area of the electrode. If each atom in the electrode surface occupies an area of (280 pm)$^2$, then the number of surface sites is $N = A\,/\,(280 \times 10^{-12}\ \text{pm})^2$, so that the number of electron-transfer events for each atom every second is

$$\frac{v}{N} = \frac{j_0A}{e\{A/(280\ \text{pm}^2)\}} = (j_0/e)\times(280\ \text{pm}^2)$$

Thus, using the values for the exchange current density from Table 18.5:

(a) For the electrode Pt | $H_2$(g) | $H^+$(aq), the rate at which electrons are transferred is

$$v = \frac{(7.9\times10^{-4}\ \text{A cm}^{-2})\times(1.0\ \text{cm}^2)}{(1.602\times10^{-19}\ \text{C})} = \mathbf{4.9\times10^{15}s^{-1}}$$

and the number of events for each atom is

$$\frac{v}{N} = \frac{\overbrace{(7.9\ \text{A m}^{-2})}^{10^{-4}\ \text{A cm}^{-2} = 1\ \text{A m}^{-2}}\times(280\times10^{-12}\ \text{m})^2}{(1.602\times10^{-19}\ \text{C})} = \mathbf{3.9\ s^{-1}}$$

(b) For the electrode Pt | $Fe^{3+}$(aq), $Fe^{2+}$(aq),

$$v = \frac{(2.5\times10^{-3}\ \text{A cm}^{-2})\times(1.0\ \text{cm}^2)}{(1.602\times10^{-19}\ \text{C})} = \mathbf{1.6\times10^{16}s^{-1}}$$

and

$$\frac{v}{N} = \frac{(2.5\ \text{A m}^{-2})\times(280\times10^{-12}\ \text{m})^2}{(1.602\times10^{-19}\ \text{C})} = \mathbf{13\ s^{-1}}$$

(c) For the electrode Pb | $H_2$(g) | $H^+$(aq)

$$v = \frac{(5.0\times10^{-12}\ \text{A cm}^{-2})\times(1.0\ \text{cm}^2)}{(1.602\times10^{-19}\ \text{C})} = \mathbf{3.1\times10^{7}s^{-1}}$$

and

$$\frac{v}{N} = \frac{(5.0 \times 10^{-12}\ \mathrm{A\,m^{-2}}) \times (280 \times 10^{-12}\ \mathrm{m})^2}{(1.602 \times 10^{-19}\ \mathrm{C})} = \mathbf{2.4 \times 10^{-8}\ s^{-1}}$$

**E18.25** The data given correspond to large positive overpotentials, and it is thus reasonable to use the simplified form of the Butler–Volmer equation, eqn 18.18,

$$j = j_0\{\mathrm{e}^{(1-\alpha)f\eta} - \mathrm{e}^{\alpha f\eta}\} \approx j_0\mathrm{e}^{(1-\alpha)f\eta}$$

Hence, taking logarithms,

$$\overbrace{\ln j}^{y} = \overbrace{\ln j_0}^{\text{intercept}} + \overbrace{(1-\alpha)f}^{\text{slope}}\,\overbrace{\eta}^{x}$$

This expression has the same form as the equation for a straight-line graph. The exchange current density may then be determined from the intercept and the transfer coefficient from the gradient. Figure 18.6 shows how the logarithm of current density varies with overpotential. The intercept of the plot is –0.2303, so that

$$j_0/\mathrm{mA\,cm^{-2}} = \mathrm{e}^{-0.2303} = 0.794$$

giving an exchange current density of **0.794 mA cm$^{-2}$**. The slope of the plot is $24.2 \times 10^{-3}$ mV$^{-1}$. Thus, the transfer coefficient is

$$\alpha = 1 - \frac{\text{slope}}{f} = 1 - \frac{24.2\ \mathrm{V^{-1}}}{38.9\ \mathrm{V^{-1}}} = \mathbf{0.378}$$

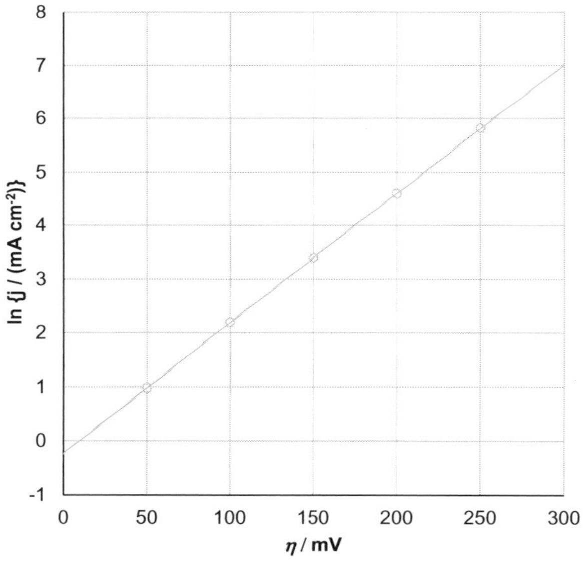


**Figure 18.6**

**E18.26** The reduction of indium is a three-electron process

$$In^{3+}(aq) + 3\,e^- \rightarrow In\,(s)$$

The Butler–Volmer equation, eqn 18.18, must therefore be modified to take account of the number of electrons, $z$, that are transferred. Thus,

$$j = j_0\{e^{z(1-\alpha)f\eta} - e^{z\alpha f\eta}\}$$

No current flows for a potential of $E = -0.388$ V. The remaining values are greater than, this value in the sense that they are more positive, and therefore all correspond to positive overpotentials. Thus, we may simplify the Butler–Volmer equation further and write

$$j = j_0 e^{z(1-\alpha)f\eta}$$

so that, taking logarithms,

$$\begin{aligned}\ln j &= \ln j_0 + z(1-\alpha)f\eta \\ &= \ln j_0 + z(1-\alpha)f(E' - E)\end{aligned}$$

This expression as the same form as the equation for a straight-line graph,

$$\overbrace{\ln j}^{y} = \overbrace{\{\ln j_0 - z(1-\alpha)fE\}}^{\text{intercept}} + \overbrace{\{z(1-\alpha)f\}}^{\text{slope}}\,\overbrace{E'}^{x}$$

Figure 18.7 shows a plot of the logarithm of the current density against applied potential.

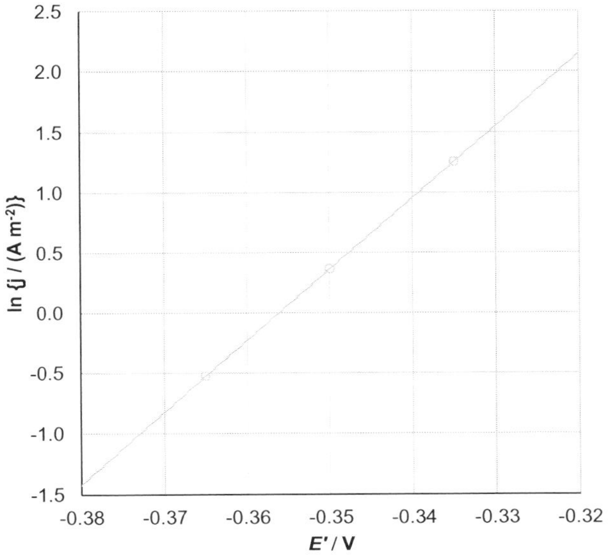


**Figure 18.7**

The slope of the graph is 59.41 $V^{-1}$, so that

$$z(1-\alpha)f = \text{slope}$$

$$\alpha = 1 - \frac{\text{slope}}{zf} = 1 - \frac{59.41\ \text{V}^{-1}}{3 \times (38.9\ \text{V}^{-1})} = \mathbf{0.491}$$

The intercept of the graph is 21.16, so that

$$\begin{aligned} \ln j_0 - z(1-\alpha)fE &= \text{intercept} \\ \ln j_0 - \text{slope} \times E &= \text{intercept} \\ \ln j_0 &= \text{intercept} + (\text{slope} \times E) \\ &= 21.16 + \{(59.41\ \text{V}^{-1}) \times (-0.388\ \text{V})\} = -1.89 \end{aligned}$$

Thus,

$$j_0/(\text{A m}^{-2}) = \text{e}^{-1.89} = 0.151$$

and the exchange current density is **0.151 A m$^{-2}$**.

The magnitude of the cathodic current density for a potential of 0.365 V is therefore

$$\begin{aligned} j_\text{c} &= j_0\text{e}^{-z\alpha f\eta} = j_0\text{e}^{z\alpha f(E'-E)} \\ &= (0.151\ \text{A m}^{-2}) \times \text{e}^{-3\times0.491\times(38.9\ \text{V}^{-1})\times\{-0.365-(-0.388)\}} \\ &= 40.4 \times 10^{-3}\ \text{A m}^{-2} = \mathbf{40.4\ mA\ m^{-2}} \end{aligned}$$

**E18.27** For large positive overpotentials, we may ignore the contribution from the cathodic current and use the simplified form of the Butler–Volmer equation, eqn 18.18,

$$j = j_0\{\text{e}^{(1-\alpha)f\eta} - \text{e}^{\alpha f\eta}\} \approx j_0\text{e}^{(1-\alpha)f\eta}$$

Taking logarithms, yields an expression with the same form as the equation for a straight-line graph

$$\overbrace{\ln j}^{y} = \overbrace{\ln j_0}^{\text{intercept}} + \overbrace{(1-\alpha)f}^{\text{slope}}\,\overbrace{\eta}^{x}$$

Figure 18.8 shows a Tafel plot of the logarithm of current density against overpotential. The intercept of the plot is –10.83, so that

$$j_0/(\text{mA cm}^{-2}) = \text{e}^{-10.83} = 1.98 \times 10^{-5}$$

giving an exchange current density of **19.8 nA cm$^{-2}$**. The slope of the plot is $19.6 \times 10^{-3}$ mV$^{-1}$ so that the transfer coefficient is

$$\alpha = 1 - \frac{\text{slope}}{f} = 1 - \frac{19.6\ \text{V}^{-1}}{38.9\ \text{V}^{-1}} = \mathbf{0.496}$$

The plot is linear throughout the range of overpotentials, implying that there are no deviations from the Tafel equation.

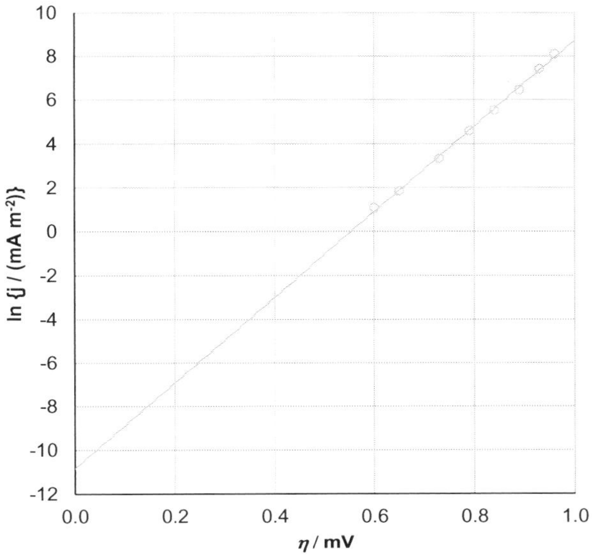


**Figure 18.8**

**E18.28** (a) The cyclic voltammogram is characteristic of a process that is reversible in both the forward and reverse directions. The electroactive species is reduced during the forward sweep of potential. The process must be reversible because the reduced species shows oxidization upon reversing the direction of the potential sweep. The peak reduction current and peak oxidation current lie symmetrically about the standard reduction potential.

(b) The electroactive species experiences a second reduction at high potential during the forward sweep of potential. Both reductions are reversible and, consequently, show oxidation currents upon reversing the potential scan toward low potentials.

(c) Reduction of the electroactive species is observed during the forward potential sweep. However, the process is not reversible and so oxidation current is observed upon reversing the sweep.

(d) The electroactive species experiences a second reduction at high potential during the forward sweep of potential. Upon reversing the potential sweep, the highly reduced species is reversibly oxidized with the loss of one electron but loss of a second electron is not observed at low potential. Thus, the complete reoxidation of the species is irreversible.

## Answers to projects

**P18.29** (a) The force acting between two charges is

$$F = -\frac{dV}{dr} = -\frac{d}{dr}\frac{Q_1Q_2}{4\pi\epsilon_0 r} = \frac{Q_1Q_2}{4\pi\epsilon_0 r^2}$$

Thus, the force acting between two electrons separated by a distance of 0.50 nm is

$$F = \frac{(-e)^2}{4\pi\epsilon_0 r^2}$$
$$= \frac{(1.602\times10^{-19}\,\text{C})^2}{4\pi\times(8.854\times10^{-12}\,\text{J}^{-1}\,\text{C}^2\,\text{m}^{-1})\times(0.50\times10^{-9}\text{m})^2} = \mathbf{9.2\times10^{-10}N}$$

The force is inversely proportional to the square of the separation. Thus, when the separation is increased to 0.60 nm, the force changes by a factor of

$$(0.50\text{ nm})^2/(0.60\text{ nm})^2 = \mathbf{0.69}$$

(b) If, instead, we assume that the potential energy may be described by a Lennard-Jones potential, eqn 15.16,

$$V = 4\epsilon\left\{\left(\frac{\sigma}{r}\right)^{12} - \left(\frac{\sigma}{r}\right)^{6}\right\}$$

then the force is

$$F = -\frac{dV}{dr} = -\frac{d}{dr}4\epsilon\left\{\left(\frac{\sigma}{r}\right)^{12} - \left(\frac{\sigma}{r}\right)^{6}\right\} = -4\epsilon\left(\sigma^{12}\frac{d}{dr}r^{-12} - \sigma^{6}\frac{d}{dr}r^{-6}\right)$$
$$= -4\epsilon(\sigma^{12}\times -12r^{-13} - \sigma^{6}\times -6r^{-7}) = \frac{24\epsilon}{\sigma}\left\{2\left(\frac{\sigma}{r}\right)^{13} - \left(\frac{\sigma}{r}\right)^{7}\right\}$$

**P18.30** We may obtain an expression for the pseudo-equilibrium constant for adsorption, $\alpha$, as a function of pressure by rearranging the Langmuir isotherm, 18.3,

$$\alpha = \frac{\theta}{(1-\theta)p}$$

Because the surface coverage is constant, this expression is of the form $\alpha = kp^{-1}$, where $k = \theta/(1-\theta)$. Thus, substituting

$$\frac{d\ln\alpha}{dT} = \frac{d}{dT}\ln\overbrace{(kp^{-1})}^{\alpha} = \frac{d}{dT}(\ln k + \ln p^{-1}) = \overbrace{\frac{d}{dT}\ln k}^{=0\text{ because k is constant}} + \frac{d\ln p}{dT} = \frac{d\ln p}{dT}$$

Hence, substituting into the van 't Hoff equation,

$$\frac{d\ln p}{dT} = \frac{\Delta_{ads}H^{\ominus}}{RT^2}$$

**P18.31** The standard cell potential is related to the standard Gibbs energy of reaction through eqn 9.16

$$E^{\ominus}_{\text{cell}} = -\frac{\Delta_r G^{\ominus}}{vF}$$

(a) For the cell reaction,

$$H_2(g) + O_2(g) \rightarrow H_2O(l)$$

the standard Gibbs energy of reaction is equal to the Gibbs energy of formation of liquid water, $\Delta_r G^{\ominus} = \Delta_f G^{\ominus}(H_2O, l) = -237$ kJ mol$^{-1}$. As written, the cell reaction is a two-electron process, so that

$$E^{\ominus}_{\text{cell}} = -\frac{-237 \times 10^3 \text{ J mol}^{-1}}{2 \times (9.6485 \times 10^4 \text{ C mol}^{-1})} = \mathbf{+1.23\ V}$$

The standard Gibbs energy of reaction for the process

$$CH_4(g) + 2\ O_2(g) \rightarrow CO_2(g) + 2\ H_2O(l)$$

may be calculated from the standard Gibbs energies of formation of the products and reactants. Thus

$$\begin{aligned}\Delta_r G^{\ominus} &= \{2\Delta_f G^{\ominus}(H_2O, l) + \Delta_f G^{\ominus}(CO_2, g)\} - \{2\Delta_f G^{\ominus}(CH_4, g) + \Delta_f G^{\ominus}(O_2, g)\}\\ &= [\{2 \times (-237.1) + (-394.4)\} - \{(-50.7) + 0\}] \text{ kJ mol}^{-1}\\ &= -817.9 \text{ kJ mol}^{-1}\end{aligned}$$

As written, the reaction corresponds to the transfer of eight electrons. It follows that, for the species in their standard states,

$$E^{\ominus}_{\text{cell}} = -\frac{-817.9 \times 10^3 \text{ J mol}^{-1}}{8 \times (9.6485 \times 10^4 \text{ C mol}^{-1})} = \mathbf{+1.06V}$$

(b) (i) Applying the Butler–Volmer equation, eqn 18.18,

$$\begin{aligned}j &= j_0\{e^{(1-\alpha)f\eta} - e^{\alpha f\eta}\}\\ &= (6.3 \times 10^{-6} \text{ A cm}^{-2}) \times \{e^{(1-0.58)\times(38.9\text{ V}^{-1})\times(0.20\text{ V})} - e^{-0.58\times(38.9\text{ V}^{-1})\times(0.20\text{ V})}\}\\ &= 0.17 \times 10^{-3} \text{ A cm}^{-2} = \mathbf{0.17\ mA\ cm^{-2}}\end{aligned}$$

(ii) If, however, we assume that the overpotential is sufficiently large and positive such that the cathodic current may be neglected, we may use the Tafel equation

$$\begin{aligned}j &= j_0 e^{(1-\alpha)f\eta}\\ &= (6.3 \times 10^{-6} \text{ A cm}^{-2}) \times e^{(1-0.58)\times(38.9\text{ V}^{-1})\times(0.20\text{ V})}\\ &= 0.17 \times 10^{-3} \text{ A cm}^{-2} = \mathbf{0.17\ mA\ cm^{-2}}\end{aligned}$$

Comparison of these two results shows that there is negligible difference between the Butler–Volmer eqn and the Tafel eqn when $\eta = 0.20$ V. The validity of the Tafel equation is unaffected by overpotentials that are greater than 0.20 V.

# Chapter 19

# Spectroscopy: molecular rotations and vibrations

## Answers to discussion questions

**D19.1** (a) For *microwave rotational spectroscopy*, the allowed transitions depend on the existence of an oscillating dipole moment, which can cause the electromagnetic field to oscillate (and vice versa for absorption). This implies that the molecule must have a permanent dipole moment, which is equivalent to an oscillating dipole when the molecule is rotating.

(b) The gross selection rule for *rotational Raman spectroscopy* is that the molecule must be anisotropically polarizable, which is to say that its polarizability, $\alpha$, depends upon the direction of the electric field relative to the molecule. Non-spherical rotors satisfy this condition. Therefore, linear and symmetric rotors are rotationally Raman active.

**D19.2** *Doppler broadening*. This contribution to the linewidth is due to the Doppler effect, which shifts the frequency of the radiation emitted or absorbed when the atoms or molecules involved are moving towards or away from the detecting device. Molecules have a wide range of speeds in all directions in a gas and the detected spectral line is the absorption or emission profile arising from all the resulting Doppler shifts. The shape of a Doppler-broadened spectral line reflects the Maxwell distribution of speeds in the sample at the temperature of the experiment; hence the line broadens as the temperature is increased because the molecules acquire a wider range of speeds. Therefore, to decrease the linewidth, the temperature of the sample should be decreased.

*Lifetime broadening*. Doppler broadening is significant in gas-phase samples, but lifetime broadening occurs in all states of matter. This kind of broadening is a quantum-mechanical effect related to the uncertainty principle and is due to the finite lifetimes of the states involved in the transition. When the lifetime is finite, the energy of the states is smeared out and hence the transition frequency is broadened as shown in eqn 19.16.

*Pressure broadening or collisional broadening*. The actual mechanism affecting the lifetime of energy states depends on various processes, one of which is collisional deactivation and another is spontaneous emission. Lowering the pressure can reduce the first of these contributions; the second cannot be changed and results in a natural linewidth. The rate of spontaneous emission cannot be changed; hence it is a natural limit to the breadth of a spectral line.

**D19.3** Strictly, the term *equilibrium bond length* refers to the separation between the atoms for which the potential energy of interaction is a minimum. Mechanical equilibrium implies that no forces are acting, and only at the equilibrium bond length is this the case. The equilibrium bond length is therefore a constant and corresponds to the position of the bottom of the potential well, marked $R_e$, in Figure 19.16 of the text. All molecules, however, possess zero-point energy as a result of their vibrational motion. There is thus not a quantum state that corresponds to this position.

The actual bond length of the molecule varies with both vibrational and rotational state. Anharmonicity means that the bond length of a molecule increases with vibrational quantum number, until at the top of the potential well, the atoms of the molecule dissociate and the separation effectively becomes infinite. The bond length also increases with rotational quantum number because of centrifugal distortion. The bond in a molecule is not completely stiff, and as the molecule rotates, the atoms within it are flung further apart, resulting in an increase in the bond length.

**D19.4** The rotational constants in vibrationally excited states are smaller than in the vibrational ground state and continue to get smaller as the vibrational level increases. Any anharmonicity in the vibration causes a slight extension of the bond length in the excited state. This results in an increase in the moment of inertia, and a consequent decrease in the rotational constant. The change in rotational constant with vibrational state is described using the equation

$$B_v = B_e - \alpha(v + ½)$$

where $B_e$ and $\alpha$ are constants and $B_v$ is the rotational constant for states with vibrational quantum number $v$. The constant $\alpha$ is related to the anharmonicity of the potential energy. For a harmonic oscillator with a strictly parabolic potential well, the mean bond length of the molecule does not change with vibrational state. Thus, $\alpha = 0$ for a strictly parabolic, harmonic potential and the rotational constant is independent of the vibrational state.

**D19.5** A total of $3N$ coordinates are necessary to specify the location in space of a molecule of $N$ atoms. In general, for a non-linear molecule, three of these coordinates are necessarily translational coordinates, corresponding to the position of the centre of mass of the molecule. A further three coordinates are required to specify the angular orientation of a non-linear molecule in space and thus describe the rotation of the molecule. The remaining $3N - 3 - 3 = 3N - 6$ coordinates therefore describe the vibration of the molecule.

For a linear molecule, three coordinates are once again required to describe translation. However, only two coordinates are required to describe rotation because a linear molecule may rotate only about the two axes perpendicular to the internuclear axis. Thus, there remain $3N - 3 - 2 = 3N - 5$ coordinates to describe the vibration of the molecule. A linear molecule therefore possesses one fewer rotational degree of freedom and one more vibrational degree of freedom than a non-linear molecule with the same number of atoms. The specification of the third angle in the nonlinear molecule effectively eliminates one of the two perpendicular bending motions that the molecule would have if it were linear. This is most easily pictured for the linear triatomic, $CO_2$, which has two perpendicular bending motions. If the molecule were permanently bent into an angular molecule, only one bending motion would remain, a bending motion that changes the dihedral angle.

**D19.6** (a) In the case of *infrared vibrational spectroscopy*, the physical basis of the gross selection rule is that the molecule must have a structure that allows for the existence of an oscillating dipole moment when the molecule vibrates. Polar molecules necessarily satisfy this requirement, but non-polar molecules may also have a fluctuating dipole moment upon vibration.

The gross selection rule for *vibrational Raman spectroscopy* is that the polarizability of the molecule must change as the molecule vibrates. All diatomic molecules satisfy this condition as the molecules swell and contract during a vibration, the control of the nuclei over the electrons varies, and the molecular polarizability changes. Hence both homonuclear and heteronuclear diatomic molecules are vibrationally Raman active. In polyatomic molecules it is usually quite difficult to judge by inspection whether or not the molecular polarizability changes upon vibration; hence group theoretical methods are relied on for judging the Raman activity of the various normal modes of vibration. The procedure is an advanced topic but the **exclusion rule** can be useful. It states that, if the molecule has a centre of inversion, then no modes can be both infrared and Raman active.

(b) The exclusion rule applies to the benzene molecule because it has a centre of inversion. Consequently, none of the normal modes of vibration of benzene can be both infrared and Raman active. If we wish to characterize all the normal modes, we must obtain both kinds of spectra.

**D19.7** In general, vibrational frequencies are determined by the effective masses of the group of atoms participating in the mode of vibration. Since the mass of $^{13}C$ is greater than the mass of $^{12}C$, in general we expect that vibrational frequencies would be different in $^{13}CO_2$ than in $^{12}CO_2$. However, in the symmetric stretch of $CO_2$, the C atom is stationary, and the effective mass of the mode depends only on the O atoms. Consequently we expect that the vibrational frequency of this mode would be independent of the mass of the carbon atom.

**D19.8** The vibration-rotation energy levels of a linear molecule are given by eqn 19.25,

$$E_{v,J} = (v + ½)h\nu + hBJ(J + 1)$$

In general, the rotation transitions accompanying a change of vibrational state correspond to $\Delta J = \pm 1$ and $\Delta J = 0$. As a result, three sets of lines may occur in the vibration–rotation spectrum. The set for which $\Delta J = -1$ correspond to a decrease in rotational energy, and are called the P branch. For a fundamental band transition with $\Delta v = +1$, the lines in the $P$ branch have energies

$$\begin{aligned}\Delta E_{\mathrm{P}} &= E_{v+1,J-1} - E_{v,J} \\ &= \overbrace{[\{(v+1)\tfrac{1}{2}\}h\nu + hB(J-1)J]}^{\substack{\text{energy of state with} \\ \text{vibrational quantum number } v+1 \\ \text{and rotational quantum number } J-1}} - \overbrace{[\{v+\tfrac{1}{2}\}h\nu + hBJ(J+1)]}^{\substack{\text{energy of state with} \\ \text{vibrational quantum number } v \\ \text{and rotational quantum number } J}} \\ &= h\nu - 2BJ\end{aligned}$$

where $J$ is the rotational quantum number of the lower state. The expression is more complicated if we take account of the change in the rotational constant of the molecule on vibrational excitation. The set with $\Delta J = +1$ correspond to an increase in rotational energy and are called the R branch. We can show that these lines have energies

$$\Delta E_{\mathrm{R}} = h\nu + 2BJ$$

The third set, with $\Delta J = 0$ correspond to vibrational transitions for which there is no accompanying change in rotational state. These transitions form the Q branch and all have energies

$$\Delta E_{\mathrm{Q}} = h\nu$$

The Q branch, however, is not always seen. The selection rule $\Delta J = 0$ corresponds to an allowed transition only when the molecule possesses angular momentum about its axis. It is, for example, observed in the vibration–rotation spectrum of the bending mode of $CO_2$, where the degeneracy of the two perpendicular bending modes results in an effective angular momentum about the axis. A Q branch is not, however, observed in either of the stretching vibrations in $CO_2$. A Q branch is also observed in open-shell molecules that possess electronic orbital angular momentum, such as the paramagnetic molecule, NO.

## Solutions to exercises

**E19.1** Applying eqn 19.2, the frequency of radiation of wavelength $\lambda = 442$ nm is

$$\begin{aligned}\nu &= c/\lambda \\ &= (2.998\times10^{8}\ \mathrm{m\ s^{-1}})/(442\times10^{-9}\mathrm{m}) = 6.78\times10^{14}\ \mathrm{s^{-1}} = \mathbf{6.78\times10^{14}\ Hz}\end{aligned}$$

and the wavenumber is

$$\tilde{\nu} = 1/\lambda = 1/(442\times10^{-9}\mathrm{m}) = 2.26\times10^{6}\mathrm{m^{-1}} = \mathbf{22600\ cm^{-1}}$$

**E19.2** (a) Rearranging eqn 19.2, the wavenumber is

$$\begin{aligned}\tilde{\nu} &= \nu/c \\ &= (88.0\times10^{6}\ \mathrm{Hz})/(2.998\times10^{8}\ \mathrm{m\ s^{-1}}) = 0.294\ \mathrm{m^{-1}} = \mathbf{2.94\times10^{-3}\ cm^{-1}}\end{aligned}$$

(b) and the wavelength is

$$\lambda = c/\nu = (2.998 \times 10^8 \text{ m s}^{-1})/(88.0 \times 10^6 \text{ Hz}) = \mathbf{3.41\ m}$$

**E19.3** The energy levels of a quantum mechanical rotor are given by eqn 19.3

$$E_J = hBJ(J+1)$$

with the rotational constant, $B$, depending upon the moment of inertia, $I$,

$$B = \frac{\hbar}{4\pi I} = \frac{\hbar}{4\pi mr^2}$$

Thus, combining these expressions and rearranging,

$$\begin{aligned} J(J+1) &= \frac{E_J}{hB} = \frac{8\pi^2 mR^2 E_J}{h^2} \\ &= \frac{8\pi^2 \times (0.75 \text{ kg}) \times (0.70 \text{ m})^2 \times (0.2 \text{ J})}{(6.626 \times 10^{-34} \text{J s})^2} = 1.3 \times 10^{67} \end{aligned}$$

It follows that $J \gg 1$, so that $J(J+1) \approx J^2$, and therefore

$$J = (1.3 \times 10^{67})^{1/2} = \mathbf{3.6 \times 10^{33}}$$

This high value is to be expected. The separation between quantum-mechanical energy levels is inversely proportional to the mass of the body. For a massive object such as a bicycle wheel, the energy levels are so close together that for most purposes we need not consider quantum-mechanical effects and a classical treatment is sufficient.

**E19.4** Expressions for the moments of inertia of various molecules are given in Table 19.1, with equilibrium bond lengths in Table 19.2

(a) Thus, for $^1H_2$, the moment of inertia is

$$\begin{aligned} I = \mu R^2 &= \frac{m_H m_H}{m_H + m_H} R^2 = \tfrac{1}{2} m_H R^2 \\ &= \tfrac{1}{2} \times (1.0078 m_u) \times (74.14 \times 10^{-12} \text{ m})^2 \\ &= \tfrac{1}{2} \times \{1.0078 \times (1.661 \times 10^{-27} \text{ kg})\} \times (74.14 \times 10^{-12} \text{ m})^2 \\ &= \mathbf{4.601 \times 10^{-48}\ kg\ m^2} \end{aligned}$$

(b) In the same way for $^2H_2$,

$$\begin{aligned} I = \mu R^2 &= \frac{m_{^2H} m_{^2H}}{m_{^2H} + m_{^2H}} R^2 = \tfrac{1}{2} m_{^2H} R^2 \\ &= \tfrac{1}{2} \times (2.0140 m_u) \times (74.14 \times 10^{-12} \text{ m})^2 \\ &= \tfrac{1}{2} \times \{2.0140 \times (1.661 \times 10^{-27} \text{ kg})\} \times (74.14 \times 10^{-12} \text{ m})^2 \\ &= \mathbf{9.196 \times 10^{-48}\ kg\ m^2} \end{aligned}$$

(c) For a symmetric linear triatomic molecule, $BA_2$, such as $^{12}C^{16}O_2$,

$$I = 2m_A R^2 = 2m_O R^2$$

$$= 2 \times (15.9949m_{\text{u}}) \times (116.00 \times 10^{-12}\ \text{m})^2$$
$$= 2 \times \{15.9949 \times (1.661 \times 10^{-27}\ \text{kg})\} \times (116.00 \times 10^{-12}\ \text{m})^2$$
$$= \mathbf{7.150 \times 10^{-46}\ kg\ m^2}$$

(d) We should expect the moment of inertia of $^{13}C^{16}O_2$ to be identical to that for $^{12}C^{16}O_2$. The isotopomers are identical apart from the mass of the central carbon atom and because this atom sits on the axis of rotation, it does not make a contribution to the moment of inertia.

**E19.5** The rotational constant is related to the moment of inertia through eqn 19.4. Thus, for $^1H_2$,

$$B = \frac{\hbar}{4\pi I} = \frac{h}{8\pi^2 I} = \frac{6.626 \times 10^{-34}\text{J s}}{8\pi^2 \times (4.601 \times 10^{-48}\ \text{kg m}^2)} = \mathbf{1.824 \times 10^{12}\ Hz}$$

which is equivalent to a wavenumber

$$\tilde{B} = B/c$$
$$= (1.824 \times 10^{12}\ \text{Hz})/(2.998 \times 10^8\ \text{m s}^{-1}) = 6084\ \text{m}^{-1} = \mathbf{60.84\ cm^{-1}}$$

For $^2H_2$,

$$B = \frac{\hbar}{4\pi I} = \frac{h}{8\pi^2 I} = \frac{6.626 \times 10^{-34}\text{J s}}{8\pi^2 \times (9.196 \times 10^{-48}\ \text{kg m}^2)} = \mathbf{9.126 \times 10^{11}\ Hz}$$

which is equivalent to a wavenumber

$$\tilde{B} = B/c$$
$$= (9.126 \times 10^{11}\ \text{Hz})/(2.998 \times 10^8\ \text{m s}^{-1}) = 3044\ \text{m}^{-1} = \mathbf{30.44\ cm^{-1}}$$

For $^{12}CO_2$ and $^{13}CO_2$,

$$B = \frac{\hbar}{4\pi I} = \frac{h}{8\pi^2 I} = \frac{6.626 \times 10^{-34}\text{J s}}{8\pi^2 \times (7.150 \times 10^{-46}\ \text{kg m}^2)} = \mathbf{1.174 \times 10^{10}\ Hz}$$

which is equivalent to a wavenumber

$$\tilde{B} = B/c$$
$$= (2.347 \times 10^{12}\ \text{Hz})/(2.998 \times 10^8\ \text{m s}^{-1}) = 39.15\ \text{m}^{-1} = \mathbf{0.3915\ cm^{-1}}$$

**E19.6** (a) An octahedral $AB_6$ molecule is classed as a spherical rotor in which all three moments of inertia are equal. The inertial axes correspond to the three orthogonal B–A–B axes. The atoms that lie on these axes do not contribute to the moment of inertia. The A–B bonds to the four remaining B atoms are all perpendicular to this axis. Thus, the perpendicular distance from the axis to these atoms is the bond length *R*. Hence, from eqn 19.5,

$$I = \sum_i m_i r_i^2 = 4m_{\text{B}} r_{\text{B}}^2$$

which is the result in Table 19.1.

(b) Thus, combining eqns 19.2 and 19.3, for $^{32}S^{19}F_6$,

$$B = \frac{\hbar}{4\pi I} = \frac{\hbar}{4\pi(4m_F r_F^2)} = \frac{h}{32\pi^2 m_F r_F^2}$$
$$= \frac{6.626\times10^{-34}\,\mathrm{J\,s}}{32\pi^2\times(18.9984m_u)\times(158\times10^{-12}\,\mathrm{m})^2}$$
$$= \frac{6.626\times10^{-34}\,\mathrm{J\,s}}{32\pi^2\times\{18.9984\times(1.661\times10^{-27}\,\mathrm{kg})\}\times(158\times10^{-12}\,\mathrm{m})^2}$$
$$= \mathbf{2.66\times10^{9}\,s^{-1}}$$

which is equivalent to a wavenumber

$$\tilde{B} = B/c$$
$$= (2.66\times10^{9}\,\mathrm{Hz})/(2.998\times10^{8}\,\mathrm{m\,s^{-1}}) = 8.88\,\mathrm{m^{-1}} = \mathbf{0.0888\,cm^{-1}}$$

**E19.7** A square planar $AB_4$ molecule such as that shown in Figure 19.1 is classed as a symmetric rotor.

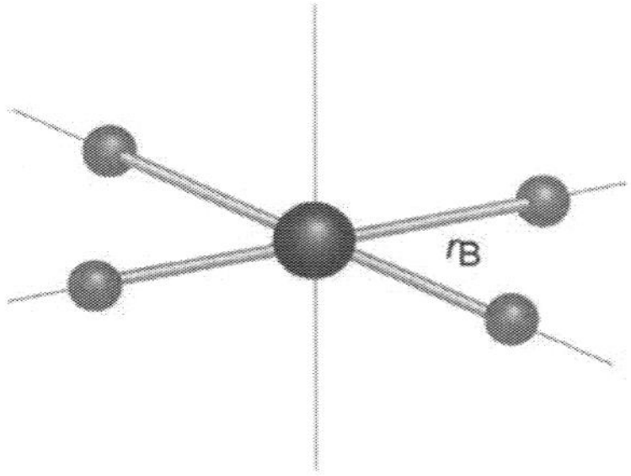


**Figure 19.1**

One inertial axis passes through the A atom at the centre of the molecule, perpendicular to the plane formed by the atoms. The other two inertial axes also pass through the centre of the molecule, but lie within the plane. These two axes are orthogonal to each other and, by symmetry, the corresponding moments of inertial are equal. These axes need not necessarily pass through the B–A–B bonds, but it is mathematically convenient to assume that they do so. Labelling the moments of inertia for the perpendicular and parallel axes as $I_\perp$ and $I_\parallel$, then using eqn 19.5, and identifying the distances of the atoms from the axes using Figure 19.1,

$$I_\perp = \sum_i m_i r_i^2 = \mathbf{4m_B r_B^2}$$

$$I_\parallel = \sum_i m_i r_i^2 = \mathbf{2m_B r_B^2}$$

The results demonstrate that, for a planar symmetric rotor such as this, $I_\perp = 2I_\parallel$.

**E19.8** Assuming $SO_3$ to be a planar molecule in which all three O atoms are identical, we may define two moments of inertia, $I_\perp$ and $I_\parallel$, corresponding to rotation about axes passing through the S atom at the centre of the molecule that are, respectively, either perpendicular or parallel to the plane containing the atoms. Thus, applying eqn 19.5,

$$I_\perp = \sum_i m_i r_i^2 = 3m_O r_O^2$$

$$I_\parallel = \sum_i m_i r_i^2 = 2m_O\{r_O \sin(\pi/3)\}^2 = (3/2)m_O r_O^2$$

It can be seen that $I_\perp = 2I_\parallel$, which is true for all planar symmetric rotors.

The rotational constant $A$ corresponds to rotation about an axis within the plane of the molecule, so that

$$A = \frac{\hbar}{4\pi I_\perp} = \frac{h}{8\pi^2(3m_O r_O^2)} = \frac{6.626\times10^{-34}\,\text{J s}}{24\pi^2\times15.9949 m_u r_O^2}$$
$$= \frac{6.626\times10^{-34}\,\text{J s}}{24\pi^2\times15.9949\times(1.661\times10^{-27}\,\text{kg})\times(143\times10^{-12}\text{m})^2}$$
$$= 5.149\times10^9\,\text{s}^{-1} = \mathbf{5.149\ GHz}$$

It follows that if $I_\perp = 2I_\parallel$, then $A = ½B$, so that

$$B = 2A = 2\times5.149\ \text{GHz} = \mathbf{10.30\ GHz}$$

(b) The sulfur atom lies on all of the inertial axes. Thus, the mass of the sulfur atom affects neither the moments of inertia, nor the rotational constants, so microwave spectroscopy could not be used to distinguish between $^{32}S^{16}O_3$ and $^{33}S^{16}O_3$.

**E19.9** For a molecule to have a pure rotational spectrum, it must possess a dipole moment. Thus, HCl, $N_2O$, $O_3$ and $SF_4$ all have pure rotational spectra. $XeF_4$ is non-polar because all of the Xe–F bonds are equivalent. Thus, it does not have a rotational spectrum.

**E19.10** For a molecule to have a rotational Raman spectrum, the polarizability must be anisotropic. This is true for all of the molecules, so all have a rotational Raman spectrum.

**E19.11** A rotational state is defined by the quantum numbers $J$, $K$ and $M_J$, although because the energy depends only upon $J$,

$$E_J = hBJ(J+1)$$

some levels are degenerate. Because the quantum number $K$, which represents the projection of the total rotational angular momentum on an internally defined axis, can take values $-J$ to $+J$, there are $(2J+1)$ possible values for a given $J$. The quantum number $M_J$ represents the projection of the rotational angular momentum on an externally defined axis in space and can also take $(2J+1)$ possible values from $-J$ to $+J$. Hence, for methane with $J = 8$, the number of degenerate states is

$$\overbrace{(2J+1)}^{\text{degeneracy due to }K} \times \overbrace{(2J+1)}^{\text{degeneracy due to }M_J} = (2J+1)^2 = \{(2\times 8)+1\}^2 = 17^2 = \mathbf{289}$$

**E19.12** For chloromethane, the energy levels depend upon both $J$ and $K$, through eqn 19.7

$$E_J = hBJ(J+1) + h(A-B)K^2$$

Thus, the levels with energy $hBJ(J+1)$ correspond to states with $K=0$. However, the energy does not depend upon the quantum number $M_J$, which corresponds to the projection of the total angular momentum on an external axis in space. There are $2J+1$ possible values of $M_J$, corresponding to $-J$ to $+J$. Hence, for chloromethane with $J=8$ and $K=0$, the number of degenerate states is

$$(2J+1) = (2\times 8)+1 = \mathbf{17}$$

**E19.13** The rotational energy levels of a rigid linear molecule are given by eqn 19.3

$$E_J = hBJ(J+1)$$

For pure rotational transitions, $\Delta J = \pm 1$, so that the transition frequencies observed in the rotational absorption spectrum are given by eqn 19.13a,

$$\begin{aligned}\nu_J = \Delta E/h &= \overbrace{\{B(J+1)(J+2)\}}^{E_{J+1}/h} - \overbrace{\{BJ(J+1)\}}^{E_J/h} \\ &= B(J^2+3J+2) - B(J^2+J) = 2B(J+1)\end{aligned}$$

Successive transitions differ by one in the quantum number $J$, so that the separation between the observed lines in the rotational spectrum is

$$\Delta\nu = \nu_{J+1} - \nu_J = 2B(J+2) - 2B(J+1) = 2B = 2\times(318.0\text{ GHz}) = \mathbf{636\ GHz}$$

This is equivalent to a wavenumber

$$\Delta\tilde{\nu} = \Delta\nu/c = \overbrace{(636\times 10^9\text{s}^{-1})}^{1\text{ GHz}=10^9\text{s}^{-1}}/(2.998\times 10^8\text{ m s}^{-1}) = 2120\text{ m}^{-1} = \mathbf{21.2\ cm^{-1}}$$

**E19.14** From eqn 19.4 and the definition of the moment of inertia for a diatomic molecule in Table 19.1,

$$\tilde{B} = B/c = \frac{\hbar}{4\pi I c} = \frac{h}{8\pi^2\mu R^2 c}$$

Thus, rearranging, and substituting the expression for the effective mass,

$$\begin{aligned}R &= \left(\frac{h}{8\pi^2\mu Bc}\right)^{1/2} = \left[\frac{h}{8\pi^2\{(m_\text{I}m_\text{Cl})/(m_\text{I}+m_\text{Cl})\}Bc}\right]^{1/2} = \left\{\frac{(m_\text{I}+m_\text{Cl})h}{8\pi^2 m_\text{I}m_\text{Cl}Bc}\right\}^{1/2} \\ &= \left\{\frac{(126.9045+34.9688)m_\text{u}\times(6.626\times 10^{-34}\text{ J s})}{8\pi^2\times(126.9045m_\text{u})\times(34.9688m_\text{u})\times\underbrace{(0.1142\times 10^2\text{ m}^{-1})}_{1\text{ cm}^{-1}=10^2\text{ m}^{-1}}\times(2.998\times 10^8\text{ m s}^{-1})}\right\}^{1/2}\end{aligned}$$

$$= 232.1 \times 10^{-12}\ \text{m} = \mathbf{232.1\ pm}$$

**E19.15** The frequencies of lines in the pure rotational spectrum of a rigid rotor are given by eqn 19.13a

$$\nu_J = 2B(J+1)$$

and are thus proportional to the rotational constant $B$. However, the value of the rotational constant is inversely proportional to the moment of inertia. Thus, using eqn 19.3 and the expression for the moment of inertia of a diatomic molecule from Table 19.1,

$$B = \frac{\hbar}{4\pi I} = \frac{h}{8\pi^2\{(m_{\text{H}}m_{\text{Cl}})/(m_{\text{H}}+m_{\text{Cl}})\}R^2} = \frac{(m_{\text{H}}+m_{\text{Cl}})h}{8\pi^2(m_{\text{H}}m_{\text{Cl}})R^2}$$

For HCl, $m_{\text{Cl}} \gg m_{\text{H}}$, so that we may make the approximation $(m_{\text{H}}+m_{\text{Cl}}) \approx m_{\text{Cl}}$ and write

$$B \approx \frac{m_{\text{Cl}}h}{8\pi^2(m_{\text{H}}m_{\text{Cl}})R^2} = \frac{h}{8\pi^2 m_{\text{H}}R^2}$$

Thus, the frequencies of the lines are inversely proportional to the mass of the isotope of hydrogen

$$\nu_J \propto m_{\text{H}}^{-1}$$

Hence, because if hydrogen is replaced by deuterium, so that the mass of the hydrogen isotope doubles,

$$m_{^2\text{H}} = 2m_{^1\text{H}}$$

the frequency and spacing between the transitions in the rotational spectrum halves.

$$\nu_J(^2\text{H}^{35}\text{Cl}) = \tfrac{1}{2}\nu_J(^1\text{H}^{35}\text{Cl})$$

**E19.16** From eqn 19.13a, lines in the rotational spectrum of $^1\text{H}^{127}\text{I}$ are given by

$$\nu_J = 2B(J+1)$$

and are therefore separated by $2B$, so that

$$B = (384\ \text{GHz})/2$$

But, from eqn 19.3

$$B = \frac{\hbar}{4\pi I} = \frac{h}{8\pi^2\mu R^2 c}$$

Thus, rearranging, and substituting the expression for the effective mass,

$$R = \left(\frac{h}{8\pi^2\mu Bc}\right)^{1/2} = \left[\frac{h}{8\pi^2\{(m_{\text{H}}m_{\text{I}})/(m_{\text{H}}+m_{\text{I}})\}B}\right]^{1/2} = \left\{\frac{(m_{\text{H}}+m_{\text{I}})h}{8\pi^2 m_{\text{H}}m_{\text{I}}B}\right\}^{1/2}$$

$$= \left\{\frac{(1.0078+126.9045)m_{\text{u}} \times (6.626\times10^{-34}\ \text{J s})}{8\pi^2 \times (1.0078m_{\text{u}}) \times (126.9045m_{\text{u}}) \times (384\times10^9\ \text{s}^{-1}/2)}\right\}^{1/2}$$

$$= 162.2 \times 10^{-12}\ \text{m} = \mathbf{162.2\ pm}$$

We demonstrated in the solution to the previous exercise that a diatomic molecule HX, because $m_X \gg m_H$, the rotational constant is inversely proportion to the mass of the isotope of hydrogen. Thus, if deuterium replaces hydrogen, so that the mass of the isotope doubles, we should expect the value of the rotational constant to half. Thus, the separation between the lines in $^2H^{127}I$ would be

$$\Delta\nu_J = 384\ \text{GHz}/2 = \mathbf{192\ GHz}$$

**E19.17** The wavenumbers of transitions to levels with rotational quantum number $J + 1$ from those with $J$ in the pure rotational spectrum of a non-rigid linear molecule are given by eqn 19.13b

$$\tilde{\nu}_J = 2\tilde{B}(J+1) - 4D(J+1)^3$$

The effect of centrifugal distortion is, however, small and we may use the rigid rotor approximation

$$\tilde{\nu}_J \approx 2\tilde{B}(J+1)$$

to assign the observed transitions. The separation between the lines is approximately 0.4 cm$^{-1}$, implying that $B \approx 0.2$ cm$^{-1}$. The first transition is thus that from $J = 2$. Following eqn 19.14, we may write

$$\overbrace{\frac{\tilde{\nu}_J}{J+1}}^{y} = \overbrace{2\tilde{B}}^{\text{intercept}} \overbrace{-4\tilde{D}}^{\text{slope}} \times \overbrace{(J+1)^2}^{x}$$

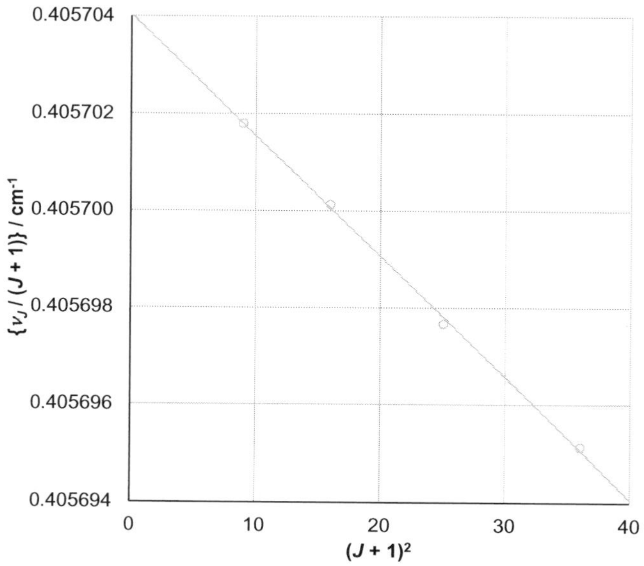


Figure 19.2

Figure 19.2 shows a plot of $\{\tilde{\nu}_J / (J+1)\}$ against $(J+1)^2$. The intercept of the graph is 0.4057 $cm^{-1}$, so that the rotational constant is

$$B = \tfrac{1}{2} \times 0.4057\ \text{cm}^{-1} = \mathbf{0.2029\ cm^{-1}}$$

and the slope of the graph is $-2.493 \times 10^{-7}$ $cm^{-1}$, giving the centrifugal distortion constant as

$$D = -\tfrac{1}{4} \times \text{slope} = -\tfrac{1}{4} \times (-2.493 \times 10^{-7}\ \text{cm}^{-1}) = \mathbf{6.233 \times 10^{-8} cm^{-1}}$$

**E19.18** We may calculate the bond lengths within OCS by first determining the rotational constants for the $^{16}O^{12}C^{32}S$ and $^{16}O^{12}C^{34}S$ isotopomers. The rotational transition frequencies in the microwave spectrum are given by eqn 19.13a

$$\overbrace{\tilde{\nu}_J}^{y} = \overbrace{2B}^{\text{slope}} \overbrace{(J+1)}^{x}$$

which has the same form as the equation for a straight-line graph. Figure 19.3 shows a plot of the transition frequencies for the two isotopomers against $J + 1$.

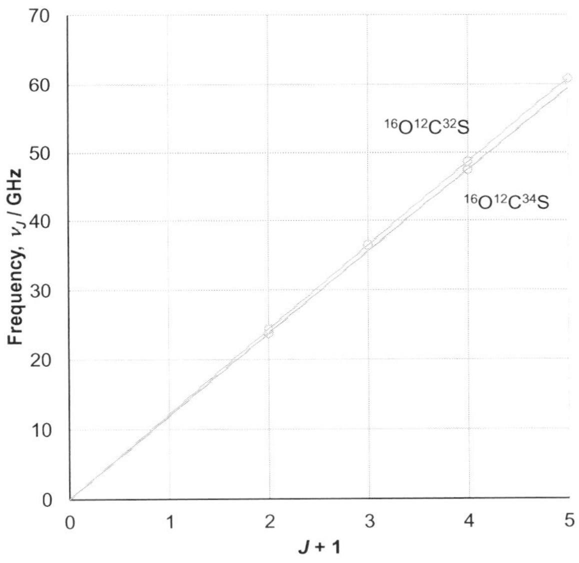


**Figure 19.3**

The slopes of the lines imply that, for the $^{16}O^{12}C^{32}S$ isotopomer,

$$B = \tfrac{1}{2} \times \text{slope} = \tfrac{1}{2} \times (12.16290\ \text{GHz}) = 6.08145\ \text{GHz}$$

and so the moment of inertia is

$$I = \frac{\hbar}{4\pi B} = \frac{h}{8\pi^2 B} = \frac{6.626 \times 10^{-34}\text{J s}}{8\pi^2 \times (6.08145 \times 10^9 \text{s}^{-1})} = 1.37992 \times 10^{-45}\ \text{kg m}^2$$

and for the $^{16}O^{12}C^{34}S$ isotopomer,

$$B = ½ \times (11.86571 \text{ GHz}) = 5.93286 \text{ GHz}$$

and so the moment of inertia is

$$I = \frac{6.626 \times 10^{-34} \text{J s}}{8\pi^2 \times (5.93286 \times 10^9 \text{s}^{-1})} = 1.41448 \times 10^{-45} \text{ kg m}^2$$

The moment of inertia, however, depends upon the atomic masses and internuclear distances as

$$I = m_O R_{OC}^2 + m_S R_{CS}^2 + \frac{(m_O R_{OC} - m_S R_{CS})^2}{m_O + m_C + m_S}$$

Although it is possible to solve the equations analytically to obtain values for the internuclear distances $R_{OC}$ and $R_{CS}$, it is easier to use mathematical software or a spreadsheet. Doing so leads to the values $R_{OC}$ = **116.28 pm** and $R_{CS}$ = **155.97 pm**.

**E19.19** A wave of wavelength $\lambda$ appears Doppler shifted at a frequency $\lambda'$ if the observer is travelling at a speed $s$ relative to a stationary source, where

$$\lambda' = \left\{\frac{1-(s/c)}{1+(s/c)}\right\}^{1/2} \lambda$$

Hence, because 1 m.p.h. is equivalent to 0.44704 m s$^{-1}$, a red traffic light of wavelength 660 nm appears at a wavelength of

$$\lambda' = \left[\frac{1-\{(65 \times 0.44704 \text{ m s}^{-1})/(2.998 \times 10^8 \text{ m s}^{-1})\}}{1+\{(65 \times 0.44704 \text{ m s}^{-1})/(2.998 \times 10^8 \text{ m s}^{-1})\}}\right]^{1/2} \times 660 \text{ nm}$$
$$= \mathbf{659.999936 \text{ nm}}$$

In order that the red traffic light appear to be of wavelength 520 nm, and hence green, the observer must be travelling at a speed

$$s = \left\{\frac{1-(\lambda/\lambda')^2}{1+(\lambda/\lambda')^2}\right\} c$$
$$= \left\{\frac{1-(660/520)^2}{1+(660/520)^2}\right\} \times (2.998 \times 10^8 \text{ m s}^{-1}) = \mathbf{7.02 \times 10^7 \text{ m s}^{-1}}$$

which is equivalent to 157 × 10$^6$ m s$^{-1}$.

**E19.20** The wavelength of the radiation appears to be lengthened because of the star's motion. we may thus infer that the star is receding and that the observed wavelength is given by

$$\lambda' = \left\{\frac{1+(s/c)}{1-(s/c)}\right\}^{1/2} \lambda$$

where $s$ is the speed of the star. Rearranging for $s$,

$$s = \left\{\frac{1-(\lambda/\lambda')^2}{1+(\lambda/\lambda')^2}\right\}c$$
$$= \left\{\frac{1-(654.2/706.5)^2}{1+(654.2/706.5)^2}\right\} \times (2.998\times10^8\ \mathrm{m\ s^{-1}}) = \mathbf{2.30\times10^7\ m\ s^{-1}}$$

The width of a Doppler broadened spectra line is given by eqn 19.15,

$$\delta\nu = \frac{2\nu}{c}\left(\frac{2RT\ln 2}{M}\right)^{1/2}$$

Writing

$$\delta\nu = \frac{c}{\lambda} - \frac{c}{\lambda'} = c\frac{(\lambda-\lambda')}{\lambda\lambda'} \approx c\frac{\delta\lambda}{\lambda^2}$$

so that, rearranging,

$$T = \left(\frac{c\delta\lambda}{2\lambda}\right)^2 \frac{M}{2R\ln 2}$$
$$= \left\{\frac{(2.998\times10^8\ \mathrm{m\ s^{-1}})\times(61.8\times10^{-12}\mathrm{m})}{2\times(654.2\times10^{-9}\mathrm{m})}\right\}^2$$
$$\times\frac{47.87\times10^{-3}\ \mathrm{kg\ mol^{-1}}}{2\times(8.3145\ \mathrm{J\ K^{-1}mol^{-1}})\times\ln 2} = \mathbf{8.3\times10^5\ K}$$

**E19.21** The width of a spectroscopic line that is lifetime broadened is given by eqn 19.16. Thus, rearranging,

$$\tau = \frac{1}{2\pi\delta\nu} = \frac{1}{2\pi c\delta\tilde{\nu}}$$

so that for a line of width 0.10 $\mathrm{cm^{-1}}$,

$$\tau = \frac{1}{2\pi\times(2.998\times10^8\ \mathrm{m\ s^{-1}})\times\underbrace{(0.10\times10^2\ \mathrm{m^{-1}})}_{1\ \mathrm{cm^{-1}}=10^2\mathrm{m^{-1}}}} = 5.3\times10^{-11}\ \mathrm{s^{-1}} = \mathbf{53\ ps}$$

for a line of width 1.0 $\mathrm{cm^{-1}}$,

$$\tau = \frac{1}{2\pi\times(2.998\times10^8\ \mathrm{m\ s^{-1}})\times\underbrace{(1.0\times10^2\ \mathrm{m^{-1}})}_{1\ \mathrm{cm^{-1}}=10^2\mathrm{m^{-1}}}} = 5.3\times10^{-12}\ \mathrm{s^{-1}} = \mathbf{5.3\ ps}$$

and for a line of width 1.0 GHz,

$$\tau = \frac{1}{2\pi\times1.0\times10^9\ \mathrm{s^{-1}}} = 1.6\times10^{-10}\ \mathrm{s^{-1}} = \mathbf{160\ ps}$$

**E19.22** The width of a spectroscopic line depends upon the lifetime of the state through eqn 19.16.

$$\delta\tilde{\nu} = \frac{1}{2\pi c\tau}$$

(a) If every collision is effective in deactivating the molecule, then the lifetime is

$$\tau = 1/(1.0 \times 10^{13}\ \mathrm{s^{-1}})$$

so that

$$\delta\tilde{\nu} = \frac{1}{2\pi \times (2.998 \times 10^{8}\ \mathrm{m\,s^{-1}})/(1.0 \times 10^{13}\ \mathrm{s^{-1}})}$$
$$= 5.3 \times 10^{3}\ \mathrm{m^{-1}} = \mathbf{53\ cm^{-1}}$$

(b) If, however, only one collision in every 200 is effective in deactivating the molecule, then the lifetime is

$$\tau = 200/(1.0 \times 10^{13}\ \mathrm{s^{-1}})$$

so that

$$\delta\tilde{\nu} = \frac{1}{2\pi \times (2.998 \times 10^{8}\ \mathrm{m\,s^{-1}}) \times \{200/(1.0 \times 10^{13}\ \mathrm{s^{-1}})\}}$$
$$= 27 \times 10^{-2}\ \mathrm{m^{-1}} = \mathbf{0.27\ cm^{-1}}$$

**E19.23** The change in frequency for a rotational Raman transition to a state with rotational quantum number $J + 2$ from one with $J$ in a linear molecule is given by eqn 19.18. Stokes radiation is scattered to lower wavenumber than the incident radiation. In this case, this is because energy is used to excite the rotational transition. The rotational constant of $O_2$ is 1.438 $\mathrm{cm^{-1}}$, so that

$$\nu_J = \nu_0 - \Delta\nu = \nu_0 - 2B(2J + 3)$$
$$= 20623\ \mathrm{cm^{-1}} - [2 \times 1.438\ \mathrm{cm^{-1}} \times \{(2 \times 2) + 3\}]$$
$$= \mathbf{20603\ cm^{-1}}$$

**E19.24** The rotational constant is related to the moment of inertia of a molecule through eqn 19.3. For a linear molecule of the form $AB_2$, such as $CO_2$, Table 19.1 shows that the moment of inertia is given by $I = 2m_A R^2$. Thus, combining these expressions

$$B = \frac{\hbar}{4\pi I} = \frac{h}{8\pi^2 I} = \frac{h}{8\pi^2 (2m_O R^2)}$$

Rearranging,

$$R = \left(\frac{h}{16\pi^2 m_O B}\right)^{1/2} = \frac{1}{4\pi}\left(\frac{h}{m_O B}\right)^{1/2}$$
$$= \frac{1}{4\pi}\left\{\frac{6.626 \times 10^{-34}\,\mathrm{J\,s}}{15.9949 m_u \times (11.70 \times 10^{9}\ \mathrm{s^{-1}})}\right\}^{1/2} = 1.162 \times 10^{-10}\ \mathrm{m} = \mathbf{116.2\ pm}$$

**E19.25** The vibrational frequency of an isolated harmonic oscillator is given by eqn 19.20b. (a) Hence, for a $^{12}C{=}^{16}O$ bond in a peptide,

$$\nu = \frac{1}{2\pi}\left(\frac{k_f}{\mu}\right)^{1/2} = \frac{1}{2\pi}\left\{\frac{k_f}{m_C m_O/(m_C + m_O)}\right\}^{1/2} = \frac{1}{2\pi}\left\{\frac{(m_C + m_O)k_f}{m_C m_O}\right\}^{1/2}$$
$$= \frac{1}{2\pi}\left\{\frac{(12.0000 + 15.9949)k_f}{(12.0000 \times 15.9949)m_u}\right\}^{1/2}$$
$$= \frac{1}{2\pi}\left\{\frac{(12.0000 + 15.9949) \times (908\ \mathrm{N\ m^{-1}})}{(12.0000 \times 15.9949) \times (1.661 \times 10^{-27}\ \mathrm{kg})}\right\}^{1/2}$$
$$= 4.49 \times 10^{13}\ \mathrm{s^{-1}} = \mathbf{4.49 \times 10^{13}\ Hz}$$

(b) and for a $^{13}C{=}^{16}O$ bond in a peptide, if we assume that the force constant remains constant upon isotopic substitution,

$$\nu = \frac{1}{2\pi}\left\{\frac{(13.0034 + 15.9949) \times (908\ \mathrm{N\ m^{-1}})}{(13.0034 \times 15.9949) \times (1.661 \times 10^{-27}\ \mathrm{kg})}\right\}^{1/2}$$
$$= 4.39 \times 10^{13}\ \mathrm{s^{-1}} = \mathbf{4.39 \times 10^{13}\ Hz}$$

**E19.26** Rearranging eqn 19.20b, the force constant is

$$k_f = (2\pi\nu)^2\mu = (2\pi\tilde{\nu}c)^2 \times \overbrace{\left(\frac{m_{Cl}m_{Cl}}{m_{Cl} + m_{Cl}}\right)}^{\substack{\text{effective mass} \\ \mu}} = (2\pi\tilde{\nu}c)^2 \times \tfrac{1}{2}m_{Cl}$$
$$= \left\{2\pi \times \overbrace{(656 \times 10^2\ \mathrm{m^{-1}})}^{1\ \mathrm{cm^{-1}}=10^2\ \mathrm{m^{-1}}} \times (2.998 \times 10^8\ \mathrm{m\ s^{-1}})\right\}^2 \times (34.9688m_u/2)$$
$$= \mathbf{443\ N\ m^{-1}}$$

**E19.27** The force constant for a harmonic oscillator may be calculated by rearranging eqn 19.20b,

$$k_f = (2\pi\nu)^2\mu = (2\pi\tilde{\nu}c)^2 \times \overbrace{\left(\frac{m_H m_X}{m_H + m_X}\right)}^{\substack{\text{effective mass} \\ \mu}}$$

so that, (a) for HF,

$$k_f = \left\{2\pi \times \overbrace{(4141.3 \times 10^2\ \mathrm{m^{-1}})}^{1\ \mathrm{cm^{-1}}=10^2\ \mathrm{m^{-1}}} \times (2.998 \times 10^8\ \mathrm{m\ s^{-1}})\right\}^2 \times \left(\frac{1.0078m_u \times 18.9984m_u}{1.0078m_u + 18.9984m_u}\right)$$
$$= \{2\pi \times (4141.3 \times 10^2\ \mathrm{m^{-1}}) \times (2.998 \times 10^8\ \mathrm{m\ s^{-1}})\}^2 \times \left(\frac{1.0078 \times 18.9984}{1.0078 + 18.9984}\right) \times \overbrace{(1.661 \times 10^{-27}\ \mathrm{kg})}^{m_u}$$
$$= \mathbf{967.4\ N\ m^{-1}}$$

(b) for HCl,

$$k_f = \{2\pi \times (2988.9 \times 10^2\ \mathrm{m^{-1}}) \times (2.998 \times 10^8\ \mathrm{m\ s^{-1}})\}^2 \times \left(\frac{1.0078 \times 34.9688}{1.0078 + 34.9688}\right) \times \overbrace{(1.661 \times 10^{-27}\ \mathrm{kg})}^{m_u}$$

$$= \mathbf{515.6\ N\ m^{-1}}$$

(c) for HBr,

$$k_f = \{2\pi \times (2988.9 \times 10^2\ \mathrm{m^{-1}}) \times (2.998 \times 10^8\ \mathrm{m\ s^{-1}})\}^2 \times \left(\frac{1.0078 \times 79.9185}{1.0078 + 79.9185}\right) \times \overbrace{(1.661 \times 10^{-27}\ \mathrm{kg})}^{m_u}$$

$$= \mathbf{411.8\ N\ m^{-1}}$$

(d) for HBr,

$$k_f = \{2\pi \times (2988.9 \times 10^2\ \mathrm{m^{-1}}) \times (2.998 \times 10^8\ \mathrm{m\ s^{-1}})\}^2 \times \left(\frac{1.0078 \times 126.9045}{1.0078 + 126.9045}\right) \times \overbrace{(1.661 \times 10^{-27}\ \mathrm{kg})}^{m_u}$$

$$= \mathbf{314.2\ N\ m^{-1}}$$

**E19.28** For a harmonic oscillator, the fundamental vibrational wavenumber may be calculated from the harmonic frequency. Thus, from eqn 19.20b,

$$\tilde{\nu} = \frac{\nu}{c} = \frac{1}{2\pi c}\left(\frac{k_f}{\mu}\right)^{1/2} = \frac{1}{2\pi c}\left\{\frac{k_f}{m_H m_X/(m_H + m_X)}\right\}^{1/2} = \frac{1}{2\pi c}\left\{\frac{(m_H + m_X)k_f}{m_H m_X}\right\}^{1/2}$$

If we assume that because the mass of the halogen atom is so much greater than that of the hydrogen atom, $m_X \gg m_H, m_D$, so that $m_D + m_X \approx m_X$, we may make the approximation

$$\tilde{\nu} \approx \frac{1}{2\pi c}\left\{\frac{m_X k_f}{m_H m_X}\right\}^{1/2} = \frac{1}{2\pi c}\left\{\frac{k_f}{m_H}\right\}^{1/2}$$

so that the fundamental vibrational wavenumber is inversely proportional to the square root of the mass of the hydrogen atom. Hence,

$$\tilde{\nu}_{DX} \approx (m_H/m_D)^{1/2}\tilde{\nu}_{HX} = (1.0078 m_u/2.0140 m_u)^{1/2}\nu_{HX} = 0.7074\nu_{HX}$$

Thus,

$$\tilde{\nu}_{DF} \approx 0.7074 \times 4141.3\ \mathrm{cm^{-1}} = \mathbf{2930\ cm^{-1}}$$
$$\tilde{\nu}_{DCl} \approx 0.7074 \times 2988.3\ \mathrm{cm^{-1}} = \mathbf{2114\ cm^{-1}}$$
$$\tilde{\nu}_{DBr} \approx 0.7074 \times 2649.7\ \mathrm{cm^{-1}} = \mathbf{1874\ cm^{-1}}$$
$$\tilde{\nu}_{DI} \approx 0.7074 \times 2309.5\ \mathrm{cm^{-1}} = \mathbf{1634\ cm^{-1}}$$

The approximation becomes more precise as the mass of the halogen atom increases. It is possible to calculate the exact value of the fundamental frequency by substituting the values of the force constants calculated in the previous question for each molecule. Doing so, we find that

$$\tilde{\nu}_{\text{DF}} = \frac{1}{2\pi c}\left(\frac{k_f}{\mu}\right)^{1/2} = \frac{1}{2\pi c}\left\{\frac{k_f}{m_{\text{D}}m_{\text{F}}/(m_{\text{D}}+m_{\text{F}})}\right\}^{1/2} = \frac{1}{2\pi c}\left\{\frac{(m_{\text{D}}+m_{\text{F}})k_f}{m_{\text{D}}m_{\text{F}}}\right\}^{1/2}$$

$$= \frac{1}{2\pi c}\left\{\frac{(1.0078+18.9984)\times 967.4\ \text{N m}^{-1}}{(1.0078\times 18.9984)\times(1.661\times 10^{-27}\ \text{kg})}\right\}^{1/2} = \mathbf{3002\ cm^{-1}}$$

In the same way for the other hydrogen halides, $\tilde{\nu}_{\text{DCl}} = 2144\ \text{cm}^{-1}$, $\tilde{\nu}_{\text{DBr}} = 1886\ \text{cm}^{-1}$ and $\tilde{\nu}_{\text{DI}} = 1640\ \text{cm}^{-1}$. The error as a result of the approximation therefore decreases down the series from 2.4 per cent for HF to 0.4 per cent for HI. Even for HF, this discrepancy is less than that introduced by assuming that the molecule is harmonic.

**E19.29** For a vibrational mode to be infrared active, the electric dipole moment must change as a result of the vibration.

(a) For $H_2$, symmetry means that the molecule does not possess an electric dipole moment even when the bond is stretched or compressed as a result of vibration.

(b) HCl, however, possesses a dipole moment, even in its equilibrium configuration. The magnitude of the dipole moment increases as the bond is stretched. Thus an infrared spectrum is observed for HCl.

(c) The equilibrium structure of $CO_2$ is nonpolar. For the symmetric stretching vibration, although the dipole moments of the individual C=O bonds do change, the symmetry means that overall, the molecule remains nonpolar. However, loss of symmetry caused by the asymmetric stretching and bending vibrations results in the molecule becoming polar. Thus, an infrared spectrum is observed for some modes of $CO_2$.

(d) For $H_2O$, the symmetric stretching, asymmetric stretching and bending vibrational modes all result in a change in the dipole moment of the molecule. Thus all vibrational modes in $H_2O$ are infrared active.

(e) $CH_3CH_3$ is nonpolar. However, many of the $3N - 6 = 18$ normal modes result in a change in the dipole moment of the molecule. Thus $CH_3CH_3$ possesses an infrared spectrum.

(f) $CH_4$ is also nonpolar. The symmetric stretching vibration does not introduce a dipole moment, and this mode is not, therefore, infrared active. However, all other vibrational modes do result in a change in dipole moment and give rise to infrared absorptions.

(g) $CH_3Cl$ is polar. The dipole moment of the molecule changes for all vibrational modes, including the symmetric stretch. Thus, $CH_3Cl$ is infrared active.

(h) $N_2$, as a homonuclear diatomic molecule and thus is nonpolar, even when the bond is stretched or compressed. Thus, $N_2$ does not possess an infrared spectrum.

**E19.30** The vibrational energy levels of a diatomic molecule are given by eqn19.23

$$E_v = (v + ½)hc\tilde{\nu} - (v + ½)^2 hc\tilde{\nu}x_{\text{e}}$$

The wavenumber of the strong fundamental transition, $v = 1 \leftarrow 0$, is thus

$$\tilde{\nu}_{1\leftarrow 0} = \frac{\Delta E}{hc} = \frac{E_1 - E_0}{hc}$$
$$= \overbrace{\{(1 + ½)\tilde{\nu} - (1 + ½)^2\tilde{\nu}x_e\}}^{v=1} - \overbrace{\{(0 + ½)\tilde{\nu} - (0 + ½)^2\tilde{\nu}x_e\}}^{v=0}$$
$$= \tilde{\nu} - 2\tilde{\nu}x_e$$

Similarly, the wavenumber of the weak overtone transition, $v = 2 \leftarrow 0$, is thus

$$\tilde{\nu}_{2\leftarrow 0} = \frac{\Delta E}{hc} = \frac{E_2 - E_0}{hc}$$
$$= \overbrace{\{(2 + ½)\tilde{\nu} - (2 + ½)^2\tilde{\nu}x_e\}}^{v=2} - \overbrace{\{(0 + ½)\tilde{\nu} - (0 + ½)^2\tilde{\nu}x_e\}}^{v=0}$$
$$= 2\tilde{\nu} - 6\tilde{\nu}x_e$$

Thus, combining these two equations, gives the vibrational wavenumber as

$$\tilde{\nu} = 3\tilde{\nu}_{1\leftarrow 0} - \tilde{\nu}_{2\leftarrow 0} = \{3 \times (2143.29\ \text{cm}^{-1})\} - (4259.66\ \text{cm}^{-1}) = \mathbf{2170.21\ cm^{-1}}$$

In a similar way, because

$$2\tilde{\nu}_{1\leftarrow 0} - \tilde{\nu}_{2\leftarrow 0} = 2\tilde{\nu}x_e$$

it follows that the anharmonicity constant is

$$x_e = \frac{2\tilde{\nu}_{1\leftarrow 0} - \tilde{\nu}_{2\leftarrow 0}}{2\tilde{\nu}} = \frac{\{2 \times (2143.29\ \text{cm}^{-1})\} - (4259.66\ \text{cm}^{-1})}{2 \times (2170.21\ \text{cm}^{-1})} = \mathbf{0.012}$$

**E19.31** For a molecule of $N$ atoms, there are $3N - 5$ normal modes of vibration if the molecule is linear, and $3N - 6$ normal modes of vibration if the molecule is nonlinear.

(a) $NO_2$ is non-linear with a bond angle of 134.3°. Thus, there are $3N - 6 = (3 \times 3) - 6 = \mathbf{3}$ normal modes of vibration.

(b) In contrast, $N_2O$ is linear. Thus, there are $3N - 5 = (3 \times 3) - 5 = \mathbf{4}$ normal modes of vibration.

(c) Cyclohexane, $C_6H_{12}$, is clearly nonlinear and so has $3N - 6 = (3 \times 18) - 6 = \mathbf{48}$ normal modes of vibration. Because of the symmetry of the molecule, some of these normal modes are degenerate. Analysis shows that for the chair conformation, these normal modes correspond to 27 different vibrational frequencies. This conformation has a centre of symmetry. Thus, according to the exclusion rule, the vibrational modes are either infrared or Raman active, but not both. As a result, we find that there are 13 fundamental bands in the infrared spectrum and 14 in the Raman spectrum. The boat conformation, however, is of lower symmetry and therefore fewer of the normal modes of vibration are degenerate. Thus, there are a total of 48 different vibrational frequencies. Of these, all 48 are Raman active, but only 37 are infrared active. The boat conformation does not possess a centre of symmetry, so there is no restriction on whether a fundamental band appears only in one or other type of spectrum.

(c) Hexane, $C_6H_{14}$, is also nonlinear and so has $3N - 6 = (3 \times 20) - 6 =$ **54** normal modes of vibration. The possibility of internal rotation about the C–C bonds means that, in general, the molecule does not possess any symmetry. Thus, none of the vibrational modes are degenerate, although some are very close in frequency. Furthermore, the molecule does not possess a centre of symmetry, so many of rhe bands appear in both the infrared and Raman spectrum.

**E19.32** Assuming that the effects of centrifugal distortion are negligible and that the value of the rotational constant is the same in the upper and lower vibrational states, then the wavenumber of a line in a vibration–rotation spectrum is given, through eqn 19.25, by the difference

$$\begin{aligned}\tilde{\nu} &= \frac{\Delta E}{hc} = \frac{E_{v',J'} - E_{v'',J''}}{hc} \\ &= [\{(v' + \tfrac{1}{2})h\nu + hBJ'(J' + 1)\} - \{(v'' + \tfrac{1}{2})h\nu + hBJ''(J'' + 1)\}]/hc\end{aligned}$$

where a single prime is used to indicate an upper state quantum number and a double prime to indicate a lower state quantum number. R branch transitions correspond to the selection rule $\Delta J = J' - J'' + 1$, with, for the fundamental band, $\Delta v = v' - v'' + 1$. Thus, the expression may be simplified to

$$\tilde{\nu}_{\mathrm{R}} = \{h\nu + hB(J'' + 2)\}/hc = \tilde{\nu} + 2\tilde{B}(J'' + 1)$$

For $^{1}H^{81}Br$, $\tilde{\nu} = 2649.7\ \mathrm{cm^{-1}}$ and $\tilde{B} = 8.48\ \mathrm{cm^{-1}}$, so that the R(2) line appears at a wavenumber of

$$\tilde{\nu}_{\mathrm{R(2)}} = (2649.7\ \mathrm{cm^{-1}}) + \{2 \times (8.48\ \mathrm{cm^{-1}}) \times (2 + 1)\} = \mathbf{2700.6\ cm^{-1}}$$

**E19.33** The vibration–rotation spectrum of a heteronuclear diatomic molecule such as HF possesses only P and R branches. At low values of rotational quantum number $J$, the effects of centrifugal distortion are negligible, and if we assume that the vibration may be treated as harmonic, the wavenumbers of the lines in these branches are given by

$$\tilde{\nu}_J = \tilde{\nu} - 2\tilde{B}J \qquad \text{P branch}$$
$$\tilde{\nu}_J = \tilde{\nu} + 2\tilde{B}(J + 1) \qquad \text{R branch}$$

We may combine these two expressions

$$\tilde{\nu}_J = \tilde{\nu} + 2m\tilde{B}$$

where $m$ is an integer such that $m = -1, -2, \ldots$ corresponds to lines in the P branch and $m = +1, +2,$ corresponds to lines in the R branch.

The transitions therefore appear to be separated by $2B$, with a gap of $4B$ between the two branches because the Q branch, with $m = 0$, is missing. We may thus assign the spectrum by considering the difference between the wavenumbers of consecutive transitions. The separation between most lines is ~22 $\mathrm{cm^{-1}}$. However the separation between the lines with wavenumbers of 2930.43 $\mathrm{cm^{-1}}$ and 2974.55 $\mathrm{cm^{-1}}$ is ~44 $\mathrm{cm^{-1}}$, indicating that these transitions must correspond to the start of the P and R branches respectively. The first line in the P branch corresponds to the transition to a rotational state $J = 0$ from $J = 1$, and is designated P(1). In the same way, the first line in the R branch corresponds to the transition to $J = 1$ from $J = 0$ and is designated R(0). The other assignments then follow:

| | P branch | | | Rbranch | | |
|---|---|---|---|---|---|---|
| | P(3) | P(2) | P(1) | R(0) | R(1) | R(2) |
| $m$ | −3 | −2 | −1 | +1 | +2 | +3 |
| $\tilde{\nu}$ /cm$^{-1}$ | 2886.50 | 2908.51 | 2930.43 | 2974.55 | 2996.57 | 3018.58 |

The combined expression has the same form as the equation of a straight-line graph. Thus, a plot of observed wavenumber against $m$ should be a straight line with a slope equal to twice the value of the rotational constant and an intercept equal to the harmonic vibrational wavenumber.

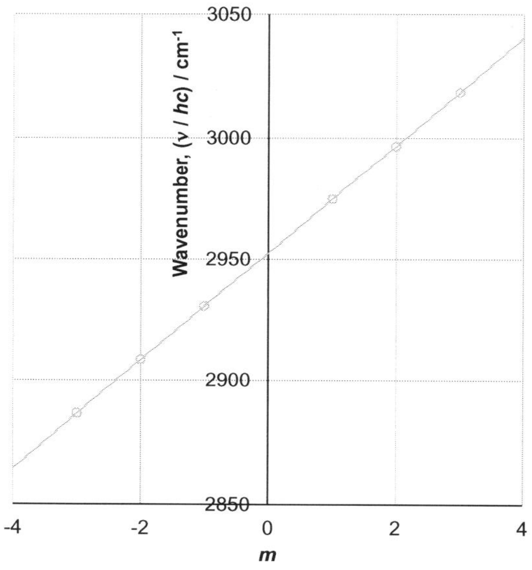


**Figure 19.3**

A plot of the data given for $^{1}H^{19}F$ is shown in Figure 19.3. The slope of the graph is 22.02 cm$^{-1}$, implying that the rotational constant is 11.01 cm$^{-1}$. The intercept, which is equal to the vibrational wavenumber, is 2952.52 cm$^{-1}$.

We may determine the bond length, $R$, from the value for the rotational constant using eqns 19.4 and 19.5. Thus,

$$\tilde{B} = \frac{\hbar}{4\pi I c} = \frac{h}{8\pi^2 c(\mu R^2)} = \frac{h}{8\pi^2 c\{m_H m_F/(m_H + m_F)\}R^2}$$

Hence, rearranging,

$$R = \left\{\frac{(m_{\rm H} + m_{\rm F})h}{8\pi^2 c m_{\rm H} m_{\rm F} B}\right\}^{1/2}$$

$$= \left\{\frac{(1.0078 + 18.9984) \times (6.626 \times 10^{-34}\,{\rm J\,s})}{8\pi^2 \times (2.998 \times 10^8\,{\rm m\,s^{-1}}) \times (1.0078 \times 18.9984) \times \underbrace{(1.661 \times 10^{-27}\,{\rm kg})}_{m_{\rm u}} \times \underbrace{(11.01 \times 10^2\,{\rm m^{-1}})}_{1\,{\rm cm^{-1}} = 10^2\,{\rm m^{-1}}}}\right\}^{1/2}$$

$$= 1.265 \times 10^{-10}\,{\rm m} = \mathbf{1.265}\,\text{Å}$$

**E19.34** The vibrational mode that corresponds to uniform expansion of the benzene ring changes the polarizability of the molecule. The vibrational mode is therefore Raman active. The centre of symmetry means that benzene is non-polar and this does not change as a result of the uniform expansion of the ring. Thus, the vibrational mode is not infrared active. The example thus illustrates the exclusion rule for Raman and infrared spectra of molecules with a centre of symmetry.

**E19.35** (a) A linear molecule of $N$ atoms, possesses $3N - 5$ normal modes of vibration. Thus, for $H_2O_2$ with $N = 4$, there are $(3 \times 4) - 5 = 7$ normal modes. For a nonlinear molecule, however, there are $3N - 6$ normal modes of vibration. Thus, for each of the conformations shown, there are $(3 \times 4) - 6 = 6$ normal modes.

(b) In total, six different bands are observed in the infrared and Raman spectra, with two bands appearing in both.

Conformation **1** possesses a centre of symmetry. The exclusion rule therefore predicts that, for this conformation, no mode should be observed in both the infrared and Raman spectrum. This is not the case, and we may therefore eliminate the possibility that the spectrum results from conformation **1**.

Conformation **2** is planar, with an additional perpendicular plane of symmetry running through the centre of the O–O bond. We should expect this symmetry to lead to the degeneracy of some of the vibrational modes. Thus, for a symmetric conformation such as this, not all of the vibrational normal modes would have different vibrational wavenumbers. In this case, however, six bands with different wavenumbers are observed, one for each of the six vibrational normal modes. Thus, we may also eliminate conformation **2**.

Conformation **3**, however, does not possess any symmetry. We therefore expect to observe six different bands, one for each vibrational normal mode, with no restriction on whether a particular band may appear in the infrared or Raman spectrum, or even both. The data are thus consistent with $H_2O_2$ adopting conformation **3**.

# Answers to projects

**P19.36** The relative population of the rotational energy level with quantum number $J$ is, from the Boltzmann distribution, eqn 0.18,

$$\frac{P_J}{P_0}=\frac{g_J}{g_0}\mathrm{e}^{-(\epsilon_J-\epsilon_0)/kT}=\frac{g_J}{g_0}\mathrm{e}^{-hBJ(J+1)/kT}$$

where the degeneracy $g_J$ allow for the consideration of energy levels rather than individual states. An expression for the rotational quantum number most populated level may be found by differentiating this expression and solving,

$$\frac{\mathrm{d}}{\mathrm{d}J}\left(\frac{P_J}{P_0}\right)=0$$

Hence, for a spherical rotor with $g_J=(2J+1)^2$,

$$\begin{aligned}&\frac{\mathrm{d}}{\mathrm{d}J}\{(2J+1)^2\mathrm{e}^{-hBJ(J+1)/kT}\}\\&=\left\{(2J+1)^2\frac{\mathrm{d}}{\mathrm{d}J}\mathrm{e}^{-hBJ(J+1)/kT}\right\}+\left\{\mathrm{e}^{-hBJ(J+1)/kT}\frac{\mathrm{d}}{\mathrm{d}J}(2J+1)^2\right\}\\&=\left[(2J+1)^2\times\{-hB(2J+1)/kT\}\mathrm{e}^{-hBJ(J+1)/kT}\right]+\{\mathrm{e}^{-hBJ(J+1)/kT}\times 4(2J+1)\}\\&=(2J+1)\{4-(2J+1)^2hB/kT\}\mathrm{e}^{-hBJ(J+1)/kT}=0\end{aligned}$$

The solutions arising from the factors

$$(2J+1)=0$$
$$\mathrm{e}^{-hBJ(J+1)/kT}=0$$

correspond to the minima in the distribution at $J=0$ and $J=\infty$. However, the factor

$$4-(2J+1)^2/kT=0$$

implies that

$$\boldsymbol{J_{\max}=(kT/hB)^{1/2}-½}$$

**P19.37** (a) Resonance Raman spectroscopy is preferable to vibrational spectroscopy for studying the O–O stretching mode because such a mode would not be infrared active, or at best, be only weakly active. The mode is not active in free $O_2$, because it would not change the molecule's dipole moment. However, in a complex in which $O_2$ is bound, the O–O stretch may change the dipole moment, but it is not certain to do so at all, let alone be strong enough to provide a good signal.

(b) The vibrational wavenumber is proportional to the frequency, and it depends on the effective mass as $\nu\propto(k_\mathrm{f}/\mu)^{1/2}$, so that

$$\tilde{\nu}(^{18}\mathrm{O}_2)/\tilde{\nu}(^{16}\mathrm{O}_2)=\{m(^{16}\mathrm{O}_2)/m(^{18}\mathrm{O}_2)\}^{1/2}=(16/18)^{1/2}=0.943$$

The vibrational wavenumber of bound $^{16}O_2$ in haemerythrin is 844 $cm^{-1}$, implying that the equivalent wavenumber for $^{18}O_2$ is $0.943\times 844\ \mathrm{cm^{-1}}=796\ \mathrm{cm^{-1}}$. This assumes that the effective masses are proportional to the isotopic masses. This assumption is valid in the free molecule, where the effective mass of $O_2$ is equal to half the mass of the O atom; it is also valid if the $O_2$ is strongly bound at one end, such that one atom is free and the other is essentially fixed to a very massive unit.

(c) The vibrational wavenumber is proportional to the square root of the force constant. The force constant is itself a measure of the strength of the bond (technically of its stiffness, which correlates with strength), which in turn is characterized by bond order. Simple molecular orbital analysis of $O_2$, $O_2^-$, and $O_2^{2-}$ results in bond orders of 2, 1½ and 1. Given the decreasing bond order, one would expect decreasing vibrational wavenumbers (and vice versa).

(d) The wavenumber of the O–O stretch is very similar to that of the peroxide anion, suggesting $Fe^{3+}{}_2\,O^{2-}{}_2$.

(e) The detection of two bands due to $^{16}O^{18}O$ implies that the two O atoms occupy non-equivalent positions in the complex. Structures **6** and 7 are consistent with this observation, but structures 4 and 5 are not.

**P19.38** (a) Many modern quantum chemistry or molecular drawing packages now allow users to predict not only the frequency, but also the intensity of bands in the infrared spectra of simple molecules. The accuracy of the spectra generated depend upon the level of calculation used.

(b) The bands responsible for the absorption of infrared radiation are those for which there is a change in the dipole moment of the molecule on excitation of the vibrational mode. For $CH_4$ and $CO_2$, all modes are infrared active apart from the symmetric stretching vibration; for $H_2O$, all modes are infrared active.

# Chapter 20

# Spectroscopy: electronic transitions

## Answers to discussion questions

**D20.1** The form of the Beer–Lambert law is justified in detail in *Further Information 20.1*. The derivation shown assumes that the concentration of the absorbing species is uniform. If not, the law will not be obeyed. This situation might apply to a substance that associates or dissociates in solution. Since the molar absorption coefficient, $\varepsilon$, depends on wavelength, the absorbance $A$ is wavelength dependent, and so if the radiation is not monochromatic, the Beer–Lambert law may not be obeyed.

**D20.2** The Franck–Condon principle states that because electrons are so much lighter than nuclei an electronic transition occurs rapidly compared to vibrational motion. We may therefore assume that the internuclear distance is unchanged in the upper and lower states. An electronic transition may thus be indicated by drawing a vertical line on a diagram showing the vibrational wavefunctions for each electronic state as a function of internuclear distance. The line should start from the most probable internuclear distance for the initial electronic state. This vertical line will, however, intersect any number of vibrational levels in the final electronic state. A vibrational progression is therefore observed, the shape of which is determined by the relative horizontal positions of the two electronic potential-energy curves. The most probable, and therefore the most intense, transitions correspond to those between vibrational states for which the overlap integral at the particular internuclear separation is large. The strongest transitions will therefore be those for which the vertical line joins vibrational states whose wavefunctions have a large amplitude.

**D20.3** Colour can arise by emission, absorption, or scattering of electromagnetic radiation by an object. Many molecules have electronic transitions that have wavelengths in the visible region of the electromagnetic spectrum. When a substance emits radiation the perceived colour of the object will be that of the emitted radiation and it may be an additive colour resulting from the emission of more than one wavelength of radiation. When a substance absorbs radiation, its colour is determined by the subtraction of those wavelengths from white light. For example, absorption of red light results in the object being perceived as green. Scattering (and diffraction) occur when light falls on a material with a periodic variation in texture or refractive index having dimensions comparable to the wavelength of light. Light of a particular wavelength may be scattered preferentially, resulting in the appearance of colour.

**D20.4** In fluorescence, a molecule is first promoted from the vibrational ground level of a lower electronic state to a higher electronic energy state by absorption of energy. Because of the requirements of the Franck–Condon principle, the transition is usually to excited vibrational levels of the upper electronic state. Therefore, the absorption spectrum shows a vibrational structure characteristic of the upper state. The excited-state molecule can now lose energy to the surroundings through radiationless transitions and decay to the lowest vibrational level of the upper state. A spontaneous radiative transition now occurs to the lower electronic level and this fluorescence spectrum has a vibrational structure characteristic of the lower state. The fluorescence spectrum is not the mirror image of the absorption spectrum because the vibrational frequencies of the upper and lower states are different due to the difference in their potential energy curves. Because the molecule loses energy through radiationless transitions in the upper electronic state, the fluorescence spectrum is typically observed to longer wavelength, and therefore lower energy than the excitation spectrum.

The first steps of phosphorescence are the same as in fluorescence: energy is absorbed in a transition to an excited state and non-radiative vibrational relaxation occurs within the excited electronic state. A radiationless transition may also occur to a nearby electronic state with a different electronic spin. The probability of such an intersystem crossing is enhanced by the presence of a heavy atom, which can provide angular momentum via strong spin–orbit coupling. Because the initial, ground state of the molecule is usually a singlet state, excitation normally occurs to another singlet state, with intersystem crossing to a nearby triplet state. The electron may remain in the triplet state for unusually long periods because the emission transition from a triplet state to a singlet state is spin-forbidden. Just as for fluorescence, the excitation spectrum is characteristic of the vibrational structure of the excited electronic state and the emission spectrum is characteristic of the ground electronic state. Similarly, radiationless transitions between vibrational states mean that the phosphorescence spectrum is also observed at a longer wavelength, lower energy than the absorption spectrum.

**D20.5** The basic requirement for a laser is that it has at least three energy levels. Of these levels, the highest lying state must be capable of being efficiently populated above its thermal equilibrium value by a pulse of radiation. A second state, lower in energy, must be a metastable state with a long enough lifetime for it to accumulate a population greater than its thermal equilibrium value by spontaneous transitions from the higher overpopulated state. The metastable state must then be capable of undergoing stimulated transitions to a third, lower lying, state. This last requirement implies not only that the population of the metastable state is greater than that at thermal equilibrium, but also that it is higher than that of the third, lower lying, state. The states must therefore achieve population inversion. The amplification process occurs when low intensity radiation of frequency equal to the transition frequency between the metastable state and the lower lying state stimulates the transition to the lower lying state and many more photons (higher intensity of the radiation) of that frequency are created.

Two important applications of lasers in chemistry have been to Raman spectroscopy and to the development of time resolved spectroscopy. Prior to the invention of lasers the source of intense monochromatic radiation required for Raman spectroscopy was a large spiral discharge tube with liquid mercury electrodes. The intense heat generated by the large current required to produce the radiation had to be dissipated by water-cooled jackets and exposures of several weeks were sometimes necessary to observe the weaker Raman lines. These problems have been eliminated with the introduction of lasers as the source of the required monochromatic radiation. As a consequence, Raman spectroscopy has been revitalized and is now almost as routine as infrared spectroscopy. Time-resolved laser spectroscopy can be used to study the dynamics of chemical reactions. Laser pulses are used to obtain the absorption, emission, and Raman spectrum of reactants, intermediates, products, and even transition states of reactions. When we want to study the rates at which energy is transferred from one mode to another in a molecule, we need femtosecond and picosecond pulses. These time scales are available from mode-locked lasers and their development has opened up the possibility of examining the details of chemical reactions at a level that would have been unimaginable before.

**D20.6** Fluorescence is the most widely used form of spectroscopy in the study of biological substances. Fluorescence is a particularly powerful technique because there are many biological reactions, solvent rearrangements, and molecular motion processes that take place on the timescale of the fluorescent lifetime. Applications of fluorescence include the measurement of ligand binding to macromolecules, the use of fluorescent labels to macromolecules as environmental probes, the monitoring of conformational changes, and as a means of following a reaction. Cellular processes can be studied by detecting with a microscope the fluorescence emission from molecules used to tag biological macromolecules. In fluorescence microscopy, images of biological cells at work are obtained by attaching a large number of fluorescent molecules to proteins, nucleic acids, and membranes and the measuring of the distribution of fluorescence intensity within the illuminated area. Special techniques permit the observation of fluorescence from single molecules in cells. A common fluorescent label is the green fluorescent protein found in certain jellyfish. With proper filtering to remove light due to Rayleigh scattering of the incident beam, it is possible to collect light from a sample that contains only fluorescence from the label.

# Solutions to exercises

**E20.1** We may combine eqns 20.1 and 20.2 and then rearrange to give an expression for the molar absorption coefficient

$$\epsilon = -\frac{\log(I/I_0)}{[\mathrm{J}]L} = \frac{A}{[\mathrm{J}]L} = \frac{A}{(n_\mathrm{J}/V)L} = \frac{A}{\{(m_\mathrm{J}/M_J)/V\}L} = \frac{M_\mathrm{J}V\,A}{m_\mathrm{J}L}$$
$$= -\frac{(502\ \mathrm{g\ mol^{-1}}) \times (0.500\ \ \mathrm{dm^3}) \times (1.011)}{(17.2 \times 10^{-3}\ \mathrm{g\ mol^{-1}}) \times (1.00\ \mathrm{cm})}$$
$$= \mathbf{1.48 \times 10^4\ \ dm^3\ mol\ cm^{-1}}$$

(b) According to the Beer–Lambert law, if the concentration of a sample doubles, the absorbance halves. Thus, the transmission is

$$T = 10^{-A} = 10^{-2\times1.011} = \mathbf{9.506 \times 10^{-3}}$$

**E20.2** Absorbance is given by the logarithm of transmittance, so that

$$A = -\log T = -\log(0.22) = \mathbf{0.66}$$

Then, applying the Beer–Lambert law, eqn 20.4,

$$\epsilon = -\frac{\log(T)}{[\mathrm{J}]L}$$
$$= -\frac{\log(0.22)}{(0.080\mathrm{mol\ dm^{-3}}) \times (1.5 \times 10^{-1}\ \mathrm{cm})} = \mathbf{55\ \ dm^3\ mol\ cm^{-1}}$$

If the path length doubles to 3.0 mm, then we should expect the absorbance also to double. Hence, the transmittance becomes

$$T = 10^{-A} = 10^{-2\times0.66} = \mathbf{0.048}$$

**E20.3** Applying the Beer–Lambert law, eqn 20.4, then for two solutions with different concentrations and path lengths that give rise to the same transmittance, we may write

$$\log T = -\epsilon[\mathrm{J}]_1 L_1 = -\epsilon[\mathrm{J}]_2 L_2$$

and hence determine the concentration of the second solution as

$$[\mathrm{J}]_2 = \frac{[\mathrm{J}]_1 L_1}{L_2} = \frac{(25\ \mathrm{\mu g\ dm^{-3}}) \times (1.55\ \mathrm{cm})}{(1.18\ \mathrm{cm})} = \mathbf{33\ \mu g\ dm^{-3}}$$

**E20.4** The total absorbance is given by the sum of the absorbance of the two substances. thus, we may write

$$A = \epsilon_\mathrm{A}[\mathrm{A}]L + \epsilon_\mathrm{B}[\mathrm{B}]L = (\epsilon_\mathrm{A}[\mathrm{A}] + \epsilon_\mathrm{B}[\mathrm{B}])L$$

at both wavelengths. Hence,

$$1.6 = \{(10.0\ \mathrm{dm^3 mol^{-1} cm^{-1}}) \times [\mathrm{A}] + (15.0\ \mathrm{dm^3 mol^{-1} cm^{-1}}) \times [\mathrm{B}]\} \times (0.200\ \mathrm{cm})$$
$$2.4 = \{(18.0\ \mathrm{dm^3 mol^{-1} cm^{-1}}) \times [\mathrm{A}] + (12.0\ \mathrm{dm^3 mol^{-1} cm^{-1}}) \times [\mathrm{B}]\} \times (0.200\ \mathrm{cm})$$

Solving these two simultaneous equations gives the concentrations of the two substances as [A] = **0.56 mol dm$^{-3}$** and [B] = **0.16 mol dm$^{-3}$**.

**E20.5** The spectrum shows that there are isosbestic points at three wavenumbers. As explained in the text, the presence of isosbestic points is good evidence that only two solutes in equilibrium with each other are present. In this example, the solutes responsible for the absorption are are Her(CNS)$_8$ and Her(OH)$_8$.

**E20.6** We may use the particle-in-a-one-dimensional box model to describe the π system of a linear polyene. The wavefunctions for the electronic states are given by eqn 12.8,

$$\psi_n = (2/L)^{1/2}\sin\frac{n\pi x}{L}$$

where $n$ = 1, 2, 3, …. The lowest energy, longest wavelength transition will be that from the highest occupied molecular orbital (HOMO) to the lowest unoccupied molecular orbital (LUMO). For a polyene with $N$ atoms, these orbitals correspond to $n_{\text{HOMO}} = (N/2)$ and $n_{\text{LUMO}} = (N/2) + 1$. The intensity of the transition is given by the overlap integral between the states

$$\begin{aligned} I &\propto \int_0^L \psi_{\text{LUMO}}\,\hat{\mu}_x\psi_{\text{HOMO}}\,\mathrm{d}x \\ &= \int_0^L (2/L)^{1/2}\sin\frac{\{(N/2)+1\}\pi x}{L}\times(xe)\times(2/L)^{1/2}\sin\frac{(N/2)\pi x}{L}\,\mathrm{d}x \\ &= (2e/L)\int_0^L \sin\frac{\{(N/2)+1\}\pi x}{L}\,x\sin\frac{(N/2)\pi x}{L}\,\mathrm{d}x \end{aligned}$$

This is a standard integral, so that

$$I \propto \frac{2eL}{\pi^2}\left\{\frac{N(N+2)}{(N+1)^2}\right\}$$

We may assume that the length of the box is given by the number of carbon–carbon bonds, which for a chain of $N$ atoms is $N+1$ multiplied by the length of a bond

$$L = (N+1)d$$

so that

$$I \propto \frac{(N+1)ed}{\pi^2}\left\{\frac{N(N+2)}{(N+1)^2}\right\} = \frac{ed}{\pi^2}\left\{\frac{N(N+2)}{(N+1)}\right\}$$

The term in brackets increases with the number of carbon atoms in the polyene. This implies that to increase the intensity of the absorption, the chain should be **lengthened**.

The energy levels of a particle in a one-dimensional box are given by eqn 12.9

$$E_n = \frac{n^2h^2}{8mL^2}$$

Thus, the wavenumber of the transition is

$$\begin{aligned}\tilde{\nu} &= \frac{\Delta E_{\text{LUMO}\leftarrow\text{HOMO}}}{hc} = \frac{E_{\text{HOMO}} - E_{\text{LUMO}}}{hc} \\ &= [\{(N/2)+1\}^2 - (N/2)^2]\frac{h}{8mcL^2} \\ &= \frac{(N+1)}{8mcL^2} = \frac{(N+1)}{8mc\{(N+1)d\}^2} = \frac{1}{8mc(N+1)d}\end{aligned}$$

Hence, for a series of linear polyenes, the wavenumber of the lowest energy transition moves to lower wavenumber as the number of atoms in the chain increases; increasing the length of the polyene shifts the absorption to the **blue**.

**E20.7** The 30000 $cm^{-1}$ absorption observed in the spectrum of $CH_3CH{=}CHCHO$ is consistent with a *n*-to-π* transition in which a carbonyl lone-pair electron on oxygen is excited to a π* orbital. The transition at 46950 $cm^{-1}$ is lower than that expected for a π-to-π* transition in an unconjugated alkene. Nevertheless, we may assume that this absorption does indeed correspond to such a π-to-π* transition because the separation between the energy levels is lowered by conjugation.

**E20.8** Tryptophan (Trp) and tyrosine (Tyr) show the characteristic absorption of a phenyl group at about 280 nm. Cysteine (Cys) and glycine (Gly) lack the phenyl group as is evident from their spectra.

**E20.9** A fluorescence spectrum gives the vibrational separations of the lower electronic state. The wavelengths stated correspond to the wavenumbers 22730, 24390, 25640, and 27030 $cm^{-1}$, indicating spacings of 1660, 1250, and 1390 $cm^{-1}$. The sharp cut off at short wavelength implies that the transition observed at 370 nm is to the ground vibrational state. The spacing of peaks in the absorption spectrum, however, gives the separation of the vibrational levels of the upper electronic state. The wavenumbers of the absorption peaks are 27800, 29000, 30300, and 32800 $cm^{-1}$. The vibrational spacings are therefore 1200, 1300, and 2500 $cm^{-1}$. The sharp increase in intensity in the absorption spectrum implies that there are no vibrational levels in the upper electronic state at lower energies, and thus longer wavelengths.

This observation that the origin band, observed at 370 nm in the fluorescence and 360 nm in the absorption spectrum, is the most intense with only limited vibrational structure implies that there is little change in the structure of the molecule upon electronic excitation.

**E20.10** The difference in the A and B spectra imply that after some vibrational decay the benzophenone can transfer its energy to naphthalene. The latter then emits the energy radiatively.

**E20.11** The lifetime of the unimolecular photochemical reaction is

$$\tau = \frac{1}{k} = \frac{1}{1.7 \times 10^{4}\ \mathrm{s}^{-1}} = 5.9 \times 10^{-5}\mathrm{s} = 59\ \mu s$$

This is much longer than that of fluorescence ($1.0 \times 10^{-9}$ s) so we conclude that the excited singlet state decays too rapidly to be the precursor of this photochemical reaction. The lifetime of phosphorescence ($1.0 \times 10^{-3}$ s) is longer than the reaction lifetime making the **triplet state** the likely reaction precursor.

**E20.12** We may write the reaction scheme as

$$\mathrm{M} + h\nu \rightarrow \mathrm{M}^* \qquad \text{excitation, } I_{\mathrm{abs}}$$
$$\mathrm{M}^* + \mathrm{Q} \rightarrow \mathrm{M} + \mathrm{Q} \qquad \text{quenching, } k_{\mathrm{Q}}$$
$$\mathrm{M}^* \rightarrow \mathrm{M} + h\nu \qquad \text{fluorescence, } k_{\mathrm{f}}$$

Hence, applying the steady-state approximation, we may assume that the concentration of the excited-state intermediate $\mathrm{M}^*$ is constant. The rate of formation therefore must equal the rate of loss, so that

$$\text{Rate of change of } [\mathrm{M}^*] = \overbrace{I_{\mathrm{abs}}}^{\substack{\text{rate of}\\ \text{formation}\\ \text{of M}^*}} - \overbrace{\{k_{\mathrm{f}}[\mathrm{M}^*] + k_{\mathrm{Q}}[\mathrm{Q}][\mathrm{M}^*]\}}^{\substack{\text{rate of}\\ \text{loss}\\ \text{of M}^*}} = 0$$

Rearranging,

$$[\mathrm{M}^*] = \frac{I_{\mathrm{abs}}}{k_{\mathrm{f}} + k_{\mathrm{Q}}[\mathrm{Q}]}$$

The intensity of the fluorescence is therefore

$$I_{\mathrm{f}} = k_{\mathrm{f}}[\mathrm{M}^*] = k_{\mathrm{f}}\frac{I_{\mathrm{abs}}}{k_{\mathrm{f}} + k_{\mathrm{Q}}[\mathrm{Q}]} = \frac{I_{\mathrm{abs}}}{1 + (k_{\mathrm{Q}}/k_{\mathrm{f}})[\mathrm{Q}]}$$

We may rearrange this expression into the form of the equation for a straight line graph

$$\overbrace{\frac{1}{I_f}}^{y} = \overbrace{\frac{1}{I_{\mathrm{abs}}}}^{\text{intercept}} + \overbrace{\left(\frac{k_{\mathrm{Q}}/k_{\mathrm{f}}}{I_{\mathrm{abs}}}\right)}^{\text{slope}} \times \overbrace{[\mathrm{Q}]}^{x}$$

Figure 20.1 shows a plot of the reciprocal of the fluorescence intensity against the quencher concentration. Denoting the units of the intensity as au, the intercept of the plot is 1.97 $\mathrm{au}^{-1}$ and the slope is 424 au $\mathrm{mol}^{-1}$ $\mathrm{dm}^{3}$. The values of the slope and intercept may be used to calculate the ratio $k_{\mathrm{Q}} / k_{\mathrm{f}}$

$$\frac{\text{slope}}{\text{intercept}} = \left(\frac{k_{\mathrm{Q}}/k_{\mathrm{f}}}{I_{\mathrm{abs}}}\right) / \left(\frac{1}{I_{\mathrm{abs}}}\right) = k_{\mathrm{Q}}/k_{\mathrm{f}}$$

so that

$$k_{\mathrm{Q}} = \frac{\text{slope}}{\text{intercept}} \times k_{\mathrm{f}} = \frac{\text{slope}}{\text{intercept}} \times \frac{1}{\tau} = \frac{\text{slope}}{\text{intercept}} \times \frac{\ln 2}{t_{1/2}}$$

$$= \frac{424\ \text{au mol}^{-1}\ \text{dm}^3}{1.97\ \text{au}} \times \frac{\ln 2}{29 \times 10^{-6}\text{s}} = \mathbf{5.16 \times 10^6\ mol^{-1}\ dm^3\ s^{-1}}$$

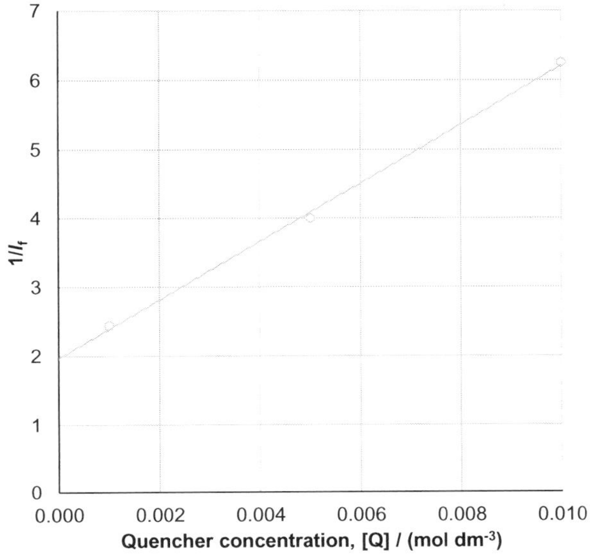


**Figure 20.1**

**E20.13** We may express the Stern–Volmer equation, eqn 20.12,

$$\frac{\phi_{F,0}}{\phi_F} = 1 + \tau_0 k_Q[Q]$$

in terms of the lifetime of excited $O_2$ in the presence and absence of a quencher as

$$\overbrace{\frac{1}{\tau}}^{y} = \overbrace{\frac{1}{\tau_0}}^{\text{intercept}} + \overbrace{k_Q}^{\text{slope}}\ \overbrace{[Q]}^{x}$$

This expression has the same form as the equation for a straight-line graph, $y = b + ax$. Figure 20.2 shows a plot of the reciprocal of the lifetime in the presence of a quencher, $1 / \tau$, against the concentration of the quencher, [Q], for the data given. The slope of the graph is $0.1276 \times \{10^9\ \text{s}^{-1} / (10^{-2}\ \text{mol dm}^{-3})\}$ so that the quenching rate constant is $\mathbf{k_f = 1.276 \times 10^{10}\ mol^{-1}\ dm^3\ s^{-1}}$.

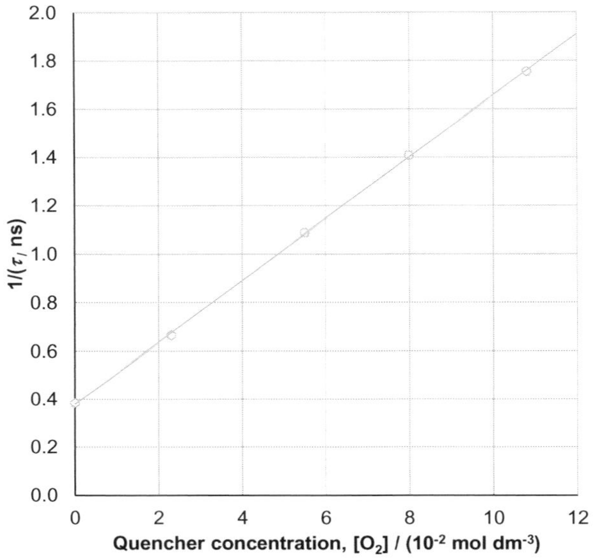


**Figure 20.2**

**E20.14** We may assume that the concentration of the excited-state of the excited state of the plant pigment, denoted $M^*$, is constant. The rate of formation by excitation must therefore equal the rate of loss, so that

$$\text{Rate of change of } [M^*] = \overbrace{I_{abs}}^{\substack{\text{rate of}\\ \text{formation}\\ \text{of } M^*}} - \overbrace{\{k_f[M^*] + k_Q[Q][M^*]\}}^{\substack{\text{rate of}\\ \text{loss}\\ \text{of } M^*}} = 0$$

Rearranging,

$$[M^*] = \frac{I_{abs}}{k_f + k_Q[Q]}$$

The intensity of the fluorescence is therefore

$$I_f = k_f[M^*] = k_f\frac{I_{abs}}{k_f + k_Q[Q]} = \frac{I_{abs}}{1 + (k_Q/k_f)[Q]}$$

We may rearrange this expression into the form of the equation for a straight line graph

$$\overbrace{(I_{abs}/I_f)}^{y} = \overbrace{1}^{\text{intercept}} + \overbrace{(k_Q/k_f)}^{\text{slope}} \times \overbrace{[Q]}^{x}$$

Figure 20.3 shows a plot of the reciprocal of the relative intensity of the fluorescent to the incident radiation, $(I_f / I_{abs})^{-1}$ against quencher concentration [Q]. The slope of the plot is $k_Q / k_f = 2.268\ \text{mmol}^{-1}\ \text{dm}^3$.

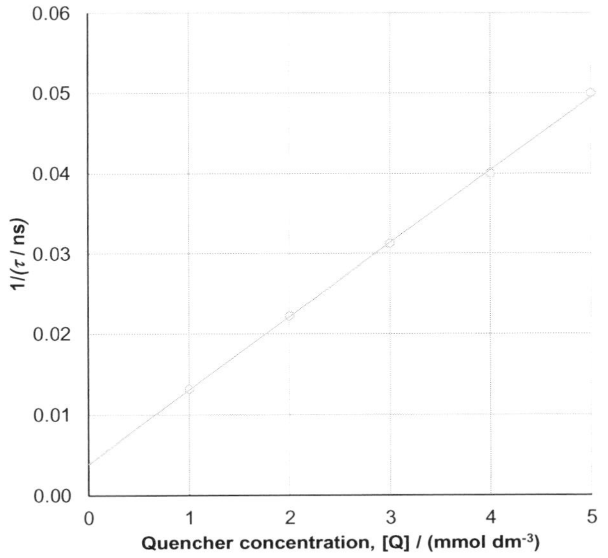


Figure 20.3

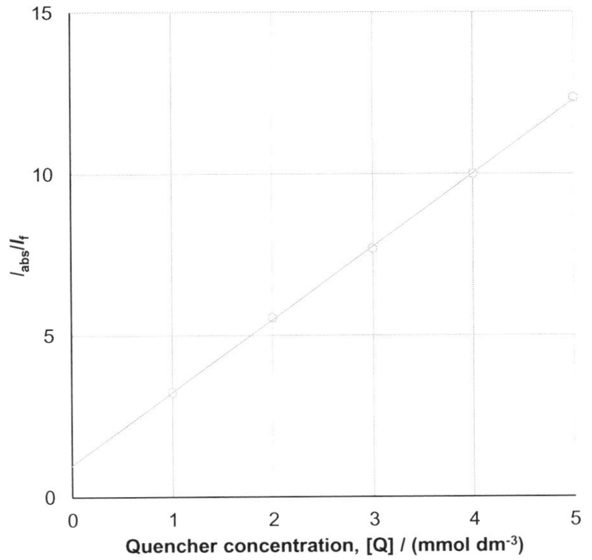


Figure 20.4

We may, however, determine the value of the quenching rate constant, $k_Q$, from the second series of measurements by writing the Stern–Volmer equation, eqn 20.12, as

$$\overbrace{\frac{1}{\tau}}^{y} = \overbrace{\frac{1}{\tau_0}}^{\text{intercept}} + \overbrace{k_Q}^{\text{slope}}\overbrace{[Q]}^{x}$$

Figure 20.4 shows how the reciprocal lifetime of the excited state of the plant pigment varies with the quencher concentration. The slope of the graph is $k_Q = 9.146 \times 10^{-3} \times \{10^9\ s^{-1} / (10^{-3}\ mol\ dm^{-3})\} = \mathbf{9.146 \times 10^9\ mol^{-1}\ dm^3\ s^{-1}}$.

The half life for fluorescence may then be calculated from the slopes of the two graphs as

$$t_{1/2} = (\ln 2) \times \tau = (\ln 2) \times \frac{1}{k_f} = (\ln 2) \times \frac{(k_Q/k_f)}{k_Q}$$
$$= (\ln 2) \times \frac{(2.268 \times 10^3 \text{mol}^{-1}\ \text{dm}^3)}{(9.146 \times 10^9 \text{mol}^{-1} \text{dm}^3\ \text{s}^{-1})} = 1.72 \times 10^{-7}\ \text{s} = \mathbf{0.172\ \mu s}$$

**E20.15** The quantum efficiency is given by the ratio of the lifetimes of the excited state in the presence and absence of the quencher

$$\frac{\phi_F}{\phi_{F,0}} = \frac{\tau}{\tau_0} = \frac{0.8\ \text{ns}}{1.2\ \text{ns}} = \mathbf{0.67}$$

**E20.16** We may rearrange eqn 20.15 to test whether the data are consistent with Förster theory. Thus, if

$$\eta_T = \frac{R_0^6}{R_0^6 + R^6}$$

then

$$\frac{1}{\eta_T} = \frac{R_0^6 + R^6}{R_0^6} = 1 + \frac{1}{R_0^6}R^6$$

This equation is of the same form as the equation for a straight-line graph. Figure 20.5 shows how the reciprocal of the efficiency, $\eta_T^{-1}$, varies with the sixth power of the separation between A and C, $R^6$. The graph is a straight line with an intercept of 1, implying that Förster theory does indeed adequately describe the data. The slope of the plot is $5.503 \times 10^{-4}\ nm^6$ so that the value of $R_0$ for the A–C pair is

$$R_0 = (\text{slope})^{-1/6} = (5.503 \times 10^{-4}\ \text{nm}^6)^{-1/6} = \mathbf{3.49\ nm}$$

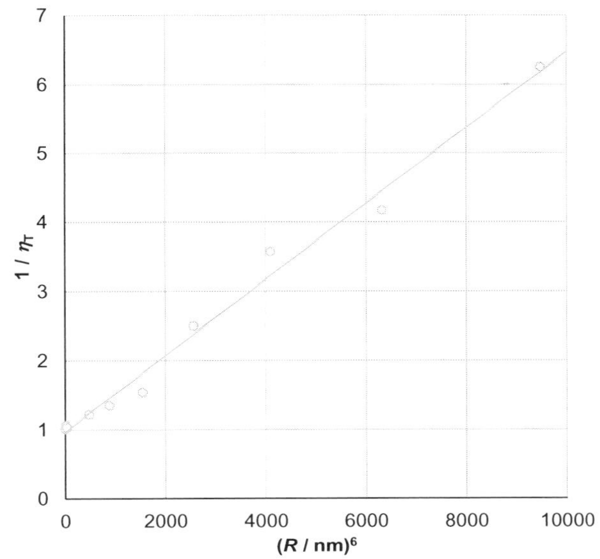


**Figure 20.5**

**E20.17** The number of photons emitted per second is given by the by the ratio of the power, $P$, to the energy of each photon, $E = hc / \lambda$. One photon is therefore emitted in a time interval of $(E / P)$. Hence, the time for $10^6$ photons to be emitted, and thus absorbed by the dye, is therefore

$$t = 10^6/(P/E) = 10^6E/P = 10^6\frac{(hc/\lambda)}{P} = 10^6\frac{hc}{P\lambda}$$
$$= \frac{10^6 \times (6.626 \times 10^{-34}\ \text{J s}) \times (2.998 \times 10^8\ \text{m s}^{-1})}{(1.0 \times 10^{-3}\ \text{J s}^{-1}) \times (488 \times 10^{-9}\ \text{m})}$$
$$= 4.07 \times 10^{-10}\text{s} = \mathbf{40.7\ ps}$$

**E20.18** The binding energy is equivalent to the ionization energy of the atom. Thus, rearranging eqn 20.16

$$I = h\nu - ½m_\text{e}v^2 = (hc/\lambda) - ½m_\text{e}v^2$$
$$= \{(6.626 \times 10^{-34}\text{J s}) \times (2.998 \times 10^8\ \text{m s}^{-1})/(100 \times 10^{-12}\ \text{m})\}$$
$$-\{½ \times (9.109 \times 10^{-31}\ \text{kg}) \times (2.34 \times 10^4 \times 10^3\ \text{ms}^{-1})^2\}$$
$$= \mathbf{1.737 \times 10^{-15}\ J}$$

**E20.19** The speed of the ejected photoelectron is related to the wavelength of the incident radiation through eqn 20.16,

$$h\nu = hc/\lambda = I + ½m_\text{e}v^2$$

Hence, rearranging,

$$\lambda = \frac{hc}{I + \tfrac{1}{2}m_e v^2}$$
$$= \frac{(6.626\times10^{-34}\,\text{J s})\times(2.998\times10^{8}\,\text{m s}^{-1})}{\{(21.4\,\text{eV})\times(1.602\times10^{-19}\,\text{J eV}^{-1})\}+\{\tfrac{1}{2}\times(9.109\times10^{-31}\,\text{kg})\times(1.03\times10^{6}\,\text{m s}^{-1})^2\}}$$
$$= 50.8\times10^{-9}\,\text{m} = \mathbf{50.8\ nm}$$

**E20.20** An electron that is accelerated through a potential difference $\Delta\phi$ acquires a kinetic energy $e\Delta\phi$. Thus, for a potential difference of 10 kV, the kinetic energy is

$$E_k = e\Delta\phi = (1.602\times10^{-19}\,\text{C})\times\overbrace{(10\times10^{3}\,\text{V})}^{1\,\text{V}=1\,\text{J C}^{-1}} = \mathbf{1.602\times10^{-16}\ J}$$

**E20.21** (a) From eqn 20.16,

$$h\nu = hc/\lambda = I + \overbrace{\tfrac{1}{2}m_e v^2}^{\text{kinetic energy, } E_k}$$

Hence, rearranging,

$$E_k = hc/\lambda - I$$
$$= \frac{(6.626\times10^{-34}\,\text{J s})\times(2.998\times10^{8}\,\text{m s}^{-1})}{(110\times10^{-9}\,\text{m})} - \{(10.0\,\text{eV})\times(1.602\times10^{-19}\,\text{J eV}^{-1})\}$$
$$= \mathbf{2.04\times10^{-19}\ J}$$

(b) This is equivalent to a speed

$$v = (2E_k/m_e)^{1/2} = \{2\times(2.04\times10^{-19}\,\text{J})/(9.109\times10^{-31}\,\text{kg})\}^{1/2}$$
$$= 669\times10^{3}\,\text{m s}^{-1} = \mathbf{669\ km\ s^{-1}}$$

**E20.22** The ionization energy for each of the orbitals is given by rearranging eqn 20.16

$$I = h\nu - E_k = 21.21\,\text{eV} - 11.01\,\text{eV} = 10.20\,\text{eV}$$
$$= 21.21\,\text{eV} - 8.23\,\text{eV} = 12.98\,\text{eV}$$
$$= 21.21\,\text{eV} - 5.22\,\text{eV} = 15.99\,\text{eV}$$

Figure 20.6 shows the relationship between the incident energy, the kinetic energy of the ejected photoelectrons and the energies of the molecular orbitals.

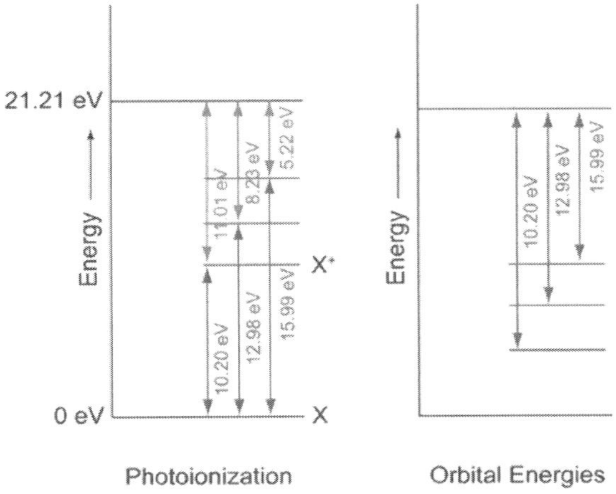


Figure 20.6

## Answers to projects

**P20.23** (a) The proportion of photons transmitted to the retina is

$$1 \times \overbrace{(1-0.30)}^{\substack{\text{not scattered}\\ \text{or absorbed}\\ \text{by atmosphere}}} \times \overbrace{(1-0.25-0.09)}^{\substack{\text{not absorbed}\\ \text{or scattered}\\ \text{by}\\ \text{cornea}}} \times \overbrace{(1-0.43)}^{\substack{\text{not absorbed}\\ \text{in ocular}\\ \text{medium}}} = 0.263$$

Flux is the number of incident particles (in this case, photons) per unit of surface area per unit time. The number of photons focused on the retina in 0.1 s is therefore

$$0.263 \times \overbrace{(4\times 10^3\ \text{mm}^{-2}\ \text{s}^{-1})}^{\text{flux from North Star}} \times \overbrace{(0.1\ \text{s})}^{\substack{\text{time}\\ \text{interval}}} \times \overbrace{(40\ \text{mm}^2)}^{\text{area}} = \mathbf{4200}$$

(b) According to the particle-in-a-box model, the energy levels of a conjugated polyene such as retinal are given by eqn 12.9

$$E = \frac{n^2h^2}{8mL^2}$$

with $n = 1, 2, 3 \ldots$ The lowest energy transition corresponds to that from the highest occupied molecular orbital (HOMO) to the lowest unoccupied molecular orbital (LUMO). Retinal consists of $N = 10$ conjugated carbon atoms, each of which contribute one electron to the π system. The molecular orbitals are doubly occupied, so the transition therefore corresponds to an excitation from a state with $n = 5$ to $n = 6$. There are $N - 1 = 9$ carbon–carbon bonds, 4 single, and 5 double, with a mean bond length $d = 140$ pm. The best agreement between theory and experiment are obtained when an extra half bond length is added to each end of box, giving a length of $Nd = 10d$.

Hence, the wavelength of the lowest energy transition is

$$\lambda = \frac{hc}{\Delta E} = \frac{hc}{(E_{\text{LUMO}} - E_{\text{HOMO}})} = \frac{hc}{(n_{\text{HOMO}}^2 - n_{\text{LUMO}}^2)h^2/(8m_e L^2)}$$

$$= \frac{8 \times (9.109 \times 10^{-31}\ \text{kg}) \times (10 \times 140 \times 10^{-12}\ \text{m})^2 \times (2.998 \times 10^8\ \text{m s}^{-1})}{(6^2 - 5^2) \times (6.626 \times 10^{-34}\text{J s})}$$

$$= 588 \times 10^{-9}\text{m} = \mathbf{588\ nm}$$

**P20.24** (a) The fluorescence quantum yield is given by eqns 20.14 and 20.15. Equating these two expressions,

$$\eta_{\text{T}} = \frac{\phi_{\text{F,0}} - \phi_{\text{F}}}{\phi_{\text{F,0}}} = \frac{R_0^6}{R_0^6 - R^6}$$

Hence, rearranging

$$\frac{R_0^6}{R_0^6 - R^6} = 1 - (\phi_{\text{F}}/\phi_{\text{F,0}})$$

$$\frac{R_0^6 - R^6}{R_0^6} = \frac{1}{1 - (\phi_{\text{F}}/\phi_{\text{F,0}})}$$

$$(R/R_0)^6 = \frac{(\phi_{\text{F}}/\phi_{\text{F,0}})}{1 - (\phi_{\text{F}}/\phi_{\text{F,0}})}$$

The ratio of the quantum yields is given by the ratio of the lifetimes in the absence and presence of the quencher,

$$(\phi_{\text{F}}/\phi_{\text{F,0}}) = \tau_{\text{F,0}}/\tau_{\text{F}} = (10 \times 10^{-12}\text{s})/(1 \times 10^{-9}\text{s}) = 0.01$$

Thus,

$$R = R_0 \times \left\{\frac{(\phi_{\text{F}}/\phi_{\text{F,0}})}{1 - (\phi_{\text{F}}/\phi_{\text{F,0}})}\right\}^{1/6} = (5.6\ \text{nm}) \times \left(\frac{0.01}{1 - 0.01}\right)^{1/6} = \mathbf{2.6\ nm}$$

(b) Although the charge-transfer reaction involving ground-state chlorophyll,

$$\text{C} + \text{Q} \rightarrow \text{C}^+ + \text{Q}^- \qquad (1)$$

is not spontaneous, the reaction between excited-state chlorophyll

$$\text{C}^* + \text{Q} \rightarrow \text{C}^+ + \text{Q}^- \qquad (2)$$

is spontaneous. The difference between the Gibbs energies of the two reactions is equal to the excitation energy of chlorophyll

$$\Delta_r G(2) - \Delta_r G(1) \approx E(\text{C}) - E(\text{C}^*) \approx E_{\text{HOMO}} - E_{\text{LUMO}} < 0$$

which may be approximated by the difference between the energy of the lowest unoccupied molecular orbital (LUMO) and highest occupied molecular orbital (HOMO). The excitation therefore lowers the Gibbs energy of reaction.

# Chapter 21

# Spectroscopy: magnetic resonance

## Answers to discussion questions

**D21.1** The local contribution to the shielding constant results from the contribution of the electrons in the atom that contains the nucleus being observed. It can be expressed as a sum of a diamagnetic and paramagnetic parts, that is $\sigma(\text{local}) = \sigma_d + \sigma_p$. The diamagnetic part, $\sigma_d$, arises because the applied field generates a circulation of charge in the ground state of the atom. In turn, the circulating charge generates a magnetic field. The direction of this field can be found through Lenz's law which states that the induced magnetic field must be opposite in direction to the field producing it. Thus, the resulting field shields the nucleus. The diamagnetic contribution is roughly proportional to the electron density on the atom and it is the only contribution for closed-shell free atoms and for distributions of charge that have spherical or cylindrical symmetry. The local paramagnetic contribution, $\sigma_p$, is somewhat harder to visualize since there is no simple and basic principle analogous to Lenz's law that can be used to explain the effect. The applied field adds a term to the Hamiltonian of the atom which mixes in excited electronic states into the ground state and any theoretical calculation of the effect requires detailed knowledge of the excited state wave functions. It is to be noted that the paramagnetic contribution does not require that the atom or molecule be paramagnetic. It is paramagnetic only in the sense in that it results in an induced field in the same direction as the applied field.

The neighbouring group contributions arise in a manner similar to the local contributions. Both diamagnetic and paramagnetic currents are induced in the neighbouring atoms and these currents results in shielding contributions to the nucleus of the atom being observed. However, there are some differences: The magnitude of the effect is much smaller because the induced currents in neighbouring atoms are much farther away. It also depends on the anisotropy of the magnetic susceptibility of the neighbouring group. Only anisotropic susceptibilities result in a contribution.

Solvents can influence the local field in many different ways. Detailed theoretical calculations of the effect are difficult due to the complex nature of the solute–solvent interaction. Polar solvent–polar solute interactions are an electric field effect that usually causes deshielding of the solute protons. Solvent magnetic anisotropy can cause shielding or deshielding, for example, for solutes in benzene solution. In addition, there are a variety of specific chemical interactions between solvent and solute that can affect the chemical shift.

**D21.2** Both spin–lattice and spin–spin relaxation are caused by fluctuating magnetic and electric fields at the nucleus in question and these fields result from the random thermal motions present in the solution or other form of matter. These random motions can be a result of a number of processes and it is hard to summarize all that could be important. In theory, every known nuclear interaction coupled with every type of motion can contribute to relaxation and detailed treatments can be exceedingly complex. However, they all depend on the magnetogyric ratio of the atom in question and the magnetogyric ratio of the proton is much larger than that of $^{13}$C. Hence, the interaction of the proton with fluctuating local magnetic fields caused by the presence of neighbouring magnetic nuclei will be greater, and the relaxation will be quicker, corresponding to a shorter relaxation time for protons. Another consideration is the structure of compounds containing carbon and hydrogen. Typically, the C atoms are in the interior of the molecule bonded to other C atoms, 99 per cent of which are nonmagnetic, so the primary relaxation effects are due to bonded protons. Protons are on the outside of the molecule and are subject to many more interactions and hence faster relaxation.

**D21.3** At room temperature, the tumbling rate of a small molecule such as benzene in a mobile solvent, may be close to the Larmor frequency, and hence its spin–lattice relaxation time will be short. As the temperature increases, the tumbling rate may increase well beyond the Larmor frequency, resulting in an increased spin–lattice relaxation time.

For a larger molecule, such as an oligopeptide at room temperature, the tumbling rate may be well below the Larmor frequency, but with increasing temperature, it will approach the Larmor frequency due to the increased thermal motion of the molecule combined with the decreased viscosity of the solvent. Therefore, the spin–lattice relaxation time may decrease.

**D21.4** Spin–spin couplings in NMR are due to a polarization mechanism, which is transmitted through bonds. The following description applies to the coupling between the protons in $H_X$–C–$H_Y$ group as is typically found in organic compounds. On $H_X$, the Fermi contact interaction causes the spins of its proton and electron to be aligned antiparallel. The spin of the electron from C in the $H_X$–C bond is then aligned antiparallel to the electron from $H_X$ due to the Pauli exclusion principle. The spin of the C electron in the bond $H_Y$ is aligned parallel to the electron from $H_X$ because of Hund's rule. Finally, the alignment is transmitted through the second bond in the same manner as the first. This progression of alignments (antiparallel × antiparallel × parallel × antiparallel × antiparallel) yields an overall energetically favourable parallel alignment of the two proton nuclear spins. Therefore, in this case, the coupling constant, $^2J_{HH}$ is negative in sign.

**D21.5** The molecular orbital occupied by the unpaired electron in an organic radical can be identified through the observation of hyperfine splitting in the electron paramagnetic resonance spectrum of the radical. The magnitude of this splitting is proportional to the spin density of the unpaired electron at those positions in the radical having atoms with nuclear moments. In addition, the spin density on carbon atoms adjacent to the magnetic nuclei can be determined indirectly through the McConnell relation. Thus, for example, in the benzene negative ion, unpaired spin densities on both the carbon atoms and hydrogen atoms can be determined from the EPR hyperfine splittings. The next step then is to construct a molecular orbital which will theoretically reproduce these experimentally determined spin densities. A good match indicates that we have found a good molecular orbital for the radical.

**D21.6** The mechanism for the hyperfine interaction of a proton in a methyl group attached to an aromatic ring is not the same as the mechanism responsible for the McConnell equation eqn 21.26 that explains the hyperfine interaction of a proton attached to a ring carbon atom. However, we still expect a proportionality between the hyperfine splitting constant, $a$, and the spin density, $\rho$, on the ring carbon atom. The hyperfine interaction in this case is due to the overlap of the proton wavefunctions in the methyl group with the $p_z$ orbital of the ring carbon atom which has unpaired electron density (spin density). The strength of the interaction will however be angularly dependent. The wavefunction for a $p_z$ orbital indicates a distribution of spin density in the plane of the ring of the form $\psi_\theta^2 = \psi_0^2 \cos^2\theta$ where $\psi_\theta^2$ and $\psi_0^2$ are the spin densities corresponding to the angles $\theta$ and 0°. On the assumption that the hyperfine splitting follows a similar relationship, one expects that the maximum splitting when the C–H bond is in a plane parallel to the $p_z$ orbital and zero interaction in a plane perpendicular to it. Therefore, for each proton in the methyl group, we can write $a = Q_{\mathrm{CCH}}\rho_{\mathrm{C}} \cos^2\theta$. The value of the parameter $a$ will be different for each proton of the group and will change as the methyl group rotates. In rapid rotation the three splittings will be averaged to one value.

## Solutions to exercises

**E21.1** Given eqns 21.1 and 21.3,

$$E_{m_I} = -\gamma_{\mathrm{N}}\hbar\mathcal{B}m_I$$
$$E_{m_I} = -g_I\mu_{\mathrm{N}}\mathcal{B}m_I$$

it follows that

$$\gamma_{\mathrm{N}} = g_I\mu_{\mathrm{N}}/\hbar$$

Nuclear $g$-factors are dimensionless numbers, the nuclear magneton $\mu_{\mathrm{N}}$ has units of J T$^{-1}$ and Planck's constant $h$ units of J s. Thus, the units of the nuclear magnetogyric ratio are

$$\mathrm{J\,T^{-1}/J\,s = T^{-1}\,s^{-1} = T^{-1}\,Hz}$$

Given that 1 T = 1 kg s$^{-2}$ A$^{-1}$, we may also express the units of the nuclear magnetogyric ratio as

$$\mathrm{T^{-1}Hz = (kg\,s^{-2}A^{-1})^{-1}s^{-1} = A\,s\,kg^{-1}}$$

**E21.2** Applying eqn 21.1 for each of the four spin states, $m_I = +3/2, +1/2, -1/2, -3/2$,

$$E_{m_I} = -\gamma_N \hbar \mathcal{B} m_I$$
$$E_{3/2} = -(2.054 \times 10^7\ \mathrm{T^{-1}s^{-1}}) \times \{(6.626 \times 10^{-34}\mathrm{J\ s})/2\pi\} \times (6.000\ \mathrm{T}) \times (-3/2)$$
$$= \mathbf{1.949 \times 10^{-26}\ J}$$

and in the same way,

$$E_{1/2} = \mathbf{6.498 \times 10^{-27}\ J}$$
$$E_{-1/2} = \mathbf{-6.498 \times 10^{-27}\ J}$$
$$E_{-3/2} = \mathbf{-1.949 \times 10^{-26}\ J}$$

The difference in energy between the states is thus $1.300 \times 10^{-26}$ J, which is equivalent to 7.826 mJ mol$^{-1}$.

**E21.3** Combining eqns 21.1 and 21.3,

$$E_{m_I} = -\gamma_N \hbar \mathcal{B} m_I$$
$$E_{m_I} = -g_I \mu_N \mathcal{B} m_I$$

it follows that

$$g_I = \hbar\gamma_N/\mu_N = \frac{\{(6.626 \times 10^{-34}\mathrm{J\ s})/2\pi\} \times (1.0840 \times 10^8\ \mathrm{T^{-1}\ s^{-1}})}{5.051 \times 10^{-27}\ \mathrm{J\ T^{-1}}} = \mathbf{2.263}$$

**E21.4** Using eqn 21.5b, the relative difference in population between the two spin states at 298 K is

(a) for protons, $^1$H nuclei,

$$\frac{N_\alpha - N_\beta}{N} = \frac{\gamma_N \hbar B}{2kT} = \frac{(26.752 \times 10^7\ \mathrm{T^{-1}s^{-1}}) \times \{(6.626 \times 10^{-34}\mathrm{J\ s})/2\pi\} \times 8.5\ \mathrm{T}}{2 \times (1.38 \times 10^{-23}\ \mathrm{J\ K^{-1}}) \times (298\ \mathrm{K})}$$
$$= \mathbf{2.9 \times 10^{-5}}$$

(b) for $^{13}$C nuclei,

$$\frac{N_\alpha - N_\beta}{N} = \frac{(6.7272 \times 10^7\ \mathrm{T^{-1}s^{-1}}) \times \{(6.626 \times 10^{-34}\mathrm{J\ s})/2\pi\} \times 8.5\ \mathrm{T}}{2 \times (1.38 \times 10^{-23}\ \mathrm{J\ K^{-1}}) \times (298\ \mathrm{K})}$$
$$= \mathbf{7.3 \times 10^{-6}}$$

**E21.5** Applying eqn 21.6, the resonance frequency is

$$\nu = \frac{\gamma_N \mathcal{B}}{2\pi} = \frac{(2.5177 \times 10^8\ \mathrm{T^{-1}s^{-1}}) \times (7.500\ \mathrm{T})}{2\pi}$$
$$= 300.5 \times 10^6\ \mathrm{s^{-1}} = \mathbf{330.5\ MHz}$$

**E21.6** Rearranging eqn 21.6,

$$\mathcal{B} = \frac{2\pi\nu}{\gamma_N} = \frac{2\pi \times (800.0 \times 10^6\ s^{-1})}{(26.752 \times 10^7\ T^{-1}s^{-1})} = \mathbf{18.79\ T}$$

**E21.7** From the definition of chemical shift, eqn 21.10,

$$\begin{aligned}\nu - \nu^o &= 10^{-6}\delta\nu^o = 10^{-6} \times 6.33 \times (500.0 \times 10^6\ s^{-1})\\ &= 3.17 \times 10^3\ s^{-1} = \mathbf{3.17\ kHz}\end{aligned}$$

**E21.8** From eqn 21.10

$$\delta = \frac{\nu - \nu^o}{\nu^o} \times 10^6$$

the difference in chemical shift is

$$\Delta\delta = \delta_{CHO} - \delta_{CH_3} = \frac{\nu_{CHO} - \nu_{CH_3}}{\nu^o} \times 10^6 = \frac{\Delta\nu}{\nu^o} \times 10^6$$

The resonance frequency is related to the local field through eqn 21.9,

$$\nu = \frac{\gamma_N}{2\pi}(1-\sigma)\mathcal{B} = \frac{\gamma_N}{2\pi}\mathcal{B}_{loc}$$

so that using eqn 21.6 to express the operating frequency of the spectrometer in terms of the applied magnetic field,

$$\Delta\mathcal{B}_{loc} = \frac{2\pi\Delta\nu}{\gamma_N} = \frac{2\pi \times \Delta\delta \times \nu^o}{10^6\gamma_N} = \frac{2\pi \times \Delta\delta \times (\gamma_N\mathcal{B}/2\pi)}{10^6\gamma_N} = \frac{\Delta\delta \times \mathcal{B}}{10^6}$$

Hence, for an applied field of 1.2 T,

$$\Delta\mathcal{B}_{loc} = \frac{(9.80 - 2.20) \times (1.2\ T)}{10^6} = 9.1 \times 10^{-6}\ T = 9.1\ \mu T$$

and

$$\Delta\mathcal{B}_{loc} = \frac{(9.80 - 2.20) \times (5.0\ T)}{10^6} = 38 \times 10^{-6}\ T = 3.8\ \mu T$$

**E21.9** Chemical shift is defined through eqn 21.10 as

$$\delta = \frac{\nu - \nu^o}{\nu^o} \times 10^6$$

The difference in frequency between the resonances is therefore,

$$\Delta\nu = \nu_{CH} - \nu_{CH_3} = 10^{-6} \times \left(\delta_{CH} - \delta_{CH_3}\right)\nu^o$$

so that for a 300 MHz spectrometer,

$$\Delta\nu = 10^{-6} \times (9.5 - 1.5) \times (300 \times 10^6\ Hz) = 2.4 \times 10^3\ Hz = \mathbf{2.4\ kHz}$$

and for a 750 MHz spectrometer,

$$\Delta\nu = 10^{-6} \times (9.5 - 1.5) \times (750 \times 10^{6}\ \text{Hz}) = 6.0 \times 10^{3}\ \text{Hz} = \mathbf{6.0\ kHz}$$

**E21.10** In general, coupling to $N$ magnetically equivalent protons results in splitting into $(N + 1)$ components. Thus, coupling to seven protons results in an **octet**.

**E21.11** A $^{14}N$ nucleus has spin $I = 1$, and thus exists in three spin states with $m_I = -1$, 0 and +1. (a) For two nuclei, the nuclear spin may combine in different ways, resulting in possible nuclear spin quantum numbers

$$I_{\text{total}} = I_1 + I_2, I_1 + I_2 - 1, \ldots |I_1 - I_2| = 1 + 1, 1 + 1 - 1, 1 - 1 = 2, 1, 0$$

For $I_{\text{total}} = 2$, there are five spin states with $m_L = -2, -1, 0, +1, +2$, each of which will give rise to a different component of the spectrum. In the same way, for $I_{\text{total}} = 1$, there are three spin states with $m_L = -1, 0, +1$ and for $I_{\text{total}} = 0$, just one spin state with $m_L = 0$. There is therefore only one way of forming spin states with $m_L = -2$ and +2. However, there are two ways of achieving each of the states with $m_L = -1$ and +1 and three ways of achieving the state with $m_L = 0$. Thus, the resonance appears as a quintet with relative intensities 1:2:3:2:1.

(b) We may follow the same process for three magnetically equivalent nuclei to demonstrate that the resonance will appear as a septet with relative intensities 1:3:6:7:6:3:1.

**E21.12** For an $AX_2$ spin system, there are eight possible spin states, with energies

$$\begin{aligned} E &= -\gamma_A h(1 - \sigma_A)\mathcal{B}m_A - \gamma_X h(1 - \sigma_X)\mathcal{B}m_{X_1} - \gamma_X h(1 - \sigma_X)\mathcal{B}m_{X_2} \\ &= -\gamma_A h(1 - \sigma_A)\mathcal{B}m_A - \gamma_X h(1 - \sigma_X)\mathcal{B}(m_{X_1} + m_{X_2}) \end{aligned}$$

It follows, by analogy with eqn 21.13, that the spin–spin coupling energy is

$$E_{\text{spin–spin}} = hJm_A(m_{X_1} + m_{X_2})$$

The table shows that the eight spin states correspond to three energy levels, with $E_{\text{spin–spin}} = -\tfrac{1}{2}hJ$, 0 and $+\tfrac{1}{2}hJ$.

| | $\alpha_A\,\alpha_{X_1}\alpha_{X_2}$ | $\alpha_A\,\alpha_{X_1}\beta_{X_2}$ | $\alpha_A\,\beta_{X_1}\alpha_{X_2}$ | $\alpha_A\,\beta_{X_1}\beta_{X_2}$ |
|---|---|---|---|---|
| $E_{\text{spin–spin}}$ | $+\tfrac{1}{2}hJ$ | 0 | 0 | $-\tfrac{1}{2}hJ$ |

| | $\beta_A\,\alpha_{X_1}\alpha_{X_2}$ | $\beta_A\,\alpha_{X_1}\beta_{X_2}$ | $\beta_A\,\beta_{X_1}\alpha_{X_2}$ | $\beta_A\,\beta_{X_1}\beta_{X_2}$ |
|---|---|---|---|---|
| $E_{\text{spin–spin}}$ | $-\tfrac{1}{2}hJ$ | 0 | 0 | $+\tfrac{1}{2}hJ$ |

The energies of the transitions that flip only the spin of the A nucleus, $\alpha \rightarrow \beta$, are

$$\Delta E = E(\beta_A\,\alpha_{X_1}\alpha_{X_2}) - E(\alpha_A\,\alpha_{X_1}\alpha_{X_2}) = (-\tfrac{1}{2}hJ) - \tfrac{1}{2}hJ = -hJ$$
$$\Delta E = E(\beta_A\,\alpha_{X_1}\beta_{X_2}) - E(\alpha_A\,\alpha_{X_1}\beta_{X_2}) = 0 - 0 = 0$$
$$\Delta E = E(\beta_A\,\beta_{X_1}\alpha_{X_2}) - E(\alpha_A\,\beta_{X_1}\alpha_{X_2}) = 0 - 0 = 0$$
$$\Delta E = E(\beta_A\,\beta_{X_1}\beta_{X_2}) - E(\alpha_A\,\beta_{X_1}\beta_{X_2}) = \tfrac{1}{2}hJ - (-\tfrac{1}{2}hJ) = hJ$$

giving rise to a triplet with transitions at energies $-hJ$, 0 and $+hJ$, with relative intensities in the ratio 1:2:1.

The energies of the transitions that flip only the spin of the $X_1$ (or $X_2$) nucleus, $\alpha \rightarrow \beta$, are

$$\Delta E = E(\alpha_A\,\beta_{X_1}\alpha_{X_2}) - E(\alpha_A\,\alpha_{X_1}\alpha_{X_2}) = 0 - \tfrac{1}{2}hJ = -\tfrac{1}{2}hJ$$
$$\Delta E = E(\alpha_A\,\beta_{X_1}\beta_{X_2}) - E(\alpha_A\,\alpha_{X_1}\beta_{X_2}) = -\tfrac{1}{2}hJ - 0 = -\tfrac{1}{2}hJ$$
$$\Delta E = E(\beta_A\,\beta_{X_1}\alpha_{X_2}) - E(\beta_A\,\alpha_{X_1}\alpha_{X_2}) = 0 - (-\tfrac{1}{2}hJ) = \tfrac{1}{2}hJ$$
$$\Delta E = E(\beta_A\,\beta_{X_1}\beta_{X_2}) - E(\beta_A\,\alpha_{X_1}\beta_{X_2}) = \tfrac{1}{2}hJ - 0 = \tfrac{1}{2}hJ$$

giving rise to a doublet with transitions at energies $-\tfrac{1}{2}hJ$ and $+\tfrac{1}{2}hJ$, with components of equal intensity.

**E21.13** The protons in acetaldehyde, $CH_3CHO$, resonate at two frequencies. Figure 21.4 of the text indicates that the chemical shift for three magnetically equivalent $CH_3$ protons is in the range $\delta = 1$–4. The resonance will be split into a doublet by the coupling to the CHO proton. The chemical shift for the CHO proton is $\delta = 9$–10, and the resonance will be split into a quartet as a result of coupling with the three $CH_3$ protons. The difference in frequency between the components of a multiplet is given by the coupling constant $J$. The splitting observed in the spectrum, however, depends upon the operating frequency of the spectrometer. From eqn 21.10

$$\delta = \frac{\nu - \nu^{o}}{\nu^{o}} \times 10^6$$

so, for a 300 MHz spectrometer, the difference in chemical shift between the components is

$$\Delta\delta = \frac{J}{\nu^{o}} \times 10^6 = \frac{2.90\ \text{Hz}}{300 \times 10^6\ \text{Hz}} \times 10^6 = 0.0096$$

and, for a 550 MHz spectrometer is

$$\Delta\delta = \frac{2.90\ \text{Hz}}{550 \times 10^6\ \text{Hz}} \times 10^6 = 0.0053$$

The integrated area under the doublet will be three times that under the triplet because it arises from three protons. The expected spectrum is shown in Figure 21.1.

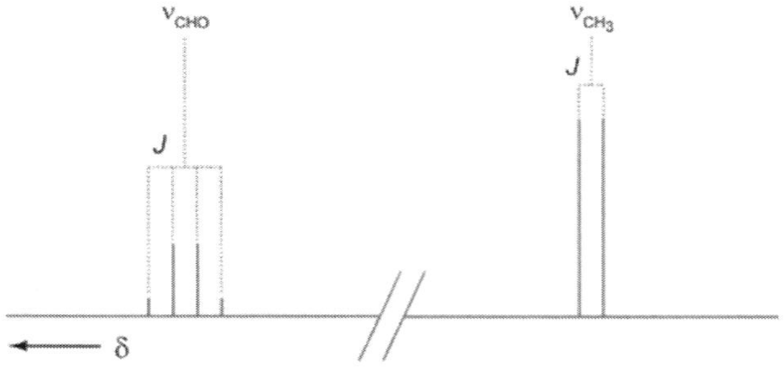


**Figure 21.1**

**E21.14** The four $^{19}F$ nuclei ($I = \frac{1}{2}$) are magnetically equivalent and are described as being isochronous. However, the $^{10}B$ nucleus ($I = 3$, 19.6 per cent abundant) splits the resonant frequency into $(2 \times 3) + 1 = 7$ components of equal intensity and the $^{11}B$ nucleus ($I = 3/2$, 80.4 per cent abundant) into $\{2 \times (3/2)\} + 1 = 4$ components of equal intensity. The splitting arising from the $^{11}B$ nucleus will be larger than that arising from the $^{10}B$ (because its magnetic moment is larger, by a factor of 1.5). Moreover, the total intensity of the four lines due to the $^{11}B$ nuclei will be greater (by a factor of $80.4/19.6 \approx 4$) than the total intensity of the seven lines due to the $^{10}B$ nuclei. The intensities of the multiplets will thus be in the ratio $(7/4) \times 4 = 7$. The spectrum is sketched in Figure 21.2.

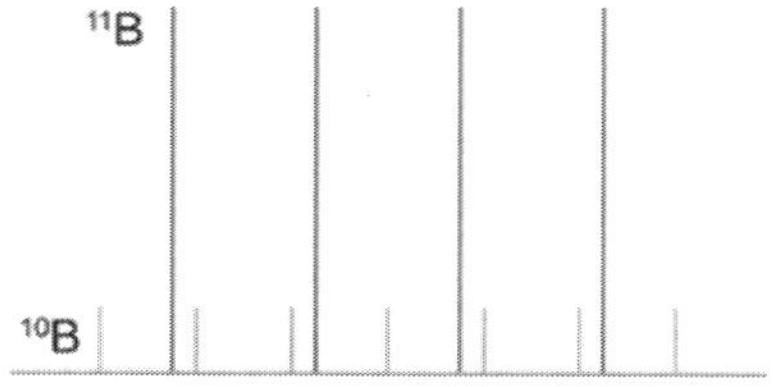


**Figure 21.2**

**E21.15** The A, M, and X resonances lie in distinctly different groups. The A resonance is split into a 1:2:1 triplet by the M nuclei, and each line of that triplet is split into a 1:4:6:4:1 quintet by the X nuclei, (with $J_{AM} > J_{AX}$). The M resonance is split into a 1:3:3:1 quartet by the A nuclei and each line is split into a quintet by the X nuclei (with $J_{AM} > J_{MX}$). The X resonance is split into a quartet by the A nuclei and then each line is split into a triplet by the M nuclei (with $J_{AX} > J_{MX}$). The spectrum is sketched in the Figure 21.3. The exact form will depend upon the specific values of the coupling constants.

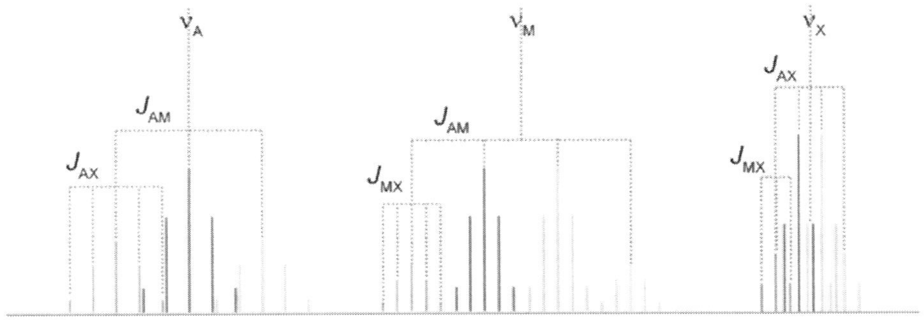


Figure 21.3

**E21.16** A nucleus with spin $I = 1$ may exist in three nuclear spin states with $m_I = -1$, 0 and +1, which for convenience we may denote α, β and γ. The intensities of the components in the fine structure expected as a result of coupling to $N$ such equivalent nuclei are given by the coefficients of the terms in the expansion $(\alpha + \beta + \gamma)^N$. These coefficients may be calculated using a version of Pascal's triangle, in which any element is given by the sum of the three values directly above. Thus, for $N = 2$, the expansion is

1
1 1 1
1 2 3 2 1
1 3 6 7 6 3 1
1 4 10 16 19 16 10 4 1
1 5 15 30 45 51 45 30 15 5 1

**E21.17** A nucleus with $I = 3/2$ may exist as four spin states, with spin quantum numbers $m_I = -3/2, -1/2, +1/2, +3/2$. We may derive the fine structure pattern for coupling to $N$ such nuclei by constructing another version of Pascal's triangle in which each value may be calculated by summing the four values in the row directly above. Thus, for $N$ up to 5, the expansion is

1
1 1 1 1
1 2 3 4 3 2 1
1 3 6 10 12 12 10 6 3 1
1 4 10 20 31 40 44 40 31 20 10 4 1
1 5 15 35 65 101 135 155 155 135 101 65 35 15 5 1

**E21.18** The relationship between the difference in resonance frequency, $\Delta\nu$, and lifetime, $\tau$, for two lines corresponding to different conformations of the same molecule that coalesce is given by eqn 21.15. Thus,

$$\tau = \frac{2^{1/2}}{\pi\Delta\nu} = \frac{2^{1/2}}{\pi \times (119\ \text{s}^{-1})} = 3.78 \times 10^{-3}\ \text{s} = \mathbf{3.78\ ms}$$

**E21.19** We may use eqn 21.10 to calculate the difference in resonance frequency for two lines of known chemical shift. Thus, if

$$\delta = \frac{\nu - \nu^{\circ}}{\nu^{\circ}} \times 10^{6}$$

then

$$\Delta\nu = (\delta_1 - \delta_2) \times \nu^{\circ} \times 10^{-6}$$

The rate of interconversion is the reciprocal of lifetime, so that, using eqn 21.15

$$k = \frac{1}{\tau} = \left(\frac{2^{1/2}}{\pi\Delta\nu}\right)^{-1} = \frac{\pi \times \{(\delta_1 - \delta_2) \times \nu^{\circ} \times 10^{-6}\}}{2^{1/2}} = \frac{\pi \times (\delta_1 - \delta_2) \times \nu^{\circ}}{2^{1/2} \times 10^{6}}$$
$$= \frac{\pi \times (4.8 - 2.7) \times (550 \times 10^{6}\ \mathrm{s^{-1}})}{2^{1/2} \times 10^{6}} = \mathbf{2600\ s^{-1}}$$

**E21.20** The difference in energy between the two spin states is given by eqn 21.22

$$\Delta E = g_e\mu_B\mathcal{B} = 2.0023 \times (9.274 \times 10^{-24}\mathrm{J\,T^{-1}}) \times 0.250\ \mathrm{T} = \mathbf{4.64 \times 10^{-24}\ J}$$

**E21.21** The difference in the relative populations of the two spin states is, from eqn 21.22

$$\frac{N_\beta - N_\alpha}{N} = \frac{g_e\mu_B\mathcal{B}}{kT}$$

Thus, for a field of 0.40 T at 298 K,

$$\frac{N_\beta - N_\alpha}{N} = \frac{2.0023 \times (9.274 \times 10^{-24}\mathrm{J\,T^{-1}}) \times (0.40\ \mathrm{T})}{(1.381 \times 10^{-23}\ \mathrm{J\,K^{-1}}) \times (298\ \mathrm{K})} = \mathbf{1.08 \times 10^{-3}}$$

which is equivalent to 0.108 per cent, and for a field of 1.2 T

$$\frac{N_\beta - N_\alpha}{N} = \frac{2.0023 \times (9.274 \times 10^{-24}\mathrm{J\,T^{-1}}) \times (1.2\ \mathrm{T})}{(1.381 \times 10^{-23}\ \mathrm{J\,K^{-1}}) \times (298\ \mathrm{K})} = \mathbf{5.4 \times 10^{-3}}$$

or 0.54 per cent.

**E21.22** Applying the condition for resonance, eqn 21.23,

$$\nu = \frac{g_e\mu_B\mathcal{B}}{h} = \frac{2.0023 \times (9.274 \times 10^{-24}\mathrm{J\,T^{-1}}) \times (0.330\ \mathrm{T})}{(6.626 \times 10^{-34}\mathrm{J\,s})}$$
$$= 9.25 \times 10^{9}\ s^{-1} = \mathbf{9.25\ GHz}$$

which corresponds to a wavelength

$$\lambda = c/\nu = (2.998 \times 10^{8}\ \mathrm{m\,s^{-1}})/(9.25 \times 10^{9}\mathrm{s^{-1}}) = 32.4 \times 10^{-3}\ \mathrm{m} = \mathbf{32.4\ mm}$$

**E21.23** Rearranging the condition for resonance, eqn 21.23,

$$g_e = \frac{h\nu}{\mu_B\mathcal{B}} = \frac{(6.626 \times 10^{-34}\mathrm{J\,s}) \times (9.2231 \times 10^{9}\ \mathrm{s^{-1}})}{(9.274 \times 10^{-24}\mathrm{J\,T^{-1}}) \times (329.12 \times 10^{-3}\ \mathrm{T})} = \mathbf{2.0022}$$

**E21.24** The separation between adjacent lines in the spectrum is 2.3 mT. Applying the condition for resonance, eqn 21.23, the hyperfine coupling constant is

$$a = \nu_1 - \nu_2 = \frac{g_e\mu_B}{h}(\mathcal{B}_1 - \mathcal{B}_2)$$
$$= \frac{2.0023 \times (9.274 \times 10^{-24}\,\mathrm{J\,T^{-1}})}{(6.626 \times 10^{-34}\,\mathrm{J\,s})} \times (2.3 \times 10^{-3}\,\mathrm{T})$$
$$= 64.5 \times 10^6\,\mathrm{s^{-1}} = \mathbf{64.5\,MHz}$$

**E21.25** (a) The electron will couple to the nuclear spin of the $^1$H nuclei in the $CH_3$ group. Because, for $^1$H, $I = ½$, the coupling results in $(2N \times I) + 1 = (2 \times 3 \times ½) + 1 = 4$ different components. The intensities are given by Pascal's triangle as 1:3:3:1.

(b) The nuclear spin of $^2$H = D is $I = 1$. The coupling therefore gives rise to $(2N \times I) + 1 = (2 \times 3 \times 1) + 1 = 7$ components. Once again, the intensities are given by Pascal's triangle. For nuclei with $I = 1$, the appropriate intensities are given in Exercise 21.16 as 1:3:6:7:6:3:1.

**E21.26** Applying the condition for resonance, eqn 21.23, so that

(a) for a frequency of 9.302 GHz,

$$\mathcal{B} = \frac{h\nu}{g_e\mu_B} = \frac{(6.626 \times 10^{-34}\,\mathrm{J\,s}) \times (9.302 \times 10^9\,\mathrm{s^{-1}})}{2.0025 \times (9.274 \times 10^{-24}\,\mathrm{J\,T^{-1}})} = 0.3319\,\mathrm{T} = \mathbf{331.9\,mT}$$

(b) and for 33.67 GHz,

$$\mathcal{B} = \frac{(6.626 \times 10^{-34}\,\mathrm{J\,s}) \times (33.67 \times 10^9\,\mathrm{s^{-1}})}{2.0025 \times (9.274 \times 10^{-24}\,\mathrm{J\,T^{-1}})} = \mathbf{1.201\,T}$$

**E21.27** In general, coupling to $N$ nuclei of spin $I$ results in $C = (2N \times I) + 1$ components. Thus, for $N = 2$ nuclei, a hyperfine pattern consisting of five components implies that the spin must be

$$I = (C - 1)/2N = (5 - 1)/(2 \times 2) = 1$$

**E21.28** See Exercise 21.17.

**E21.29** Applying the McConnell equation, eqn 21.26, the electron density at each carbon atom is

$$\rho = a/Q$$

For 1,2-dinitrobenzene (**3**), the observed hyperfine splitting constants correspond to electron density

$$\rho = (0.011\,\mathrm{mT})/(2.25\,\mathrm{mT}) = 0.0048$$
$$\rho = (0.172\,\mathrm{mT})/(2.25\,\mathrm{mT}) = 0.0764$$

For 1,3-dinitrobenzene (**4**), the observed hyperfine splitting constants correspond to electron density

$$\rho = (0.272\ \text{mT})/(2.25\ \text{mT}) = 0.1208$$
$$\rho = (0.450\ \text{mT})/(2.25\ \text{mT}) = 0.2000$$
$$\rho = (0.108\ \text{mT})/(2.25\ \text{mT}) = 0.0480$$

For 1,4-dinitrobenzene (**5**), the observed hyperfine splitting constants correspond to electron density

$$\rho = (0.112\ \text{mT})/(2.25\ \text{mT}) = 0.0497$$

## Answers to projects

**P21.30** Considering the Karplus equation, eqn 21.14,

$${}^3J_{\text{HH}} = A + B\cos\phi + C\cos 2\phi$$

the minimum in the coupling constant corresponds to

$$\frac{\text{d}\,{}^3J_{\text{HH}}}{\text{d}\phi} = \frac{\text{d}}{\text{d}\phi}\,{}^3J_{\text{HH}}$$
$$= \frac{\text{d}}{\text{d}\phi}(A + B\cos\phi + C\cos 2\phi) = -(B\sin\phi + 2C\sin 2\phi) = 0$$

Using the relationship

$$\sin 2\phi = 2\sin\phi\cos\phi$$

and so, substituting,

$$B\sin\phi + 2C\sin\phi\cos\phi = \sin\phi\,(B + 4C\cos\phi) = 0$$

Thus, either

$$\sin\phi = 0$$

such that $\phi = 0$, or

$$B + 4C\cos\phi = 0$$

or

$$\cos\phi = -B/4C = B/4C$$

The second derivative is

$$\frac{\text{d}^2}{\text{d}\phi^2}\,{}^3J_{\text{HH}} = \frac{\text{d}}{\text{d}\phi}\frac{\text{d}\,{}^3J_{\text{HH}}}{\text{d}\phi}$$
$$= \frac{\text{d}}{\text{d}\phi}\{-(B\sin\phi + 2C\sin 2\phi)\} = -(B\cos\phi + 4C\cos 2\phi)$$

Using the relationship

$$\cos 2\phi = 2(\cos^2\phi - 1)$$

then if $\cos\phi = -B/4C = B/4C$

$$\frac{d^2}{d\phi^2}\,{}^3J_{HH} = -\{B\cos\phi + 8C(\cos^2\phi - 1)\} = -B[(B/4C) + 8C\{(B/4C)^2 - 1\}]$$
$$= -B^2/4C - B^2/2C + 8C = -3B^2/4C + 8C$$

This quantity is positive if $16C^2 > 3B^2$. This is certainly true for typical values of $B$ and $C$, namely $B = -1$ Hz and C = 5 Hz. Therefore the condition for a minimum is as stated, namely, $\cos\phi = B/4C$.

**P21.31** We may express the rate of reaction as

$$v = \frac{[I]}{[I]+[EI]}v_I + \frac{[EI]}{[I]+[EI]}v_{EI} = \frac{[I]_0 - [EI]}{[I]_0}v_I + \frac{[EI]}{[I]_0}v_{EI}$$

where we have used the fact that total amount of I is constant, so that

$$[I] + [EI] = [I]_0$$

Rearranging for [EI]

$$[EI] = \frac{[I]_0(v - v_I)}{v_{EI} - v_I} = \frac{[I]_0\delta v}{\Delta v}$$

We notice that the frequency differences that appear in the second equality are the ones defined in the problem. Now, considering the equilibrium constant, and noting that $[I]_0 \gg [EI]$ so that $[I]_0 - [EI] \approx [I]_0$,

$$K_I = \frac{[E][I]}{[EI]} = \frac{([E]_0 - [EI])([I]_0 - [EI])}{[EI]} \approx \frac{([E]_0 - [EI])[I]_0}{[EI]}$$

The assumption is valid because the total amount of I is much greater than the total E, so it must also be much greater than [EI], even if all E binds I. Now, solving this expression for $[E]_0$

$$[E]_0 = \frac{K_I + [I]_0}{[I]_0}[EI] = \left(\frac{K_I + [I]_0}{[I]_0}\right)\left(\frac{[I]_0\delta v}{\Delta v}\right) = \frac{(K_I + [I]_0)\delta v}{\Delta v}$$

Solving for $[I]_0$ yields

$$\overbrace{[I]_0}^{y} = \overbrace{[E]_0\Delta v}^{\text{slope}} \times \overbrace{(1/\delta v)}^{x} + \overbrace{(-K_I)}^{\text{intercept}}$$

This expression has the same form as the equation for a straight-line graph.

**P21.32** (a) Applying the resonance condition,

$$\nu = \frac{\gamma_N}{2\pi}(1-\sigma)\mathcal{B}$$

then because shielding constants are quite small, $1 - \sigma \approx 1$, we may write

$$\delta\nu = \nu_1 - \nu_2 = \frac{\gamma_N}{2\pi}(\mathcal{B}_1 - \mathcal{B}_2) = \frac{\gamma_N}{2\pi}\frac{d\mathcal{B}}{dx}\delta x$$

Rearranging, the field gradient required for a difference in frequency $\delta\nu$ over a distance $\delta x$ is

$$\frac{d\mathcal{B}}{dx} = \frac{2\pi\delta\nu}{\gamma_N\delta x} = \frac{2\pi \times (100\ \mathrm{s^{-1}})}{26.752 \times 10^7\ \mathrm{T^{-1}\ s^{-1}} \times (8 \times 10^{-2}\ \mathrm{m})}$$
$$= 29.4 \times 10^{-6}\mathrm{T\ m^{-1}} = \mathbf{29.4\ \mu T\ m^{-1}}$$

(b) The intensity at a particular depth through the disk-shaped organ depends upon the width of the organ. We may measure the depth in terms of the parameter $d$, where $d$ runs from $-R$ to $+R$, with $R$ the radius of the organ. The width at distance $d$ is thus, by Pythagoras' theorem,

$$2(R^2 - d^2)^{1/2} = 2R\{1 - (d/R)^2\}^{1/2}$$

Figure 21.4 shows a plot of this function.

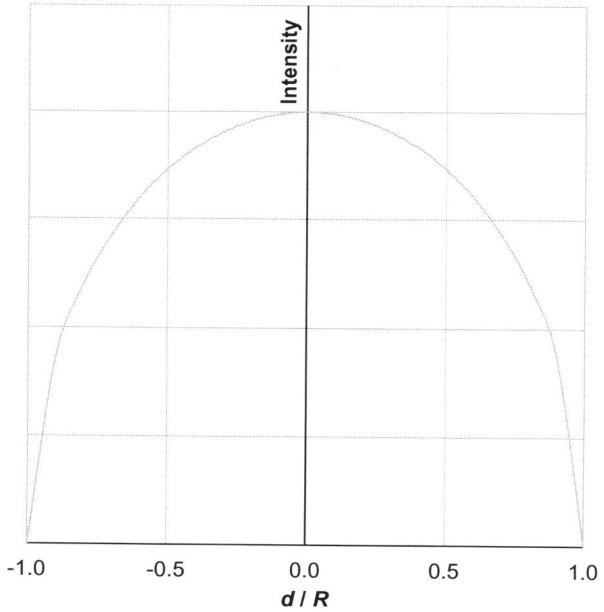


Figure 21.4

# Chapter 22

# Statistical thermodynamics

## Answers to discussion questions

**D22.1** The complete derivation of the Boltzmann distribution is beyond the scope of this text. We can, however, summarize the basic steps of that derivation. We start with the concept of a distribution that is the arrangement of $N$ molecules in the allowed states of the system, with $N_1$ molecules in state 1 with energy $\epsilon_1$, $N_2$ molecules in state 2 with energy $\epsilon_2$, etc. Then we look for the most probable of the allowed distributions, because the most probable distribution is, for all practical purposes, the only one that determines the actual properties of the system. The most probable distribution is the distribution with the maximum value of the statistical weight, $W$,

$$W = \frac{N!}{N_1!\,N_2!\,N_3!\ldots}$$

where $W$ is the number of ways of arranging the $N$ molecules within the allowed states. We must, however, look for the maximum value of $W$ subject to the constraints that the total energy of the system, $\epsilon$, and the number of molecules, $N$, in the system be constant.

$$\epsilon = \textstyle\sum_i N_i\epsilon_i$$

and

$$N = \sum_i N_i$$

This maximization technique subject to constraints is known as the method of undetermined multipliers. When these two constraints are taken into account we arrive at the formula for the Boltzmann distribution, eqn 22.1a,

$$\frac{N_2}{N_1} = \mathrm{e}^{-(\epsilon_2-\epsilon_1)/kT}$$

For a complete derivation, see *Atkins' Physical Chemistry*, P. Atkins and J. de Paula, 9th edition, Oxford University Press, (2010).

**D22.2** We may define temperature in many ways. However, because this chapter focuses on the application of statistics to the distribution of physical states in systems that contain a large number of atoms or molecules, we begin with the statistical answer: the thermodynamic temperature is the one quantity that determines the most probable populations of those states in systems at thermal equilibrium. This is because the relative populations of states with energies $\epsilon_1, \epsilon_2, \ldots$ etc. are given by the Boltzmann formula, eqn 22.1a,

$$\frac{N_2}{N_1} = e^{-(\epsilon_2-\epsilon_1)/kT}$$

The Boltzmann formula shows us that for such a system, the relative population of high-energy states increases with temperature.

As a consequence, the temperature provides a necessary condition for thermal equilibrium; a system is at thermal equilibrium only if all of its sub-systems have the same temperature. Note that this is not a circular definition of temperature, for thermal equilibrium is not defined by uniformity of temperature: systems whose sub-systems can exchange energy tend toward thermal equilibrium. In this context, sub-systems can be different materials placed in contact, such as a block of copper in a beaker of water, or can be more abstract, such as rotational and vibrational modes of motion.

Statistical thermodynamics provides a link with this definition of temperature with the empirical concept of temperature developed in previous chapters through concepts such as the equipartition theorem.

**D22.3** The molecular partition function $q$, may be defined through eqns 22.3 and 22.4 in terms of a summation over the states

$$q = \sum_i e^{-(\epsilon_i-\epsilon_0)/kT}$$

or the levels

$$q = \sum_L g_L e^{-(\epsilon_L-\epsilon_0)/kT}$$

of the system. It represents the average number of states thermally accessible to a molecule at the temperature of the system. Consider the value of the partition function at the extremes of temperature. The limit of $q$ as $T$ approaches zero, is simply $g_0$, the degeneracy of the ground state. As $T$ approaches infinity, all states become equally populated and each term in the sum is simply the degeneracy of the energy level. If the number of levels is infinite, the partition function is infinite as well. In some special cases where we can effectively limit the number of states, the upper limit of the partition function is just the number of states.

**D22.4** Particles with the same chemical composition are not necessarily identical. For example, *ortho-* and *para*-hydrogen are of the same chemical composition, but are not identical. Stereoisomers also have the same chemical composition, but are not identical. The words *identical* and *indistinguishable* have related, but slightly different meanings. Particles of the same composition can be regarded as distinguishable when they are localized as in a crystal lattice where we can assign a set of coordinates to each particle. Strictly speaking, it is the lattice site that carries the set of coordinates, but as long as the particle is fixed to the site, it too can be considered distinguishable. In the gas phase, however, particles of the same composition would be indistinguishable.

**D22.5** For convenience, consider a two-state system in which the lower state is assigned an energy equal to zero, with the upper state having an energy that is $\epsilon$ higher. Each state is assumed to have a degeneracy equal to 1. Thus, the partition function for the system is defined, through eqn 22.3 as

$$q = 1 + \mathrm{e}^{-\epsilon/kT}$$

For this simple system of non-interacting states, the internal energy is equal to the average energy $\epsilon$ of the occupied states. From eqn 22.11 and 22.12,

$$\begin{aligned} U(T) &= \overbrace{U(0)}^{0} + \epsilon = \epsilon = \frac{NkT^2}{q}\frac{\mathrm{d}q}{\mathrm{d}T} \\ &= \frac{NkT^2}{1+\mathrm{e}^{-\epsilon/kT}}\frac{\mathrm{d}}{\mathrm{d}T}(1+\mathrm{e}^{-\epsilon/kT}) = \frac{NkT^2}{1+\mathrm{e}^{-\epsilon/kT}} \times \frac{\epsilon}{kT^2}\mathrm{e}^{-\epsilon/kT} = \frac{\mathrm{e}^{-\epsilon/kT}}{1+\mathrm{e}^{-\epsilon/kT}}N\epsilon \\ &= \frac{1}{1+\mathrm{e}^{\epsilon/kT}}N\epsilon \end{aligned}$$

This equation for $U(T)$ indicates that, at the absolute zero of temperature $U(0) = 0$. At absolute zero, the upper state is unpopulated; all particles are in the ground state. At very high temperature the exponential term $\mathrm{e}^{\epsilon/kT}$ approaches 1 and the internal energy approaches $\frac{1}{2}N\epsilon$. The two levels are equally populated as $T$ approaches infinity and the internal energy equals the average of the two state energies.

The entropy of distinguishable particles is given by eqn 22.13a. Thus

$$\begin{aligned} S(T) &= \frac{U(T) - U(0)}{T} + Nk\ln q = \frac{U(\mathrm{T})}{T} + Nk\ln q \\ &= \frac{\mathrm{e}^{-\epsilon/kT}}{1+\mathrm{e}^{-\epsilon/kT}}\frac{N\epsilon}{T} + Nk\ln(1+\mathrm{e}^{-\epsilon/kT}) \end{aligned}$$

This equation for $S(T)$ indicates that, at the absolute zero of temperature, $S(0) = 0$ and the system is perfectly ordered with all particles in the lowest level. At very high temperature the exponential term $\mathrm{e}^{-\epsilon/kT}$ approaches 1 and the internal energy approaches $Nk \ln 2$. Comparing this result with the Boltzmann formula for entropy ($S = k \ln W$) reveals that $W = 2^N$. This happens because each particle has an equal probability of being in either the lower or the upper level at very high temperature.

**D22.6** The thermodynamic entropy is defined through eqn 4.1, which in differential form may be written as

$$\mathrm{d}S = \frac{\mathrm{d}q_{\mathrm{rev}}}{T}$$

where $\mathrm{d}q_{\mathrm{rev}}$ is the infinitesimal quantity of energy supplied as heat to the system reversibly at a temperature $T$.

The statistical entropy is defined in terms of the Boltzmann formula, eqn 4.11,

$$S = k \ln W$$

where $k$ is the Boltzmann constant and $W$ is the number of microstates, the total number of ways in which the molecules of the system can be arranged to achieve the same total energy of the system. These two definitions turn out to be equivalent provided the thermodynamic entropy is taken to be zero at $T = 0$.

The concept of the number of microstates is related to the ill-defined qualitative concepts of disorder and dispersal of matter and energy that are used widely to introduce the concept of entropy: a more disorderly distribution of energy and matter corresponds to a greater number of microstates. The more molecules that can participate in the distribution of energy, the more microstates there are for a given total energy and the greater the entropy.

The molecular interpretation of entropy given by the Boltzmann formula also suggests the thermodynamic definition. At high temperatures where the molecules of a system can occupy a large number of available energy levels, a small additional transfer of energy as heat will cause only a small change in the number of accessible energy levels, whereas at low temperatures the transfer of the same quantity of heat will increase the number of accessible energy levels and microstates significantly. Hence, the change in entropy upon heating will be greater when the energy is transferred to a cold body than when it is transferred to a hot body. This argument suggests that the change in entropy should be inversely proportional to the temperature at which the transfer takes place as in indicated in the thermodynamic definition.

**D22.7** The general expression for the equilibrium constant of the reaction

$$\mathrm{A} + \mathrm{B} \rightleftharpoons \mathrm{C}$$

in terms of the partition functions and difference in molar energy, $\Delta E$, of the products and reactants is given as eqn 22.18

$$K = \frac{q_{\mathrm{m}}^{\ominus}(\mathrm{C})}{q_{\mathrm{m}}^{\ominus}(\mathrm{A})q_{\mathrm{m}}^{\ominus}(\mathrm{B})} N_{\mathrm{A}} \mathrm{e}^{-\Delta E/RT}$$

The derivation is given in Further Information 22.2. The partition functions are functions of temperature and the ratio of partition functions in eqn 22.18 will therefore vary with temperature. However, the most direct effect of temperature on the equilibrium constant is through the exponential term. The manner in which both factors affect the magnitudes of the equilibrium constant and its variation with temperature depend upon the particular reaction.

The molecular partition function gives an indication of the number of states that are thermally accessible to a molecule at the temperature of the system. The fact that a ratio of partition functions for products and reactants appears in eqn 22.18 reveals the important method of comparing molecular distributions over available energy levels when evaluating an equilibrium constant. This ratio accounts for the role of entropy in the establishment of equilibrium. The exponential factor accounts for the role of energy.

## Solutions to exercises

**E22.1** The ratio of the populations of the two states is given by the Boltzmann distribution, eqn 22.1b,

$$\frac{N_2}{N_1} = \mathrm{e}^{-\Delta E/RT} = \mathrm{e}^{-(2.4\times10^3\ \mathrm{J\ mol^{-1}})/\{(8.3145\ \mathrm{J\ K^{-1}mol^{-1}})\times(273.15+20)\mathrm{K}\}} = \mathbf{0.37}$$

**E22.2** The difference in energy between the two spin states of a proton in a magnetic field $B$ is given by eqn 21.4,

$$\Delta E = \gamma_{\mathrm{N}}\hbar B$$

(a) Thus, applying the Boltzmann distribution, the ratio of the populations of the α and β spin states for a magnetic field of 1.5 T is

$$\frac{N_\beta}{N_\alpha} = \mathrm{e}^{-\Delta E/RT} = \mathrm{e}^{-\gamma_{\mathrm{H}}\hbar B/RT}$$
$$= \mathrm{e}^{-\{(\ 26.752\times 107\ \mathrm{T^{-1}s^{-1}})\times(6.626\times10^{-34}\mathrm{J\ s})\times(1.5\ \mathrm{T})\}/\{2\pi\times(8.3145\ \mathrm{J\ K^{-1}mol^{-1}})\times(273.15+20)\mathrm{K}\}}$$
$$= \mathbf{0.999990}$$

The population difference is thus 10 nuclei in 1 million.

(b) And for a magnetic field of 15 T,

$$\frac{N_\beta}{N_\alpha} = \mathrm{e}^{-\Delta E/RT} = \mathrm{e}^{-\gamma_{\mathrm{H}}\hbar B/RT}$$
$$= \mathrm{e}^{-\{(\ 26.752\times 107\ \mathrm{T^{-1}s^{-1}})\times(6.626\times10^{-34}\mathrm{J\ s})\times(15\ \mathrm{T})\}/\{2\pi\times(8.3145\ \mathrm{J\ K^{-1}mol^{-1}})\times(273.15+20)\mathrm{K}\}}$$
$$= \mathbf{0.999895}$$

which is equivalent to 105 nuclei in 1 million.

**E22.3** For an electron in a magnetic field $B$, the difference in energy between the two spin states is given by eqn 21.21

$$\Delta E = g_{\mathrm{e}}\mu_{\mathrm{B}}B$$

where $g_{\mathrm{e}} = 2.0023$ and $\mu_{\mathrm{B}}$ is the Bohr magneton. Applying the Boltzmann distribution, the ratio of the populations of the α and β spin states for a magnetic field of 0.33 T is

$$\frac{N_\beta}{N_\alpha} = e^{-\Delta E/RT} = e^{-g_e\mu_B B/RT}$$

$$= e^{-\{(2.0023)\times(9.274\times10^{-24}\,\mathrm{J\,T^{-1}})\times(0.33\,\mathrm{T})\}/\{2\pi\times(8.3145\,\mathrm{J\,K^{-1}mol^{-1}})\times(273.15+20)\mathrm{K}\}}$$

$$= \mathbf{0.99849}$$

**E22.4** The quantum number $J$ defines the rotational energy of a linear molecule through the relationship

$$\epsilon_J = hBJ(J+1)$$

For each energy level, however, there are $2J+1$ possible values of the quantum number $M_J$. The degeneracy of a level with quantum number $J$ is therefore $g_J = 2J+1$. Thus, using the form of the Boltzmann distribution appropriate for energy levels, as opposed to states, eqn 22.4,

$$N_J = \frac{g_J e^{-\epsilon_J/kT}}{q}$$

and so, the relative populations of two levels with rotational quantum numbers $J_1$ and $J_2$, is given by

$$\frac{N_{J_2}}{N_{J_1}} = \frac{(g_{J_2}e^{-\epsilon_{J_2}/kT})/q}{(g_{J_1}e^{-\epsilon_{J_1}/kT})/q} = \frac{g_{J_2}}{g_{J_1}}e^{-(\epsilon_{J_2}-\epsilon_{J_1})/kT} = \frac{(2J_2+1)}{(2J_1+1)}e^{-hB\{J_2(J_2+1)-J_1(J_1+1)\}/kT}$$

so that for the levels with $J = 2$ and $J = 4$,

$$\frac{N_4}{N_2} = \frac{\{(2\times4)+1\}}{\{(2\times2)+1\}}e^{-\frac{(6.626\times10^{-34}\,\mathrm{J\,s})\times(11.70\times10^{9}\,\mathrm{s^{-1}})\times\{4\times(4+1)-2(2+1)\}}{(1.38\times10^{-23}\,\mathrm{J\,K^{-1}})\times(25+273.15)\,\mathrm{K}}} = \mathbf{1.753}$$

Thus, there are almost twice as many molecules in the level with $J = 4$ than that with $J = 2$.

**E22.5** For a spherical molecule such as $CH_4$, although the energy of the rotational levels is given by the same expression as for a linear molecule,

$$\epsilon_J = hBJ(J+1)$$

the degeneracy is

$$g_J = (2J+1)^2$$

Hence, following the same approach as in the previous exercise, the ratio of the populations of two levels in a spherical rotor is

$$\frac{N_{J_2}}{N_{J_1}} = \frac{(g_{J_2}e^{-\epsilon_{J_2}/kT})/q}{(g_{J_1}e^{-\epsilon_{J_1}/kT})/q} = \frac{g_{J_2}}{g_{J_1}}e^{-(\epsilon_{J_2}-\epsilon_{J_1})/kT} = \frac{(2J_2+1)^2}{(2J_1+1)^2}e^{-hB\{J_2(J_2+1)-J_1(J_1+1)\}/kT}$$

Thus, for $J = 4$ and $J = 2$,

$$\frac{N_4}{N_2} = \frac{\{(2\times 4)+1\}^2}{\{(2\times 2)+1\}^2}\mathrm{e}^{-\frac{(6.626\times10^{-34}\,\mathrm{J\,s})\times(157\times10^{9}\,\mathrm{s}^{-1})\times\{4\times(4+1)-2(2+1)\}}{(1.38\times10^{-23}\,\mathrm{J\,K^{-1}})\times(25+273.15)\,\mathrm{K}}} = \mathbf{2.27}$$

**E22.6** (a) The partition function is defined through eqn 22.4

$$q = \sum_L g_L \mathrm{e}^{-\epsilon_L/kT}$$

where the summation runs over the levels rather than the states of the system. Thus, for the example given,

$$q = (1\times\mathrm{e}^{-0/kT}) + (6\times\mathrm{e}^{-2\epsilon/kT}) + (3\times\mathrm{e}^{-5\epsilon/kT}) = \mathbf{1 + 6e^{-2\epsilon/kT} + 3e^{-5\epsilon/kT}}$$

(b) If $T = 0$, then all but the first term in the summation disappear, because $\mathrm{e}^{-\infty} = 0$, so that

$$\boldsymbol{q = 1}$$

(c) At $T = \infty$, the exponential terms, $\mathrm{e}^0 = 1$ and so the partition function becomes

$$q = 1 + 6 + 3 = \mathbf{10}$$

**E22.7** The translational partition function for a molecule of mass $m$ is given by eqn 22.5

$$q^{\mathrm{T}} = \frac{(2\pi mkT)^{3/2}V}{h^3}$$

(a) Thus, for $N_2$, with a molecular mass of $28.02m_{\mathrm{u}}$, the translational partition function at a temperature of 298 K is

$$q^{\mathrm{T}} = \frac{\{2\pi\times\{28.02\times(1.661\times10^{-27}\,\mathrm{kg})\}\times(1.381\times10^{-23}\,\mathrm{J\,K^{-1}})\times(298\,\mathrm{K})\}^{3/2}\times(10.0\times10^{-6}\,\mathrm{m^3})}{(6.626\times10^{-34}\,\mathrm{J\,s})^3}$$

$$= \mathbf{1.448\times10^{27}}$$

(b) In the same way for $CS_2$ with a molecular mass of $76.14m_{\mathrm{u}}$

$$q^{\mathrm{T}} = \frac{\{2\pi\times\{76.14\times(1.661\times10^{-27}\,\mathrm{kg})\}\times(1.381\times10^{-23}\,\mathrm{J\,K^{-1}})\times(298\,\mathrm{K})\}^{3/2}\times(10.0\times10^{-6}\,\mathrm{m^3})}{(6.626\times10^{-34}\,\mathrm{J\,s})^3}$$

$$= \mathbf{6.485\times10^{27}}$$

The partition function for $CS_2$ is therefore greater than that for $N_2$. This is to be expected. The greater mass of $CS_2$ means that the translational states are closer together. Thus, for a given energy, more states can be accessed in $CS_2$ than $N_2$. This difference is reflected in the value of the partition function, which is a measurement of the number of states that may be populated at a given temperature.

**E22.8** The translational partition function for a molecule of mass $m$ is given by eqn 22.5.

$$q^{\mathrm{T}} = \frac{(2\pi mkT)^{3/2}V}{h^3}$$

(a) Thus, for methane, $CH_4$, with molecular mass $m = 16.05m_{\mathrm{u}}$ in a spherical cavity of radius $r$,

$$q^{\mathrm{T}} = \frac{(2\pi \times 16.05m_{\mathrm{u}} \times kT)^{3/2}\overbrace{\{(4/3)\pi r^3\}}^{\text{Volume of a sphere}}}{h^3}$$

$$= \frac{(2\pi \times 16.05m_{\mathrm{u}} \times kT)^{3/2}\overbrace{\{(4/3)\pi(d/2)^3\}}^{\text{Volume of a sphere}}}{h^3}$$

$$= \frac{(2\pi \times 16.05m_{\mathrm{u}} \times kT)^{3/2}\pi d^3}{6h^3}$$

$$= \frac{\{2\pi \times \{16.05 \times (1.661 \times 10^{-27}\ \mathrm{kg})\} \times (1.381 \times 10^{-23}\ \mathrm{J\ K^{-1}}) \times (298\ \mathrm{K})\}^{3/2} \times \pi \times (0.50 \times 10^{-9}\mathrm{m})^3}{6 \times (6.626 \times 10^{-34}\mathrm{J\ s})^3}$$

$$= \mathbf{3.2 \times 10^{4}}$$

(b) For a larger volume, $V = 100\ \mathrm{cm}^3$,

$$q^{\mathrm{T}} = \frac{\{2\pi \times \{16.05 \times (1.661 \times 10^{-27}\ \mathrm{kg})\} \times (1.381 \times 10^{-23}\ \mathrm{J\ K^{-1}}) \times (298\ \mathrm{K})\}^{3/2} \times (100 \times 10^{-6}\mathrm{m}^3)}{6 \times (6.626 \times 10^{-34}\mathrm{J\ s})^3}$$

$$= \mathbf{6.2 \times 10^{27}}$$

**E22.9** (a) The energy levels of a rigid diatomic molecule are given by eqn 19.3

$$\epsilon_J = hc\tilde{B}J(J+1)$$

with a degeneracy

$$g_J = 2J + 1$$

Thus, the rotational partition function, as defined through eqn 22.4, is

$$q^{\mathrm{R}} = \sum_{J=0}^{\infty} g_J\, \mathrm{e}^{-\epsilon_J/kT} = \sum_{J=0}^{\infty}(2J+1)\, \mathrm{e}^{-hc\tilde{B}J(J+1)/kT}$$

$$= 1 + 3\mathrm{e}^{-2hc\tilde{B}/kT} + 5\mathrm{e}^{-6hc\tilde{B}/kT} + 7\mathrm{e}^{-12hc\tilde{B}/kT} + \cdots$$

For a rotational constant of $8.465\ \mathrm{cm}^{-1}$, then

$$\frac{hc\tilde{B}}{kT} = \frac{(6.626 \times 10^{-34}\mathrm{J\ s}) \times (2.998 \times 10^{8}\ \mathrm{m\ s^{-1}}) \times (8.465 \times 10^{2}\ \mathrm{m^{-1}})}{(1.381 \times 10^{-23}\ \mathrm{J\ K^{-1}}) \times (298\ \mathrm{K})}$$

$$= 0.0409$$

Direct summation of terms up to an including $J = 15$ leads to a value for the partition function of $q^{\mathrm{R}} = $ **24.816.**

(b) Alternatively, using the approximate expression for the partition function, eqn 22.6,

$$q^{\mathrm{R}} = \frac{kT}{hc\tilde{B}} = \frac{1}{0.0409} = \mathbf{24.474}$$

The difference between the values of the partition function calculated by exact summation and by approximation is thus

$$\frac{24.816 - 24.474}{24.816} = 0.014$$

which is equivalent to 1.4 per cent.

**E22.10** Using a spreadsheet, we find that the temperature at which the difference between the values of the partition function calculated by exact summation and by approximation is 10 per cent is 38.96 K. The agreement becomes better as the temperature increases.

**E22.11** The approximate form of the rotational partition function, which is valid for heavy rotors or at high temperature, is given as eqn 22.6,

$$q^{\mathrm{R}} = \frac{kT}{\sigma hB}$$

where $\sigma = 1$ for heteronuclear diatomic molecules such as HCl and $\sigma = 2$ for symmetric linear molecules such as $CO_2$.

(a) Hence, for $^{1}H^{35}Cl$,

$$q^{\mathrm{R}} = \frac{(1.38\times10^{-23}\ \mathrm{J\ K^{-1}})\times(298\ \mathrm{K})}{1\times(6.626\times10^{-34}\mathrm{J\ s})\times\underbrace{(318\times10^{9}\ \mathrm{s^{-1}})}_{1\ \mathrm{GHz}=10^{-9}\mathrm{s}^{-1}}} = \mathbf{19.5}$$

(b) and for $^{12}C^{16}O_2$,

$$q^{\mathrm{R}} = \frac{(1.38\times10^{-23}\ \mathrm{J\ K^{-1}})\times(298\ \mathrm{K})}{2\times(6.626\times10^{-34}\mathrm{J\ s})\times(11.70\times10^{9}\ \mathrm{s^{-1}})} = \mathbf{265}$$

The higher rotational partition function for $CO_2$ in comparison with HCl shows that more rotational states are accessible. $CO_2$ is heavier, and has a higher moment of inertia than HCl, and even though half of the rotational states are missing because of nuclear spin statistics, the energy levels are still much closer together.

**E22.12** The Pauli principle excludes certain rotational states for symmetric molecules. Thus, for $CO_2$ for example, rotational states with odd values of the rotational quantum number $J$ are missing. This is reflected in the approximate formula for the rotational partition function, eqn 22.6,

$$q^{\mathrm{R}} = \frac{kT}{\sigma hB}$$

where the symmetry $\sigma$ takes account of the absence of some states. For $CO_2$ for example, because half of the rotational states are missing, $\sigma = 2$. Although $N_2O$ is linear, it has a non-symmetric NNO structure, and all rotational states are allowed. Hence, for $N_2O$, $\sigma = 1$. Thus, although the rotational constants for the two molecules are similar, the partition function for $N_2O$ is almost twice that of $CO_2$ at the same temperature.

**E22.13** The exact form of the vibrational partition function is given by eqn 22.7,

$$q^{\mathrm{V}} = \frac{1}{1 - \mathrm{e}^{-hc\tilde{\nu}/kT}}$$

For HBr, with vibrational wavenumber 264 cm$^{-1}$, the exponent has a value at 298 K

$$\frac{hc\tilde{\nu}}{kT} = \frac{(6.626 \times 10^{-34}\,\mathrm{J\,s}) \times (2.998 \times 10^{8}\,\mathrm{m\,s^{-1}}) \times (264 \times 10^{2}\,\mathrm{m^{-1}})}{(1.38 \times 10^{-23}\,\mathrm{J\,K^{-1}}) \times (298\,\mathrm{K})} = 1.27$$

giving a partition function

$$q^{\mathrm{V}} = \frac{1}{1 - \mathrm{e}^{-1.27}} = \mathbf{1.39}$$

At higher temperatures, however, we may use the approximate form of the partition function, eqn 22.8

$$q^{V} = \frac{kT}{hc\tilde{\nu}}$$

Use of a spreadsheet to calculate values for the partition function at different temperatures shows that the difference becomes 10 per cent of the true value at a temperature of 1680 K.

**E22.14** For a polyatomic molecule with more than one vibrational mode, the overall vibrational partition function, $q^{\mathrm{V}}$, is given by the product of the partition functions for the individual vibrations, $q_1^{\mathrm{V}}, q_2^{\mathrm{V}}, \ldots$

$$q^{\mathrm{V}} = q_1^{V} q_2^{V} q_3^{V} \ldots$$

where, for molecules that have one or more degenerate vibrational modes, we must remember to include the partition function for each of the modes. Hence, for $CO_2$, using eqn 22.7

$$q^{\mathrm{V}} = \frac{1}{1 - \mathrm{e}^{-hc\tilde{\nu}/kT}}$$

to calculate the partition functions of the separate vibrational modes, at 500 K,

$$\frac{hc}{kT} = \frac{(6.626 \times 10^{-34}\,\mathrm{J\,s}) \times (2.998 \times 10^{8}\,\mathrm{m\,s^{-1}})}{(1.38 \times 10^{-23}\,\mathrm{J\,K^{-1}}) \times (500\,\mathrm{K})} = 2.876 \times 10^{-5}\,\mathrm{m}$$

and so,

$$q_1^V = \frac{1}{1 - e^{-(2.876\times10^{-5}\ m)\times(1388\times10^2\ m)}} = 1.019$$
$$q_2^V = \frac{1}{1 - e^{-(2.876\times10^{-5}\ m)\times(667\times10^2\ m)}} = 1.621$$
$$q_3^V = \frac{1}{1 - e^{-(2.876\times10^{-5}\ m)\times(2349\times10^2\ m)}} = 1.035$$

Hence, the overall vibrational partition function is

$$q^V = 1.019 \times 1.172 \times 1.172 \times 1.001 = \mathbf{1.401}$$

Repeating the calculation at 1000 K gives

$$q^V = 1.157 \times 1.621 \times 1.621 \times 1.035 = \mathbf{3.147}$$

**E22.15** The electronic partition function may be calculated as a direct summation over energy levels using eqn 22.4

$$q = \sum_L g_L\, e^{-\epsilon_L/kT}$$

where $g_L$ is the degeneracy of the level $L$ with energy $\epsilon_L$. The degeneracy of a level with total angular momentum quantum number $J$, which is indicated by the subscript to the term symbol, is $g = 2J + 1$. Thus for the lowest, $^3P_0$ level, $J = 0$ and so this level of the carbon atom is singly degenerate. The $^3P_1$ level has $J = 1$, and so has a degeneracy of 3, and the $^3P_2$ level has $J = 2$, and thus a degeneracy of 5. The separations between the levels are expressed in terms of wavenumber, but may be converted into energies by multiplication by $hc$. Hence

$$\begin{aligned} q^E &= \overbrace{(g_1 \times e^{-\epsilon_1/kT})}^{^3P_0} + \overbrace{(g_2 \times e^{-\epsilon_2/kT})}^{^3P_1} + \overbrace{(g_3 \times e^{-\epsilon_3/kT})}^{^3P_2} \\ &= 1 \times e^{-0\times(hc/kT)} + \{3 \times e^{-16.4\ cm^{-1}\times(hc/kT)}\} + \{5 \times e^{-43.5\ cm^{-1}\times(hc/kT)}\} \end{aligned}$$

It is reasonable to assume that other electronic levels lie at such high energies that they are not thermally accessible, even at moderate temperatures. We need therefore include only the three lowest levels in the summation.

At 10 K,

$$\begin{aligned} hc/kT &= \frac{(6.626 \times 10^{-34} J\ s) \times (2.998 \times 10^8\ m\ s^{-1})}{(1.381 \times 10^{-23}\ J\ K^{-1}) \times (10\ K)} \\ &= 1.438 \times 10^{-3} m = 0.1438\ cm \end{aligned}$$

so that

$$\begin{aligned} q^E &= 1 + \{3 \times e^{-16.4\ cm^{-1}\times0.1438\ cm}\} + \{5 \times e^{-43.5\ cm^{-1}\times0.1438\ cm}\} \\ &= 1 + (3 \times 0.095) + (5 \times 0.002) = \mathbf{1.293} \end{aligned}$$

At 298 K, however

$$hc/kT = \frac{(6.626\times10^{-34}\,\text{J s})\times(2.998\times10^{8}\,\text{m s}^{-1})}{(1.381\times10^{-23}\,\text{J K}^{-1})\times(298\,\text{K})}$$
$$= 4.827\times10^{-5}\text{m} = 4.827\times10^{-3}\text{cm}$$

so that, at this higher temperature

$$q^{\text{E}} = 1 + \{3\times \text{e}^{-16.4\,\text{cm}^{-1}\times 4.827\times10^{-3}\text{cm}}\} + \{5\times \text{e}^{-43.5\,\text{cm}^{-1}\times 4.827\times10^{-3}\text{cm}}\}$$
$$= 1 + (3\times0.924) + (5\times0.811) = \mathbf{7.825}$$

The values for the partition function confirm that as the temperature is increased, more electronic states become accessible.

**E22.16** (a) At a temperature $T = 0$, all atoms must be in the lowest electronic, $^3P_2$, level. This level has a total angular momentum quantum number $J = 2$, and so a degeneracy of $(2J + 1) = 5$. Hence, the atoms may occupy any of five states at absolute zero, so that the partition function is $\boldsymbol{q}^{\text{E}} = \mathbf{5}$.

(b) At higher temperatures, however, we must calculate the electronic partition function as a direct summation over energy levels using eqn 22.4

$$q = \sum_L g_L\,\text{e}^{-\epsilon_L/kT}$$

where $g_L$ is the degeneracy of the level $L$ with energy $\epsilon_L$. If the energies are expressed relative to that of the lowest level, the summation becomes

$$q = g_0 + \sum_L g_L\,\text{e}^{-(\epsilon_L-\epsilon_0)/kT}$$

At $T = 0$, the exponential terms in the summation also equal zero, and only the first term, $g_0$ remains. Thus, $q^{\text{E}} = 5$. At higher temperatures, however,

$$q^{\text{E}} = \overbrace{g_0}^{^3P_2} + \overbrace{(g_1\times \text{e}^{-\epsilon_1/kT})}^{^3P_1} + \overbrace{(g_3\times \text{e}^{-\epsilon_2/kT})}^{^3P_0}$$
$$= 5 + \{3\times \text{e}^{-158.5\,\text{cm}^{-1}\times(hc/kT)}\} + \{1\times \text{e}^{-226.5\,\text{cm}^{-1}\times(hc/kT)}\}$$

At 298 K,

$$hc/kT = \frac{(6.626\times10^{-34}\,\text{J s})\times(2.998\times10^{8}\,\text{m s}^{-1})}{(1.381\times10^{-23}\,\text{J K}^{-1})\times(298\,\text{K})}$$
$$= 4.827\times10^{-5}\text{m} = 4.827\times10^{-3}\text{cm}$$

so that

$$q^{\text{E}} = 5 + \{3\times \text{e}^{-158.5\,\text{cm}^{-1}\times 4.827\times10^{-3}\text{cm}}\} + \{1\times \text{e}^{-226.5\,\text{cm}^{-1}\times 4.827\times10^{-3}\text{cm}}\}$$
$$= 5 + (3\times0.465) + (1\times0.335) = \mathbf{6.730}$$

**E22.17** The molecular partition function is given by the product of the partition functions for the different modes of motion. Thus,

$$q = q^T q^R q^V q^E$$

The value of the translational partition function follows from eqn 22.5,

$$q^{\mathrm{T}} = \frac{(2\pi mkT)^{3/2}V}{h^3}$$

The molecular mass of ethyne is $m = 24.04m_{\mathrm{u}}$, so that

$$q^{\mathrm{T}} = \frac{\{2\pi \times 24.04 \times (1.661 \times 10^{-27}\ \mathrm{kg}) \times (1.381 \times 10^{-23}\ \mathrm{J\ K^{-1}}) \times (298\ \mathrm{K})\}^{3/2} \times (1.00\ \mathrm{m^3})}{(6.626 \times 10^{-34}\mathrm{J\ s})^3}$$
$$= 1.140 \times 10^{32}$$

Using the approximate form of the rotational partition function, eqn 22.6, and noting that because the molecule is symmetric, the symmetry number $\sigma = 2$,

$$q^{\mathrm{R}} = \frac{kT}{\sigma hc\tilde{B}}$$
$$= \frac{(1.381 \times 10^{-23}\ \mathrm{J\ K^{-1}}) \times (298\ \mathrm{K})}{2 \times (6.626 \times 10^{-34}\mathrm{J\ s}) \times (2.998 \times 10^{8}\ \mathrm{m\ s^{-1}}) \times (1.177 \times 10^{2}\ \mathrm{m^{-1}})}$$
$$= 88.0$$

The vibrational partition function is given by the product of the partition functions for the seven normal modes. Applying eqn 22.7,

$$q^{\mathrm{V}} = \frac{1}{1 - \mathrm{e}^{-hc\tilde{\nu}/kT}}$$

for the mode at 612 $\mathrm{cm^{-1}}$ the exponent has a value at 298 K

$$\frac{hc\tilde{\nu}}{kT} = \frac{(6.626 \times 10^{-34}\mathrm{J\ s}) \times (2.998 \times 10^{8}\ \mathrm{m\ s^{-1}}) \times (612 \times 10^{2}\ \mathrm{m^{-1}})}{(1.381 \times 10^{-23}\ \mathrm{J\ K^{-1}}) \times (298\ \mathrm{K})} = 2.954$$

giving a partition function for this mode of

$$q^{\mathrm{V}}_{612} = \frac{1}{1 - \mathrm{e}^{-2.954}} = 1.055$$

In the same way for the other modes, we find that

$$q^{\mathrm{V}}_{729} = 1.031,\ q^{\mathrm{V}}_{1974} = 1.000,\ q^{\mathrm{V}}_{3287} = 1.000,\ q^{\mathrm{V}}_{3374} = 1.000$$

so that the overall vibrational partition function is

$$q^{\mathrm{V}} = \overbrace{q^{\mathrm{V}}_{612}q^{\mathrm{V}}_{612}}^{\text{doubly degenerate}}\ \overbrace{q^{\mathrm{V}}_{729}q^{\mathrm{V}}_{729}}^{\text{doubly degenerate}}\ q^{\mathrm{V}}_{3374}q^{\mathrm{V}}_{3287}q^{\mathrm{V}}_{1974} = 1.055^2 \times 1.031^2 \times 1.000^3 = 1.18$$

Ethyne is a closed-shell molecule. It is thus reasonable to assume that there are no low-lying electronic states that could be accessed at 298 K, so that

$$q^{\mathrm{E}} = 1$$

Hence, the overall partition function, which is given by the product of each of the individual partition functions is

$$q = \overbrace{1.140 \times 10^{32}}^{q^{\mathrm{T}}} \times \overbrace{88.0}^{q^{\mathrm{R}}} \times \overbrace{1.182}^{q^{V}} \times \overbrace{1}^{q^{\mathrm{E}}} = \mathbf{1.185 \times 10^{34}}$$

**E22.18** According to the Boltzmann distribution, in a sample of molecules, the number in the first excited level, with energy $\epsilon$ and degeneracy 5 is

$$N_1 = N_0 \times 5\mathrm{e}^{-\epsilon/kT}$$

and in the second excited level with energy $3\epsilon$ and degeneracy 3 is

$$N_2 = N_0 \times 3\mathrm{e}^{-3\epsilon/kT}$$

The average energy of a molecule within the sample is thus

$$\begin{aligned}\bar{E} &= \frac{N_0\epsilon_0 + N_1\epsilon_1 + N_2\epsilon_2}{N} \\ &= \frac{N_0 \times 0 + \{\overbrace{5N_0\mathrm{e}^{-\epsilon/kT}}^{N_1} \times \epsilon\} + \{\overbrace{3N_0\mathrm{e}^{-3\epsilon/kT}}^{N_2} \times 3\epsilon\}}{N_0 + \underbrace{5N_0\mathrm{e}^{-\epsilon/kT}}_{N_1} + \underbrace{3N_0\mathrm{e}^{-3\epsilon/kT}}_{N_2}} \\ &= \left(\frac{\mathbf{5e^{-\epsilon/kT} + 9e^{-3\epsilon/kT}}}{\mathbf{1 + 5e^{-\epsilon/kT} + 9e^{-3\epsilon/kT}}}\right)\boldsymbol{\epsilon}\end{aligned}$$

Alternatively, we may derive the same result using eqn 22.11,

$$\bar{E} = E/N = \frac{kT^2}{q} \times \frac{\mathrm{d}q}{\mathrm{d}T}$$

with the partition function for the system described as

$$\begin{aligned}q = \sum g_L\mathrm{e}^{-\epsilon_L/kT} &= (1 \times \mathrm{e}^{-0/kT}) + (5 \times \mathrm{e}^{-\epsilon/kT}) + (3 \times \mathrm{e}^{-3\epsilon/kT}) \\ &= 1 + 5\mathrm{e}^{-\epsilon/kT} + 3\mathrm{e}^{-3\epsilon/kT}\end{aligned}$$

and

$$\frac{dq}{dT} = \frac{d}{dT}q = \frac{d}{dT}(1 + 5e^{-\epsilon/kT} + 3e^{-3\epsilon/kT})$$
$$= 5 \times \frac{\epsilon}{kT^2} \times e^{-\epsilon/kT} + 3 \times \frac{3\epsilon}{kT^2} \times e^{-3\epsilon/kT}$$
$$= \frac{\epsilon}{kT^2}(5e^{-\epsilon/kT} + 9e^{-3\epsilon/kT})$$

so that

$$\bar{E} = \frac{kT^2}{1 + 5e^{-\epsilon/kT} + 3e^{-3\epsilon/kT}} \times \frac{\epsilon}{kT^2}(5e^{-\epsilon/kT} + 9e^{-3\epsilon/kT})$$
$$= \left(\frac{5e^{-\epsilon/kT} + 9e^{-3\epsilon/kT}}{1 + 5e^{-\epsilon/kT} + 9e^{-3\epsilon/kT}}\right)\epsilon$$

**E22.19** From eqn 22.11 and 22.12, the electronic contribution to the molar internal energy is

$$U_m(T) = U_m(0) + \epsilon_m = \frac{N_A kT^2}{q} \times \frac{dq}{dT} = \frac{RT^2}{q} \times \frac{dq}{dT}$$

From the solution to exercise 22.15, the partition function is

$$q^E = 1 + 3e^{-16.4\ cm^{-1} \times (hc/kT)} + 5e^{-43.5\ cm^{-1} \times (hc/kT)}$$
$$= 1 + 3e^{-23.59\ K/T} + 5e^{-62.57\ K/T}$$

with the derivative

$$\frac{dq}{dT} = \frac{d}{dT}q = \frac{d}{dT}(1 + 3e^{-23.59\ K/T} + 5e^{-62.57\ K/T})$$
$$= 3 \times \frac{23.59\ K}{T^2}e^{-23.59\ K/T} + 5 \times \frac{62.57\ K}{T^2} \times e^{-62.57\ K/T}$$
$$= (70.77e^{-23.59\ K/T} + 312.85e^{-62.57\ K/T})/T^2$$

so that

$$U_m(T) = \frac{R}{1 + 3e^{-23.59\ K/T} + 5e^{-62.57\ K/T}} \times 70.77e^{-23.59\ K/T} + 312.85e^{-62.57\ K/T}$$

Figure 22.1 shows a plot of the variation of this function with temperature. Reading from the graph, at $T = 298$ K, $U_m(T) = 339$ J mol$^{-1}$. As temperature increases, the system converges towards a configuration in which the molecules are distributed equally between the states. For one mole of molecules, at $T = \infty$, the population of each state is thus

$$N_0 = N_1 = N_2 = N = \frac{N_A}{g_0 + g_1 + g_2} = \frac{N_A}{1 + 3 + 5} = \frac{N_A}{9}$$

This configuration corresponds to an energy

$$U_m(T) = g_0N_0\epsilon_0 + g_1N_1\epsilon_1 + g_2N_2\epsilon_2 = N(g_0\epsilon_0 + g_1\epsilon_1 + g_2\epsilon_2)$$
$$= (N_A/9)\{0 + (3 \times hc \times 16.4\ cm^{-1}) + (5 \times hc \times 43.5\ cm^{-1})\}$$
$$= (N_A hc/9) \times \{(49.2 + 217.5)\ cm^{-1}\}$$

$$= (6.022 \times 10^{23}\ \mathrm{mol^{-1}}) \times (6.626 \times 10^{-34}\ \mathrm{J\ s}) \times (2.998 \times 10^{8}\ \mathrm{m\ s^{-1}}) \times (266.7 \times 10^{2}\ \mathrm{m^{-1}})/9$$
$$= 355\ \mathrm{J\ mol^{-1}}$$

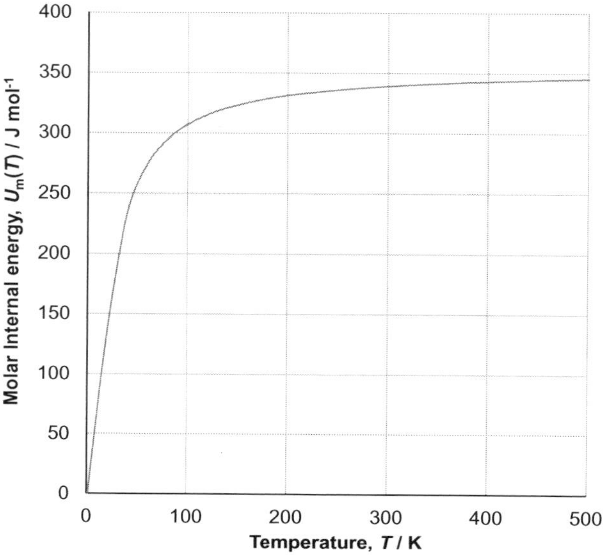


**Figure 22.1**

**E22.20** Molar heat capacity at constant volume is defined as the rate of change of molar internal energy with temperature,

$$C_{V,\mathrm{m}} = \frac{\mathrm{d}U_\mathrm{m}}{\mathrm{d}T}$$

Using eqn 22.11 and 22.12 to derive an expression for the molar internal energy,

$$C_{V,\mathrm{m}} = \frac{\mathrm{d}}{\mathrm{d}T}U_\mathrm{m}(T) = \frac{\mathrm{d}}{\mathrm{d}T}(U(0) + \epsilon) = \frac{\mathrm{d}}{\mathrm{d}T}\left(U(0) + \frac{N_\mathrm{A}kT^2}{q} \times \frac{\mathrm{d}q}{\mathrm{d}T}\right)$$
$$= \overbrace{\frac{\mathrm{d}}{\mathrm{d}T}U(0)}^{0} + \frac{\mathrm{d}}{\mathrm{d}T}\left(\frac{1}{q} \times RT^2 \times \frac{\mathrm{d}q}{\mathrm{d}T}\right)$$
$$= \frac{1}{q}\frac{\mathrm{d}q}{\mathrm{d}T}\frac{\mathrm{d}}{\mathrm{d}T}(RT^2) + RT^2\frac{\mathrm{d}q}{\mathrm{d}T}\frac{\mathrm{d}}{\mathrm{d}T}(q^{-1}) + \left(\frac{RT^2}{q}\right)\frac{\mathrm{d}}{\mathrm{d}T}\frac{\mathrm{d}q}{\mathrm{d}T}$$
$$= \frac{2RT}{q}\frac{\mathrm{d}q}{\mathrm{d}T} - \frac{RT^2}{q^2}\left(\frac{\mathrm{d}q}{\mathrm{d}T}\right)^2 + \left(\frac{RT^2}{q}\right)\frac{\mathrm{d}^2q}{\mathrm{d}T^2}$$

The electronic partition function for the oxygen atom is, from exercise 22.16,

$$q^\mathrm{E} = 5 + \left\{3 \times \mathrm{e}^{-158.5\ \mathrm{cm^{-1}} \times (hc/kT)}\right\} + \left\{1 \times \mathrm{e}^{-226.5\ \mathrm{cm^{-1}} \times (hc/kT)}\right\}$$

and because

$$hc/k = \frac{(6.626 \times 10^{-34} \text{J s}) \times (2.998 \times 10^{8} \text{ m s}^{-1})}{(1.381 \times 10^{-23} \text{ J K}^{-1})} = 1.438 \times 10^{-2} \text{ K}$$

it follows that

$$q^{\text{E}} = 5 + 3\text{e}^{-228.0 \text{ K}/T} + \text{e}^{-325.7 \text{ K}/T}$$

and so

$$\begin{aligned}\frac{\text{d}q}{\text{d}T} &= \frac{\text{d}}{\text{d}T}q = \frac{\text{d}}{\text{d}T}(5 + 3\text{e}^{-228.0 \text{ K}/T} + \text{e}^{-325.7 \text{ K}/T}) \\ &= 3 \times \frac{228.0}{T^2}\text{e}^{-228.0 \text{ K}/T} + \frac{325.7 \text{ K}}{T^2}\text{e}^{-325.7 \text{ K}/T} \\ &= \frac{983.9 \text{ K}}{T^2}\text{e}^{-228.0 \text{ K}/T} + \frac{325.7 \text{ K}}{T^2}\text{e}^{-325.7 \text{ K}/T}\end{aligned}$$

with

$$\begin{aligned}\frac{\text{d}^2q}{\text{d}T^2} &= \frac{\text{d}}{\text{d}T}\frac{\text{d}q}{\text{d}T} = \frac{\text{d}}{\text{d}T}\left(\frac{983.9 \text{ K}}{T^2}\text{e}^{-228.0 \text{ K}/T} + \frac{325.7 \text{ K}}{T^2}\text{e}^{-325.7 \text{ K}/T}\right) \\ &= \frac{983.9 \text{ K}}{T^2}\frac{\text{d}}{\text{d}T}\text{e}^{-228.0 \text{ K}/T} + \text{e}^{-228.0 \text{ K}/T}\frac{\text{d}}{\text{d}T}\frac{983.9 \text{ K}}{T^2} \\ &\qquad + \frac{325.7 \text{ K}}{T^2}\frac{\text{d}}{\text{d}T}\text{e}^{-325.7 \text{ K}/T} + \text{e}^{-325.7 \text{ K}/T}\frac{\text{d}}{\text{d}T}\frac{325.7 \text{ K}}{T^2} \\ &= \left(\frac{2.243 \times 10^5 \text{ K}^2}{T^4} - \frac{328.0 \text{ K}}{T^3}\right)\text{e}^{-228.0 \text{ K}/T} \\ &\qquad + \left(\frac{1.061 \times 10^5 \text{ K}^2}{T^4} - \frac{108.6 \text{ K}}{T^3}\right)\text{e}^{-325.7 \text{ K}/T}\end{aligned}$$

We may then substitute these expressions into our equation for the molar heat capacity at constant volume. Figure 22.2 shows how the molar heat capacity at constant volume varies with temperature. The value of the molar heat capacity at constant volume at 298 K can be read from the graph as $C_{V,\text{m}} = \mathbf{3.253 \text{ J K}^{-1} \text{ mol}^{-1}}$.

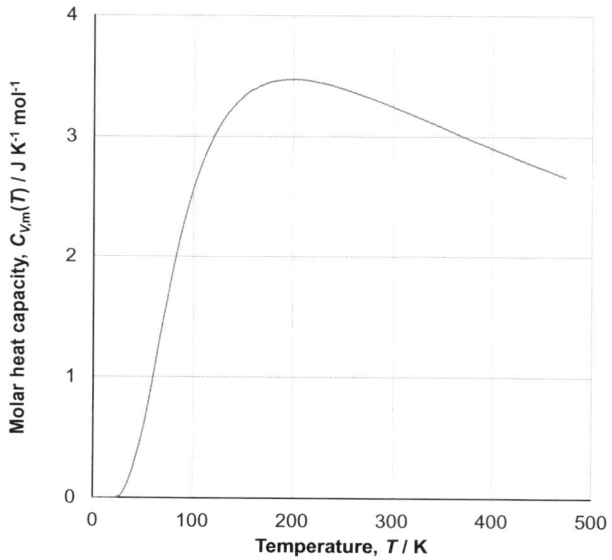


**Figure 22.2**

**E22.21** The heat capacity reflects how the internal energy changes with temperature. If the density of states is high, so that the partition function is large, then a small increase in temperature causes a large change in internal energy. This is consistent with a high heat capacity. A large partition function also leads to a high entropy, because the energy may be dispersed over a large number of states.

**E22.22** The molar entropy of a sample of indistinguishable molecules such as $N_2$ gas is given by eqn 22.13b

$$S = \frac{U(T) - U(0)}{T} + Nk\ln q - Nk(\ln N - 1)$$

$$S_m = \frac{U_m(T) - U_m(0)}{T} + N_A k\ln q - N_A k(\ln N_A - 1)$$

$$= \frac{U_m(T) - U_m(0)}{T} + R\ln q - R(\ln N_A - 1)$$

At high temperatures, it is reasonable to assume that the value for the internal energy may be calculated using the theory of equipartition, and that each quadratic mode makes a contribution of ½$RT$ to the molar internal energy. Thus, because for $N_2$ there are three quadratic contributions from translational modes and two contributions from the two rotational modes, making five quadratic modes in total,

$$U_m(T) - U_m(0) = 5 \times ½RT = (5/2)RT$$

The overall partition function is given by the product of the partition function for each of the separate modes,

$$q = q^{\mathrm{T}}q^{\mathrm{V}}q^{\mathrm{R}}q^{\mathrm{E}}$$

The translational partition function is given by eqn 22.5, with the molar volume expressed using the perfect gas equation,

$$q^{\mathrm{T}} = \frac{(2\pi mkT)^{3/2}V_{\mathrm{m}}}{h^3} = \frac{(2\pi mkT)^{3/2}(RT/p^{\ominus})}{h^3} = \frac{(2\pi mk)^{3/2}RT^{5/2}}{p^{\ominus}h^3}$$

Thus, for $N_2$, with a molecular mass of $28.02m_{\mathrm{u}}$, the translational partition function at 298 K and 1 bar = $10^5$ Pa, is

$$q^{\mathrm{T}} = \frac{[2\pi \times \{28.02 \times (1.661 \times 10^{-27}\ \mathrm{kg})\} \times (1.38 \times 10^{-23}\ \mathrm{J\ K^{-1}})]^{3/2} \times (8.3145\ \mathrm{J\ K^{-1}mol^{-1}}) \times (298\ \mathrm{K})^{5/2}}{(10^5\ \mathrm{Pa}) \times (6.626 \times 10^{-34}\mathrm{J\ s})^3}$$
$$= 3.507 \times 10^{30}$$

The value of the rotational partition function at 298 K is, from eqn 22.6,

$$q^{\mathrm{R}} = \frac{kT}{\sigma hc\tilde{B}}$$
$$= \frac{(1.38 \times 10^{-23}\ \mathrm{J\ K^{-1}}) \times (298\ \mathrm{K})}{2 \times (6.626 \times 10^{-34}\mathrm{J\ s}) \times (2.998 \times 10^{8}\ \mathrm{m\ s^{-1}}) \times (1.987 \times 10^{2}\ \mathrm{m^{-1}})}$$
$$= 51.81$$

The separation between the electronic energy levels and between the vibrational energy levels is so great in comparison with the thermal energy, $\Delta E \gg kT$, that we may assume that only the ground state is accessible. Thus,

$$q^{\mathrm{V}} = 1$$
$$q^{\mathrm{E}} = 1$$

Hence, substituting,

$$S_{\mathrm{m}} = \frac{5RT}{2T} + R\ln q^{\mathrm{T}}q^{\mathrm{R}}q^{\mathrm{V}}q^{\mathrm{E}} - R(\ln N_{\mathrm{A}} - 1)$$
$$= R\{(7/2) + \ln(q^{\mathrm{T}}q^{\mathrm{R}}q^{\mathrm{V}}q^{\mathrm{E}}/N_{\mathrm{A}})\}$$
$$= (8.3145\ \mathrm{J\ K^{-1}mol^{-1}}) \times \left\{(7/2) + \ln\frac{(3.507 \times 10^{30} \times 51.81)}{(6.022 \times 10^{23}\ \mathrm{mol^{-1}})}\right\}$$
$$= \mathbf{191.4\ J\ K^{-1}mol^{-1}}$$

**E22.23** In general, the greater the complexity of the system, the greater the standard entropy.

(a) Monatomic gases with greater numbers of particles and greater molar mass have greater standard translational entropies. More energy levels are accessible and the partition function is greater Hence, $S^{\ominus}(\mathrm{Xe}) > S^{\ominus}(\mathrm{Ne})$.

(b) All contributions, translational, rotational, and vibrational, to the molecular partition functions depend on the mass of the molecule. The greater the mass, the greater the partition functions and the greater the entropy. Hence, $S^\ominus(D_2O) > S^\ominus(H_2O)$.

(c) Diamond has a very rigid and orderly lattice. Graphite has a layer-like structure in which the layers can slide past each other, resulting in much more disorder in the graphite structure; hence $S^\ominus$(Graphite) > $S^\ominus$(Diamond).

**E22.24** We may model the dispersion of the molecules within the micelle as the expansion of a gas. The change in entropy upon expansion of a perfect gas is given by eqn 4.2

$$\Delta S = k\ln(V_f/V_i)$$

so that the change in entropy per molecule is

$$\Delta S = k\ln(V_{\text{solution}}/V_{\text{micelle}})$$

and, for a micelle containing $N$ molecules, the change in entropy per micelle is

$$\Delta S = Nk\ln(V_{\text{solution}}/V_{\text{micelle}})$$

In the absence of specific data on the volumes involved we can arrive at a rough value of $\Delta S$ by making some reasonable estimates. Let us assume that the micelle is spherical in shape. Let us also assume that the radius of this sphere is roughly the same as the length of the hydrocarbon chain of the amphiphile. Assume that the chain consists of 10 zigzag carbon atoms with an average C–C–C length of 250 pm, or about 125 pm per carbon atom. Thus, the radius of the micelle may be estimated as about 1.25 nm. The volume of the micelle is thus

$$V_{\text{micelle}} = (4/3)\pi r^3 = (4/3)\pi \times (1.25\times 10^{-9}\text{ m})^3 = 6\times 10^{-27}\text{ m}^3$$

We may assume that the volume of the solution is that of a typical 100 cm$^3$ beaker

$$V_{\text{solution}} = 100\text{ cm}^3 = 100\times 10^{-6}\text{m}^3 = 10^{-4}\text{ m}^3 1$$

Thus, for a micelle consisting of $N = 100$ molecules,

$$\Delta S = 100\times(1.381\times 10^{-23}\text{ J K}^{-1})\times \ln\{(10^{-4}\text{ m}^3)/(6\times 10^{-27}\text{ m}^3)\}$$
$$= 7\times 10^{-20}\text{ J K}^{-1}$$

which is equivalent to a change in molar entropy of

$$\Delta S_m = N_A\Delta S = (6.022\times 10^{23}\text{ mol}^{-1})\times(7\times 10^{-20}\text{ J K}^{-1})$$
$$= 40\times 10^3\text{ J K}^{-1}\text{mol}^{-1} = \mathbf{4\ kJ\ K^{-1}mol^{-1}}$$

The observed value is significantly less than that estimated. In our estimation, end effects contributing to the length of the amphiphile have been neglected and the number of carbon atoms for amphiphiles that could form a micelle of 100 amphiphiles may be larger than the 10 assumed.

**E22.25** The standard molar Gibbs energy of a substance may be expressed in terms of partition functions using eqn 22.17

$$G_m^{\ominus}(T) - G_m^{\ominus}(0) = -RT\ln(q_m^{\ominus}/N_A)$$

The standard molar partition function is given by the product of the partition functions for the different modes of motion

$$q_m^{\ominus} = q^T q^R q^V q^E$$

The standard translational partition function is given by eqn 22.5, with the molar volume expressed using the perfect gas equation,

$$q^T = \frac{(2\pi mkT)^{3/2}V_m}{h^3} = \frac{(2\pi mkT)^{3/2}(RT/p)}{h^3} = \frac{(2\pi mk)^{3/2}RT^{5/2}}{ph^3}$$

Thus, for $CO_2$, with a molecular mass of $44.02m_u$, the translational partition function at 298 K and 1 bar = $10^5$ Pa, is

$$q^T = \frac{[2\pi \times \{44.04 \times (1.661 \times 10^{-27}\ \text{kg})\} \times (1.381 \times 10^{-23}\ \text{J K}^{-1})]^{3/2} \times (8.3145\ \text{J K}^{-1}\text{mol}^{-1}) \times (298\ \text{K})^{5/2}}{(10^5\ \text{Pa}) \times (6.626 \times 10^{-34}\text{J s})^3}$$

$$= 7.01 \times 10^{30}$$

The rotational partition function at 298 K is given by eqn 22.6,

$$q^R = \frac{kT}{\sigma hc\tilde{B}}$$

The rotational constant of $CO_2$ is 0.3903 $\text{cm}^{-1}$, so that

$$q^R = \frac{(1.381 \times 10^{-23}\ \text{J K}^{-1}) \times (298\ \text{K})}{2 \times (6.626 \times 10^{-34}\text{J s}) \times (2.998 \times 10^8\ \text{m s}^{-1}) \times (0.3903 \times 10^2\ \text{m}^{-1})}$$

$$= 265$$

The vibrational partition function for a polyatomic molecule is given by the product of the partition function for each of the separate modes of vibration. $CO_2$ has four normal modes of vibration, with non-degenerate stretching vibrational modes with wavenumbers 1388 $\text{cm}^{-1}$ and 2349 $\text{cm}^{-1}$ and doubly degenerate bending modes with wavenumber 667 $\text{cm}^{-1}$. The vibrational partition function is, using eqn 22.7

$$q^V = \frac{1}{1 - e^{-hc\tilde{\nu}/kT}}$$

and so, for $CO_2$, if

$$\frac{hc}{kT} = \frac{(6.626 \times 10^{-34}\text{J s}) \times (2.998 \times 10^8\ \text{m s}^{-1})}{(1.38 \times 10^{-23}\ \text{J K}^{-1}) \times (298\ \text{K})} = 4.827 \times 10^{-5}\ \text{m}$$

then,

$$q^V_{1388} = \frac{1}{1 - e^{-(4.827\times10^{-5}\ \text{m})\times(1388\times10^2\ \text{m})}} = 1.001$$

$$q^{\mathrm{V}}_{667} = \frac{1}{1 - \mathrm{e}^{-(4.827\times10^{-5}\ \mathrm{m})\times(667\times10^{2}\ \mathrm{m})}} = 1.042$$

$$q^{\mathrm{V}}_{2349} = \frac{1}{1 - \mathrm{e}^{-(4.827\times10^{-5}\ \mathrm{m})\times(2349\times10^{2}\ \mathrm{m})}} = 1.000$$

Hence, the overall vibrational partition function is

$$q^{\mathrm{V}} = \overbrace{1.001}^{\substack{\text{singly}\\\text{degenerate}\\\text{stretch}}} \times \overbrace{1.042 \times 1.042}^{\substack{\text{doubly}\\\text{degenerate}\\\text{bend}}} \times \overbrace{1.000}^{\substack{\text{singly}\\\text{degenerate}\\\text{stretch}}} = 1.086$$

We may assume that because $CO_2$ is a closed-shell molecule, there are no low-lying electronic states, and therefore that

$$q^{\mathrm{E}} = 1$$

Thus,

$$q^{\ominus}_{\mathrm{m}} = \overbrace{7.01 \times 10^{30}}^{q^{\mathrm{T}}} \times \overbrace{265}^{q^{\mathrm{R}}} \times \overbrace{1.086}^{q^{\mathrm{V}}} \times \overbrace{1}^{q^{\mathrm{E}}} = 2.02 \times 10^{33}$$

Hence,

$$G^{\ominus}_{\mathrm{m}}(T) - G^{\ominus}_{\mathrm{m}}(0) = -(8.3145\ \mathrm{J\ K^{-1}mol^{-1}}) \times (298\ \mathrm{K}) \times \ln\left(\frac{2.02 \times 10^{33}}{6.022 \times 10^{23}\ \mathrm{mol^{-1}}}\right)$$

$$= -54.3 \times 10^{3}\ \mathrm{J\ mol^{-1}} = \mathbf{-54.3\ kJ\ mol^{-1}}$$

**E22.26** Following the method used in Example 22.5, the equilibrium constant for the reaction

$$N_2(g) + 3\ H_2(g) \rightleftharpoons 2\ NH_3(g)$$

may be written as

$$K = \frac{\left(q^{\ominus}_{\mathrm{NH_3,m}}/N_{\mathrm{A}}\right)^2}{\left(q^{\ominus}_{\mathrm{N_2,m}}/N_{\mathrm{A}}\right)\left(q^{\ominus}_{\mathrm{H_2,m}}/N_{\mathrm{A}}\right)^3}\mathrm{e}^{-\Delta E/RT}$$

The overall molar partition function for each species is given by the product

$$q^{\ominus}_{\mathrm{m}} = q^{\mathrm{T}}_{\mathrm{m}} q^{\mathrm{R}}_{\mathrm{m}} q^{\mathrm{V}}_{\mathrm{m}} q^{\mathrm{E}}_{\mathrm{m}}$$

although, because all three species are closed shell systems with non-degenerate ground states, all electronic partition functions $q^{\mathrm{E}} = 1$.

**E22.27** For the ionization of sodium,

$$Na(g) \rightleftharpoons Na^{+}(g) + e^{-}(g)$$

the equilibrium constant is given by

$$K = \frac{\left(q^{\ominus}_{\mathrm{Na^+(g),m}}/N_{\mathrm{A}}\right)\left(q^{\ominus}_{\mathrm{e^-(g),m}}/N_{\mathrm{A}}\right)}{\left(q^{\ominus}_{\mathrm{Na(g),m}}/N_{\mathrm{A}}\right)}\mathrm{e}^{-\Delta E/RT}$$

The molar partition function of each species is given by the product

$$q_{\mathrm{m}}^{\ominus} = q^{\mathrm{T}} q^{\mathrm{E}}$$

so that, substituting,

$$K = \frac{q_{\mathrm{Na^+(g)}}^{\mathrm{T}} q_{\mathrm{Na^+(g)}}^{\mathrm{E}} q_{\mathrm{e^-(g)}}^{\mathrm{T}} q_{\mathrm{e^-(g)}}^{\mathrm{E}}}{q_{\mathrm{Na(g)}}^{\mathrm{T}} q_{\mathrm{Na(g)}}^{\mathrm{E}}} \mathrm{e}^{-\Delta E/RT} / N_{\mathrm{A}}$$

Because the translational partition function is a function only of mass and temperature, and $m_{\mathrm{Na^+}} \approx m_{\mathrm{Na^+}}$

$$q^{\mathrm{T}}{}_{\mathrm{Na^+(g)}} \approx q^{\mathrm{T}}{}_{\mathrm{Na(g)}}$$

so that these terms cancel. The standard molar translational partition function for the electron follows from eqn 22.5,

$$q^{\mathrm{T}} = \frac{(2\pi mkT)^{3/2} V_{\mathrm{m}}}{h^3} = \frac{(2\pi m_{\mathrm{e}} kT)^{3/2} (RT/p^{\ominus})}{h^3} = \frac{(2\pi m_{\mathrm{e}} k)^{3/2} RT^{5/2}}{p^{\ominus} h^3}$$

The lowest energy level of the sodium atom corresponds to a ${}^2\mathrm{S}_{1/2}$ level, with a degeneracy $g_{\mathrm{Na(g)}} = 2J + 1 = (2 \times \frac{1}{2}) + 1 = 2$, so that

$$q_{\mathrm{Na(g)}}^{\mathrm{E}} = 2$$

Similarly, because an electron may exist in two spin states,

$$q_{\mathrm{e^-(g)}}^{\mathrm{E}} = 2$$

so that these terms also cancel. The sodium ion, however, is a closed-shell species, with no low-lying electronic states. Thus

$$q_{\mathrm{Na^+(g)}}^{\mathrm{E}} = 1$$

The difference in the energies of the ground states of the products and reactants is equal to the ionization energy of sodium,

$$\Delta E = I(\mathrm{Na}) = +495.8\ \mathrm{kJ\ mol^{-1}}$$

Hence, substituting into the expression for the equilibrium constant,

$$K = \frac{q_{\mathrm{e^-(g)}}^{\mathrm{T}} \mathrm{e}^{-\Delta E/RT}}{N_{\mathrm{A}}} = \frac{(2\pi m_{\mathrm{e}} k)^{3/2} RT^{5/2}}{p^{\ominus} h^3} \times \frac{\mathrm{e}^{-\Delta E/RT}}{N_{\mathrm{A}}} = \frac{(2\pi m_{\mathrm{e}})^{3/2} (kT)^{5/2}}{p^{\ominus} h^3} \mathrm{e}^{-\Delta E/RT}$$

$$= \frac{\{2\pi \times (9.109 \times 10^{-31}\ \mathrm{kg})\}^{3/2} \times \{(1.381 \times 10^{-23}\ \mathrm{J\ K^{-1}}) \times (1000\ \mathrm{K})\}^{5/2}}{(10^5\ \mathrm{Pa}) \times (6.626 \times 10^{-34}\ \mathrm{J\ s})^3} \times \mathrm{e}^{-(495.8 \times 10^3\ \mathrm{J\ mol^{-1}})/\{(8.3145\ \mathrm{J\ K^{-1} mol^{-1}}) \times (1000\ \mathrm{K})\}}$$

$$= \mathbf{1.336 \times 10^{-25}}$$

**E22.28** For the dissociation of $I_2(g)$,

$$\mathrm{I_2(g)} \rightleftharpoons \mathrm{2I(g)}$$

the equilibrium constant may be expressed in terms of molar partition functions as

$$K = \frac{\left(q^{\ominus}_{\mathrm{I(g),m}}/N_{\mathrm{A}}\right)^2}{\left(q^{\ominus}_{\mathrm{I_2(g),m}}/N_{\mathrm{A}}\right)}\mathrm{e}^{-\Delta E/RT} = \frac{{q^{\ominus}_{\mathrm{I(g),m}}}^2}{q^{\ominus}_{\mathrm{I_2(g),m}}N_{\mathrm{A}}}\mathrm{e}^{-\Delta E/RT}$$

For the iodine atom,

$$q^{\ominus}_{\mathrm{I(g),m}} = q^{\mathrm{T}}_{\mathrm{I(g)}}q^{\mathrm{E}}_{\mathrm{I(g)}}$$

The standard molar translational partition function is given by eqn 22.5,

$$q^{\mathrm{T}}_{\mathrm{I(g)}} = \frac{(2\pi mkT)^{3/2}V_{\mathrm{m}}}{h^3} = \frac{(2\pi m_{\mathrm{I}}kT)^{3/2}(RT/p^{\circ})}{h^3} = \frac{(2\pi m_{\mathrm{I}}k)^{3/2}RT^{5/2}}{p^{\circ}h^3}$$

$$= \frac{[2\pi \times \{126.90 \times (1.661 \times 10^{-27}\ \mathrm{kg})\} \times (1.381 \times 10^{-23}\ \mathrm{J\ K^{-1}})]^{3/2} \times (8.3145\ \mathrm{J\ K^{-1}mol^{-1}}) \times (500\ \mathrm{K})^{5/2}}{(10^5\ \mathrm{Pa}) \times (6.626 \times 10^{-34}\mathrm{J\ s})^3}$$

$$= 1.250 \times 10^{32}$$

The lowest level of the iodine atom is $^2\mathrm{P}_{3/2}$. The degeneracy of this level is therefore $g_{\mathrm{I(g)}} = 2J + 1 = \{2 \times (3/2)\} + 1 = 4$, so that

$$q^{\mathrm{E}}_{\mathrm{I(g)}} = 4$$

For the iodine molecule,

$$q^{\ominus}_{\mathrm{I(g),m}} = q^{\mathrm{T}}_{\mathrm{I(g)}}q^{\mathrm{R}}_{\mathrm{I(g)}}q^{\mathrm{V}}_{\mathrm{I(g)}}q^{\mathrm{E}}_{\mathrm{I(g)}}$$

The standard molar translational partition function is

$$q^{\mathrm{T}}_{\mathrm{I_2(g)}} = \frac{\left(2\pi m_{\mathrm{I_2}}k\right)^{3/2}RT^{5/2}}{p^{\ominus}h^3} = 2^{3/2}q^{\mathrm{T}}_{\mathrm{I(g)}} = 3.534 \times 10^{32}$$

The rotational partition function is, from eqn 22.6,

$$q^{\mathrm{R}}_{\mathrm{I_2(g)}} = \frac{kT}{\sigma hc\tilde{B}}$$

$$= \frac{(1.381 \times 10^{-23}\ \mathrm{J\ K^{-1}}) \times (500\ \mathrm{K})}{2 \times (6.626 \times 10^{-34}\mathrm{J\ s}) \times (2.998 \times 10^8\ \mathrm{m\ s^{-1}}) \times \underbrace{(0.0373 \times 10^2\ \mathrm{m^{-1}})}_{\tilde{B}=0.0373\ \mathrm{cm^{-1}}}}$$

$$= 4660$$

and the vibrational partition function is, from 22.7,

$$q^{\mathrm{V}} = \frac{1}{1 - \mathrm{e}^{-hc\tilde{\nu}/kT}}$$

$$= \frac{1}{1 - \mathrm{e}^{-\frac{\{(6.626\times10^{-34}\mathrm{J\ s})\times(2.998\times10^8\ \mathrm{m\ s^{-1}})\times(214.36\times10^2\mathrm{m^{-1}})\}}{\{(1.381\times10^{-23}\ \mathrm{J\ K^{-1}})\times(500\ \mathrm{K})\}}}}$$

$$= 2.172$$

The iodine molecule is a closed-shell species, with no low-lying electronic states, so that

$$q^{\mathrm{E}}_{\mathrm{I_2(g)}} = 1$$

We may assume that the difference in the energy of the ground states of the product and reactant is approximately equal to the I–I bond enthalpy,

$$\Delta E = H_B(\text{I}-\text{I}) = 151\ \text{kJ mol}^{-1}$$

Hence,

$$K = \frac{\{4 \times (1.250 \times 10^{32})\}^2}{1 \times 2.172 \times 4660 \times (3.534 \times 10^{32}) \times (6.022 \times 10^{23}\ \text{mol}^{-1})} \times \text{e}^{-(151\times10^3\ \text{J mol}^{-1})/\{(8.3145\ \text{J K}^{-1}\text{mol}^{-1})\times(500\ \text{K})\}}$$

$$= \mathbf{1.951 \times 10^{-11}}$$

## Answers to projects

**P22.29** (a) The internal energy is given by eqn 22.11 and eqn 22.12

$$U(T) = \overbrace{U(0)}^{0} + \epsilon = \overbrace{\frac{NkT^2}{q} \times \frac{\text{d}q}{\text{d}T}}^{\epsilon}$$

The vibrational partition function for a series of harmonic oscillators is, from eqn 22.6,

$$q = \frac{1}{1-\text{e}^{-h\nu/kT}}$$

so that

$$\frac{\text{d}q}{\text{d}T} = \frac{(h\nu/kT^2)\text{e}^{-h\nu/kT}}{(1-\text{e}^{-h\nu/kT})^2}$$

Substituting,

$$U(T) = NkT^2 \times (1-\text{e}^{-h\nu/kT}) \times \frac{(h\nu/kT^2)\text{e}^{-h\nu/kT}}{(1-\text{e}^{-h\nu/kT})^2}$$

$$= \frac{\text{e}^{-h\nu/kT}}{(1-\text{e}^{-h\nu/kT})}Nh\nu = \frac{1}{(\text{e}^{h\nu/kT}-1)}Nh\nu$$

We may expand the exponential term using the relationship

$$\text{e}^x = 1 + x + x^2/2! + x^3/3! + \cdots$$

so that

$$\text{e}^{h\nu/kT} = 1 + \frac{h\nu}{kT} + \frac{1}{2}\left(\frac{h\nu}{kT}\right)^2 + \frac{1}{6}\left(\frac{h\nu}{kT}\right)^3 + \cdots$$

If $h\nu \ll kT$, we may neglect all but the first two terms in the expansion, so that

$$\text{e}^{h\nu/kT} \approx 1 + \frac{h\nu}{kT}$$

and therefore,

$$U(T) = \frac{1}{\{1 + (h\nu/kT) - 1\}} Nh\nu = \frac{Nh\nu}{h\nu/kT} = NkT$$

This is equal to the result obtained from the equipartition theorem, which was described in *Foundations*.

(b) The heat capacity at constant volume is given by

$$C_V = \frac{\mathrm{d}U}{\mathrm{d}T} = \frac{\mathrm{d}}{\mathrm{d}T} U(T)$$

Substituting the expression for the internal energy derived in part (a),

$$C_V = \frac{\mathrm{d}}{\mathrm{d}T} \overbrace{\left\{ \frac{Nh\nu}{\mathrm{e}^{h\nu/kT} - 1} \right\}}^{U(T)} = -(h\nu/kT^2)\mathrm{e}^{h\nu/kT} \frac{Nh\nu}{(\mathrm{e}^{h\nu/kT} - 1)^2}$$

$$= Nk\mathrm{e}^{h\nu/kT} \left( \frac{h\nu/kT}{\mathrm{e}^{h\nu/kT} - 1} \right)^2$$

In the high-temperature limit, so that

$$\mathrm{e}^{h\nu/kT} \approx 1 + \frac{h\nu}{kT}$$

then

$$C_V = Nk(1 + h\nu/kT) \left\{ \frac{h\nu/kT}{(1 + h\nu/kT) - 1} \right\}^2 = Nk(1 + h\nu/kT) = Nk + \frac{Nh\nu}{T} \approx Nk$$

Printed and bound by CPI Group (UK) Ltd, Croydon, CR0 4YY